Custom Integrated Edition • Grade 6

interactive SCIENCE

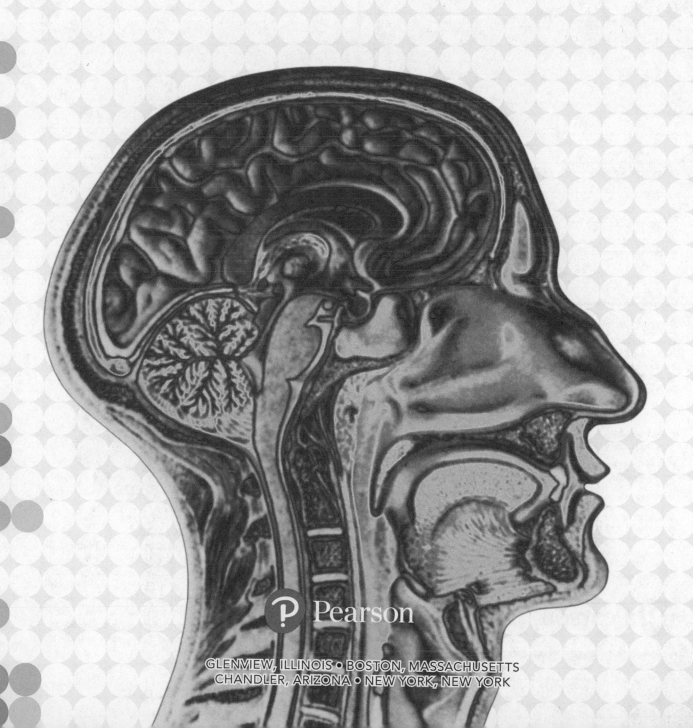

Pearson

GLENVIEW, ILLINOIS • BOSTON, MASSACHUSETTS
CHANDLER, ARIZONA • NEW YORK, NEW YORK

You're an author!

As you write in this science book, your answers and personal discoveries will be recorded for you to keep, making this book unique to you. That is why you are one of the primary authors of this book.

✎ **In the space below, print your name, school, town, and state. Then write a short autobiography that includes your interests and accomplishments.**

YOUR NAME _____

SCHOOL _____

TOWN _____

AUTOBIOGRAPHY _____

_____

_____

_____

_____

_____

Your Photo

Acknowledgments appear on pages 736–740, which constitute an extension of this copyright page.

Copyright © 2017 by Pearson Education, Inc., or its affiliates. All Rights Reserved. Printed in the United States of America. This publication is protected by copyright, and permission should be obtained from the publisher prior to any prohibited reproduction, storage in a retrieval system, or transmission in any form or by any means, electronic, mechanical, photocopying, recording, or otherwise. For information regarding permissions, request forms and the appropriate contacts within the Pearson Education Global Rights & Permissions Department, please visit www.pearsoned.com/permissions/.

Certain materials herein are adapted from Understanding by Design, 2nd Edition, by Grant Wiggins & Jay McTighe © 2005 ASCD. Used with permission.

Pearson, Prentice Hall, Pearson Prentice Hall, Lab Zone, and Pearson Flipped Videos for Science, are trademarks, in the U.S. and/or other countries, of Pearson Education, Inc., or its affiliates.

Untamed Science is a US registered mark licensed to Pearson from EcoMedia.

Unless otherwise indicated herein, any third-party trademarks that may appear in this work are the property of their respective owners and any references to third-party trademarks, logos or other trade dress are for demonstrative or descriptive purposes only. Such references are not intended to imply any sponsorship, endorsement, authorization, or promotion of Pearson's products by the owners of such marks, or any relationship between the owner and Pearson Education, Inc. or its affiliates, authors, licensees or distributors.

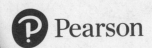

ISBN-13:   978-1-323-20594-5
ISBN-10:   1-323-20594-2
6   20

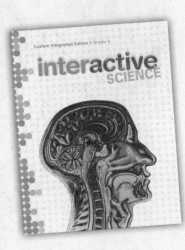

ON THE COVER

Seeing Inside

Magnetic resonance imaging (MRI) uses magnetism, radio waves, and a computer to produce images of structures inside a person's body. Scientists developed a way to add color to this MRI so that specific organs and tissues are easier to see than if they were in black and white.

Program Authors

DON BUCKLEY, M.Sc.
Director of Technology & Innovation,
The School at Columbia University, New York, New York
Don Buckley has transformed learning spaces, textbooks, and media resources so that they work for students and teachers. He has advanced degrees from leading European universities, is a former industrial chemist, published photographer, and former consultant to MOMA's Education Department. He also teaches a graduate course at Columbia Teacher's College in Educational Technology and directs the Technology and Innovation program at the school. He is passionate about travel, architecture, design, change, the future, and innovation.

ZIPPORAH MILLER, M.A.Ed.
Coordinator for K-12 Science Programs, Anne Arundel County Public Schools.
Mrs. Zipporah Miller served as a reviewer during the development of Next Generation Science Standards and provides national training to teachers, administrators, higher education staff and informal science stakeholders on the Next Generation Science Standards. Prior to her appointment in Anne Arundel, Mrs. Miller served as the Associate Executive Director for Professional Development Programs and Conferences at the National Science Teachers Association (NSTA).

MICHAEL J. PADILLA, Ph.D.
Eugene P. Moore School of Education, Clemson University, Clemson, South Carolina
A former middle school teacher and a leader in middle school science education, Dr. Michael Padilla has served as president of the National Science Teachers Association and reviewed the Next Generation Science Standards. He is a former professor of science education at Clemson University. As lead author of the *Science Explorer* series, Dr. Padilla has inspired the team in developing a program that promotes student inquiry and meets the needs of today's students.

KATHRYN THORNTON, Ph.D.
Professor, Mechanical & Aerospace Engineering, University of Virginia, Charlottesville, Virginia
Selected by NASA in May 1984, Dr. Kathryn Thornton is a veteran of four space flights. She has logged more than 975 hours in space, including more than 21 hours of extravehicular activity. As an author on the *Scott Foresman Science* series, Dr. Thornton's enthusiasm for science has inspired teachers around the globe.

MICHAEL E. WYSESSION, Ph.D.
Associate Professor of Earth and Planetary Science, Washington University, St. Louis, Missouri
An author on more than 50 scientific publications, Dr. Wysession was awarded the prestigious Packard Foundation Fellowship and Presidential Faculty Fellowship for his research in geophysics. Dr. Wysession is an expert on Earth's inner structure and has mapped various regions of Earth using seismic tomography. He is known internationally for his work in geoscience education and research, and was an author of the Next Generation Science Standards.

Instructional Design Author

GRANT WIGGINS, Ed.D.
Dr. Wiggins is a co-author with Jay McTighe of *Understanding by Design, 2nd Edition* (ASCD 2005). His approach to instructional design provides teachers with a disciplined way of thinking about curriculum design, assessment, and instruction that moves teaching from covering content to ensuring understanding. He was also the President of Authentic Education, Hopewell, New Jersey. UNDERSTANDING BY DESIGN® and UbD™ are trademarks of ASCD, and are used under license.

Activities Author

KAREN L. OSTLUND, Ph.D.
Past President, National Science Teachers Association, Arlington, Virginia
Dr. Ostlund has over 40 years of experience teaching at the elementary, middle school, and university levels. She was Director of WINGS Online (Welcoming Interns and Novices with Guidance and Support) and the Director of the UTeach/Dell Center for New Teacher Success with the UTeach program in the College of Natural Sciences at the University of Texas at Austin. She also served as Director of the Center for Science Education at the University of Texas at Arlington, as President of the Council of Elementary Science International, and as a member of the Board of Directors of the National Science Teachers Association. As an author of Scott Foresman Science, Dr. Ostlund was instrumental in developing inquiry activities.

ELL Consultant

JIM CUMMINS, Ph.D.
Professor and Canada Research Chair, Curriculum, Teaching and Learning Department at the University of Toronto
Dr. Cummins's research focuses on literacy development in multilingual schools and the role technology plays in learning across the curriculum. *Interactive Science* incorporates research-based principles for integrating language with the teaching of academic content based on Dr. Cummins's work.

Reviewers

Program Consultants

William Brozo, Ph.D.
Professor of Literacy, Graduate School of Education, George Mason University, Fairfax, Virginia.
Dr. Brozo is the author of numerous articles and books on literacy development. He co-authors a column in The Reading Teacher and serves on the editorial review board of the Journal of Adolescent & Adult Literacy.

Kristi Zenchak, M.S.
Biology Instructor, Oakton Community College, Des Plaines, Illinois

Kristi Zenchak helps elementary teachers incorporate science, technology, engineering, and math activities into the classroom. STEM activities that produce viable solutions to real-world problems not only motivate students but also prepare students for future STEM careers. Ms. Zenchak helps elementary teachers understand the basic science concepts, and provides STEM activities that are easy to implement in the classroom.

Content Reviewers

Brad Armosky, M.S.
Texas Advanced Computing Center
University of Texas at Austin
Austin, Texas

Alexander Brands, Ph.D.
Department of Biological Sciences
Lehigh University
Bethlehem, Pennsylvania

Paul Beale, Ph.D.
Department of Physics
University of Colorado
Boulder, Colorado

Joy Branlund, Ph.D.
Department of Earth Science
Southwestern Illinois College
Granite City, Illinois

Constance Brown, Ph.D
Atmospheric Science Program
Geography Department
Indiana University
Bloomington, Indiana

Dana Dudle, Ph.D.
Biology Department
DePauw University
Greencastle, Indiana

Rick Duhrkopf, Ph. D.
Department of Biology
Baylor University
Waco, Texas

Mark Henriksen, Ph.D.
Physics Department
University of Maryland
Baltimore, Maryland

Andrew Hirsch, Ph.D.
Department of Physics
Purdue University
W. Lafayette, Indiana

Linda L. Cronin Jones, Ph.D.
School of Teaching & Learning
University of Florida
Gainesville, Florida

T. Griffith Jones, Ph.D.
College of Education
University of Florida
Gainesville, Florida

Candace Lutzow-Felling, Ph.D.
Director of Education
State Arboretum of Virginia & Blandy Experimental Farm
Boyce VA 22620

Cortney V. Martin, Ph.D.
Virginia Polytechnic Institute
Blacksburg, Virginia

Sadredin Moosavi, Ph.D.
University of Massachusetts Dartmouth
Fairhaven, Massachusetts

Klaus Newmann, Ph.D.
Department of Geological Sciences
Ball State University
Muncie, Indiana

Scott M. Rochette, Ph.D.
Department of the Earth Sciences
SUNY College at Brockport
Brockport, New York

Ursula Rosauer Smedly, M.S.
Alcade Science Center
New Mexico State University
Alcade, New Mexico

Frederick W. Taylor, Ph.D.
Jackson School of Geosciences
University of Texas at Austin
Austin, Texas

Karyn Rogers, Ph.D.
Department of Geological Sciences
University of Missouri
Columbia, Missouri

Laurence Rosenhein, Ph.D.
Dept. of Chemistry and Physics
Indiana State University
Terre Haute, Indiana

Sara Seager, Ph.D.
Department of Planetary Science and Physics
Massachusetts Institute of Technology
Cambridge, MA

William H. Steinecker. Ph.D.
Research Scholar
Miami University
Oxford, Ohio

Paul R. Stoddard, Ph.D.
Department of Geology and Environmental Geosciences
Northern Illinois University
DeKalb, Illinois

Janet Vaglia, Ph. D.
Department of Biology
DePauw University
Greencastle, Indiana

Ed Zalisko, Ph.D.
Professor of Biology
Blackburn College
Carlinville, Illinois

K-8 National Master Teacher Board

Table of Contents

Lab zone Enter the Lab zone for hands-on inquiry.

Scenario Investigation: Plants in Space

Chapter Lab Investigation:
- Directed Inquiry: Investigating Stomata
- Open Inquiry: Investigating Stomata

Inquiry Warm-Ups: • What Do Leaves Reveal About Plants? • Will Mosses Absorb Water? • Which Plant Part Is It? • Make the Pollen Stick • Can a Plant Respond To Touch? • Feeding the World

Quick Labs: • Algae and Other Plants • Local Plant Diversity • Masses of Mosses • Examining a Fern • Common Characteristics • The In-Seed Story • Modeling Flowers • Plant Life Cycles • Where Are the Seeds? • Watching Roots Grow • Seasonal Changes • Everyday Plants

PearsonRealize.com

Go online for engaging videos, interactivities, and virtual labs.

 **Enter the Lab zone for hands-on inquiry.**

Scenario Investigation: Mealworm Migration

Chapter Lab Investigation:
  • Directed Inquiry: A Snail's Pace
  • Open Inquiry: A Snail's Pace

Inquiry Warm-Ups: Will It Bend and Move? • Sending Signals • Hydra Doing? • How Do Snakes Feed? • Making More • "Eggs-amination"

Quick Labs: • Comparing Bone and Cartilage • What Do Muscles Do? • Design a Nervous System • Compare Nervous Systems • Webbing Along • Planarian Feeding Behavior • Comparing Respiratory Systems • Comparing Circulatory Systems • Types of Reproduction • Types of Fertilization "Eggs-tra" Production • Cycles of Life • To Care or Not to Care

PearsonRealize.com

Go online for engaging videos, interactivities, and virtual labs.

Lab zone® Enter the Lab zone
for hands-on inquiry.

Scenario Investigation: That Can't Possibly
Work!

△ **Chapter Lab Investigation:**
  • Directed Inquiry: World in a Bottle
  • Open Inquiry: World in a Bottle

△ **Inquiry Warm-Ups:** • What's in the Scene?
  • Populations • Can You Hide a Butterfly?
  • How Communities Change

△ **Quick Labs:** • Organisms and Their Habitats
  • Organizing an Ecosystem • Growing and
  Shrinking • Elbow Room • Adaptations for
  Survival • Competition and Predation • Type
  of Symbiosis

PearsonRealize.com

**Go online for engaging
videos, interactivities,
and virtual labs.**

 Enter the Lab zone for hands-on inquiry.

STEM Activity: River Works

Chapter Lab Investigation:
  • Directed Inquiry: Ecosystem Food Chains
  • Open Inquiry: Ecosystem Food Chains

Inquiry Warm-Ups: • Where Did Your Dinner Come From? • Are You Part of a Cycle? • How Much Rain Is That? • Where Does It Live?

Quick Labs: • Observing Decomposition • Consequences of Human Activity • Following Water • Carbon and Oxygen Blues • Playing Nitrogen Cycle Roles • Inferring Forest Climates • Dissolved Oxygen

PearsonRealize.com

Go online for engaging videos, interactivities, and virtual labs.

CHAPTER 5

Balance Within Ecosystems

 Enter the Lab zone for hands-on inquiry.

Scenario Investigation: Fantasy Food Chain

Chapter Lab Investigation:
- Directed Inquiry: Consequences of Human Activity
- Open Inquiry: Consequences of Human Activity

Inquiry Warm-Ups: Populations • Can You Hide a Butterfly? • How Communities Change • How Do You Interact With Your Environment? • How Much Variety Is There?

Quick Labs: Growing and Shrinking • Elbow Room • Adaptations for Survival • Bird Beak Adaptations • Primary or Secondary • How Do Humans Impact Ecosystems? • Consequences of Human Activity • Technology and the Environment • Modeling Keystone Species • Grocery Gene Pool • Humans and Biodiversity

PearsonRealize.com

Go online for engaging videos, interactivities, and virtual labs.

 Enter the Lab zone for hands-on inquiry.

STEM Activity: Sail Away
Scenario Investigation: Please Drop In

△ **Chapter Lab Investigation:**
• Directed Inquiry: Sticky Sneakers
• Open Inquiry: Sticky Sneakers

△ **Inquiry Warm-Ups:** • Is the Force With You?
• Observing Friction • What Changes Motion?
• How Pushy Is a Straw? • What Makes an
Object Move in a Circle? • Why Redesign?

△ **Quick Labs:** • What Is Force? • Modeling
Unbalanced Forces • Calculating • Around and
Around • Newton's Second Law • Interpreting
Illustrations • Colliding Cars • Which Lands
First? • Orbiting Earth • Using Scientific
Thinking • How Close Is It?

PearsonRealize.com

Go online for engaging videos, interactivities, and virtual labs.

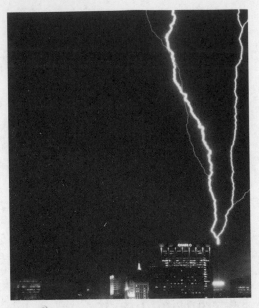

Lab zone® Enter the Lab zone for hands-on inquiry.

Scenario Investigation: My House Is Wired!

Chapter Lab Investigation:
• Directed Inquiry: Build a Flashlight
• Open Inquiry: Build a Flashlight

Inquiry Warm-Ups: • Can You Move a Can Without Touching It? • How Can Current Be Measured? • Do the Lights Keep Shining? • How Can You Make a Bulb Burn More Brightly?

Quick Labs: • Drawing Conclusions • Sparks Are Flying • Producing Electric Current • Conductors and Insulators • Modeling Potential Difference • Ohm's Law • Calculating Electric Power and Energy Use • Electric Shock and Short Circuit Safety

PearsonRealize.com

Go online for engaging videos, interactivities, and virtual labs.

CHAPTER

8

Magnetism and Electromagnetism

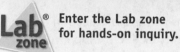 **Enter the Lab zone
for hands-on inquiry.**

Scenario Investigation: Is the North Pole
Really the South Pole?

Chapter Lab Investigation:
• Directed Inquiry: Detecting Fake Coins
• Open Inquiry: Detecting Fake Coins

Inquiry Warm-Ups: • Natural Magnets
• Predict the Field • Electromagnetism • How
Are Electricity, Magnets, and Motion Related?
• Electric Current Without a Battery

Quick Labs: • Magnetic Poles • Spinning
in Circles • Earth's Magnetic Field • Electric
Current and Magnetism • Magnetic Fields
From Electric Current • Electromagnet • Can a
Magnet Move a Wire? • How Galvanometers
Work • Parts of an Electric Motor • Inducing
an Electric Current • How Generators Work
• How Transformers Work

PearsonRealize.com

**Go online for engaging
videos, interactivities,
and virtual labs.**

 Enter the Lab zone
for hands-on inquiry.

Scenario Investigation: Mile-High Baseball

Chapter Lab Investigation:
• Directed Inquiry: Heating Earth's Surface
• Open Inquiry: Heating Earth's Surface

Inquiry Warm-Ups: • How Long Will
the Candle Burn? • Does Air Have Mass?
• Is Air There? • Does a Plastic Bag
Trap Heat? • What Happens When Air Is
Heated? • Does the Wind Turn?

Quick Labs: • Breathe In, Breathe Out
• What Is the Source of Earth's Energy?
• Properties of Air • Soda Bottle Barometer
• Effects of Altitude on the Atmosphere
• Layers of the Atmosphere • Calculating
Temperature Changes • How Does the Sun's
Energy Reach Earth? • Measuring Temperature
• Temperature and Height • Build a Wind Vane
• Modeling Global Wind Belts

PearsonRealize.com

**Go online for engaging
videos, interactivities,
and virtual labs.**

CHAPTER 10

Weather

Lab zone® Enter the Lab zone
for hands-on inquiry.

Scenario Investigation: Predicting the
Weather Is No Sport

Chapter Lab Investigation:
• Directed Inquiry: Reading a Weather Map
• Open Inquiry: Reading a Weather Map

Inquiry Warm-Ups: • Where Did the Water
Go? • How Does Fog Form? • How Can You
Make Hail? • How Do Fluids of Different
Densities Move? • Can You Make a Tornado?
• Predicting Weather

Quick Labs: • Water in the Air • Measuring
to Find the Dew Point • How Clouds Form
• Identifying Clouds • Types of Precipitation
• Floods and Droughts • Tracking Air Masses
• Weather Fronts • Cyclones and Anticyclones
• Where Do Hurricanes Come From? • Storm
Safety • Modeling Weather Satellites

PearsonRealize.com

**Go online for engaging
videos, interactivities,
and virtual labs.**

CHAPTER 11

Earth, Moon, and Sun

Lab zone® Enter the Lab zone
for hands-on inquiry.

Scenario Investigation: Smearing Causes
Seasons

Chapter Lab Investigation:
• Directed Inquiry: Reasons for the Seasons
• Open Inquiry: Reasons for the Seasons

Inquiry Warm-Ups: • Earth's Sky • What
Causes Day and Night? • What Factors
Affect Gravity? • How Does the Moon Move?
• When Is High Tide? • Why Do Craters Look
Different From Each Other?

Quick Labs: • Observing the Night Sky
• Watching the Skies • Sun Shadows • What's
Doing the Pulling? • Around and Around We
Go • Moon Phases • Eclipses • Modeling the
Moon's Pull of Gravity • Moonwatching

PearsonRealize.com

**Go online for engaging
videos, interactivities,
and virtual labs.**

 Enter the Lab zone for hands-on inquiry.

STEM Activity: Life on Mars

Chapter Lab Investigation:
• Directed Inquiry: Speeding Around the Sun
• Open Inquiry: Speeding Around the Sun

Inquiry Warm-Ups: • What Is at the Center? • How Big Is Earth? • How Can You Safely Observe the Sun? • Ring Around the Sun • How Big Are the Planets? • Collecting Micrometeorites

Quick Labs: • Going Around in Circles • A Loopy Ellipse • Clumping Planets • Layers of the Sun • Viewing Sunspots • Characteristics of the Inner Planets • Greenhouse Effect • Density Mystery • Make a Model of Saturn • Changing Orbits

PearsonRealize.com

Go online for engaging videos, interactivities, and virtual labs.

Science, Engineering, and Technology Skills Handbook

PART 1

What Is Science?

 Enter the Lab zone for hands-on inquiry.

Scenario Investigation: This Isn't Science!

△ **Chapter Lab Investigation:**
• Directed Inquiry: Changing Pitch
• Open Inquiry: Changing Pitch

△ **Inquiry Warm-Ups:** • Exploring Science
• How to Think Scientifically • Doing Science Is
Asking Questions

△ **Quick Labs:** • Practicing Science Skills
• Exploring Scientific Thinking • Using
Scientific Reasoning • Scientific Discovery
• Making a Hypothesis • Theory or Not?

PearsonRealize.com

Go online for engaging videos, interactivities, and virtual labs.

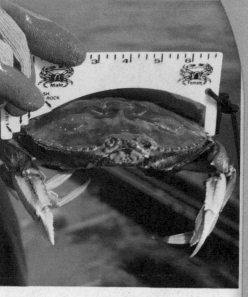

 Enter the Lab zone for hands-on inquiry.

STEM Activity: Out of the Corner of Your Eye

Chapter Lab Investigation:
• Directed Inquiry: Super Models
• Open Inquiry: Super Models

Inquiry Warm-Ups: • Taking Measurements • Making Models • Picturing Information • Models and Science • Is Science Safe?

Quick Labs: • Measurement Systems • Measuring Volume in Metric • Understanding Significant Figures • Math Tools in Science • Making Graphs • Graphs and Predictions • Systems of Science • Models of Natural Systems • Be Prepared to Be Safe in the Lab. • In Case of an Emergency

PearsonRealize.com

Go online for engaging videos, interactivities, and virtual labs.

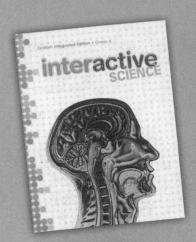

Interactive Science

Interactive Science is a program that features 3 pathways to match the way you learn.

- The write-in student edition enables you to become an active participant as you read about science.

- A variety of hands-on activities will not only engage you but also provide you with a deep understanding of science concepts.

- Go to PearsonRealize.com to access a wide array of digital resources built especially for students like you!

 Interact with your textbook.

 Interact with inquiry.

 Interact online.

interactive SCIENCE

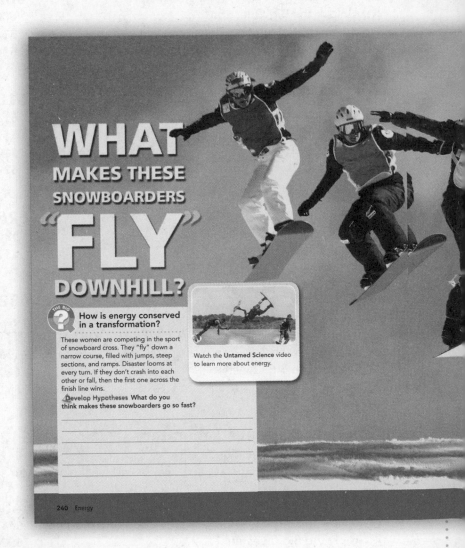

WHAT MAKES THESE SNOWBOARDERS "FLY" DOWNHILL?

How is energy conserved in a transformation?

These women are competing in the sport of snowboard cross. They "fly" down a narrow course, filled with jumps, steep sections, and ramps. Disaster looms at every turn. If they don't crash into each other or fall, then the first one across the finish line wins.

Develop Hypotheses What do you think makes these snowboarders go so fast?

Watch the **Untamed Science** video to learn more about energy.

240 Energy

 ## Get Engaged!

At the start of each chapter, you will see two questions: an Engaging Question and the Big Question. Each chapter's Big Question will help you start thinking about the Big Ideas of Science. Look for the Big Q symbol throughout the chapter!

Start with the Big Question

Energy

CHAPTER
7

PearsonRealize.com

241

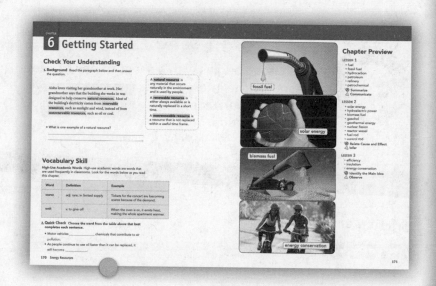

Build Reading, Inquiry, and Vocabulary Skills

In every lesson you will learn new Reading and Inquiry skills to help you read and think like a scientist.

PearsonRealize.com

Go to **PearsonRealize.com** for a variety of digital activities.

Unlock the Big Question

PearsonRealize.com

Go to PearsonRealize.com to access a wide array of digital resources such as Virtual Labs, videos, and assessments.

Explore the Key Concepts

Each lesson begins with a series of Key Concept questions. The interactivities in each lesson will help you understand these concepts and Unlock the Big Question.

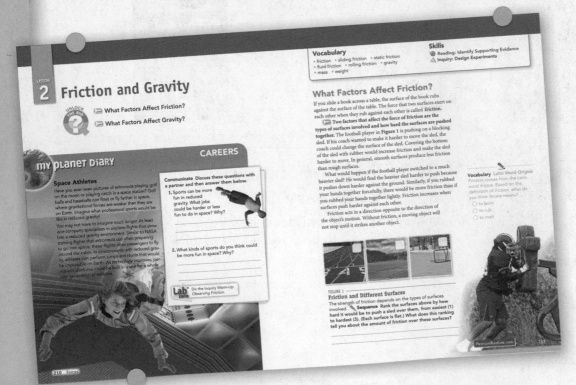

Desertification If the soil of moisture and nutrients, th advance of desertlike conditi fertile is called **desertificatio**

One cause of desertificati is a period when less rain th droughts, crops fail. Without blows away. Overgrazing of cutting down trees for firew

Desertification is a seriou and graze livestock where d people may face famine and central Africa. Millions of r cities because they can no lo

apply it!

Desertification affects many areas around the world.

1 Name Which continent has the most existing deser

2 Interpret Maps Where i the United States is the gre risk of desertification?

3 Infer Is desertification is existing desert? Explain. your answer.

4 CHALLENGE If an area is things people could do to p

516 Land, Air, and Water

my planet diary

At the start of each lesson, My Planet Diary will introduce you to amazing events, significant people, and important discoveries in science or help you to overcome common misconceptions about science concepts.

apply it!

Elaborate further with the Apply It activities. This is your opportunity to take what you've learned and apply those skills to new situations.

Lab zone

Look for the Lab zone triangle. This means that it's time to do a hands-on inquiry lab. In every lesson, you'll have the opportunity to do a hands-on inquiry activity that will help reinforce your understanding of the lesson topic.

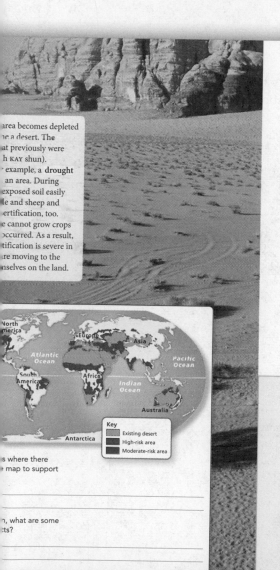

...area becomes depleted
...e a desert. The
...at previously were
...h KAY shun).
...example, a **drought**
...an area. During
...exposed soil easily
...le and sheep and
...ertification, too.
...e cannot grow crops
...occurred. As a result,
...tification is severe in
...re moving to the
...nselves on the land.

...s where there
... map to support

...n, what are some
...ts?

Land Reclamation Fortunately, it is possible to replace land damaged by erosion or mining. The process of restoring an area of land to a more productive state is called **land reclamation**. In addition to restoring land for agriculture, land reclamation can restore habitats for wildlife. Many different types of land reclamation projects are currently underway all over the world. But it is generally more difficult and expensive to restore damaged land and soil than it is to protect those resources in the first place. In some cases, the land may not return to its original state.

FIGURE 4 ·····
Land Reclamation
These pictures show land before and after it was mined.

✎ **Communicate** Below the pictures, write a story about what happened to the land.

📋 Assess Your Understanding

1a. Review Subsoil has ((less)/more) plant and animal matter than topsoil.

c. Apply Concepts Wh...
that could preven...
land reclamati...

b. Explain What can happen to soil if plants are removed?

got it? ·····

O **I get it!** Now I know that soil management is important because ___

O **I need extra help with** ___

Lab zone — Do the Quick Lab *Modeling Soil Conservation*

got it?

Evaluate Your Progress

After answering the Got It question, think about how you're doing. Did you get it or do you need a little help?

Assess the Big Question

Explore the Big Question

At one point in the chapter, you'll have the opportunity to take all that you've learned to further explore the Big Question.

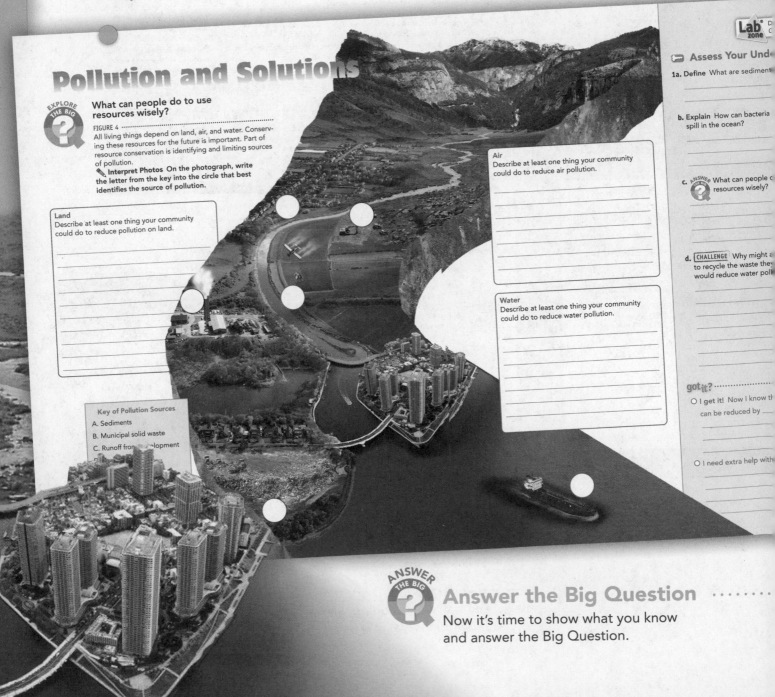

Pollution and Solutions

What can people do to use resources wisely?

FIGURE 4 ....
All living things depend on land, air, and water. Conserving these resources for the future is important. Part of resource conservation is identifying and limiting sources of pollution.

✎ **Interpret Photos** On the photograph, write the letter from the key into the circle that best identifies the source of pollution.

Land
Describe at least one thing your community could do to reduce pollution on land.

Key of Pollution Sources
A. Sediments
B. Municipal solid waste
C. Runoff from ___lopment

Air
Describe at least one thing your community could do to reduce air pollution.

Water
Describe at least one thing your community could do to reduce water pollution.

Assess Your Und

1a. Define What are sediment

b. Explain How can bacteria spill in the ocean?

c. ANSWER What can people c resources wisely?

d. CHALLENGE Why might a to recycle the waste they would reduce water poll

got it?
○ I get it! Now I know th can be reduced by ___

○ I need extra help with

Answer the Big Question ....

Now it's time to show what you know and answer the Big Question.

Review What You've Learned

Use the Chapter Study Guide to review the
Big Question and prepare for the test.

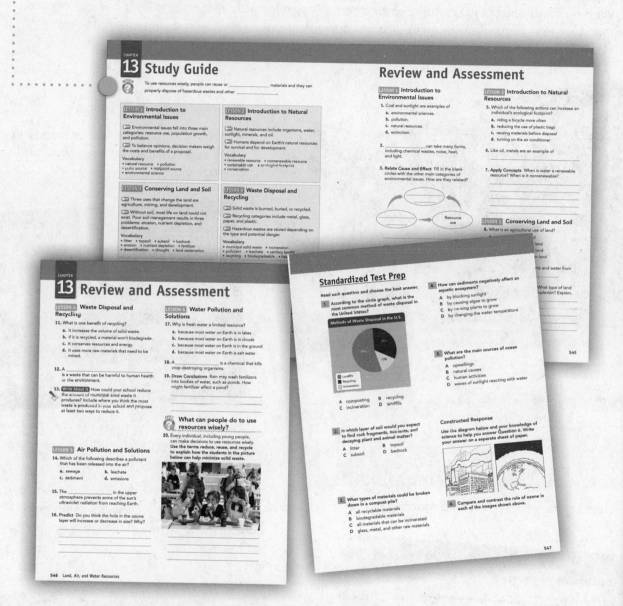

Practice Taking Tests

Apply the Big Question and take a practice test in
standardized test format.

What is Pearson Realize?

Interactive Science is now part of Pearson's brand-new learning management system, Realize! With rich and engaging content, embedded assessment with instant data, and flexible classroom management tools, Realize gives you the power to raise interest and achievement for every student in your classroom.

Engaging Videos

Engage with science topics through videos! Start each chapter with an Untamed Science video.

Pearson Flipped Videos for Science give you another way to learn.

Interactivities and Virtual Labs

Practice science content with engaging online activities.

At **PearsonRealize.com** go online and conduct labs virtually! No goggles and no mess.

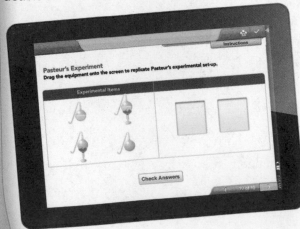

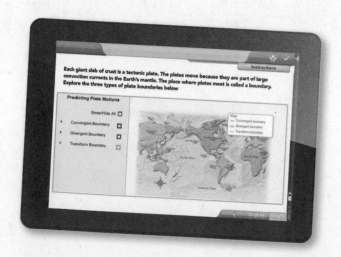

Connect to What You Know

Check what you know at the end of each lesson and chapter.

Get More Practice on skills and content, based on your performance.

Predict your exam readiness with benchmark assessments.

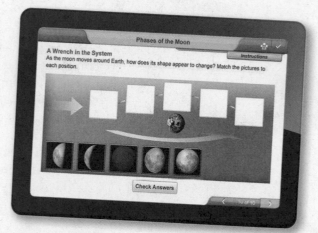

Pearson Realize offers powerful classroom management functionality, including:

Standards-aligned content — search by standard

Powerful Search tools — search by keyword, topic or standards

Customizable curriculum — reorder the table of contents, upload files and media, add links and create custom lessons and assessments

Flexible class management tools — create classes, organize students, and create assignments targeted to students, groups of students, or the entire class.

Tracks student progress — instantly access student and class data that shows standards mastery on assessments, online activity and overall progress.

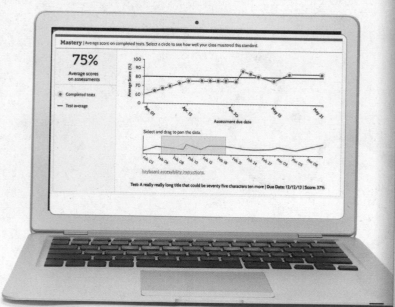

Track Your Learning Online.

PearsonRealize.com

BIG IDEAS OF SCIENCE

Have you ever worked on a jigsaw puzzle? Usually a puzzle has a theme that leads you to group the pieces by what they have in common. But until you put all the pieces together you can't solve the puzzle. Studying science is similar to solving a puzzle. The big ideas of science are like puzzle themes. To understand big ideas, scientists ask questions. The answers to those questions are like pieces of a puzzle. Each chapter in this book asks a big question to help you think about a big idea of science. By answering the big questions, you will get closer to understanding the big idea.

Before you read each chapter, use the pages that follow to write about what you know and what more you'd like to know.

Grasses and wildflowers look different, but they all grow in soil and need sunlight and water.

BIG IDEA

Living things are alike yet different.

What do you already know about how all living things are alike yet different? ✏️ **What more would you like to know?**

_____

_____

_____

Big Question:

❓ How do you know a plant when you see it? Plants

✏️ **After reading the chapter, write what you have learned about the Big Idea.**

_____

_____

_____

_____

A giraffe's long neck allows it to feed on vegetation that other animals cannot reach. Its long legs allow it to run at a speed of about 56 kilometers (35 miles) per hour for a short distance.

Arco Images GmbH/Alamy

BIGIDEA

Structures in living things are related to their functions.

What do you already know about how animals move in water, on land, or in air? ✎ **What more would you like to know?**

_____

_____

_____

_____

_____

Big Question:

❓ How do animals move? Animal Life Processes

✎ **After reading the chapter, write what you have learned about the Big Idea.**

_____

_____

_____

_____

These prairie dogs live in grasslands and make their homes underground. To stay alive, prairie dogs search for food and water and hide from animals that eat them.

Living things interact with their environment.

What do you already know about how the animals and plants in your neighborhood live together?
✏️ **What more would you like to know?**

_____
_____
_____
_____

Big Question:

❓ **How do living things affect one another?**
Populations and Communities

❓ **How do energy and matter move through ecosystems?** Ecosystems and Biomes

❓ **How do natural and human activities change ecosystems?**
Balance Within Ecosystems

✏️ **After reading the chapter, write what you have learned about the Big Idea.**

_____
_____
_____
_____

By hitting the soccer ball with her head, this athlete changes the direction of the soccer ball.

BIGIDEA

A net force causes an object's motion to change.

What do you already know about how the force of one object can affect the movement of another object? ✏ **What more would you like to know?**

_____
_____
_____
_____
_____

Big Question

❓ How do objects react to forces? Forces

✏ **After reading the chapter, write what you have learned about the Big Idea.**

_____
_____
_____
_____
_____
_____

Energy can take different forms but is always conserved.

What do you already know about what happens to the mass and energy of a candle as it burns?
🖉 **What more would you like to know?**

_____

_____

_____

_____

_____

_____

Big Questions:

❓ How does an electric circuit work? Electricity

❓ How are electricity and magnetism related? Magnetism and Electromagnetism

🖉 **After reading the chapters, write what you have learned about the Big Idea.**

_____

_____

_____

_____

_____

_____

As these skydivers fall, they don't lose any energy—the energy just takes different forms.

BIGIDEA
Earth's land, water, air, and life form a system.

Many forms of marine life, such as this orca breaching near the coastline, interact every day with Earth's land, air, and water.

What do you already know about how land, water, air, and life interact on Earth?

✏️ **What would you like to know?**

_____

_____

_____

Big Questions

❓ How does the sun's energy affect Earth's atmosphere?
The Atmosphere

❓ How do meteorologists predict the weather? Weather

✏️ **After reading the chapters, write what you have learned about the Big Idea.**

_____

_____

_____

_____

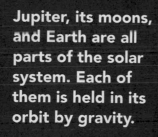

Jupiter, its moons, and Earth are all parts of the solar system. Each of them is held in its orbit by gravity.

Earth: Apollo 17 Crew. Jupiter/moons: NASA.

BIGIDEA

Earth is part of a system of objects that orbit the sun.

What do you already know about Earth and the other objects in the solar system? **What more would you like to know?**

_____

_____

_____

_____

Big Questions

? How do Earth, the moon, and the sun interact? Earth, Moon, and Sun

? Why are objects in the solar system different from each other? The Solar System

After reading the chapters, write what you have learned about the Big Idea.

_____

_____

_____

_____

_____

_____

WHAT'S UNUSUAL ABOUT THESE TREES?

How do you know a plant when you see it?

With its wide trunk and short stubby branches, the baobab tree looks like a sweet potato or an upside-down tree. Seen for miles across the dry African savannah, the baobab can live for over 1,000 years and can grow to over 23 meters high and 27 meters around the trunk. It would take about 18 teenagers with arms spread wide and fingertips touching to encircle a tree that wide!

Draw Conclusions Why do you think the baobab tree has such a wide trunk and short branches only at the very top?

_____
_____
_____
_____
_____

Watch the **Untamed Science** video to learn more about plants.

1 Getting Started

Check Your Understanding

1. **Background** Read the paragraph below and then answer the question.

Rahim and Malika were in the park after school. "Plants are such cool **organisms**," said Rahim. "Can you imagine if humans had green **pigment** in their skin?" "Yeah," said Malika. "If we were **autotrophs**, I'd never have to get up early to pack my lunch!"

> An **organism** is a living thing.
>
> A **pigment** is a colored chemical compound that absorbs light.
>
> An **autotroph** is an organism that makes its own food.

- Give an example of an autotrophic organism that has green pigment.

_____

_____

Vocabulary Skill

Greek Word Origins Many science words come to English from ancient Greek. Learning the Greek word parts can help you understand some of the vocabulary in this chapter.

Greek Word Part	Meaning	Example Word
chloros	pale green	chloroplast, _n._ green cellular structure in which photosynthesis occurs
petalon	leaf	petal, _n._ colorful, leaflike flower structure

2. **Quick Check** _Chlorophyll_ is a pigment found in plants. Which part of the word _chlorophyll_ tells you that it is a green pigment?

_____

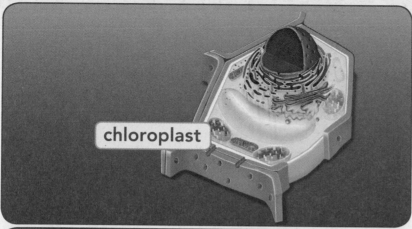

chloroplast

monocot

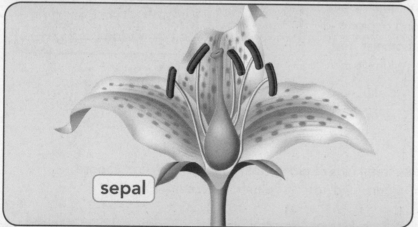

sepal

fruit

Chapter Preview

Scenario Investigation

Plants in Space

Purpose   To select the best plant for a space station on Mars

Materials   • paper   • pen or pencil

Scenario

Each spring, farmers and gardeners begin planting seeds and tending their gardens. It's a tradition with a history that may be as many as 23,000 years old. Someday this annual gardening ritual could make the difference between life and death for the residents of a space station on the planet Mars.

Science-fiction novels often describe space colonies on alien planets. Often these fictional colonies contain Earth plants that support the people living in the colony. Plants are vital for human survival on another planet. The plants provide food for the colonists and make the air breathable and the water drinkable.

NASA scientists agree that colonizing another planet must include plants. They are figuring out what kind of plants to use for the planned Mars colony. You are a botanist. You have been asked to help. The fate of NASA's plans is in your hands.

Life on Mars

Although Mars is the planet in our solar system that most closely resembles Earth, life on Mars would be very different from what we are used to. Consider the environment on Mars:

- Average Temperature: $-63°C$ ($-81.4°F$)

- Average Daily Temperature Range: -89 to $-31°C$ (-128.2 to $-23.8°F$)

- Atmosphere: 95.32 percent carbon dioxide (CO_2); 2.7 percent nitrogen (N_2); 1.6 percent argon (Ar); 0.13 percent oxygen (O_2); 0.08 percent carbon monoxide (CO)

Procedure

☐ **1. What Are the Choices?** There are three kinds of plants from which NASA can choose: nonvascular plants, seedless vascular plants, and vascular plants with seeds.

☐ **2. Choosing the Best** NASA is looking for a kind of plant that will absorb carbon dioxide, release oxygen, and provide the space colonists with food to eat. Use your textbook to research the characteristics of the three different kinds of plants. Which kind do you believe will do the best job of supporting the Mars explorers? Explain your answer.

_____

_____

_____

Procedure *(continued)*

☑ **3. Selecting One Example** Once you have chosen the best type of plant, select one example that you believe will provide a good source of food for the crew. (You can use the examples in the chart below, or you can use your own.) Explain why your choice is a good one.

_____

_____

Plant Examples				
		Vascular with Seeds		
Nonvascular	**Seedless Vascular**	**Gymnosperms**	**Angiosperms**	
moss	ferns	cycads	wheat	corn
liverworts	club mosses	conifers	rice	rye
hornworts	horsetails	ginkgoes	beans	potatoes
		gnetophytes	apples	oranges
			tomatoes	spinach

Conclusion

Let's see what you learned about plants and their benefits to humans living in space.

☑ **1.** What is the name of the gas that plants absorb from the air and use to grow?

_____

☑ **2.** Plants release a different gas back into the air. What is the name of that gas?

_____

☑ **3.** What is the process by which plants use light to produce their food called?

_____

☑ **4.** Which of the three kinds of plants produce most of the foods that humans eat?

_____

Prepare your recommendation for NASA in the form of a business letter. In your letter:

- name the plant you recommend
- give the name of the gas the plant will absorb and the gas it will release
- explain how this gas exchange will benefit the residents of the Mars colony

Use your textbook or the Internet to find the nutritional value of the food produced by the plant you recommend, and include that information in your report.

What Is a Plant?

UNLOCK THE BIG ?

🔑 **What Characteristics Do All Plants Share?**

🔑 **What Do Plants Need to Live Successfully on Land?**

my planeT DiaRY

How Does Your Garden Grow?

Students at The Hilldale School in Daly City, California, get to play in the dirt during class. The students planted and maintain a garden filled with native species. Native plants, or plants that have been in an area for a long time, can struggle to survive if new plants are introduced. This creates problems for the insects, animals, and other organisms that rely on the native plants. The students spent three months removing nonnative plants before creating a garden that will help local organisms right outside their school.

Communicate Discuss the question with a group of classmates. Write your answer below.

Describe a plant project you would like to do at your school.

_____

_____

_____

_____

_____

_____

Lab zone® Do the Inquiry Warm-Up *What Do Leaves Reveal About Plants?*

What Characteristics Do All Plants Share?

Which organisms were the ancestors of today's plants? In search of answers, biologists studied fossils, the traces of ancient life forms preserved in rock and other substances. The oldest plant fossils are about 400 million years old. These fossils show that even at that early date, plants already had many adaptations for life on land.

Vocabulary

- chlorophyll • photosynthesis • tissue • chloroplast
- vacuole • cuticle • vascular tissue

Skills

↻ Reading: Compare and Contrast

△ Inquiry: Predict

Better clues to the origin of plants came from comparing the chemicals in modern plants to those in other organisms. Biologists studied a pigment called chlorophyll. **Chlorophyll** (KLAWR uh fil) is a green pigment found in the chloroplasts of plants, algae, and some bacteria. Land plants and green algae contain the same forms of chlorophyll. Further comparisons of genetic material clearly showed that plants and green algae are very closely related. Today, green algae are classified as plants.

Members of the plant kingdom share several characteristics. **Nearly all plants are autotrophs, organisms that produce their own food. With the exception of some green algae, all plants contain many cells. In addition, all plant cells are surrounded by cell walls.**

Plants Are Autotrophs

You can think of a typical plant as a sun-powered, food-making factory. Sunlight provides the energy for this food-making process, called **photosynthesis.** During photosynthesis, a plant uses carbon dioxide gas and water to make food and oxygen.

↻ **Compare and Contrast**
How do you think the ancient environment of the leaf in the fossil differed from that of the modern leaf in the pictures below?

_____

_____

_____

_____

_____

_____

_____

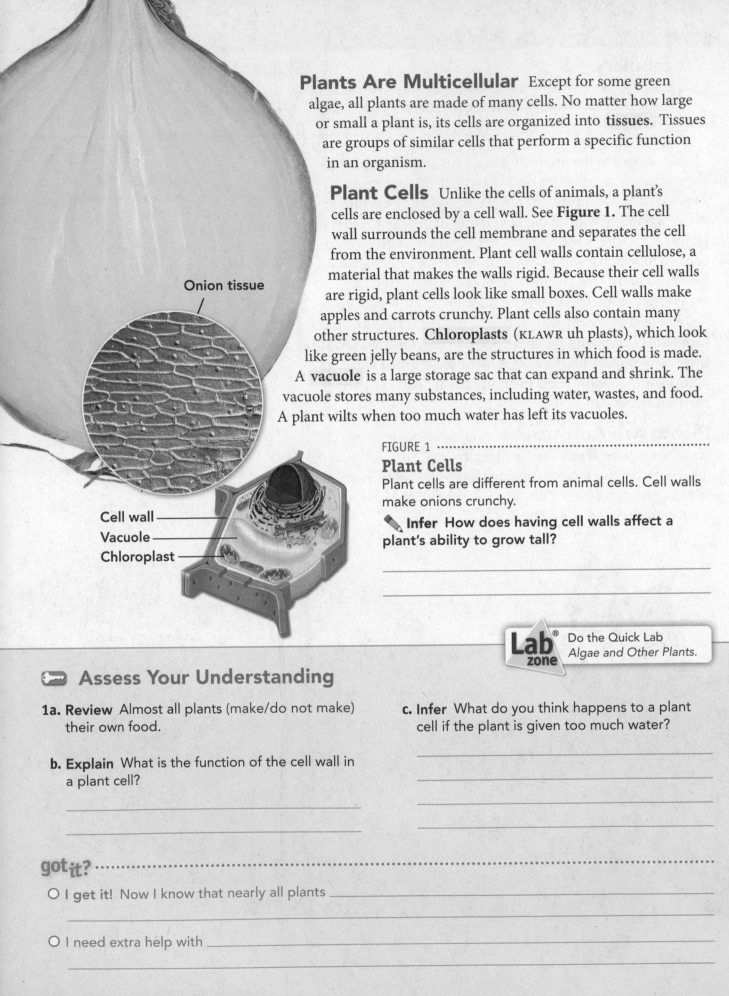

Plants Are Multicellular

Except for some green algae, all plants are made of many cells. No matter how large or small a plant is, its cells are organized into **tissues.** Tissues are groups of similar cells that perform a specific function in an organism.

Plant Cells

Unlike the cells of animals, a plant's cells are enclosed by a cell wall. See **Figure 1.** The cell wall surrounds the cell membrane and separates the cell from the environment. Plant cell walls contain cellulose, a material that makes the walls rigid. Because their cell walls are rigid, plant cells look like small boxes. Cell walls make apples and carrots crunchy. Plant cells also contain many other structures. **Chloroplasts** (KLAWR uh plasts), which look like green jelly beans, are the structures in which food is made. A **vacuole** is a large storage sac that can expand and shrink. The vacuole stores many substances, including water, wastes, and food. A plant wilts when too much water has left its vacuoles.

Onion tissue

Cell wall
Vacuole
Chloroplast

FIGURE 1 ··

Plant Cells

Plant cells are different from animal cells. Cell walls make onions crunchy.

✎ **Infer** How does having cell walls affect a plant's ability to grow tall?

_____

_____

Lab zone® Do the Quick Lab
Algae and Other Plants.

⚷ Assess Your Understanding

1a. Review Almost all plants (make/do not make) their own food.

b. Explain What is the function of the cell wall in a plant cell?

_____

_____

c. Infer What do you think happens to a plant cell if the plant is given too much water?

_____

_____

_____

_____

got it? ··

O **I get it!** Now I know that nearly all plants _____

_____

O **I need extra help with** _____

_____

What Do Plants Need to Live Successfully on Land?

Imagine multicellular algae floating in the ocean. The algae obtain water and other materials directly from the water around them. They are held up toward the sunlight by the water. Now imagine plants living on land. What adaptations would help them meet their needs without water all around them? 🔑 **For plants to survive on land, they must have ways to obtain water and other nutrients from their surroundings, retain water, support their bodies, transport materials, and reproduce.**

Obtaining Water and Other Nutrients

Recall that all organisms need water to survive. Obtaining water is easy for algae because water surrounds them. To live on land, plants need adaptations for obtaining water from the soil. One adaptation is the way the plant produces its roots, as shown in **Figure 2**. Plants must also have ways of obtaining other nutrients from the soil.

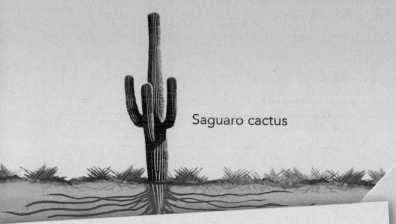

Saguaro cactus

Acacia tree

FIGURE 2 ·······
Getting Water in the Desert

The saguaro cactus and the acacia tree both live in deserts with limited water. Saguaro roots spread out horizontally. When it rains, the roots quickly absorb water over a wide area. Acacia trees in the Negev Desert of Israel get their water from deep underground instead of at the surface.

✏️ **Interpret Diagrams** Draw the roots of the acacia tree. Then describe how the growth of the roots differs between the plants.

_____

_____

_____

FIGURE 3 ·······························

Waterproof Leaves
The waxy cuticle of many leaves, like the one below, looks shiny under light.

Retaining Water When there is more water in plant cells than in the air, the water leaves the plant and enters the air. The plant could dry out if it cannot hold onto water. One adaptation that helps a plant reduce water loss is a waxy, waterproof layer called the **cuticle.** You can see the cuticle on the leaf in **Figure 3.**

Support A plant on land must support its own body. It's easier for small, low-growing plants to support themselves. In larger plants, the food-making parts must be exposed to as much sunlight as possible. Cell walls and tissue strengthen and support the large bodies of these plants.

Transporting Materials A plant needs to transport water, minerals, food, and other materials from one part of its body to another. In general, water and minerals are taken up by the bottom part of the plant, while food is made in the top part. But all of the plant's cells need water, minerals, and food.

In small plants, materials can simply move from one cell to the next. Larger plants need a more efficient way to transport materials from one part of the plant to another. These plants have tissue for transporting materials called vascular tissue. **Vascular tissue** is a system of tubelike structures inside a plant through which water, minerals, and food move. See vascular tissue in action in **Figure 4.**

apply it!

This graph shows how much water a plant loses during the day. Give the graph a title.

❶ **Interpret Graphs** During what part of the day did the plant lose the most water?

_____

❷ **Predict** How might the line in the graph look from 10 P.M. to 8 A.M.? Why?

_____
_____
_____
_____
_____
_____

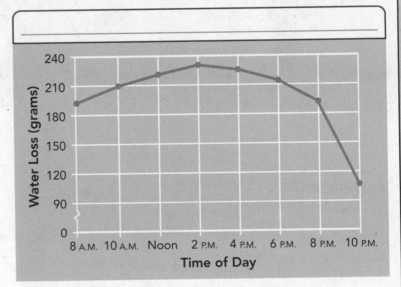

❸ **CHALLENGE** Do you think this graph would be the same for plants all around the world? Why?

_____
_____
_____

Reproduction

For algae and some other plants, reproduction can only occur if there is water in the environment. This is because the sperm cells of these plants swim through the water to the egg cells. Land plants need to have adaptations that make reproduction possible in dry environments.

FIGURE 4 ·······················

Colorful Carnations

These three carnations were left overnight in glasses of water. Blue dye was added to the glass in the middle. The stem of the flower on the right was split in half. Part of the stem was placed in water with blue dye and the other part was placed in water with red dye.

✏️ **Draw Conclusions** Why did the flowers in the glasses with dye change color?

_____
_____
_____
_____
_____

Lab zone® Do the Quick Lab *Local Plant Diversity.*

🔑 Assess Your Understanding

2a. Define What is a cuticle?

_____
_____
_____

b. Apply Concepts Describe the pros and cons of being a tall land plant.

_____
_____
_____
_____
_____

got it?

○ **I get it!** Now I know that to live on land, plants need to _____
_____
_____
_____

○ **I need extra help with** _____
_____
_____
_____

Classifying Plants

UNLOCK
THE BIG
?

🔑 **What Are the Characteristics of Nonvascular Plants?**

🔑 **What Are the Characteristics of Seedless Vascular Plants?**

🔑 **What Are the Characteristics of Seed Plants?**

my planet diary

CAREER

The Moss Is Greener on the Other Side

Tired of mowing the lawn? Never want to pull out another weed? Hire a moss landscaper! Landscapers design beautiful yards, usually planting trees, flowers, bushes, and grasses. These plants need a lot of care. Moss doesn't. Moss grows in the shade where other plants can't.

Landscapers can use moss to cover an entire yard if the conditions are right. Mosses are also better for the environment. People don't have to put toxic chemicals on their moss lawns to kill weeds or keep it green.

Write your answer below.

Do you think people should use moss instead of grass for their lawns? Why?

_____

_____

_____

_____

Lab ® Do the Inquiry Warm-Up
zone *Will Mosses Absorb Water?*

What Are the Characteristics of Nonvascular Plants?

Plants that lack vascular tissue for transporting materials are known as **nonvascular plants**. 🔑 **Nonvascular plants are low-growing, have thin cell walls, and do not have roots for absorbing water from the ground.** Instead, they obtain water and materials directly from their surroundings. The materials then pass from one cell to the next. This means that materials do not travel far or quickly. This slow method helps explain why most nonvascular plants live in damp, shady places. The thin cell walls are why these plants cannot grow more than a few centimeters tall.

Vocabulary

- nonvascular plant • rhizoid • vascular plant • phloem
- xylem • frond • pollen • seed • gymnosperm
- angiosperm • cotyledon • monocot • dicot

Skills

⟳ **Reading: Outline**

△ **Inquiry: Communicate**

Mosses Have you ever seen mosses growing in the cracks of a sidewalk or in a shady spot? With more than 10,000 species, mosses are by far the most diverse group of nonvascular plants.

If you were to look closely at a moss, you would see a plant that looks something like **Figure 1.** Structures that look like tiny leaves grow off a small, stemlike structure. Thin, rootlike structures called **rhizoids** anchor the moss and absorb water and nutrients. Moss grows a long, slender stalk with a capsule at the end. The capsule contains spores for reproduction.

FIGURE 1 ···

Moss Structure

Diagrams can be easier to read than photographs, but photographs are more realistic.

✎ **Relate Diagrams and Photos** Label the capsule, stalk, and leaflike structure in the photo. Draw lines from your labels to the structure itself, like in the diagram below.

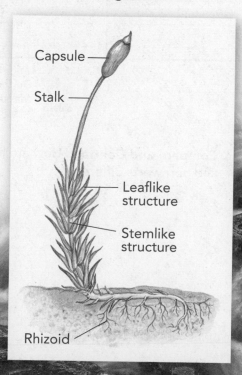

Capsule

Stalk

Leaflike structure

Stemlike structure

Rhizoid

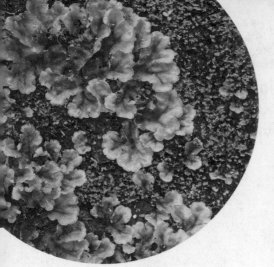

Liverwort ▲

Liverworts and Hornworts Liverworts and hornworts are two other groups of nonvascular plants. There are more than 8,000 species of liverworts. This group of plants is named for the shape of the plant's body, which looks somewhat like a human liver. *Wort* is an old English word for "plant." Liverworts are often found growing as a thick crust on moist rocks or soil along the sides of a stream. There are fewer than 100 species of hornworts. If you look closely at a hornwort, you can see slender, curved structures that look like horns growing out of the plant. Unlike mosses or liverworts, hornworts are seldom found on rocks or tree trunks. Instead, hornworts usually live in moist soil, often mixed in with grass plants.

✎ **Outline** Fill in the table to the right with what you have learned about liverworts and hornworts.

Hornwort ▶

Nonvascular Plants

Plant	Identifiable Physical Characteristic	Where Found
Mosses	Fuzzy appearance	Shady spots, rocks, tree trunks
Liverworts		
Hornworts		

Lab zone ® Do the Quick Lab *Masses of Mosses.*

🔑 Assess Your Understanding

1a. Review (Vascular tissues/Rhizoids) anchor moss and absorb water and nutrients.

b. Explain Why are most nonvascular plants short?

c. Compare and Contrast How are liverworts and hornworts different?

got**it?**

○ **I get it!** Now I know the characteristics of nonvascular plants are _____

○ **I need extra help with** _____

What Are the Characteristics of Seedless Vascular Plants?

If you could have walked through the ancient forests that existed long before the dinosaurs lived, they would have looked very strange to you. You might have recognized the mosses and liverworts that carpeted the moist soil, but you would have seen very tall, odd-looking trees. Among the trees grew huge, tree-sized ferns. Other trees resembled giant sticks with leaves up to one meter long. The odd-looking plants in the ancient forests are the ancestors of the ferns, clubmosses, and horsetails of today. **🔑 Ferns, club mosses, and horsetails share two characteristics. They have vascular tissue and they do not produce seeds. Instead of seeds, these plants reproduce by releasing spores.**

Vascular Tissue   Ancient trees were vascular plants. **Vascular plants** are plants with true vascular tissue. Vascular plants can grow tall because their vascular tissue provides an effective way of transporting materials throughout the plant. The vascular tissue also strengthens the plants' bodies. You can see vascular tissue in **Figure 2.** The cells making up the vascular tissue have strong cell walls. Imagine a handful of drinking straws bundled together with rubber bands. The bundle of straws is stronger and more stable than a single straw would be. Arranged similarly, the strong, tubelike structures in vascular plants give the plants strength and stability.

There are two types of vascular tissue. **Phloem** (FLOH um) is the vascular tissue through which food moves. After food is made in the leaves, it enters the phloem and travels to other parts of the plant. Water and minerals, on the other hand, travel in the vascular tissue called **xylem** (ZY lum). The roots absorb water and minerals from the soil. These materials enter the root's xylem and move upward into the stems and leaves.

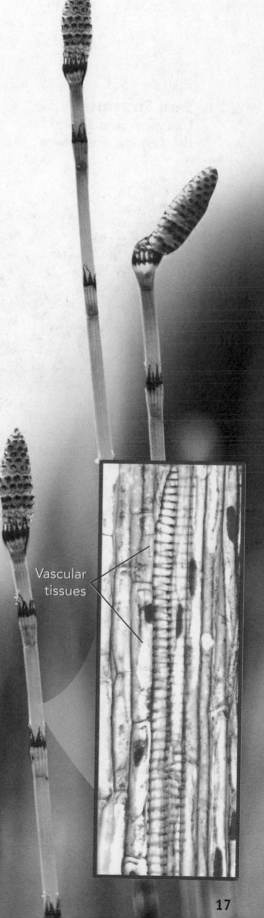

Vascular tissues

FIGURE 2 ························

Vascular Tissue
Vascular plants have xylem and phloem.

✏️ **Identify** In the text, underline the roles of vascular tissue.

Ferns

There are more than 12,000 species of ferns alive today. They range in size from tiny plants about the size of this letter *M* to tree ferns that grow up to five meters tall. Ferns thrive in shaded areas with moist soil. Some remain green year-round while others turn brown in the fall and regrow in spring.

The Structure of Ferns

Like other vascular plants, ferns have stems, roots, and leaves. The stems of most ferns are underground. Leaves grow upward from the top side of the stems, while roots grow downward from the bottom of the stems. Water and nutrients enter the root's vascular tissue and travel through the tissue into the stems and leaves.

Figure 3 shows a fern's structure. Notice that the fern's leaves, or **fronds,** are divided into many smaller parts that look like small leaves. The upper surface of each frond is coated with a cuticle that helps the plant retain water. In many ferns, the developing leaves are coiled at first. Because they resemble the top of a violin, these young leaves are often called fiddleheads. Fiddleheads uncurl as they mature.

FIGURE 3 ·······························

Fern Structure

Like other plants, ferns have roots, stems, and leaves.

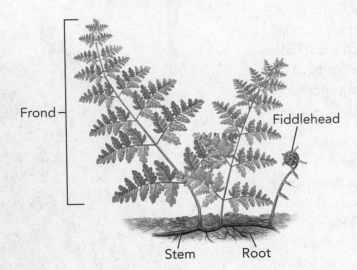

Frond

Fiddlehead

Stem   Root

apply it!

Caring for Your Fern

Suppose you ran a flower shop that sold cut flowers and potted plants. You have just received a shipment of potted ferns and several customers are interested in purchasing them. Before they are ready to be sold, you need to make sure your customers can take care of the ferns so they won't regret their purchase.

1 Communicate On the tag at left, write the care instructions that will be given to your customers who buy potted ferns. Include the conditions that the fern needs for light and water.

2 CHALLENGE Florists recommend not putting plants like ferns in south- or west-facing windows. Why?

◄ Horsetail

Club Mosses and Horsetails

Like ferns, club mosses and horsetails have true stems, roots, and leaves. However, there are relatively few species of club mosses and horsetails alive today.

Do not be confused by the name *club moss*. Unlike true mosses, club mosses have vascular tissue. You may be familiar with the club moss in **Figure 4.** The plant, which looks a little like a small branch of a pine tree, is sometimes called ground pine or princess pine. Club mosses usually grow in moist woodlands and near streams.

There are about 30 species of horsetails on Earth today. The whorled pattern of growth somewhat resembles the appearance of a horse's tail. The stems contain silica, a gritty substance also found in sand. During colonial times, Americans used the plants to scrub their pots and pans. Another common name for horsetails is scouring brushes.

Club moss ▼

FIGURE 4 ···

Moss Imposter?
A club moss is pictured at left.

✎ **Describe** Why is a club moss not a true moss?

_____

_____

_____

_____

_____

Lab zone® Do the Quick Lab
Examining a Fern.

🗝 Assess Your Understanding

2a. Identify In plants, water moves through (phloem/xylem). Food moves through (phloem/xylem).

b. Infer Why do you think the developing leaves of a fern are coiled?

_____

_____

c. Develop Hypotheses Why do you think there are more ferns than club mosses?

_____

_____

_____

_____

got it? ···

○ **I get it!** Now I know the characteristics of seedless vascular plants include _____

_____

○ **I need extra help with** _____

_____

19

What Are the Characteristics of Seed Plants?

Seed plants outnumber seedless plants by more than ten to one. You eat many seed plants—rice, peas, and squash, for example. You wear clothes made from seed plants, such as cotton and flax. You may live in a home built from seed plants—oak, pine, or maple trees. In addition, seed plants produce much of the oxygen you breathe.

Seed plants share two important characteristics. 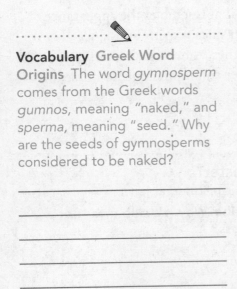 **Seed plants have vascular tissue, and they use pollen and seeds to reproduce.** In addition, the bodies of all seed plants have roots, stems, and leaves. Most seed plants live on land. Recall that land plants face many challenges, including standing upright and supplying all their cells with food and water. Like ferns, seed plants meet these two challenges with vascular tissue.

Pollen and Seeds Unlike seedless plants, seed plants can live in a wide variety of environments. Seedless plants need water in their surroundings for fertilization to occur. Seed plants do not need water for sperm to swim to the eggs. Instead, seed plants produce **pollen,** tiny structures that contain the cells that will later become sperm cells. Pollen deliver sperm cells directly near the eggs. After sperm cells fertilize the eggs, seeds develop. A **seed** is a structure that contains a young plant inside a protective covering. Seeds protect the young plant from drying out.

Gymnosperms The giant sequoia trees belong to the group of seed plants known as gymnosperms. A **gymnosperm** (JIM noh spurm) is a seed plant that produces naked seeds. The seeds of gymnosperms are referred to as "naked" because they are not enclosed by a protective fruit.

Many gymnosperms have needlelike or scalelike leaves and deep-growing root systems. Gymnosperms are the oldest type of seed plant. According to fossil evidence, gymnosperms first appeared on Earth about 360 million years ago. Fossils also indicate that there were many more species of gymnosperms on Earth in the past than there are today. Four types of gymnosperms exist today, as shown in **Figure 5.**

Vocabulary Greek Word Origins The word *gymnosperm* comes from the Greek words *gumnos*, meaning "naked," and *sperma*, meaning "seed." Why are the seeds of gymnosperms considered to be naked?

_____

_____

_____

_____

GYMNOSPERM	DESCRIPTION/FUNCTION
Cycads 	About 175 million years ago, the majority of plants were cycads (SY kadz). Today, cycads grow mainly in tropical and subtropical areas. Cycads look like palm trees with cones that can grow as large as a football!
Conifers 	Conifers (KAHN uh furz), or cone-bearing plants, are the largest and most diverse group of modern gymnosperms. Most conifers are evergreens, meaning they keep their leaves or needles year-round.
Ginkgoes 	Ginkgoes (GING kohz) also grew hundreds of millions of years ago. Today, only one species, *Ginkgo biloba*, exists. It probably survived because the Chinese and Japanese cared for it in their gardens. Today, ginkgo trees are planted along city streets because they can tolerate air pollution.
Gnetophytes 	Gnetophytes (NEE tuh fyts) live in hot deserts and in tropical rain forests. Some are trees, some are shrubs, and others are vines. The *Welwitschia* (shown at left) of West Africa can live for more than 1,000 years!

FIGURE 5 ....

Types of Gymnosperms
The chart describes the four main groups of gymnosperms.

✎ **Answer these questions.**

1. **Name** Which group of gymnosperms has the most species?

_____

2. **Apply Concepts** What could have happened to the ecosystem the *Ginkgo biloba* tree lived in if the tree had become extinct?

_____
_____
_____
_____
_____
_____
_____

_____

_____

Angiosperms You probably associate the word *flower* with a sweet-smelling plant growing in a garden. You certainly wouldn't think of something that smells like rotting meat. That's exactly what the corpse flower, or rafflesia, smells like. This flower, which grows in Asia, produces a meat smell, which attracts flies that spread the flower's pollen. You won't be seeing rafflesia in your local florist shop any time soon! Rafflesia belongs to the group of seed plants known as angiosperms (AN jee uh spurmz). **Angiosperms,** or flowering plants, share two important characteristics. First, they produce flowers. Second, in contrast to gymnosperms, which produce uncovered seeds, angiosperms produce seeds that are enclosed in fruits.

Angiosperms live almost everywhere on Earth. They grow in frozen areas in the Arctic, tropical jungles, and barren deserts. A few angiosperms, such as mangrove trees, live at the ocean's edge.

Types of Angiosperms Angiosperms are divided into two major groups: monocots and dicots. "Cot" is short for cotyledon (kaht uh LEED un). The **cotyledon,** or seed leaf, provides food for the embryo. *Mono-* means "one" and *di-* means "two." **Monocots** are angiosperms that have only one seed leaf. Grasses, including corn, wheat, and rice, and plants such as lilies and tulips, are monocots. **Dicots,** on the other hand, produce seeds with two seed leaves. Dicots include plants such as roses and violets, as well as dandelions. Both oak and maple trees are dicots, as are food plants such as beans and apples. **Figure 6** shows the characteristics of monocots and dicots.

FIGURE 6 ·······················

Monocots and Dicots
Use the table below to find your answers.

🖉 **Interpret Photos** Label the rafflesia (top) and the other flowers on this page as *monocots* or *dicots*.

_____

Characteristics of Monocots and Dicots

	Seeds	Leaves	Flowers	Stems	Roots
Monocots	Single cotyledon	Parallel veins	Floral parts often in multiples of 3	Vascular tissue bundles scattered throughout stem	Many roots spread out
Dicots	Two cotyledons	Branched veins	Floral parts often in multiples of 4 or 5	Vascular tissue bundles arranged in a ring	One main root

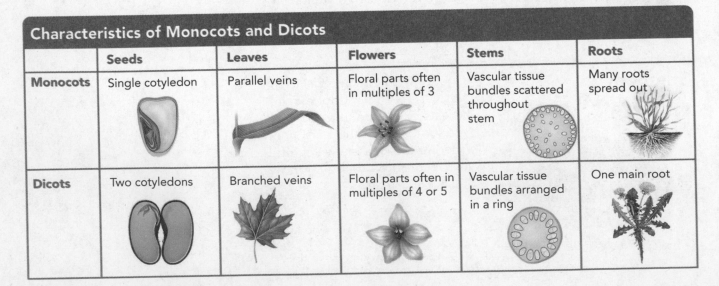

do the math!

Use the graph of known plant species to answer the questions.

1 **Interpret Graphs** Which plant group has the fewest species?

_____

2 **Calculate** Figure out the percentage that each of the following plant groups represents. Round your answer to the nearest tenth.

Green algae _____

Ferns and relatives _____

Angiosperms _____

3 **CHALLENGE** Why do you think angiosperms are the largest group?

_____

_____

_____

_____

_____

_____

Major Groups of Known Plants

Green Algae: 7,000 species

Mosses and Relatives: 18,500 species

Ferns and Relatives: 12,000 species

Gymnosperms: 800 species

Angiosperms: 260,000 species

Lab **zone** Do the Quick Lab *Common Characteristics.*

Assess Your Understanding

3a. Define What are pollen?

_____

_____

_____

_____

_____

b. Draw Conclusions Why do you think angiosperms enclose their seeds in fruits?

_____

_____

_____

_____

_____

got it?

○ **I get it!** Now I know the characteristics of seed plants include _____

_____

○ **I need extra help with** _____

_____

UNLOCK
THE BIG
?

🔑 **What Are the Functions of Roots, Stems, and Leaves?**

🔑 **How Do Seeds Become New Plants?**

🔑 **What Are the Structures of a Flower?**

MY PLANET DIARY

SCIENCE STATS

Plant Giants

- The aroid plant (as shown here) on the island of Borneo in Asia has leaves that can grow three meters long! These are the largest undivided leaves on Earth!

- The rafflesia flower can grow up to one meter wide and weigh seven kilograms.

- The jackfruit can weigh up to 36 kilograms. That's the world's largest fruit that grows on trees!

Write your answer below.

Why do you think the aroid plant has such big leaves?

_____

_____

_____

Lab zone® Do the Inquiry Warm-Up
Which Plant Part Is It?

What Are the Functions of Roots, Stems, and Leaves?

Each part of a plant plays an important role in its structure and function. Roots, stems, and leaves are just three structures we will look into further.

Roots Have you ever tried to pull a dandelion out of the soil? It's not easy, is it? That is because most roots are good anchors. Roots have three main functions. 🔑 **Roots anchor a plant in the ground, absorb water and minerals from the soil, and sometimes store food.** The more root area a plant has, the more water and minerals it can absorb.

Vocabulary

- root cap • cambium • stoma • transpiration
- embryo • germination • flower • pollination
- sepal • petal • stamen • pistil • ovary

Skills

🔄 Reading: Relate Cause and Effect
⚠ Inquiry: Observe

Types of Roots The two main types of root systems are shown in **Figure 1.** A fibrous root system consists of many similarly sized roots that form a dense, tangled mass. Plants with fibrous roots take a lot of soil with them when you pull them out of the ground. Lawn grass, corn, and onions have fibrous root systems. In contrast, a taproot system has one long, thick main root. Many smaller roots branch off the main root. A plant with a taproot system is hard to pull out of the ground. Carrots, dandelions, and cacti have taproots.

FIGURE 1 ⋯⋯⋯⋯⋯⋯⋯⋯⋯⋯⋯⋯⋯⋯

Root Systems and Structure

There are two main root systems with many structures.

✏ **Interpret Photos** Label the taproot *T* and the fibrous roots *F*.

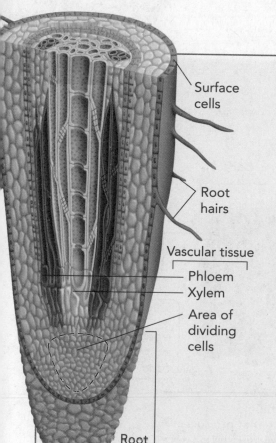

Surface cells

Root hairs

Vascular tissue
— Phloem
— Xylem
— Area of dividing cells

Root cap

Root Structure

In **Figure 2,** you can see the structure of a typical root. The tip of the root is rounded and is covered by the root cap. The **root cap** protects the root from injury as the root grows through the soil. Behind the root cap are the cells that divide to form new root cells.

Root hairs grow out of the root's surface. These tiny hairs can enter the spaces between soil particles, where they absorb water and minerals. The root hairs also help to anchor the plant in the soil.

Locate the vascular tissue in the center of the root. The water and nutrients that are absorbed from the soil quickly move into the xylem. From there, these substances are transported upward to the plant's stems and leaves. Phloem transports food manufactured in the leaves to the root. The root tissues then use the food for growth or store it for future use by the plant.

FIGURE 2 ⋯⋯⋯⋯⋯⋯⋯⋯⋯⋯⋯⋯⋯⋯⋯⋯⋯⋯⋯⋯⋯⋯⋯

Root Structure

Roots have many structures.

✏ **Define** What is the function of the root cap?

_____

_____

Stems

The stem of a plant has two main functions. 🗝 **The stem carries substances between the plant's roots and leaves. The stem also provides support for the plant and holds up the leaves so they are exposed to the sun.** In addition, some stems, such as those of asparagus, store food.

The Structure of a Stem

Stems can be either woody or herbaceous (hur BAY shus). Woody stems are hard and rigid, such as in maple trees. Herbaceous stems contain no wood and are often soft. Plants with herbaceous stems include daisies, ivy, and asparagus (pictured left).

Herbaceous and woody stems consist of phloem and xylem tissue as well as many other supporting cells. As you can see in **Figure 3**, a woody stem contains many layers of tissue. The outermost layer is bark. Bark includes an outer protective layer and an inner layer of living phloem, which transports food through the stem. Next is a layer of cells called the **cambium** (KAM bee um), which divides to produce new phloem and xylem. It is xylem that makes up most of what you call "wood." Sapwood is active xylem that transports water and minerals through the stem. The older, darker, heartwood is inactive but provides support.

FIGURE 3 ···

Stem Structure

The woody stem of a tree contains many different structures.

✎ **Interpret Diagrams** Label the active xylem and phloem on the tree trunk below.

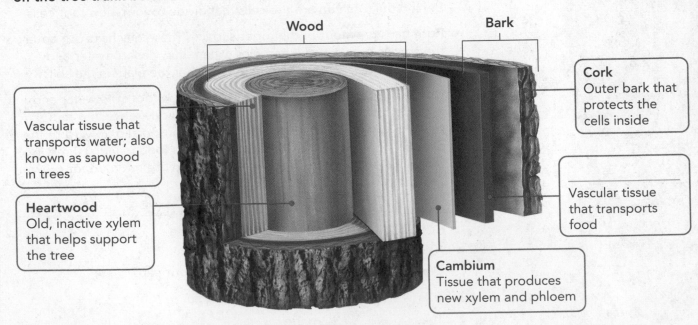

Wood

Bark

Cork
Outer bark that protects the cells inside

Vascular tissue that transports water; also known as sapwood in trees

Vascular tissue that transports food

Heartwood
Old, inactive xylem that helps support the tree

Cambium
Tissue that produces new xylem and phloem

Annual Rings Have you ever looked at a tree stump and seen a pattern of circles that looks something like a target? These circles are called annual rings. They represent a tree's yearly growth. Annual rings are made of xylem. Xylem cells that form in the spring are large and have thin walls because they grow rapidly. They produce a wide, light brown ring. Xylem cells that form in the summer grow slowly and, therefore, are small and have thick walls. They produce a thin, dark ring. One pair of light and dark rings represents one year's growth. You can estimate a tree's age by counting its annual rings.

The width of a tree's annual rings can provide important clues about past weather conditions, such as rainfall. In rainy years, more xylem is produced, so the tree's annual rings are wide. In dry years, rings are narrow. By examining annual rings from some trees in the southwestern United States, scientists were able to infer that severe droughts occurred in the years 840, 1067, 1379, and 1632.

◄ **The annual rings in a tree reveal the tree's history.**

apply it!

1 Calculate How old was the tree when it was cut down?

_____

_____

2 Observe The area at Area C is blackened from a fire that affected one side of the tree. Describe how the tree grew after the fire.

_____

_____

_____

_____

3 CHALLENGE Areas A and B both represent four years of growth. What might account for their difference in size?

_____

_____

_____

_____

_____

_____

_____

Vocabulary Greek Word
Origins The Greek word *stoma*
means "mouth." How are the
stomata of a plant like mouths?

_____

_____

_____

_____

_____

_____

_____

_____

Leaves

Leaves Leaves vary greatly in size and shape. Pine trees have needle-shaped leaves. Birch trees have small rounded leaves with jagged edges. Regardless of their shape, leaves play an important role in a plant. 🔑 **Leaves capture the sun's energy and carry out the food-making process of photosynthesis.**

The Structure of a Leaf If you were to cut through a leaf and look at the edge under a microscope, you would see the structures in **Figure 4.** The leaf's top and bottom surface layers protect the cells inside. Between the layers of cells are veins that contain xylem and phloem.

The surface layers of the leaf have small openings, or pores, called stomata (stoh MAH tuh; *singular* stoma). The stomata open and close to control when gases enter and leave the leaf. When the stomata are open, carbon dioxide enters the leaf, and oxygen and water vapor exit.

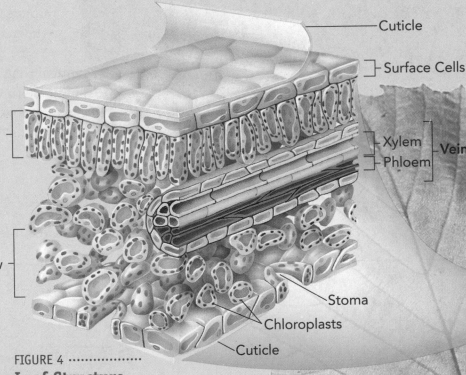

Upper Leaf Cells
Tightly packed cells trap the energy in sunlight.

Lower Leaf Cells
Widely spaced cells allow carbon dioxide to reach cells for photosynthesis and oxygen to escape into the air.

Cuticle

Surface Cells

Xylem
Phloem
Vein

Stoma

Chloroplasts

Cuticle

FIGURE 4 ··················

Leaf Structure
Each structure helps a leaf produce food.

✏️ **Review** Circle the best answer to complete the sentences.

(Cuticles/Chloroplasts) are the structures in which food is made. (Cuticles/Chloroplasts) are the waxy layers that help plants reduce water loss.

The Leaf and Photosynthesis The structure of a leaf is ideal for carrying out photosynthesis. The cells that contain the most chloroplasts are located near the leaf's upper surface, where they get the most light. The chlorophyll in the chloroplasts traps the sun's energy.

Carbon dioxide enters the leaf through open stomata. Water, which is absorbed by the plant's roots, travels up the stem to the leaf through the xylem. During photosynthesis, sugar and oxygen are produced from the carbon dioxide and water. Oxygen passes out of the leaf through the open stomata. The sugar enters the phloem and then travels throughout the plant.

Controlling Water Loss Because such a large area of a leaf is exposed to the air, water can quickly evaporate from a leaf into the air. The process by which water evaporates from a plant's leaves is called **transpiration.** A plant can lose a lot of water through transpiration. A corn plant, for example, can lose almost 4 liters of water on a hot summer day. Without a way to slow down the process of transpiration, a plant would shrivel up and die.

Fortunately, plants have ways to slow down transpiration. One way plants retain water is by closing the stomata. The stomata often close when leaves start to dry out.

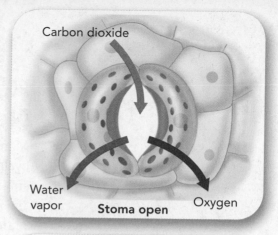

Carbon dioxide

Water vapor   **Stoma open**   Oxygen

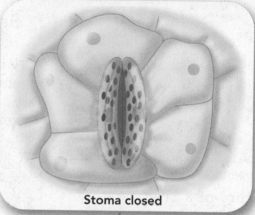

Stoma closed

FIGURE 5 ··

Stomata
Stomata can slow water loss.

✏ **Name** What three substances enter and leave a plant through stomata?

_____

_____

 Do the Lab Investigation
Investigating Stomata.

🔑 Assess Your Understanding

1a. List What are the functions of a stem?

_____

_____

_____

_____

b. Infer If you forget to water a houseplant for a few days, would its stomata be open or closed? Why?

_____

_____

_____

got it? ··

○ **I get it!** Now I know that roots, stems, and leaves perform functions like _____

_____

○ **I need extra help with** _____

_____

How Do Seeds Become New Plants?

Many plants begin their life cycle as a seed. You can follow the cycle from seed to plant in **Figure 6.** All seeds share important similarities. 🔑 **Inside a seed is a partially developed plant. If a seed lands in an area where conditions are favorable, the plant sprouts out of the seed and begins to grow.**

Seed Structure A seed has three main parts—an embryo, stored food, and a seed coat. The young plant that develops from the zygote, or fertilized egg, is called the **embryo.** The embryo already has the beginnings of roots, stems, and leaves. In the seeds of most plants, the embryo stops growing when it is quite small. When the embryo begins to grow again, it uses the food stored in the seed until it can make its own food by photosynthesis. In all seeds, the embryo has one or more seed leaves, or cotyledons. In some seeds, food is stored in the cotyledons. In others, food is stored outside the embryo.

The outer covering of a seed is called the seed coat. The seed coat acts like plastic wrap, protecting the embryo and its food from drying out. This allows a seed to remain inactive for a long time. In many plants, the seeds are surrounded by a structure called a fruit.

FIGURE 6 ·······················

Story of a Seed
Read the text on this page and the next page. Then complete the activities about seeds becoming new plants.

✎ **Complete each task.**

1. **Review** On the diagram, label the seed's embryo, cotyledons, and seed coat.

Stem and root

Stored food

Seed Dispersal

After seeds form, they are usually scattered. The scattering of seeds is called seed dispersal. Seeds can be dispersed in many different ways. When animals eat fruit, the seeds inside the fruit pass through the animal's digestive system and are deposited in new areas. Other seeds are enclosed in barblike structures that hook onto fur or clothing. The seeds fall off in a new area. Water also disperses seeds that fall into oceans and rivers. Wind disperses lightweight seeds, such as those of dandelions and maple trees. Some plants eject their seeds. The force scatters the seeds in many directions. A seed that is dispersed far from its parent plant has a better chance of survival. Far away, a seed does not have to compete with its parent for light, water, and nutrients.

Germination

After a seed is dispersed, it may remain inactive for a while before it germinates. **Germination** (jur muh NAY shun) occurs when the embryo begins to grow again and pushes out of the seed. Germination begins when the seed absorbs water. Then the embryo uses stored food to begin to grow. The roots first grow downward. Then its stem and leaves grow upward.

✎

➲ **Relate Cause and Effect**
Underline a cause of seed dispersal and circle its effect in the text on this page.

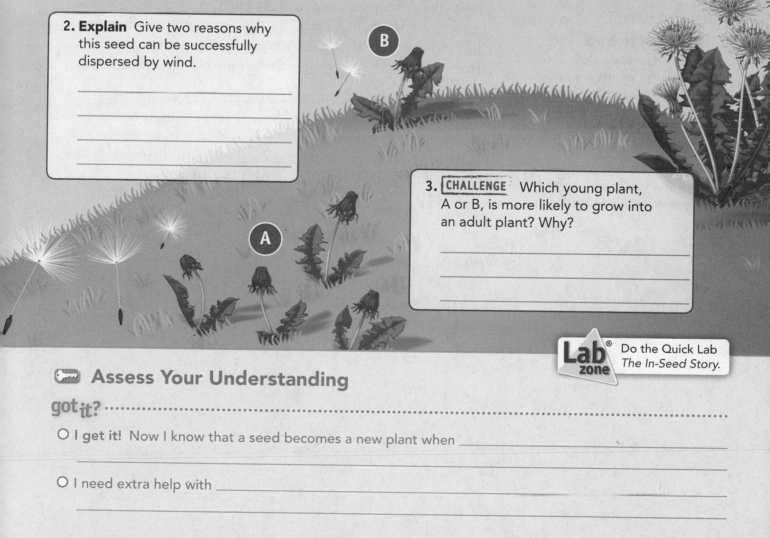

2. **Explain** Give two reasons why this seed can be successfully dispersed by wind.

_____
_____
_____
_____

3. CHALLENGE Which young plant, A or B, is more likely to grow into an adult plant? Why?

_____
_____
_____

B

A

Lab zone® Do the Quick Lab *The In-Seed Story.*

🔑 Assess Your Understanding

got it? ....

O **I get it!** Now I know that a seed becomes a new plant when _____
_____

O **I need extra help with** _____
_____

What Are the Structures of a Flower?

Flowers come in all sorts of shapes, sizes, and colors. But, despite their differences, all flowers have the same function—reproduction. A **flower** is the reproductive structure of an angiosperm. 🗝️ **A typical flower contains sepals, petals, stamens, and pistils.**

The colors and shapes of most flower structures and the scents produced by most flowers attract insects and other animals. These organisms ensure that pollination occurs. **Pollination** is the transfer of pollen from male reproductive structures to female reproductive structures. Pollinators, such as those shown in **Figure 7**, include birds, bats, and insects such as bees and flies. As you read, keep in mind that some flowers lack one or more of the parts. For example, some flowers have only male reproductive parts, and some flowers do not have petals.

Sepals and Petals

When a flower is still a bud, it is enclosed by leaflike structures called **sepals** (SEE pulz). Sepals protect the developing flower and are often green in color. When the sepals fold back, they reveal the flower's colorful, leaflike **petals**. The petals are generally the most colorful parts of a flower. The shapes, sizes, and number of petals vary greatly between flowers.

Stamens

Within the petals are the flower's male and female reproductive parts. The **stamens** (STAY munz) are the male reproductive parts. Locate the stamens inside the flower in **Figure 8.** The thin stalk of the stamen is called the filament. Pollen is made in the anther, at the top of the filament.

FIGURE 7 ·······················

Pollinator Matchup
Some pollinators are well adapted to the plants they pollinate. For example, the long tongue of the nectar bat helps the bat reach inside the agave plant, as shown below.

✏️ **Apply Concepts** Write the letter of the pollinator on the plant it is adapted to pollinate.

Pistils The female parts, or **pistils** (PIS tulz), are found in the center of most flowers, as shown in **Figure 8.** Some flowers have two or more pistils; others have only one. The sticky tip of the pistil is called the stigma. A slender tube, called a style, connects the stigma to a hollow structure at the base of the flower. This hollow structure is the **ovary**, which protects the seeds as they develop. An ovary contains one or more ovules.

FIGURE 8 ·····························

Structures of a Typical Flower

Flowers have many structures.

✎ **Relate Text and Visuals**
Use the word bank to fill in the missing labels.

_____
are the small, leaflike parts of a flower. They protect the developing flower.

_____
are usually the most colorful parts of a flower. Pollinators are attracted by their color and scent.

_____
are the male reproductive parts of a flower. Pollen is produced in the anther, at the top of the stalklike filament.

_____
are the female reproductive parts of a flower. They consist of a sticky stigma, a slender tube called the style, and a hollow structure called the ovary at the base.

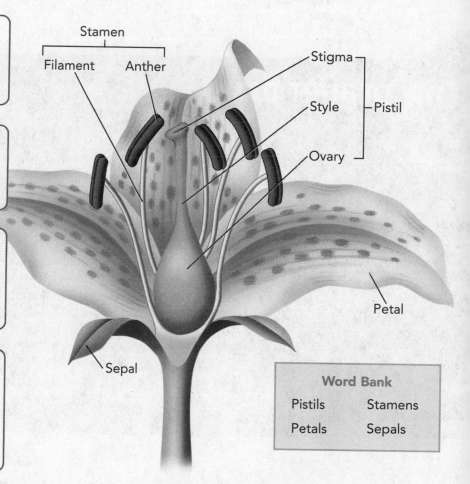

Word Bank

Pistils	Stamens
Petals	Sepals

Lab® zone Do the Quick Lab *Modeling Flowers.*

Assess Your Understanding

got it? ···

○ **I get it!** Now I know that the structures of a flower include _____

_____

○ **I need extra help with** _____

_____

33

Plant Reproduction

UNLOCK
THE BIG
?

🔑 **What Are the Stages of a Plant Life Cycle?**

🔑 **How Do Plants Reproduce?**

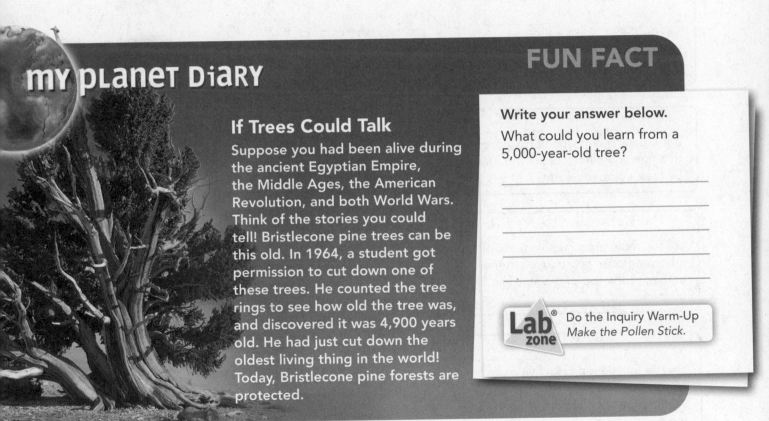

my planeT DiaRY

FUN FACT

If Trees Could Talk

Suppose you had been alive during the ancient Egyptian Empire, the Middle Ages, the American Revolution, and both World Wars. Think of the stories you could tell! Bristlecone pine trees can be this old. In 1964, a student got permission to cut down one of these trees. He counted the tree rings to see how old the tree was, and discovered it was 4,900 years old. He had just cut down the oldest living thing in the world! Today, Bristlecone pine forests are protected.

Write your answer below.

What could you learn from a 5,000-year-old tree?

_____

_____

_____

_____

_____

Lab zone® Do the Inquiry Warm-Up
Make the Pollen Stick.

What Are the Stages of a Plant's Life Cycle?

Like other living things, plants develop and reproduce through life stages. 🔑 **Plants have complex life cycles that include two different stages, the sporophyte stage and the gametophyte stage.** In the **sporophyte** (SPOH ruh fyt) stage, the plant produces spores. The spore develops into the plant's other stage, called the gametophyte. In the **gametophyte** (guh MEE tuh fyt) stage, the plant produces two kinds of sex cells: sperm cells and egg cells. See **Figure 1.**

Vocabulary

- sporophyte • gametophyte • annual • biennial
- perennial • fertilization • zygote • cone
- ovule • fruit

Skills

↻ Reading: Summarize
△ Inquiry: Infer

FIGURE 1 ··

Plant Life Cycle

All plants go through two stages in their life cycle.

✎ **Interpret Diagrams** Label the sporophyte and gametophyte stages.

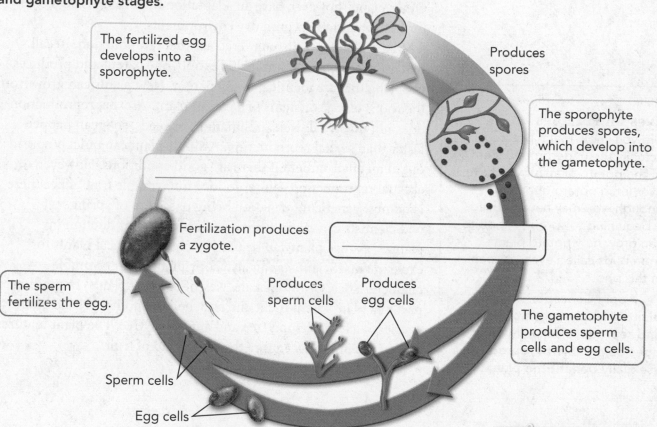

The fertilized egg develops into a sporophyte.

Produces spores

The sporophyte produces spores, which develop into the gametophyte.

_____

Fertilization produces a zygote.

The sperm fertilizes the egg.

Produces sperm cells

Produces egg cells

_____

The gametophyte produces sperm cells and egg cells.

Sperm cells

Egg cells

Angiosperms are classified based on the length of their life cycles. Flowering plants that complete a life cycle within one growing season are called **annuals.** Annuals include marigolds, petunias, wheat, and cucumbers. Angiosperms that complete their life cycle in two years are called **biennials** (by EN ee ulz). In the first year, biennials germinate and grow roots, very short stems, and leaves. During their second year, biennials lengthen their stems, grow new leaves, and then produce flowers and seeds. Parsley, celery, and foxglove are biennials. Flowering plants that live for more than two years are called **perennials.** Most perennials flower every year.

Do the Quick Lab
Plant Life Cycles.

🔑 Assess Your Understanding

got it? ··

○ I get it! Now I know that the stages of a plant's life cycle include_____

_____

_____

○ I need extra help with _____

_____

How Do Plants Reproduce?

Plants reproduce in different ways depending on their specialized structures and the environment they live in.  **All plants undergo sexual reproduction that involves fertilization.** Fertilization occurs when a sperm cell unites with an egg cell. The fertilized egg is called a **zygote.** For algae and some plants, fertilization can only occur if there is water in the environment. This is because the sperm cells of these plants swim through the water to the egg cells. Other plants, however, have an adaptation that makes it possible for fertilization to occur in dry environments.

Many plants can also undergo asexual reproduction. Recall that asexual reproduction includes only one parent and produces offspring that are identical to the parent. New plants can grow from the roots, leaves, or stems of a parent plant. Asexual reproduction does not involve flowers, pollination, or seeds, so it can happen faster than sexual reproduction. A single plant can quickly spread out in an environment if there are good conditions. However, asexual reproduction can reproduce unfavorable traits since there is no new genetic information being passed to offspring.

Scientists can take advantage of asexual reproduction in plants. A single plant can be used to create identical plants for experiments. Scientists can also copy plants with favorable characteristics. Grafting is one way of copying plants. In grafting, part of a plant's stem is cut and attached to another related plant species, such as a lemon tree and an orange tree. The plant matures and can then produce more than one kind of fruit.

FIGURE 2 ·········

Eyes on Potatoes

Did you know that a potato is actually the underground stem of the potato plant? If you have ever left a potato out long enough, you may have noticed it beginning to sprout. A potato can grow new potato plants from buds called eyes, as seen in this photo.

✎ **Apply Concepts** Potato plants also produce flowers and reproduce sexually. How does being able to reproduce asexually benefit the plant?

_____

_____

_____

_____

_____

_____

_____

apply it!

A citrus farmer was able to graft a lemon tree branch onto an orange tree. Now the same tree produces lemons and oranges! The farmer plans to use branches from the same lemon trees to create other combined fruit trees.

1 Review The farmer used the lemon tree's ability to (sexually/asexually) reproduce.

2 ⚠Infer Name at least one negative effect of using the same lemon tree to create new trees the farmer should know about.

_____

_____

3 CHALLENGE Why might the public be opposed to using this method to create new fruit trees?

_____

_____

Nonvascular and Seedless Vascular Plants

Mosses, liverworts, hornworts, ferns, club mosses, and horsetails need to grow in moist environments. This is because the plants release spores into their surroundings, where they grow into gametophytes. When the gametophytes produce egg cells and sperm cells, there must be enough water available for the sperm to swim toward the eggs.

For example, the familiar fern, with its visible fronds, is the sporophyte stage of the plant. On the underside of mature fronds, spores develop in tiny spore cases. Wind and water can carry the spores great distances. If a spore lands in moist, shaded soil, it develops into a gametophyte. Fern gametophytes are tiny plants that grow low to the ground.

Spore cases on the fronds of a fern

Gymnosperms You can follow the process of gymnosperm reproduction in **Figure 3**.

1 **Cone Production**

Most gymnosperms have reproductive structures called **cones.** Cones are covered with scales. Most gymnosperms produce two types of cones: male cones and female cones. Usually, a single plant produces both male and female cones. In some types of gymnosperms, however, individual trees produce either male cones or female cones. A few gymnosperms produce no cones.

2 **Pollen Production and Ovule Development**

(A) Male cones produce pollen grains. Cells in the pollen will mature into sperm cells. (B) The female gametophyte develops in structures called ovules. An **ovule** (OH vyool) is a structure that contains an egg cell. Female cones contain at least one ovule at the base of each scale. The ovule later develops into the seed.

3 **Egg Production**

Two egg cells form inside each ovule on the female cone.

4 **Pollination**

The transfer of pollen from a male reproductive structure to a female reproductive structure is called pollination. In gymnosperms, wind often carries the pollen from the male cones to the female cones. The pollen collect in a sticky substance produced by each ovule.

5 **Fertilization**

Once pollination has occurred, the ovule closes and seals in the pollen. The scales also close, and a sperm cell fertilizes an egg cell inside each ovule. The zygote then develops into the embryo part of the seed.

6 **Seed Development**

Female cones remain on the tree while the seeds mature. As the seeds develop, the female cone increases in size. It can take up to two years for the seeds of some gymnosperms to mature. Male cones, however, usually fall off the tree after they have shed their pollen.

7 **Seed Dispersal**

When the seeds are mature, the scales open. The wind shakes the seeds out of the cone and carries them away. Only a few seeds will land in suitable places and grow into new plants.

FIGURE 3 ·······················

Gymnosperm Reproduction Cycle
The reproduction cycle of a gymnosperm is shown at right.

✎ **Complete each task.**

1. **Identify** Underline the sentence(s) on this page that use the vocabulary terms *cone* and *ovule.*

2. **Describe** What is the relationship between cones and ovules?

_____
_____
_____
_____

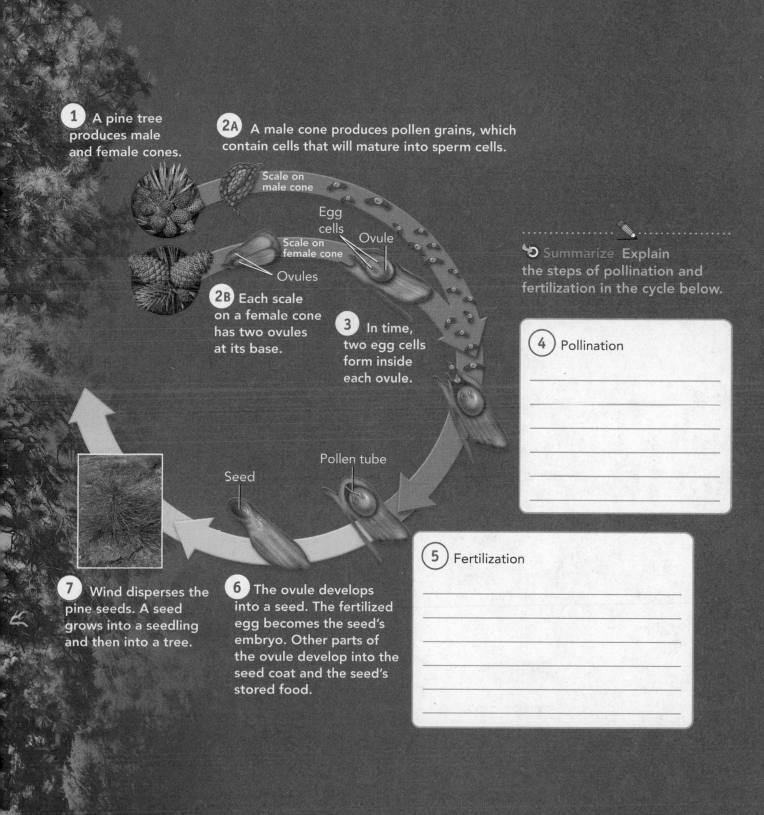

1 A pine tree produces male and female cones.

2A A male cone produces pollen grains, which contain cells that will mature into sperm cells.

Scale on male cone

Egg cells

Scale on female cone

Ovule

Ovules

2B Each scale on a female cone has two ovules at its base.

3 In time, two egg cells form inside each ovule.

↩ Summarize **Explain** the steps of pollination and fertilization in the cycle below.

4 Pollination

_____

_____

_____

_____

Seed

Pollen tube

5 Fertilization

_____

_____

_____

_____

_____

7 Wind disperses the pine seeds. A seed grows into a seedling and then into a tree.

6 The ovule develops into a seed. The fertilized egg becomes the seed's embryo. Other parts of the ovule develop into the seed coat and the seed's stored food.

FIGURE 4 ·····················

Angiosperm Reproduction

Reproduction in angiosperms begins with flowers.

✎ **Relate Text and Visuals** Look back at the plant life and gymnosperm reproduction cycles in this lesson. What do the yellow and purple colors of the arrows represent?

_____

_____

_____

_____

_____

Angiosperms You can follow angiosperm reproduction in Figure 4. First, pollen fall on a flower's stigma. In time, the sperm cell and egg cell join together in the flower's ovule. The zygote develops into the embryo part of the seed.

Pollination A flower is pollinated when a grain of pollen falls on the stigma. Some angiosperms are pollinated by the wind, but most rely on other organisms. When an organism enters a flower to obtain food, it becomes coated with pollen. Some of the pollen can drop onto the flower's stigma as the animal leaves. The pollen can also be brushed onto the stigma of the next flower the animal visits.

Fertilization If the pollen fall on the stigma of a similar plant, fertilization can occur. A sperm cell joins with an egg cell inside an ovule within the ovary at the base of the flower. The zygote then begins to develop into the seed's embryo. Other parts of the ovule develop into the rest of the seed.

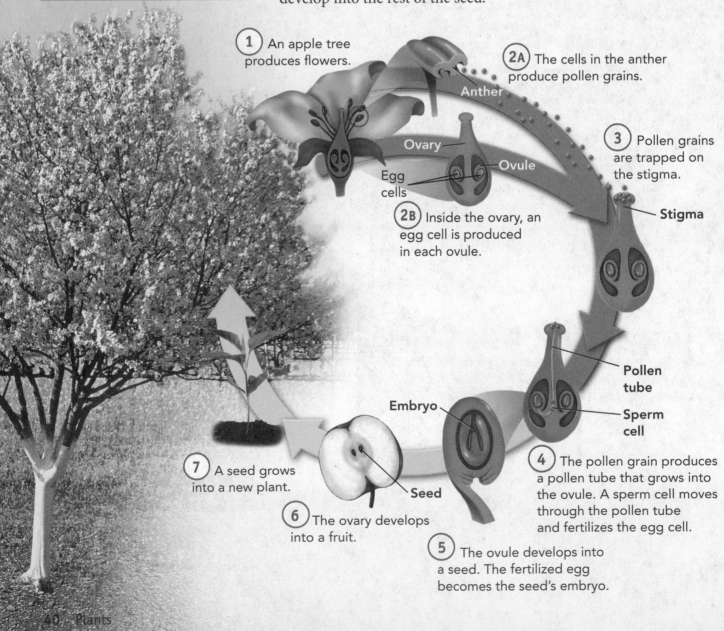

1. An apple tree produces flowers.

2A. The cells in the anther produce pollen grains.

Anther

Ovary

Ovule

Egg cells

2B. Inside the ovary, an egg cell is produced in each ovule.

3. Pollen grains are trapped on the stigma.

Stigma

Pollen tube

Sperm cell

4. The pollen grain produces a pollen tube that grows into the ovule. A sperm cell moves through the pollen tube and fertilizes the egg cell.

Embryo

Seed

7. A seed grows into a new plant.

6. The ovary develops into a fruit.

5. The ovule develops into a seed. The fertilized egg becomes the seed's embryo.

Fruit Development and Seed Dispersal As the seed develops, the ovary changes into a **fruit.** A fruit is the ripened ovary and other structures that enclose one or more seeds. Fruits include apples, cherries, tomatoes, squash, and many others. Fruits are the means by which angiosperm seeds are dispersed. Animals that eat fruits help to disperse their seeds by depositing them in new areas.

FIGURE 5 ···

Flower to Fruit
Flowers eventually develop into fruit.

✎ **Sequence** Write the numbers 1 through 4 in the blank circles to show the progression from flower to fruit.

Lab zone Do the Quick Lab
Where Are the Seeds?

🔑 Assess Your Understanding

1a. Review (Fertilization/Asexual reproduction) occurs when a sperm cell unites with an egg cell.

b. Explain Why do plants like liverworts need to live in moist environments?

_____

_____

c. Relate Cause and Effect Underline the cause and circle the effect in the sentences below.
Pollination can occur when pollen on an insect is dropped onto the stigma.
Animals eating fruit is one way seeds are dispersed.

got it? ···

O **I get it!** Now I know that all of the major plant groups reproduce _____

_____

O **I need extra help with** _____

_____

5 Plant Responses and Growth

UNLOCK THE BIG Q?

🔑 **What Are Three Stimuli That Produce Plant Responses?**

🔑 **How Do Plants Respond to Seasonal Changes?**

MY PLANET DIARY

DISCOVERY

Flower Power

What makes a plant flower? Plants detect the amount of light each day. When there is just enough light, the plant sends a signal to the flower. But what is this signal? For almost 80 years, the answer remained a mystery. In 2008, scientists discovered the protein that was responsible. They linked the protein they thought controlled flowering to a fluorescent, or glowing, protein they obtained from a jellyfish. Then they watched the bright green protein travel with the flowering protein through the stem to make the plant bloom. Why does this experiment matter?

Global climate change is starting to hurt crops. Some places near the equator are becoming too warm to farm. Areas closer to Earth's poles may be needed to grow more crops as they warm. These areas, however, do not get as much sunlight. Scientists could use the flowering protein to encourage plants to flower without direct sunlight.

Communicate Discuss the question with a group of classmates. Then write your answer below.

In addition to getting the plants to flower with no light, what other challenges might scientists have to overcome when trying to get plants to succeed in a new area?

_____

_____

_____

_____

_____

Lab zone® Do the Inquiry Warm-Up *Can a Plant Respond to Touch?*

The green you see in these plant cells is from a fluorescent protein like the one used in the flowering experiment.

Vocabulary

- tropism • hormone • auxin • photoperiodism
- critical night length • short-day plant • long-day plant
- day-neutral plant • dormancy

Skills

🔁 Reading: Relate Text and Visuals
△ Inquiry: Draw Conclusions

What Are Three Stimuli That Produce Plant Responses?

You may be one of those people who close their window shades at night because the morning light wakes you up. People respond to many stimuli each day. Did you know plants also respond to some of the same stimuli, including light?

Tropisms Animals usually respond to stimuli by moving. Unlike animals, plants usually respond by growing either toward or away from a stimulus. A plant's growth response toward or away from a stimulus is called a **tropism** (TROH piz um). If a plant grows toward the stimulus, it is said to show a positive tropism. If a plant grows away from a stimulus, it shows a negative tropism. 🔑 **Touch, gravity, and light are three important stimuli that trigger growth responses, or tropisms, in plants.**

Touch

Some plants show a response to touch called thigmotropism. The prefix *thigmo-* comes from a Greek word that means "touch." The stems of many vines, such as morning glories, sweet peas, and grapes, show a positive thigmotropism. As the vines grow, they coil around any object they touch.

FIGURE 1 ·······························

Plant Responses to Stimuli

The stimuli in space are not always the same as those on Earth.

✎ **Develop Hypotheses** How might the roots of a plant grow in space without the influence of gravity?

_____

_____

_____

_____

_____

Gravity

Plants can respond to gravity. This response is called gravitropism. Roots show positive gravitropism if they grow downward. Stems, on the other hand, show negative gravitropism. Stems grow upward against gravity.

✏️ **Relate Text and Visuals** Use what you have read to label the side of the plant with more auxin and the side with less auxin.

Light

All plants exhibit a response to light called phototropism. The leaves, stems, and flowers of plants grow toward light. This shows a positive phototropism. A plant receives more energy for photosynthesis by growing toward the light.

Plants are able to respond to stimuli because they produce hormones. A **hormone** produced by a plant is a chemical that affects how the plant grows and develops. One important plant hormone is named **auxin** (AWK sin). Auxin speeds up the rate at which a plant's cells grow and controls a plant's response to light. When light shines on one side of a plant's stem, auxin builds up in the shaded side of the stem. The cells on the shaded side begin to grow faster. The cells on the stem's shaded side are longer than those on its sunny side. The stem bends toward the light.

Lab zone® Do the Quick Lab
Watching Roots Grow.

🔖 Assess Your Understanding

1a. Define What is a tropism?

_____
_____
_____
_____

b. Predict What do you think would happen if a plant did not create enough of the hormone that controlled flower formation?

_____
_____
_____

got it? ....

○ **I get it!** Now I know that plants respond to _____
_____

○ **I need extra help with** _____
_____

How Do Plants Respond to Seasonal Changes?

People have long observed that plants respond to the changing seasons. Some plants bloom in early spring, while others don't bloom until summer. The leaves on some trees change color in autumn and then fall off by winter.

Photoperiodism What triggers a plant to flower? **The amount of darkness a plant receives determines the time of flowering in many plants.** A plant's response to seasonal changes in the length of night and day is called **photoperiodism.**

Plants respond differently to the length of nights. Some plants will only bloom when the nights last a certain length of time. This length, called the **critical night length,** is the number of hours of darkness that determines whether or not a plant will flower. For example, if a plant has a critical night length of 11 hours, it will flower only when nights are longer than 11 hours. You can read more on how different plants respond to night length in **Figure 2.**

Photoperiodism

Plants and Night Length		Examples
Short-day plants flower when the nights are longer than a critical length. They bloom in fall or winter.	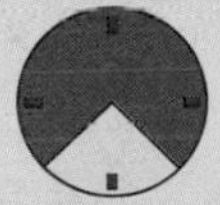 Midnight / Noon	Chrysanthemums, poinsettias 
Long-day plants flower when nights are shorter than a critical length. They bloom in spring or summer.	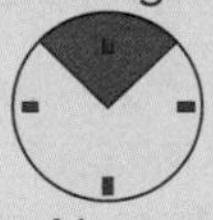 Midnight / Noon	Irises, lettuce 
Day-neutral plants have a flowering cycle that is not sensitive to periods of light and dark. They can bloom year-round depending on weather.	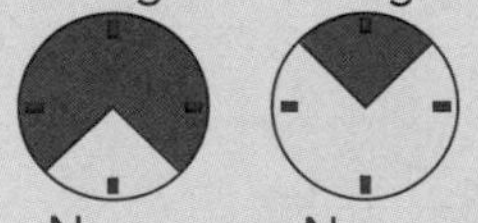 Midnight / Noon Midnight / Noon	Dandelions, rice, tomatoes 

FIGURE 2 ....
Photoperiodism
Flowering plants can be grouped as short-day plants, long-day plants, and day-neutral plants.

Infer Suppose you are a farmer in a climate that supports plant growth all year-round but night length varies. Based on the categories in the chart, would you plant mostly one type of plant or a mixture of all three? Explain.

_____

_____

_____

_____

_____

Winter Dormancy Some plants prepare differently than others for certain seasons. As winter draws near, many plants prepare to go into a state of **dormancy.** Dormancy is a period when an organism's growth or activity stops. 🔑 **Dormancy helps plants survive freezing temperatures and the lack of liquid water.**

With many trees, the first visible change is that the leaves begin to turn color. Cooler weather and shorter days cause the leaves to stop making chlorophyll. As chlorophyll breaks down, yellow and orange pigments become visible. In addition, the plant begins to produce new red pigments. This causes the brilliant colors of autumn leaves. Over the next few weeks, sugar and water are transported out of the tree's leaves. When the leaves fall to the ground, the tree is ready for winter.

apply it!

One hundred radish seeds were planted in two identical trays of soil. One tray was kept at 10°C. The other tray was kept at 20°C. The trays received equal amounts of sun and water. The graph shows how many seeds germinated over time at each temperature.

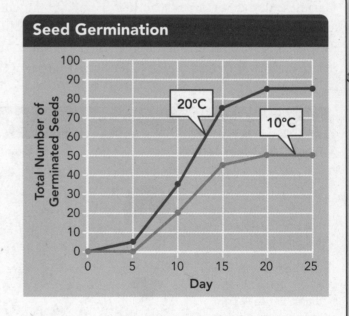

1 Read Graphs About how many seeds in the 20°C tray germinated on Day 13?

_____

_____

2 Draw Conclusions Based on the graph, what can you conclude about the relationship between the two temperatures and germination?

_____

_____

_____

3 CHALLENGE After the experiment, a fellow scientist concludes that more seeds will *always* germinate at higher temperatures. Is the scientist right? Why?

_____

_____

_____

_____

EXPLORE THE BIG ?

Roving for Life in Space

How do you know a plant when you see it?

FIGURE 3 ···

You are a scientist researching distant planets. You have sent a rover to collect samples from one of the planets and you get some exciting results. The rover has found three living things, and one of them is a plant! But, on the way back to Earth, the rover has a rough landing and the samples get mixed up. You run some tests in your lab to find which sample is the plant. The results are shown below.

✎ Circle the sample that is a plant. Then answer the question below.

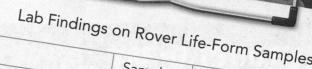

Lab Findings on Rover Life-Form Samples

	Sample 1	Sample 2	Sample 3
Reproduces sexually	Yes	Yes	No
Cells have cell walls	No	Yes	Yes
Contains vascular tissue	Yes	No	No
Multicellular	Yes	Yes	No
Autotroph	No	Yes	No
Responds to light	Yes	Yes	Yes
	Yes	Yes	No

Choose one of the samples you did not circle. Why is this sample not a plant?

_____

_____

_____

_____

_____

Do the Quick Lab
Seasonal Changes.

🔑 Assess Your Understanding

2a. Review (Short-day/Long-day) plants flower when nights are shorter than a critical length.

b. Explain Why do the leaves of some trees change color in autumn?

_____

_____

c. ANSWER THE BIG ? How do you know a plant when you see it?

_____

_____

_____

_____

got it? ···

○ **I get it!** Now I know that plants respond to seasonal changes because_____

_____

○ **I need extra help with** _____

_____

Plants in Everyday Life

How Are Plants Important to Everyday Life?

MY PLANET DIARY

Posted by: George

Location: Tacoma, Washington

I never really thought much about how important trees are until my dad and I planted a plum tree in our yard. I've watched it grow over the last couple of years. The first year we didn't get any plums. The next year, we had tons of plums and they were good! This made me think more about all that we get from plants —food to eat, wood to build houses, and cotton to make clothes!

Communicate Discuss the question with a group of classmates. Then write your answer below.

Describe a plant that is important to your everyday life.

_____

_____

_____

_____

_____

_____

Lab ® **zone** Do the Inquiry Warm-Up *Feeding the World.*

Vocabulary
- peat

Skills
- Reading: Identify the Main Idea
- Inquiry: Pose Questions

How Are Plants Important to Everyday Life?

What did you have for breakfast today? Cereal? Toast? Orange juice? Chances are you have already eaten something today that came from plants. Besides providing food, plants play many roles on Earth. **In addition to food, plants provide habitats. Plants can clean the water and protect the soil in an environment. Plants are also the base of many products important to human life, such as medicines, paper, and clothing.**

The Role of Plants in an Ecosystem Plants play many roles in an ecosystem. You can see some of these roles in **Figure 1.** Recall that an ecosystem contains living things and the nonliving surroundings. People are included in ecosystems too!

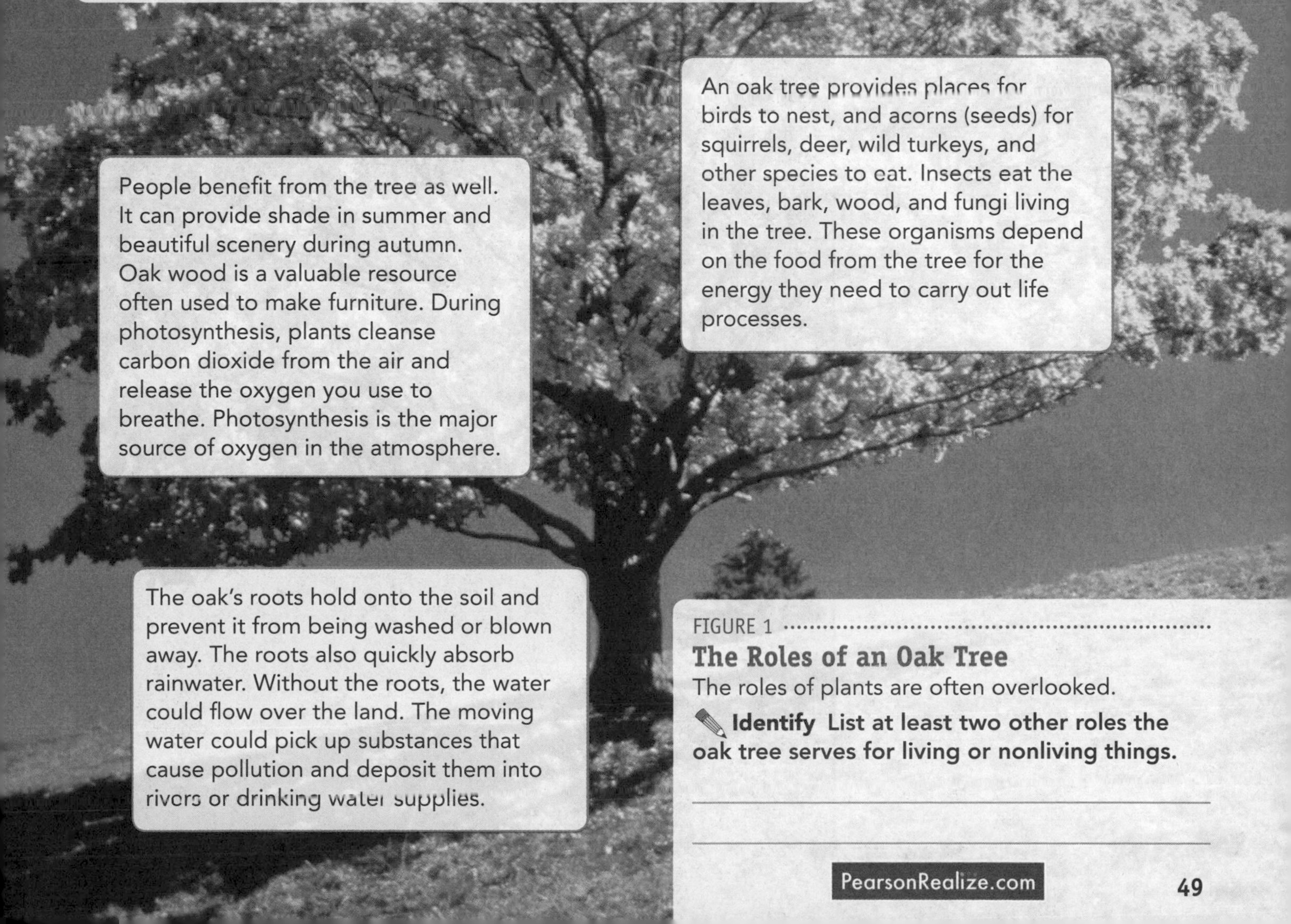

An oak tree provides places for birds to nest, and acorns (seeds) for squirrels, deer, wild turkeys, and other species to eat. Insects eat the leaves, bark, wood, and fungi living in the tree. These organisms depend on the food from the tree for the energy they need to carry out life processes.

People benefit from the tree as well. It can provide shade in summer and beautiful scenery during autumn. Oak wood is a valuable resource often used to make furniture. During photosynthesis, plants cleanse carbon dioxide from the air and release the oxygen you use to breathe. Photosynthesis is the major source of oxygen in the atmosphere.

The oak's roots hold onto the soil and prevent it from being washed or blown away. The roots also quickly absorb rainwater. Without the roots, the water could flow over the land. The moving water could pick up substances that cause pollution and deposit them into rivers or drinking water supplies.

FIGURE 1
The Roles of an Oak Tree
The roles of plants are often overlooked.
Identify **List at least two other roles the oak tree serves for living or nonliving things.**

____

____

⟳ Identify the Main Idea In the text under the heading How People Use Plants, underline at least three plant groups and circle one product made from each.

apply it!

You are at a grocery store buying cleaning products to clean your bathroom. You can choose a cleaner made from chemicals made in a lab or one made from plant-derived chemicals.

❶ Pose Questions What questions should you ask before making your decision?

_____
_____
_____
_____
_____
_____
_____
_____

❷ CHALLENGE What could be some disadvantages of the plant-based cleaner?

_____
_____
_____
_____
_____
_____
_____
_____

How People Use Plants People have found ways to directly use almost all plants. Green algae is often used in scientific research and as a thickening agent in some foods. Liverworts, club mosses, and other plants are used in parts of the world to treat conditions from fevers to itchy skin.

Many people use moss in agriculture and gardening. The moss that gardeners use contains sphagnum (SFAG num) moss. Sphagnum moss grows in a type of wetland called a bog. The still water in a bog is so acidic that decomposers cannot live in the water. When the plants die, they do not decay. Instead, the dead plants accumulate at the bottom of the bog. Over time, the mosses become compressed into layers and form a blackish-brown material called **peat.** In some parts of Europe and Asia, people use peat as a fuel to heat homes and to cook food.

Peat drying after being extracted from a bog

Gymnosperms provide many useful products. Paper and the lumber used to build homes come from conifers. The rayon fibers in clothes as well as the cellophane wrappers on some food also come from conifers. Turpentine and the rosin used by baseball pitchers, gymnasts, and musicians are made from conifer sap.

Angiosperms are an important source of food, clothing, and medicine. People eat a variety of vegetables, fruits, and cereals, all of which are angiosperms. The seeds of cotton plants are covered with cotton fibers. The stems of flax plants provide linen fibers. The sap of rubber trees is used to make rubber for tires and other products. Furniture is often made from the wood of maple, cherry, and oak trees. Some important medications come from angiosperms, too. For example, the heart medication digitalis comes from the leaves of the foxglove plant.

FIGURE 2 ·································

Plants in Your Life

You may not have realized how many things, like clothes and sports equipment, are made of plants!

✎ **Name** List at least five things in your everyday life that come from plants.

_____
_____
_____
_____

Lab zone® Do the Quick Lab *Everyday Plants.*

🔑 Assess Your Understanding

1a. List Give two uses of moss.

_____

b. Describe Why is conifer sap important?

_____
_____
_____

c. Make Judgments Should governments spend more money on plant research than they currently do? Why?

_____
_____
_____
_____

got it? ·································

○ **I get it!** Now I know that plants provide many useful things, such as _____
_____

○ **I need extra help with** _____
_____

Study Guide

REVIEW THE BIG

Nearly all plants have cells surrounded by _____, are _____ that photosynthesize, and are made of many cells.

LESSON 1 What Is a Plant?

🔑 Nearly all plants are autotrophs and contain many cells surrounded by cell walls.

🔑 For plants to survive on land, they must have ways to obtain water and nutrients, retain water, support their bodies, transport materials and reproduce.

Vocabulary
- chlorophyll
- photosynthesis • tissue
- chloroplast • vacuole
- cuticle • vascular tissue

LESSON 2 Classifying Plants

🔑 Nonvascular plants are low-growing, have thin cell walls, and do not have roots.

🔑 Seedless vascular plants have vascular tissue and produce spores.

🔑 Seed plants have vascular tissue and seeds.

Vocabulary
- nonvascular plant • rhizoid • vascular plant
- phloem • xylem • frond • pollen • seed
- gymnosperm • angiosperm
- cotyledon • monocot • dicot

LESSON 3 Plant Structures

🔑 A plant's roots, stems, and leaves anchor the plant, absorb water and minerals, capture the sun's energy, and make food.

🔑 A seed contains a partially developed plant.

🔑 A typical flower contains sepals, petals, stamens, and pistils.

Vocabulary
- root cap • cambium • stoma • transpiration
- embryo • germination • flower • pollination
- sepal • petal • stamen • pistil • ovary

LESSON 4 Plant Reproduction

🔑 Plants have complex life cycles that include a sporophyte stage and a gametophyte stage.

🔑 All plants undergo sexual reproduction that involves fertilization.

Vocabulary
- sporophyte • gametophyte • annual • biennial
- perennial • fertilization • zygote • cone
- ovule • fruit

LESSON 5 Plant Responses and Growth

🔑 Plants show growth responses, or tropisms, toward touch, gravity, and light.

🔑 The amount of darkness a plant receives determines the time of flowering in many plants. Dormancy helps plants survive winter.

Vocabulary
- tropism • hormone • auxin • photoperiodism
- critical night length • short-day plant
- long-day plant • day-neutral plant • dormancy

LESSON 6 Plants in Everyday Life

🔑 In addition to food, plants provide habitats, clean water, and protect soil. Plants are also the base of many products, including medicine, paper, and clothing.

Vocabulary
- peat

Review and Assessment

LESSON 1 **What Is a Plant?**

1. In which cellular structure do plants store water and other substances?

   a. cuticle   **b.** vacuole

   c. cell wall   **d.** chloroplast

2. The pigment _____ is found in chloroplasts.

3. **Make Generalizations** Complete the table below to describe plant adaptions for life on land.

Structure	Function
Roots	Help obtain water and nutrients
Cuticle	_____ _____
Vascular tissue	_____ _____

LESSON 2 **Classifying Plants**

4. Which of the following are seedless vascular plants?

   a. ferns   **b.** liverworts

   c. gymnosperms   **d.** angiosperms

5. Nonvascular plants have rootlike structures called _____

6. **Compare and Contrast** How are gymnosperms and angiosperms alike and different?

_____

_____

_____

_____

_____

_____

LESSON 3 **Plant Structures**

7. A plant absorbs water and minerals through

   a. roots.   **b.** stems.

   c. leaves.   **d.** stomata.

8. Transpiration slows down when _____ are closed.

9. **Relate Cause and Effect** When a strip of bark is removed all the way around the trunk of a tree, the tree dies. Explain why.

_____

_____

_____

10. **Write About It** Plant structures do not look the same among all plants. For example, some leaves are short and others long. Explain why you think there is so much variation.

LESSON 4 **Plant Reproduction**

11. A zygote is the direct result of

   a. pollination.

   b. fertilization.

   c. biennial growth.

   d. the sporophyte stage.

12. _____ complete their life cycles within one growing season.

13. **Sequence** Describe the major events in the plant life cycle. Use the terms *zygote*, *sperm*, *sporophyte*, *spores*, *gametophyte*, and *egg*.

_____

_____

_____

_____

_____

_____

_____

LESSON 5 Plant Responses and Growth

14. A plant's response to gravity is an example of a

  a. dormancy.   **b.** hormone.

  c. tropism.   **d.** critical night length.

15. The plant hormone _____ affects the rate of cell growth.

16. Predict A particular short-day plant has a critical night length of 15 hours. Fill in the chart below to predict when this plant would flower.

Day Length	Night Length	Will It Flower?
9 h	15 h	_____
10 h	14 h	_____
7.5 h	16.5 h	_____

17. Develop Hypotheses Suppose climate change alters the environment of an oak tree from one with cold and snowy winters to one with warmer winters. Will the tree still go into a state of dormancy? Explain.

_____

_____

_____

_____

_____

_____

_____

_____

LESSON 6 Plants in Everyday Life

18. Which of the following is *not* a way that people use plants?

  a. for food   **b.** for clothing

  c. for medicines   **d.** for metal extracts

19. Over time, mosses may compact into _____

20. Make Judgments Should the government put as much effort into protecting plants as they do animals? Why or why not?

_____

_____

_____

_____

_____

_____

APPLY THE BIG ? How do you know a plant when you see it?

21. Plants are all around us. Describe a plant that you see often and then explain what makes it a plant.

_____

_____

_____

_____

_____

_____

_____

_____

_____

Standardized Test Prep

Read each question and choose the best answer.

1. The diagram below shows the parts of a flower. In which flower part does pollination take place?

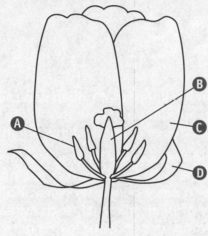

   A   part A   B   part B
   C   part C   D   part D

2. You examine plant cells under a microscope and notice many round, green structures within the cells. The structures are most likely

   A   tissues.   B   vacuoles.
   C   cell walls.   D   chloroplasts.

3. In order to reproduce, most gymnosperms produce _____, while most angiosperms produce _____.

   A   sperm, eggs   B   pollen, cones
   C   cones, flowers   D   flowers, fruits

4. What kind of tropism do roots display when they respond to the environment by growing downward into the soil?

   A   gravitropism   B   phototropism
   C   thigmotropism   D   photoperiodism

5. The vegetables, fruits, and cereals that people eat all come from which type of producer?

   A   peat   B   angiosperms
   C   moss   D   nonvascular plants

Constructed Response

Use the diagrams below to help you answer Question 6. Write your answer on a separate piece of paper.

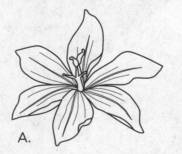

A.

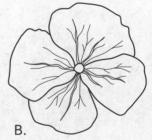

B.

6. Which of the plants above is a monocot? Which is a dicot? Explain your answers.

GRAINS
OF EVIDENCE

You probably know that pollen can cause allergies, but did you know that it can also be used as evidence in criminal investigations?

A growing field of research, called forensic botany, is helping investigators use plant evidence to solve crimes. Forensic botany is the study of plant material, such as leaves, pollen, wood, or seeds, to investigate a crime. Because certain plants grow in specific areas and flower at specific times, plant material can help identify the time or place that a crime occurred.

Seeds or pollen found on a suspect's clothing can be used to link a suspect to a crime scene. Botanical evidence can also be found in a victim's stomach. Because certain plant parts cannot be digested, forensic botanists can even determine a victim's last meal!

Write About It Find out more about the life cycle of a plant described in this chapter. Draw a life cycle for the plant. Then describe how investigators could use knowledge of the plant's life cycle to solve a crime.

◄ Back in 1997 in New Zealand, pollen grains such as this one were used as the evidence to prove that a suspect was involved in a struggle at the crime scene.

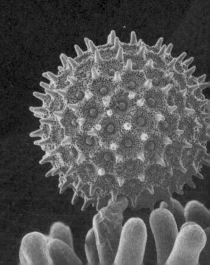

PLANTING
ROOTS IN OUTER
SPACE

Far from farms and greenhouses on Earth, future space explorers will need to grow their own food, and recycle and purify their air and water. Astronauts from the National Aeronautics and Space Administration (NASA) have been experimenting with plants in space for many years.

Which Way Is Up?

On Earth, plant roots grow downward and outward in response to Earth's gravity, while plant shoots grow upward. In space, where there is no clear up or down, roots and shoots both grow toward the light! In order to grow with the roots at the bottom and the stems at the top, plants need gravity. So space stations need special plant chambers that rotate continuously to create artificial gravity for plants.

Tomatoes From Outer Space

To study whether radiation in space will affect the ability of seeds to grow, NASA scientists placed 12.5 million tomato seeds in a satellite that orbited Earth for six years! Students around the world then planted the seeds, which grew normally and produced normal tomatoes. So scientists now know that seeds will survive for a long time in orbit.

Design It Scientists are still learning about how to grow plants to support space travel. Find out about current NASA research on plants in space. Identify one question you have about plant growth in space. Then write a proposal for an experiment to investigate your question.

A researcher holds tiny *Arabidopsis* seedlings. *Arabidopsis* plants are related to the cabbage plant, and are often used as model plants in research projects. ▽

WHAT MAKES A BAT AGILE IN FLIGHT?

THE BIG ?

How do animals move?

Bats are the only mammals that can truly fly. The wings of a bat are made of a thin skin that stretches from its shoulders to the tips of its long, flexible finger bones. When the bat moves its wings up and down, the skin billows out like a balloon. As a bat flies, its wings are more flexible than your hand waving because the wing bones bend. This little brown bat can reach speeds of 35 km/h as it flies, swoops, or dives after a moth.

△ Develop Hypotheses How can a bat alter its course so quickly?

_____

_____

_____

_____

Watch the **Untamed Science** video to learn more about how animals move.

Animal Life Processes

2 Getting Started

Check Your Understanding

1. **Background** Read the paragraph below and then answer the question.

Why can you not leap like a frog? Like a frog, you are a **vertebrate**. But frogs have **adaptations** for leaping. A frog's powerful hind legs and sturdy **endoskeleton** allow it to leap and land without injury.

> An animal that has a backbone is a **vertebrate.**
>
> An **adaptation** is a characteristic that enables an animal to live successfully in its environment.
>
> An **endoskeleton** is an internal skeleton.

- What adaptations do frogs have that enable them to leap?

_____

_____

_____

_____

Vocabulary Skill

Identify Multiple Meanings Some words have different meanings in science and in everyday use. The table below lists the multiple meanings for some words in this chapter.

Word	Everyday Meaning	Scientific Meaning
impulse	n. a sudden desire, urge, or inclination	n. an electrical message that moves from one neuron to another
stimulus	n. something that encourages an activity to begin	n. a change that an animal detects in its environment

2. **Quick Check** In the table above, circle the meaning of the word *stimulus* as it is used in the following sentence.

- The smell of pancakes was the *stimulus* that made Theo's mouth water.

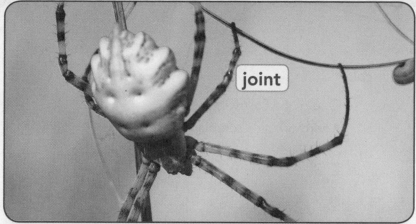
joint

response

carnivore

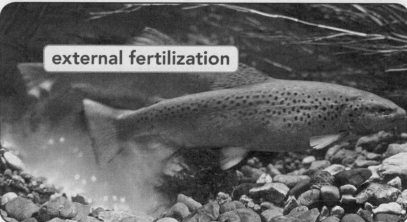
external fertilization

Chapter Preview

Scenario Investigation

Mealworm Migration

Purpose   To investigate migration on a small scale

Materials
- petri dish with lid
- 5 mealworms in a cup
- white construction paper
- scissors
- permanent marker

One of the Following:
- herb or spice sample
- ice cubes
- light sources

Scenario

When you hear the word "migration," what comes to your mind? Do you think of birds flying south for the winter? Do you think of monarch butterflies flying to Mexico in the fall? Migration means to move from one location to another, often over long distances. This move is usually triggered by the seasons.

Many insects migrate, but instead of going south for the winter, they move to a warmer place nearby. For example, some insects burrow into the ground to avoid freezing. Others form tight clusters in the hollows of trees, or even enter people's homes. In the spring, the insects emerge from their hiding places and continue with their life cycles.

How do insects know when to begin migrating? In some cases, changes in temperature signal them to move. When the temperature drops, they seek a warmer place. Insects and other animals also change location in response to other conditions such as light intensity or the presence of a particular scent.

You are a behavioral scientist who studies large- and small-scale migrations. Today you will be conducting an experiment with mealworms, the grub-like larvae of the darkling beetle (*Tenebrio molitor*). You want to know if anything in the environment tells a mealworm when to begin migrating.

Procedure

☑ **1. Environmental Signals** Variables in the environment (temperature, light, odor, etc.) can trigger movement. The migrations can be positive or negative. Mealworms will move toward a positive trigger and away from a negative one.

☑ **2. Finding a Group** Your teacher will assign you to a group and a variable that your group will test (temperature, light, or odor).

☑ **3. Gathering Materials** Based on your assigned variable, gather the supplies you will need for your investigation from your teacher.

☑ **4. Five Trials Will Do It** Divide your petri dish in half. Create an environment such that the variable you are testing is present on only one side of the petri dish. Place a mealworm in the center of the dish and observe it for three minutes. Make note of whether it moves toward (positive) or away from (negative) the side with your variable. Repeat this process five times, using a new mealworm each time.

☑ **5. Reporting Your Data** Use the table at the right to record your data.

Procedure *(continued)*

☑ **6. Analyzing Team Data** Is there a strong positive or strong negative response in your data? If at least four mealworms respond the same way, that is a strong response.

Trial	Response (Positive or Negative)
1	
2	
3	
4	
5	

_____

☑ **7. Reporting Your Results** Based on your assigned variable, gather the supplies you will need for your investigation from your teacher.

☑ **8. Adding and Analyzing Similar Data** After every team has posted their data, add the total positive and negative responses for each variable. How do the mealworms appear to respond to each variable? If other groups tested the same variable as your group, how did their results compare to yours?

_____

_____

Conclusion

Let's see what you learned about animal migration and movement.

☑ **1.** Animals move for a number of reasons. Identify three of them.

_____

☑ **2.** What three organ systems of the body are involved in movement? Explain briefly each system's role in movement.

_____

_____

_____

☑ **3.** Do the positive and/or negative responses of mealworms qualify as migrations? Explain.

_____

☑ **4.** Animals are adapted to move in different environments. What adaptation do mealworms have that enables them to move on dry land?

_____

You have been invited to present the results of your experiments at the annual convention of the Animal Behavior Society. They have asked you to summarize your findings in a paragraph so that they can advertise your talk. Write a paragraph that identifies the variables you and your class tested and briefly explains your results.

Skeletons and Muscles

UNLOCK THE BIG Q?

🔑 **What Supports and Protects Animal Bodies?**

🔑 **What Is the Role of Muscles?**

my planet diary

Fast Felines

Which animal is the fastest sprinter? It is a cheetah. The cheetah's body structure and muscles allow it to reach speeds of up to 112 km/h in only three seconds. Its flexible spine enables the cheetah to extend its limbs to great lengths. This ability allows the cheetah to cover as much ground in one stride as a racehorse. The cheetah also has a high percentage of fast-twitch muscle fibers. These fibers provide power and allow the cheetah to reach its incredible speed faster than a race car can reach the same speed. It's no wonder that the cheetah holds the title of "World's Fastest Land Animal."

FUN FACTS

Read the following questions. Then write your answers below.

1. What are two parts of a cheetah's body that help it run fast?

_____

_____

_____

2. Why do you think a cheetah's speed is an advantage to the animal?

_____

_____

_____

_____

 Lab zone Do the Inquiry Warm-Up *Will It Bend and Move?*

Vocabulary
- molting
- joint
- cartilage
- muscle

Skills
- Reading: Compare and Contrast
- Inquiry: Infer

What Supports and Protects Animal Bodies?

Imagine you are watching lions moving slowly through tall grass. They are surrounding a young zebra that has wandered away from its mother. Flies buzz, and beetles chew on grass blades. Buzzards circle in the distance. Nearby, a snake slithers away from one of the lions. Unaware, the zebra continues to graze.

Think about all these different animals. Do they have anything in common? The answer is yes. All of their bodies are supported by skeletons, which have similar functions. **A skeleton is a framework that shapes and supports an animal, protects its internal organs, and allows it to move in its environment.**

Types of Skeletons Most animals have one of three types of skeletons: skeletons without hard parts, exoskeletons, and endoskeletons. An exoskeleton is a hard outer covering, while an endoskeleton is a framework inside the body. Some animals, such as sponges, do not have skeletons. However, most sponges have hard, spikelike structures scattered among their cells. These structures help support and protect them.

Endoskeleton   Exoskeleton

Both

Compare and Contrast
Complete the Venn diagram to show how endoskeletons and exoskeletons are alike and how they are different.

Skeletons Without Hard Parts

Have you ever seen blobs that look like clear gelatin washed up on beach sand? These blobs are the bodies of jellyfish. They still have some shape because of their skeleton. Jellyfish and other cnidarians, as well as earthworms and some other annelids, have skeletons without hard parts. These skeletons have fluid-filled cavities surrounded by muscle, a tissue used in movement. Like all skeletons, this type of skeleton helps an animal keep its shape and move about.

Exoskeletons

Mollusks and arthropods have exoskeletons. Clam and scallop shells are mollusk exoskeletons made of calcium-containing compounds. The exoskeletons of arthropods are made of a different substance. Exoskeletons have some disadvantages. First, exoskeletons have no cells, so they cannot grow the way organisms grow. A mollusk's shell does get larger over time as the animal secretes calcium. But to grow, arthropods must shed their exoskeletons periodically and produce new ones in a process called **molting**. Second, an exoskeleton can be heavy. This weight prevents an animal from growing very large. Look at the skeletons in **Figure 1**.

FIGURE 1 ·······························

Two Types of Skeletons

Some animals have skeletons without hard parts, while others have exoskeletons.

✎ **Relate Text and Visuals** In each box, write a description of the type of the animal's skeleton.

Earthworm

Cicada

Old skeleton

Scallop

Endoskeletons Echinoderms and vertebrates have endoskeletons. Like exoskeletons, endoskeletons may contain different materials. For example, a sea star's endoskeleton is made of plates that contain calcium. Sharks and some other fishes have endoskeletons made of **cartilage,** a tissue that is more flexible than bone. The endoskeletons of most other vertebrates are made of mostly bone with some cartilage.

Bone and cartilage contain living cells. As a result, a vertebrate's endoskeleton can grow. In addition, because endoskeletons are relatively light, vertebrates with endoskeletons can grow larger than animals with exoskeletons. Some animals with endoskeletons are shown in **Figure 2.**

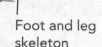

Polar Bear

FIGURE 2 ···

Endoskeletons

Endoskeletons are made of different materials.

✎ **Complete these tasks.**

1. **Relate Text and Visuals** In the table, identify the material that each animal's endoskeleton is made of.

Animal	Material in Endoskeleton
Sea Star	
Shark	
Bear	

2. **Draw Conclusions** Why is having an endoskeleton an advantage to a bird?

_____

_____

Foot and leg skeleton

Sea Star

Spines

Great White Shark

Skull

Jaws

Spine

Skeletal plates

Tube foot

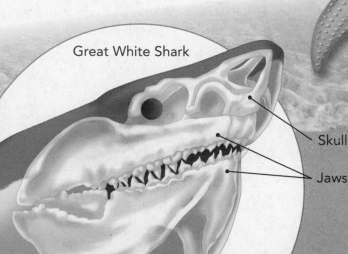

Joint

Costa Rican Spider

Joints
Have you ever tried to run without bending your legs? If you have, then you know it is difficult. Fortunately, most exoskeletons and endoskeletons have joints. A **joint** is a place where two or more parts of a skeleton meet. The way the parts are held together in a joint determines how the joint can move.

Both arthropods and vertebrates have joints. An arthropod's appendages, or jointed attachments, enable the arthropod to move these appendages in different ways. For example, an insect's mouthparts may move from side to side and crush blades of grass. Its legs, however, may move forward and backward, enabling the insect to crawl. Vertebrates also have jointed appendages. As with arthropods, different joints enable vertebrates to move their appendages in different ways.

apply it!

Joints provide flexibility for animals. Look at the picture of the lemur on the right. Then answer the questions.

1 Interpret Photos Circle the joints you see.

2 Infer Describe how the leg joints enable the lemur to move.

_____
_____
_____
_____

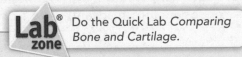
Do the Quick Lab *Comparing Bone and Cartilage.*

Assess Your Understanding

1a. Define What is cartilage?

_____
_____

b. [CHALLENGE] Why is a lobster more vulnerable to predators when it molts?

_____
_____
_____

got it?

○ **I get it!** Now I know that a skeleton is a framework that _____
_____

○ **I need extra help with** _____
_____

What Is the Role of Muscles?

🔑 **Muscles help animals move their body parts.** Tissues that contract or relax to create movement are **muscles.** Some muscles are part of an organ. For example, muscles make up most of the walls of some blood vessels. When these muscles contract, or get shorter, they squeeze blood through the vessels.

Other muscles attach to parts of skeletons. Muscles attach to the inside of exoskeletons. In an endoskeleton, muscles attach to the outsides of the bones or cartilage. For both types of skeletons, movement occurs when muscles pull on skeletons.

Muscles attached to skeletons always work in pairs, as shown in **Figure 3.** When one muscle contracts, the other muscle relaxes, or returns to its original length. The contracted muscle pulls on the skeleton and causes it to move in a certain direction. Then, as the contracted muscle relaxes, the relaxed muscle contracts. This action causes the skeleton to move in the opposite direction.

FIGURE 3 ···································

Muscle Pairs

✏️ **Complete these tasks.**

1. **Use Context to Determine Meaning** In the text above, underline key phrases that help you understand the terms *relaxed* and *contracted*.

2. **Interpret Diagrams** Label each muscle as *relaxed* or *contracted* for both types of skeletons.

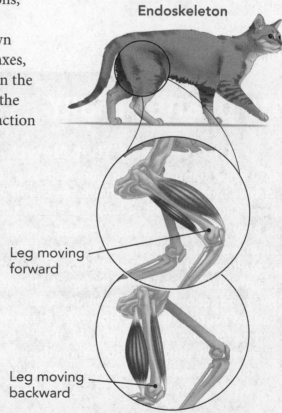

Endoskeleton

Leg moving forward

Leg moving backward

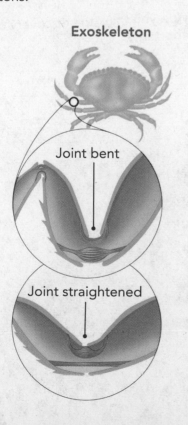

Exoskeleton

Joint bent

Joint straightened

Lab zone® Do the Quick Lab *What Do Muscles Do?*

🔑 **Assess Your Understanding**

got it? ···································

⭕ **I get it!** Now I know that muscles help animals _____

_____

⭕ **I need extra help with** _____

_____

_____

The Nervous System

UNLOCK THE BIG Q?

🔑 **What Is the Role of the Nervous System?**

🔑 **How Do Nervous Systems Differ?**

my planet diary

DISCOVERY

The Nerve of That Newt!

What happens when a newt loses a limb? It grows back! So a newt that loses a limb is not necessarily doomed to having a life on three legs.

In 2007, a team of British scientists made an intriguing discovery. They learned that a protein called nAG is needed for a newt to regrow a missing limb. If the nerve that triggers the production of nAG is removed, the newt cannot regrow its limb. However, the scientists developed a way to make the newt's cells artificially produce nAG. When they did this, the newt was able to regrow its limbs, even without the nerve.

Read the following questions. Write your answers below.

1. What role does a nerve play in the newt's ability to regrow a missing limb?

_____
_____
_____
_____

2. Why do you think the discovery of nAG is important?

_____
_____
_____
_____

Lab zone® Do the Inquiry Warm-Up *Sending Signals.*

Vocabulary

- nervous system • stimulus • response • neuron
- impulse • sensory neuron • interneuron
- motor neuron • brain

Skills

↻ Reading: Identify Supporting Evidence

△ Inquiry: Draw Conclusions

What Is the Role of the Nervous System?

You are in the yard studying. Your dog, Rugger, is lying beside you. Suddenly, Rugger lifts his head and perks his ears. A few seconds later, a car pulls into the driveway.

Interactions Rugger's actions resulted from interactions of his nervous system. A **nervous system** receives information from the environment and coordinates a response. In this way, it acts like the body's control panel. 🗝 **A nervous system allows animals to detect signals in their environments, process the signals, and react to them.**

A signal that causes an animal to react in some way is called a **stimulus** (plural *stimuli*). Touch, sound, and the things animals smell, taste, or see are stimuli. After a nervous system detects a stimulus, it processes the information. For animals like Rugger, this process happens in the brain. Processing information results in a response. A **response** is an animal's reaction to a stimulus. Rugger's response to hearing the car was to lift his head and perk his ears. Rugger could have also responded by barking or running.

A chameleon eats insects. When it sees an insect, a chameleon snaps out its long, sticky tongue, which traps the insect on the end.

❶ **Identify** What is the stimulus for this chameleon? What is the response?

_____

_____

❷ △ **Draw Conclusions** Why is this response important to the chameleon?

_____

_____

Types of Cells

Animals often respond to a stimulus in fractions of seconds. If they didn't, they might not eat, or they might be eaten. The basic unit of the nervous system, a neuron, enables speedy responses. A **neuron** is a nerve cell with a unique structure for receiving and passing on information. In a nerve cell, information travels as an electrical message called an **impulse**.

Complex animals have three kinds of neurons that work together to take in information, process it, and enable an animal to respond. **Sensory neurons** are nerve cells that detect stimuli. Organs, such as eyes and ears, contain many sensory neurons. **Interneurons** are nerve cells that pass information between neurons. **Motor neurons** are nerve cells that carry response information to muscles and other organs.

✏️ **Identify Supporting Evidence** In the second paragraph, underline three examples of supporting evidence for the statement, "Complex animals have three kinds of neurons."

In complex animals, different kinds of neurons work together to transfer information.

❶ **Classify** Under each picture, write the type of neuron the mouse is using.

❷ **Describe** Based on these pictures, what stimulus is the mouse receiving? What is its response?

_____

_____

_____

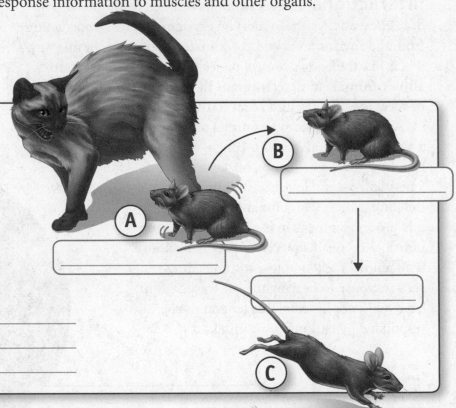

Do the Quick Lab *Design a Nervous System.*

🔑 Assess Your Understanding

1a. Review What is a stimulus?

_____

_____

b. Apply Concepts What kind of stimulus would produce a response from a hungry animal?

_____

_____

got**it?**

○ **I get it!** Now I know that a nervous system allows animals to _____

_____

○ **I need extra help with** _____

_____

_____

How Do Nervous Systems Differ?

It is hard to imagine an animal without a nervous system. This is because most familiar animals have complex nervous systems. But sponges don't have a nervous system, and many other animals have very simple ones. 🔑 **The simplest nervous systems are a netlike arrangement of neurons throughout the body. The most complex systems have a nerve cord and a brain.**

Types of Nervous Systems A cnidarian's nervous system consists of neurons arranged like a net, as you can see in **Figure 1.** This type of nervous system is called a nerve net. Animals with nerve nets have no specialized neurons. Therefore, a stimulus to one neuron sends impulses in all directions.

Many animals have more organized nervous systems than those of cnidarians. For example, a planarian's nervous system has nerve cords formed from groups of interneurons. Arthropods, mollusks, and vertebrates have nervous systems with brains. A **brain** is an organized grouping of neurons in the head of an animal with bilateral symmetry. A brain receives information, interprets it, and controls an animal's response. A complex animal with a brain and nerve cord may have billions of neurons.

A hydra has a nerve net with no specialized neurons.

Cnidarian

Neurons

FIGURE 1 ··
Nervous Systems
Different types of nervous systems have different functions.

✎ **Identify** In the table, write the structures that make up each animal's nervous system.

Groups of interneurons

Nerve cord

Flatworm

A planarian has two small structures in its head that are formed from groups of interneurons.

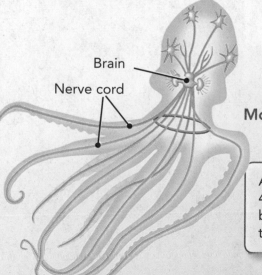

Brain

Nerve cord

Mollusk

An octopus has about 40 million neurons in its brain. Octopuses seem to be able to learn.

Nervous System Structures	
Cnidarian	
Flatworm	
Mollusk	

Sense Organs The more complex an animal's nervous system is, the more specialized its sense organs are. Sense organs such as ears, eyes, and noses detect stimuli in the form of sound, light, odor, and touch. Many, but not all, sense organs are located in the head. For example, a grasshopper has compound eyes and antennae on its head, which detect chemicals and touch. It also has membranes on its body that detect vibrations.

Animals with many sense organs can process many stimuli at the same time. This is because different areas of the brain respond to different stimuli at the same time. For example, when an animal such as your dog is around food, its brain processes messages about the food's color, smell, taste, and temperature all at the same time. Look at Figure 2 to learn about some animals' sense organs.

While under water, a platypus uses its bill to detect the movements of other animals.
_____
_____
_____
_____

FIGURE 2 ···
Sense Organs
✎ Read about each animal. Then answer the questions below.

1. **Infer** Write in the boxes how the sense organ might help the animal.
2. CHALLENGE Where are the sense organs located on most animals with bilateral symmetry? Why?

_____
_____

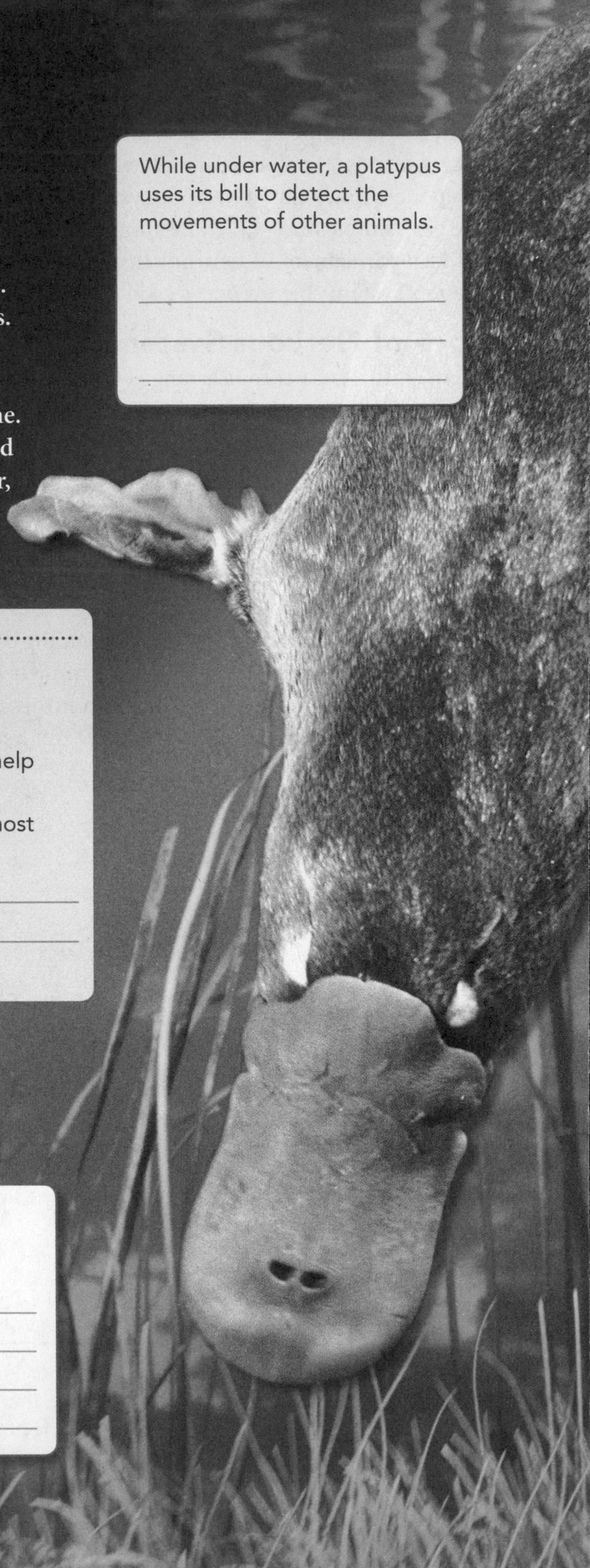

A frog detects vibrations in the air with its tympanic membrane.
_____
_____
_____
_____

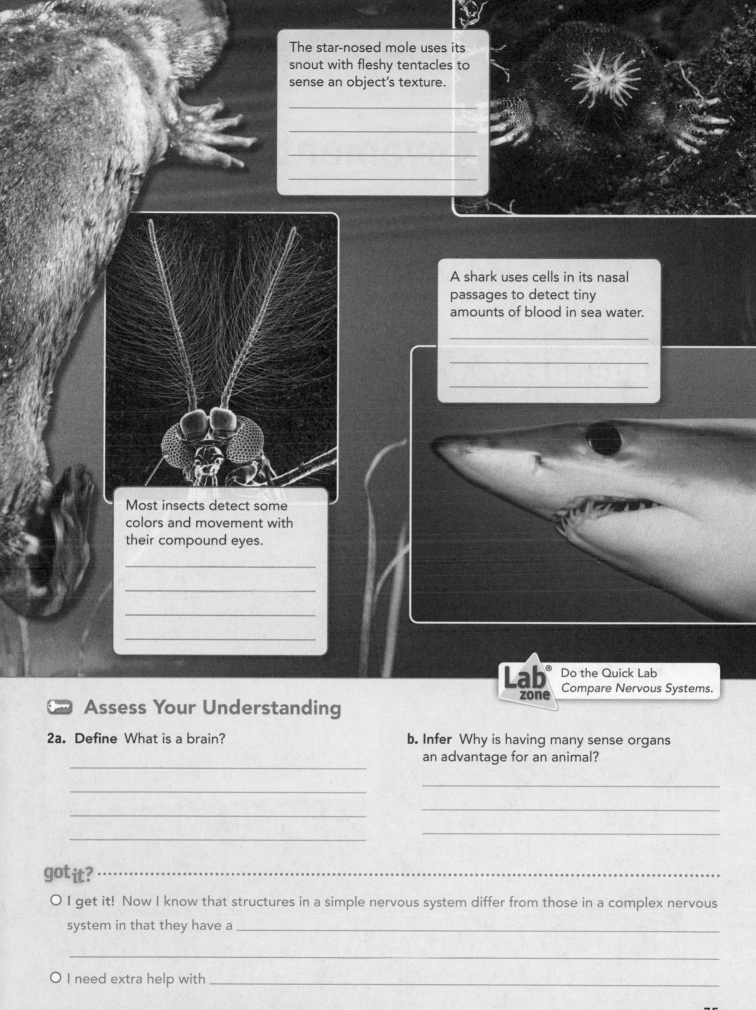

The star-nosed mole uses its snout with fleshy tentacles to sense an object's texture.

_____
_____
_____
_____

A shark uses cells in its nasal passages to detect tiny amounts of blood in sea water.

_____
_____
_____

Most insects detect some colors and movement with their compound eyes.

_____
_____
_____
_____

Lab® zone
Do the Quick Lab
Compare Nervous Systems.

Assess Your Understanding

2a. Define What is a brain?

_____
_____
_____
_____

b. Infer Why is having many sense organs an advantage for an animal?

_____
_____
_____

gotit? ···

○ **I get it!** Now I know that structures in a simple nervous system differ from those in a complex nervous system in that they have a _____

_____

○ **I need extra help with** _____

Animal Movement

UNLOCK THE BIG ?

🔑 **What Causes Animals to Move?**

🔑 **How Do Adaptations for Movement Compare?**

my planeT DiaRY

BLOG

Posted by Emily

Location Bronxville, NY

If I could choose one thing to do that I can't do today, it would be flying. I look at birds in New York and imagine the great adventures they must have.

I imagined taking off from my roof and heading south to the Atlantic Ocean. As I soared over Long Island, I decided I wanted to see the ocean all around me, so I flew east to Montauk Point. I perched on top of a lighthouse and looked at the view below me. Then I flew over Fire Island without stopping because I didn't want to miss the concert at Jones Beach before returning home.

Communicate Discuss the following questions with a partner. Then write your answers below.

1. In what ways can people fly today?

_____
_____
_____

2. Would it affect your life in a positive or negative way if people could fly unassisted? Why?

_____
_____
_____
_____

 Do the Inquiry Warm-Up *Hydra Doing?*

Vocabulary
- water vascular system
- swim bladder

Skills
- Reading: Relate Text and Visuals
- Inquiry: Calculate

What Causes Animals to Move?

All animals move about in certain ways during their lives. They may swim, walk, slither, crawl, run, hop, fly, soar, jump, or swing through trees. However, all animal movements have something in common. **An animal moves about when its nervous system, muscular system, and skeletal system work together to make movement happen.** First, an animal's nervous system receives a signal from the environment. Second, its nervous system processes the signal. Finally, its nervous system signals the muscles, which contract, causing the skeleton to move.

Animals move for many reasons. They move to obtain food, defend and protect themselves, maintain homeostasis, and find mates.

Relate Text and Visuals For each photo, write a reason why the animal might be moving.

Raccoon

Hermit Crab

Peacock

Lab zone Do the Lab Investigation *A Snail's Pace.*

Assess Your Understanding

got it? ....

○ I get it! Now I know that animals move about _____

_____

○ I need extra help with _____

_____

How Do Adaptations for Movement Compare?

Animals live nearly everywhere on Earth. **Animals that live in water, on land, or in the air have different adaptations for movement.**

Moving in Water If you have ever tried to walk in a swimming pool, you know that moving in water is more difficult than moving on land. This is because water is resistant to movement through it. Many animals that swim, such as fishes, dolphins, and penguins, have streamlined bodies that help them move through water. They also have appendages for swimming. Fishes have fins, dolphins have flippers, and penguins have wings.

Some animals that live in water do not swim but move through water in other ways. For example, sea stars and other echinoderms have a **water vascular system,** a system of fluid-filled tubes. The tubes produce suction, which enables an echinoderm to grip surfaces and move along. Look at **Figure 1** to see some different animal adaptations for moving in water.

FIGURE 1 ···

Moving Through Water

✎ **Complete the activity and then answer the question.**

1. **Summarize** In the table on the next page, identify each animal's adaptation for moving. Then describe how the animal moves.

2. **Make Judgments** How is a fish helped by staying at a certain depth without using a lot of energy?

_____

_____

_____

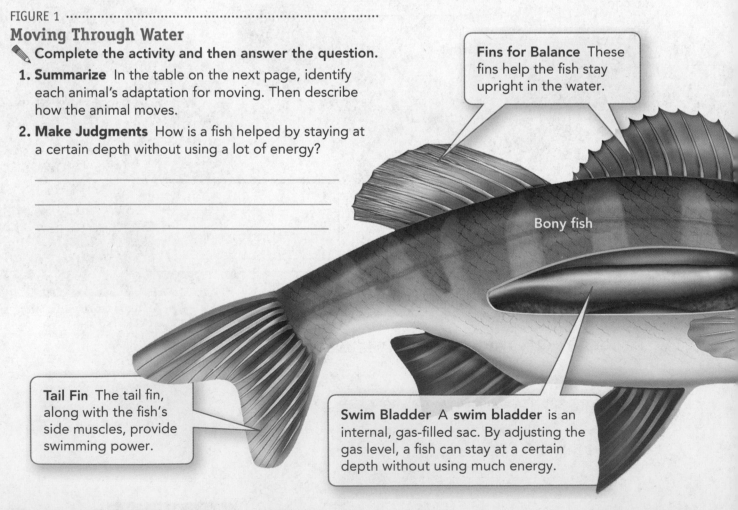

Fins for Balance These fins help the fish stay upright in the water.

Bony fish

Tail Fin The tail fin, along with the fish's side muscles, provide swimming power.

Swim Bladder A **swim bladder** is an internal, gas-filled sac. By adjusting the gas level, a fish can stay at a certain depth without using much energy.

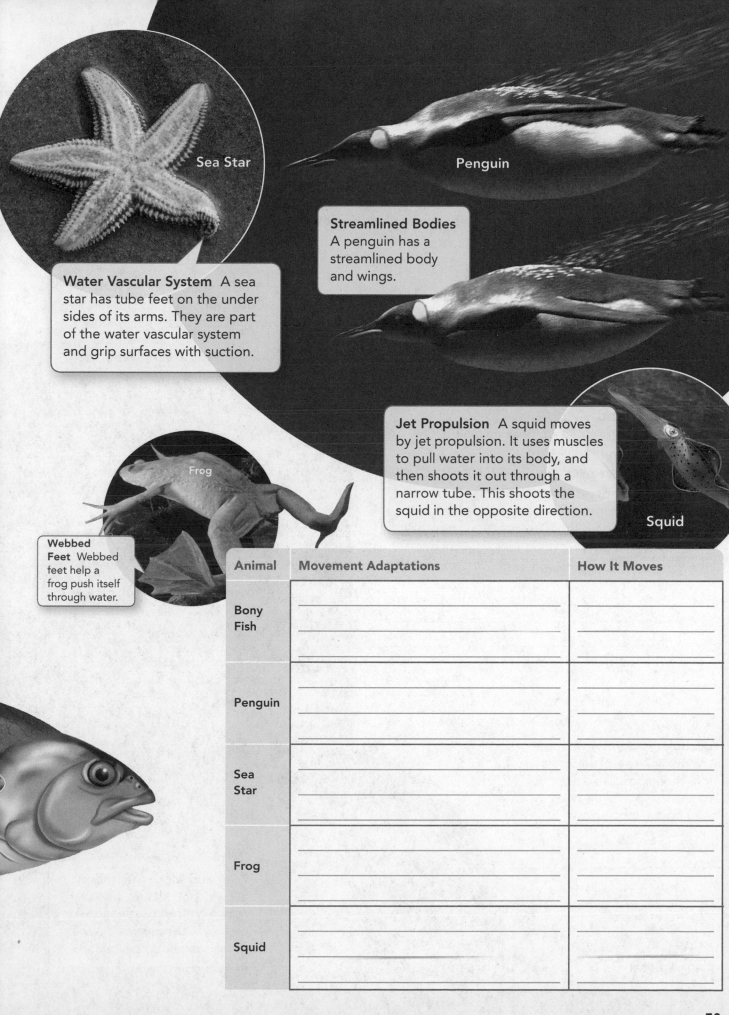

Sea Star

Penguin

Streamlined Bodies
A penguin has a streamlined body and wings.

Water Vascular System A sea star has tube feet on the under sides of its arms. They are part of the water vascular system and grip surfaces with suction.

Jet Propulsion A squid moves by jet propulsion. It uses muscles to pull water into its body, and then shoots it out through a narrow tube. This shoots the squid in the opposite direction.

Squid

Frog

Webbed Feet Webbed feet help a frog push itself through water.

Animal	Movement Adaptations	How It Moves
Bony Fish		
Penguin		
Sea Star		
Frog		
Squid		

Muscles and Bristles
A segmented worm, such as this fireworm, has muscles that contract to extend the worm forward. It also has bristles that grip the soil.

Moving on Land Have you ever watched a snake slither through the grass? Perhaps you've watched ants walk across the ground. Both snakes and ants move on land, but their adaptations for moving on land are different. A snake contracts its muscles and pushes against the ground with its body. An ant uses its jointed appendages to walk. **Figure 2** shows some of the many adaptations that animals have for moving on land.

Body Muscles This sidewinding adder snake uses its muscles to lift loops of its body off the hot desert sand as it moves along.

FIGURE 2 ···

Moving on Land
The different adaptations of these animals allow them to move in different ways.

✎ **Complete these activities.**

1. **Apply Concepts** In the graphic organizer on the next page, describe an adaptation for moving that three other animals you know have.

2. CHALLENGE Describe the adaptations that a kangaroo has for movement.

_____

_____

_____

_____

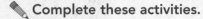

Vocabulary Identify Multiple Meanings The word *foot* has other meanings besides appendage. Write another meaning for *foot* below.

_____

_____

Foot and Mucus To move, a snail contracts its muscular foot. The foot oozes slippery mucus, which makes it easier for the snail to move along.

Foot

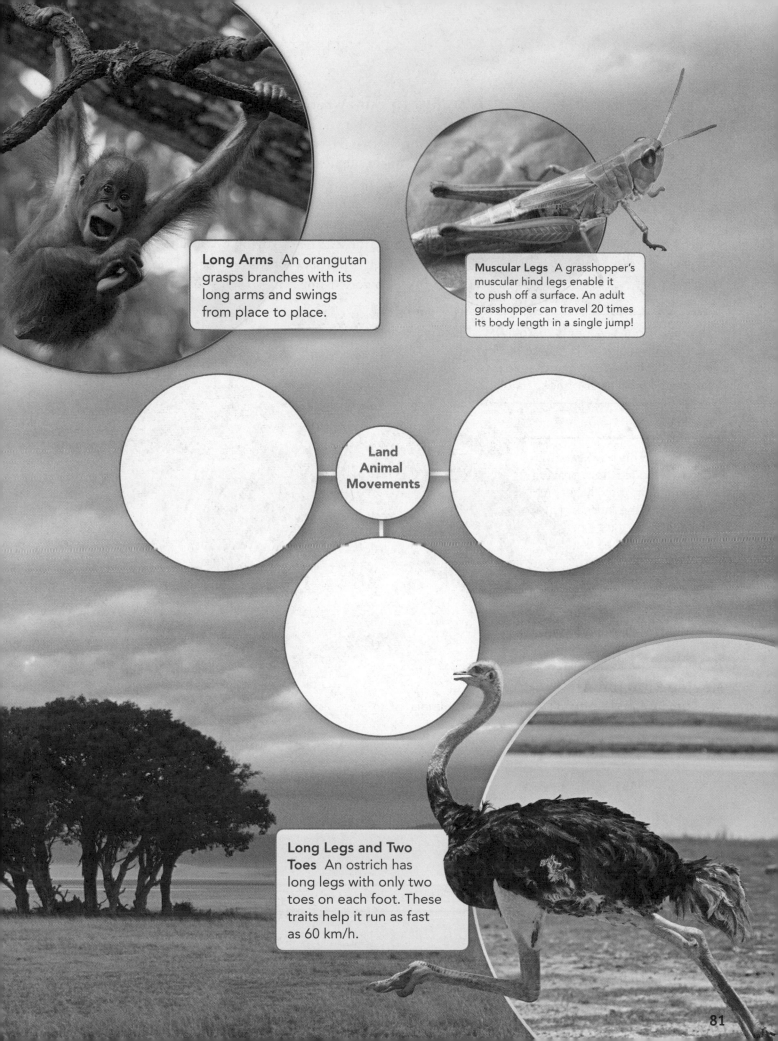

Long Arms An orangutan grasps branches with its long arms and swings from place to place.

Muscular Legs A grasshopper's muscular hind legs enable it to push off a surface. An adult grasshopper can travel 20 times its body length in a single jump!

Land Animal Movements

Long Legs and Two Toes An ostrich has long legs with only two toes on each foot. These traits help it run as fast as 60 km/h.

Moving in Air What do beetles, birds, and bats have in common? The answer, of course, is that they can fly. When you think of animals that fly, you probably first think about birds. Birds are uniquely adapted for flight, as shown in **Figure 3**. But many insects are also flight experts. Their wings grow from their exoskeletons and can move up, down, forward, and backward. A few insects can even twist their wings. Some insects warm up their flight muscles before flying by vibrating their wings, much like a pilot warms up an airplane's engines before taking off.

Skin and Bones A bat is the only mammal that flies. A bat wing is made of thin skin stretched over the bat's long finger bones.

Feathers This hawk's long, broad wing feathers provide lift, enabling it to fly very high. Also, the large surface area of its feathers help the hawk soar.

FIGURE 3 ···

Moving Through Air

✎ **Compare and Contrast** Choose two animals on these pages. Then, in the table, write how their wings are alike and different.

Wings	Animals
Alike	
Different	

Paired Wings A dragonfly has two wings on each side of its body. The wings enable it to fly a long time and change direction quickly.

Wings for Hovering The small, narrow wings of this hummingbird can flap rapidly. This allows hummingbirds to fly forward, backward, and even hover like a helicopter.

Short, Round Wings Some forest birds, such as this pheasant, have short, rounded wings that enable them to take off rapidly.

Front and Hind Wings Butterflies have front and hind wings that are linked by a thin layer of cells. This helps the butterfly flap both pairs of wings at the same time.

do the math!

Different insects beat their wings at different rates, which are measured in beats per second (bps).

Insect	Wing bps
Housefly	190
Horsefly	96
Large white butterfly	12

1 Interpret Data How many times does a housefly beat its wings in one minute?

_____

_____

2 Calculate How many times faster does a horsefly beat its wings than a large white butterfly?

_____

_____

EXPLORE THE BIG Q

A MOVING STORY

How do animals move?

FIGURE 4

A raccoon scurries over rocks as a bald eagle soars above it looking for a meal. Nearby, dragonflies skim over a stream where trout surface to snatch a meal. Movement is everywhere.

✎ Answer the questions in the boxes.

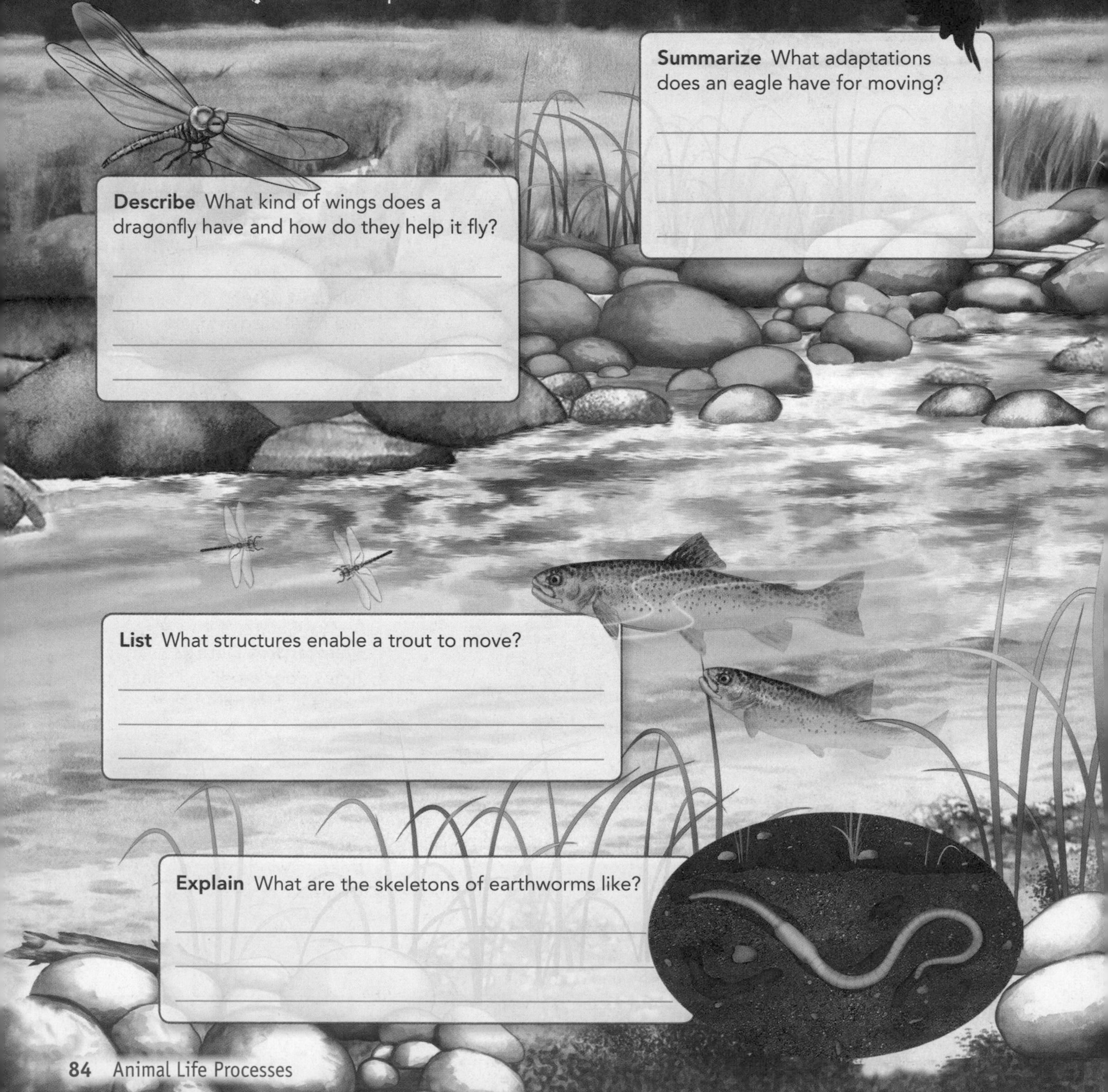

Summarize What adaptations does an eagle have for moving?

Describe What kind of wings does a dragonfly have and how do they help it fly?

List What structures enable a trout to move?

Explain What are the skeletons of earthworms like?

Summarize How does a raccoon's nervous system work with its muscular system to escape an eagle?

_____

_____

_____

_____

Identify When a moose smells a leafy plant, what kinds of neurons are involved? What roles do the neurons serve?

_____

_____

_____

_____

_____

Lab ® Do the Quick Lab
zone *Webbing Along.*

🔑 Assess Your Understanding

1a. Explain What adaptation does a grasshopper have to move on land?

_____

_____

_____

b. ANSWER THE BIG **?** How do animals move?

_____

_____

_____

got it? ....

○ **I get it!** Now I know that animals have different adaptations for movement depending on _____

_____

○ **I need extra help with** _____

_____

Obtaining Energy

LESSON

4

UNLOCK THE BIG ?

🔑 **How Do Animals Obtain and Digest Food?**

🔑 **How Do Animals Obtain Oxygen?**

🔑 **What Are the Two Types of Circulatory Systems?**

my planet Diary

Owl Pellets

You chew your food before you swallow it using your teeth. Owls, however, do not have teeth. They swallow their food whole. Their food includes mice and insects. After an owl swallows, the food travels into its digestive system to be digested.

What happens to the body parts that an owl cannot digest? Any bones, teeth, and fur travel to the gizzard, a part of an owl's digestive system. Then the owl regurgitates, or spits up, the undigested parts as a pellet. Scientists can examine a pellet to find out what an owl eats.

Owl pellet

FUN FACTS

Read the following questions. Write your answers below.

1. What happens to the food that an owl eats?

_____

_____

_____

2. What might you learn about an owl's environment by looking at its pellet?

_____

_____

_____

Lab® zone Do the Inquiry Warm-Up *How Do Snakes Feed?*

How Do Animals Obtain and Digest Food?

Think about the last time you had pizza and how good it tasted. That pizza was more than just a great meal. It also gave you the energy you needed to ride a bike or use a computer. All animals—including you—need food to provide the raw materials and energy that their cells need to carry out their functions.

Vocabulary

• carnivore • herbivore • omnivore • filter feeder • digestion
• digestive system • cellular respiration • diffusion
• respiratory system • circulatory system

Skills

👁 Reading: Compare and Contrast
△ Inquiry: Classify

What Animals Eat

🦴 **The different ways that an animal obtains food depends on what it eats and its adaptations for getting food.** Animals may be grouped based on what type of food they eat. Most animals, like those in **Figure 1,** are carnivores, herbivores, or omnivores. Animals that eat only other animals are **carnivores.** Animals that eat only plant material are **herbivores.** Animals that eat both plant material and other animals are **omnivores.** A few types of animals—such as earthworms, snails, and crabs—eat decaying plants and animals.

Caterpillar

FIGURE 1 ·····························

Animal Diets

All animals need food, but they differ in what they eat and how they get it.

✎ **Infer** Choose one animal from each of the three groups and write in the box what you think it eats.

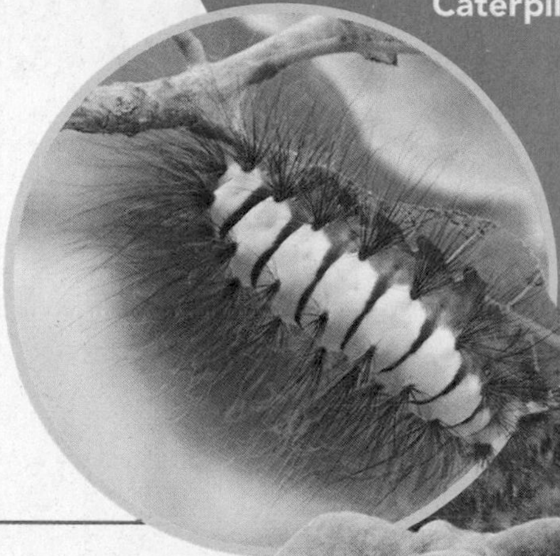

Herbivores

_____

_____

_____

Raccoon

Lion

Elephant

Carnivores

_____

_____

_____

Omnivores

_____

_____

_____

Bear

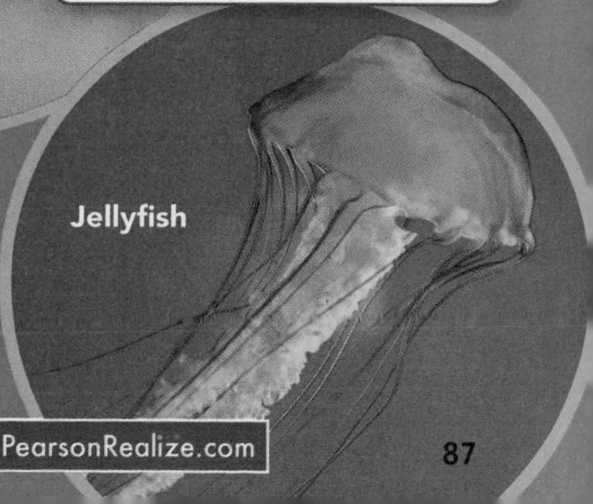

Jellyfish

Animal Mouthparts If you have ever watched animals eating, you may have noticed some of the different adaptations that animals have for eating. Some animals have mouthparts that are specialized for tearing, chewing, or sucking food. For example, grasshoppers have sharp mouthparts that tear and chew leaves. Hummingbirds and butterflies have mouthparts that enable them to suck plant juices from flowers, stems, and leaves.

Other animals have teeth that are specialized for eating certain types of food. Carnivores, such as wolves, have pointed teeth used for tearing meat. Herbivores, such as rabbits, have flat teeth for grinding plant material. Omnivores usually have both pointed and flat teeth for eating their food.

Some animals that live in water strain their food from the water. They are called **filter feeders.** Some filter feeders include baleen whales and clams. Most filter feeders trap and eat microscopic organisms that live in the water.

apply it!

Many animals use teeth to eat.

❶ ◢Classify Look at the teeth of each animal. Based on its teeth, classify each animal as a carnivore, herbivore, or omnivore.

❷ **Relate Evidence and Explanation** In each box, explain why you classified the animal as you did.

Adaptations for Obtaining Food

Animals have an amazing variety of adaptations for obtaining food. These adaptations include structures and behaviors. For example, animals have an opening through which food enters their bodies. This opening is usually called a mouth. Structures such as beaks and claws enable animals to get food into their mouths. Behaviors also help animals obtain food. For example, most spiders make webs that help them capture their prey. In **Figure 2,** you can see some adaptations that animals have for obtaining food.

Hawk

Birds use their beaks to obtain food. The shapes of beaks are specialized for eating different kinds of food.

✏️ **Communicate** Look at the beaks of the hawk and pileated woodpeckers. With a partner, decide which beak shape is best for probing soft material and which is best for eating meat.

_____
_____
_____
_____
_____

FIGURE 2 ·····························

Obtaining Food

Adaptations help organisms such as a grasshopper and a spider obtain food.

✏️ **Study the photos and read the description about how each animal obtains food. Then answer the questions in the boxes.**

Grasshopper   **Spider**

Insects have different mouthparts. Grasshoppers have mouthparts for chewing grass.

✏️ **Develop Hypotheses** This spider is a carnivore. Describe how you think it uses its fangs.

_____
_____

Pileated Woodpeckers

This type of snake stretches its jaws, opens its mouth very wide, and swallows its food whole.

✏️ CHALLENGE Explain how this adaptation might help this type of snake survive.

_____
_____

Egg-Eating Snake

89

Animal Digestion

Animal Digestion You already know that the food animals eat provides needed materials to their cells. However, the food that animals eat is too large to enter the cells. It must be broken down first. The process that breaks down food into small molecules is called **digestion**. Some types of animals digest food mainly inside their cells, but most animals digest food outside their cells.

Digestion Inside Cells Sponges and a few other animals digest food inside specialized cells in their bodies. The digested food then diffuses into other cells, where it is used. This process is called intracellular digestion. **Figure 3** shows how intracellular digestion occurs in sponges.

Digestion Outside Cells Most animals digest their food outside their cells. This process is called extracellular digestion. Digestion outside cells occurs in a digestive system. A **digestive system** is an organ system that has specialized structures for obtaining and digesting food. Most carnivores, herbivores, and omnivores have digestive systems.

Internal Body Cavity The simplest kind of digestive system has only one opening. Food enters the body and wastes exit the body through the same opening. Cnidarians and flatworms have this type of digestive system.

FIGURE 3 ·····························

Intracellular Digestion

Structures surrounding the central cavity of a sponge are adapted for digestion.

✎ **Sequence** Read each box carefully. Then write a number in each circle to show the order in which intracellular digestion occurs in sponges.

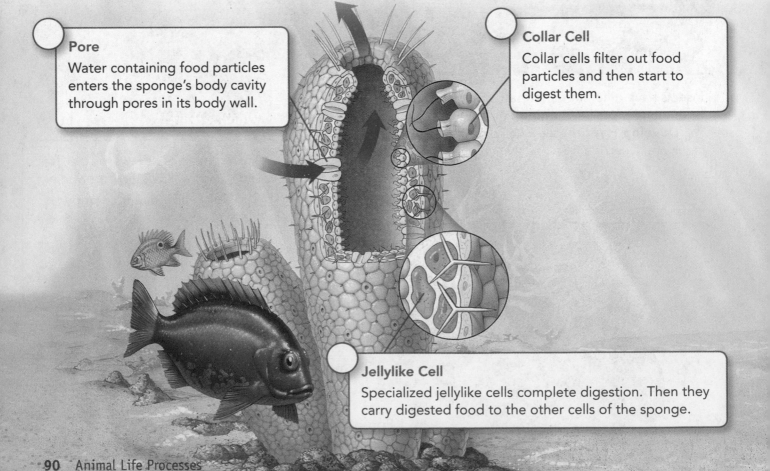

Pore
Water containing food particles enters the sponge's body cavity through pores in its body wall.

Collar Cell
Collar cells filter out food particles and then start to digest them.

Jellylike Cell
Specialized jellylike cells complete digestion. Then they carry digested food to the other cells of the sponge.

Digestive Tube Complex animals have digestive systems that consist of a tube with two openings. One opening is a mouth for taking in food. The other opening is an anus through which wastes leave. A digestive tube has specialized areas where food is processed for digestion, digested, and absorbed. You can see the specialized areas of an earthworm's and a fish's digestive tubes in **Figure 4.** A digestive system with two openings is more efficient than a system with one opening. This is more efficient because digested food does not mix with undigested food.

FIGURE 4 ······························
Digestive Tubes
The digestive tubes of earthworms and fishes have specialized areas in common. These areas have the same functions.

✏ **Interpret Diagrams** In each box, list the names of each area of the tube in the order through which food passes.

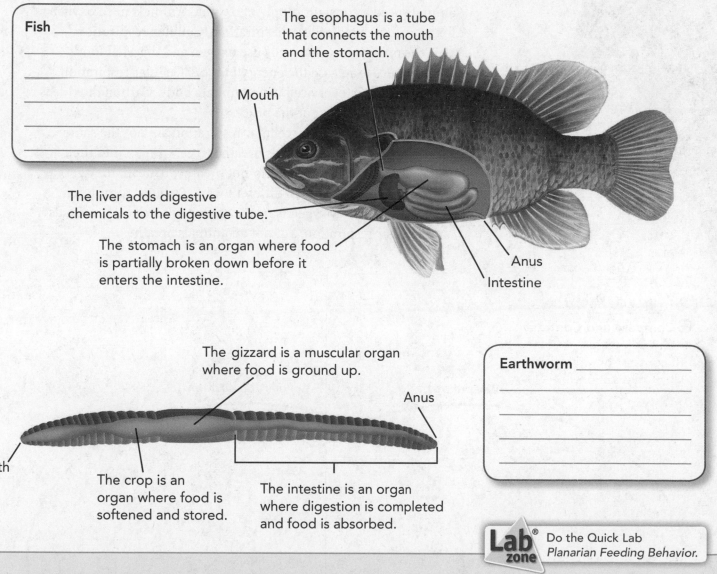

Fish _____
_____
_____
_____
_____
_____

The esophagus is a tube that connects the mouth and the stomach.

Mouth

The liver adds digestive chemicals to the digestive tube.

The stomach is an organ where food is partially broken down before it enters the intestine.

Anus

Intestine

The gizzard is a muscular organ where food is ground up.

Anus

Mouth

The crop is an organ where food is softened and stored.

The intestine is an organ where digestion is completed and food is absorbed.

Earthworm _____
_____
_____
_____
_____

Lab ® Do the Quick Lab
zone *Planarian Feeding Behavior.*

🔑 Assess Your Understanding

got it?

○ **I get it!** Now I know that the way an animal obtains energy depends on _____
_____
_____

○ **I need extra help with** _____
_____
_____
_____

How Do Animals Obtain Oxygen?

What happens when you try to hold your breath? It is not easy after a while, is it? It is difficult because you must breathe to exchange two important gases with your surroundings. Your body cannot function without constantly taking in oxygen and getting rid of carbon dioxide.

Why Animals Need Oxygen Just like you, all other animals need a constant supply of oxygen. Animals need oxygen for a process called cellular respiration. **Cellular respiration** is the process in which cells use oxygen and digested food molecules to release the energy in food. Cellular respiration occurs in every cell in an animal's body. Carbon dioxide is a waste product of the process.

Breathing and cellular respiration are not the same process. Some animals breathe to get oxygen into their bodies. But other animals do not breathe. Instead, they get oxygen into their bodies in different ways. Cellular respiration cannot occur until oxygen is inside an animal's cells. All animals have cellular respiration, but not all animals breathe.

⟲ **Compare and Contrast**
In the Venn diagram, compare and contrast breathing and cellular respiration.

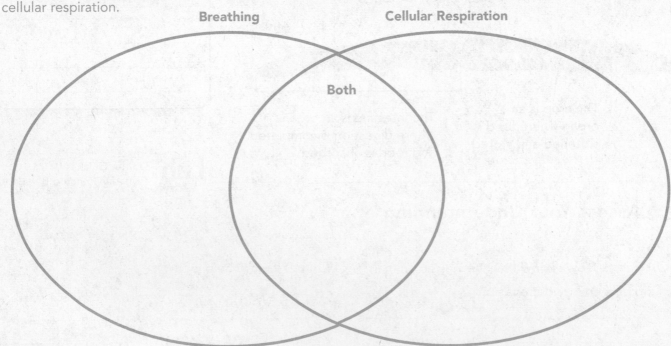

Breathing   Cellular Respiration

Both

Exchanging Gases

Animals exchange oxygen and carbon dioxide with their surroundings by diffusion. In the process of **diffusion,** particles move from an area of high concentration to an area of low concentration.  **Animal cells exchange oxygen and carbon dioxide with their surroundings by diffusion across the outer coverings, or membranes, of cells.** Cell membranes are moist and thin, which enable efficient diffusion.

Cells use oxygen in the process of cellular respiration. Therefore, the concentration of oxygen inside cells is usually lower than it is outside cells. So, oxygen tends to diffuse into cells. Because cellular respiration produces carbon dioxide, there is usually a higher concentration of carbon dioxide inside cells than outside cells. As a result, carbon dioxide tends to diffuse out of cells.

Comparing Animal Respiratory Systems

The structures that an animal uses to exchange gases with its surroundings make up the **respiratory system.** Respiratory systems include structures such as skin, gills, and lungs. The type of respiratory system an animal has depends on how complex the animal is and where it lives.

Animals that exchange gases across their skin live in water or in moist places on land. However, most animals that live in water, which contains dissolved oxygen, have gills. Gills are featherlike structures where gases are exchanged between water and blood. In contrast, most animals that breathe air, which contains oxygen, have lungs. Lungs are saclike structures made up of a thin layer of cells where gases are exchanged between air and blood. Lungs are located inside the body where they can stay moist.

apply it!

Use this model of an animal's muscle cell to complete the activity.

❶ **Identify** Is the concentration of oxygen greater inside or outside the cell?

_____

❷ **Predict** Draw X's to represent the concentration of carbon dioxide inside and outside the cell. Explain what you drew.

_____

_____

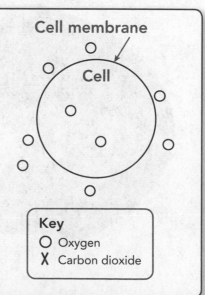

Key
O Oxygen
X Carbon dioxide

Animals Living in Water Think about animals that live in water, such as jellyfishes, clams, sharks, and whales. Just as these animals are different, so are their respiratory structures. Most of these animals use either their outer body coverings or gills as respiratory structures, as shown in **Figure 5**. For example, cnidarians use their outer body coverings for gas exchange. Fishes, mollusks, and arthropods use their gills. However, some animals that live in water have lungs and get oxygen from the air. Whales, dolphins, and alligators breathe air at the surface and hold their breath when they dive.

FIGURE 5 ·····························

Respiration Without Lungs
Animals that live in water and do not have lungs use their outer body covering or gills to exchange gases.

✎ **Relate Text and Visuals** In each box, identify the animal's respiratory structure.

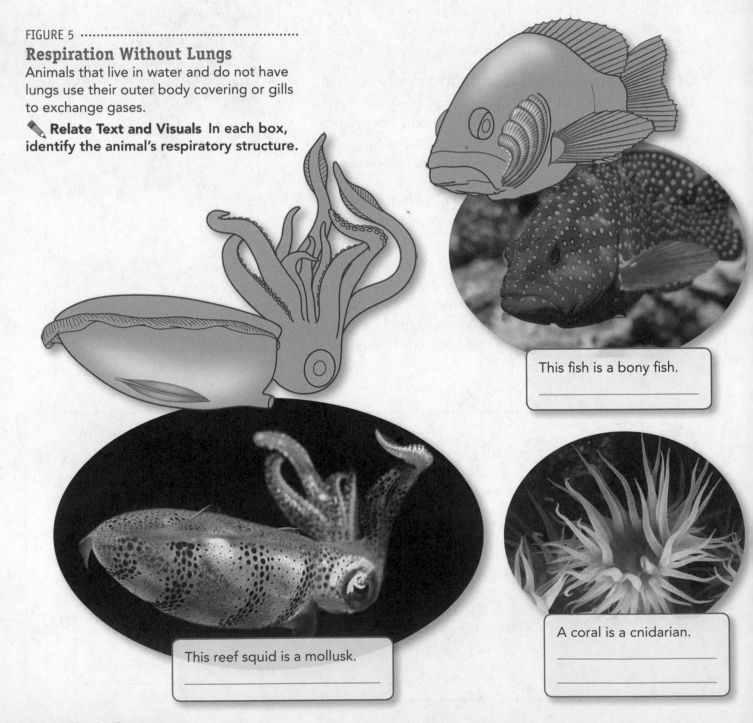

This fish is a bony fish.
_____

This reef squid is a mollusk.
_____

A coral is a cnidarian.
_____
_____

Animals Living on Land

You might think that all animals living on land use their lungs to exchange gases. Some animals do use lungs, but others do not. For example, amphibians may use their skin as their main respiratory structure. Arthropods and other invertebrates have some unique respiratory structures. Although the respiratory structures of land-dwelling animals are diverse, they do have something in common. They all are made up of thin layers of moist cells. In addition, in more complex animals, the layers have folds or pockets that increase the surface area for gas exchange. The respiratory structures of invertebrates and vertebrates are different.

Invertebrate Structures Just a few of the invertebrates that live on land are shown in **Figure 6**. Their respiratory structures include skin, book lungs, and tracheal tubes.

Earthworms exchange gases through their moist skin.

FIGURE 6 ·····················

Invertebrate Respiration

Skin, book lungs, and tracheal tubes are respiratory structures of invertebrates.

✎ **Summarize** In the chart, list each animal shown, and write the name of its respiratory structure.

Spiders have structures called book lungs, which are made of thin, stacked cell layers.

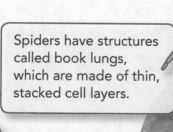

Grasshoppers have tracheal tubes, which have openings for gases to enter and leave the body.

Animal	Respiratory Structure

Vertebrate Structures Most vertebrates, including reptiles, birds, mammals, and most adult amphibians, use lungs to breathe. However, lungs are not all the same. Because some lungs have more pockets or folds than others, the amount of surface area for gas exchange differs. For example, adult amphibian lungs are small and do not have many pockets. Therefore, the main respiratory structure for an adult amphibian is its skin. In contrast, the lungs of mammals are large. A mammal's lungs have many more pockets than those of reptiles and adult amphibians. Additional pockets make the lungs of mammals very efficient.

Specialized Respiratory Structures Birds require a lot of energy to fly. Therefore, their cells must receive plenty of oxygen to release the energy contained in food. To obtain more oxygen from each breath of air, birds have a system of air sacs in their bodies. Most birds have nine air sacs. As you can see in **Figure 7,** air sacs connect to the lungs.

FIGURE 7 ·······························
A Bird's Lungs
In this simplified diagram, you can see how the fresh air a bird inhales flows through a long tube into the lower air sacs. It then flows into the lungs. From there, it flows into the upper air sacs until it is exhaled.

✎ **Observe** On the diagram, draw arrows to trace the path of air through the bird's respiratory structures.

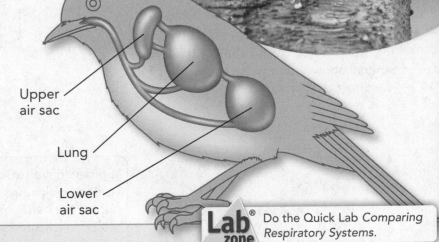

Upper air sac

Lung

Lower air sac

Lab zone® Do the Quick Lab *Comparing Respiratory Systems.*

🔑 **Assess Your Understanding**

1a. Explain What do all respiratory structures have in common?

_____

_____

_____

b. Apply Concepts Why is having several air sacs an advantage for a bird?

_____

_____

_____

got**it?** ··

○ **I get it!** Now I know that the type of respiratory structure an animal has depends on _____

_____

_____

○ **I need extra help with** _____

_____

What Are the Two Types of Circulatory Systems?

You have probably seen ants coming and going from their nest. Did you know that ants work as a team? Each ant has a specific job. While worker ants are out searching for food, other ants are protecting the nest. A soldier ant may even put its head in the nest's opening to stop enemies from entering. By working together, these ants are able to get food and stay safe. What teamwork!

Getting materials to an animal's cells and taking away wastes also takes teamwork. The circulatory system must work with both the digestive and respiratory systems to do so. The **circulatory system** transports needed materials to cells and takes away wastes.

🔑 **Complex animals have one of two types of circulatory systems: open or closed.** Both types of systems include blood, vessels, and a heart. A heart is a hollow, muscular structure that pumps blood through vessels. Blood vessels are a connected network of tubes that carries blood. Blood transports digested food from the digestive system and oxygen from the respiratory system to the cells. In addition, blood carries carbon dioxide and other wastes from cells to the organs that eliminate them from the body.

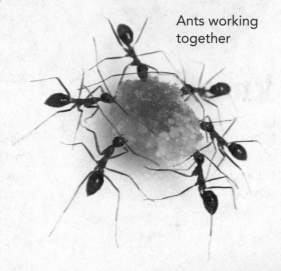
Ants working together

Summarize On the clipboard, write in your own words how the digestive, respiratory, and circulatory systems work as a team.

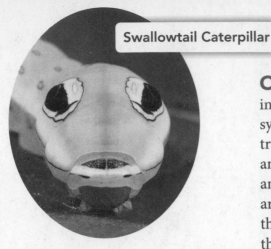

Swallowtail Caterpillar

Did you know that many insects have green blood? Their blood is clear or yellowish green. Unlike your blood, insect blood does not contain the protein that makes it red.

Open Circulatory Systems

Many invertebrates, including arthropods and most mollusks, have open circulatory systems. In an open circulatory system, blood does not always travel inside vessels. One or more hearts pump blood to the head and organs. Then the blood flows into the spaces around the animal's organs. There, food particles, oxygen, water, and wastes are exchanged between the blood and cells directly. Eventually, the blood moves back into the heart or hearts to be pumped out to the body again. You can see this type of circulatory system in the grasshopper shown in **Figure 8**.

FIGURE 8 ....

An Open Circulatory System

Grasshoppers have several hearts that pump blood into short vessels. These vessels open into the body spaces containing the internal organs. The blood washes over the organs and eventually returns to the hearts.

✎ **Sequence** In the graphic organizer, describe the flow of blood in the grasshopper's body. Start with blood in the hearts.

Hearts   Blood vessels

Step 1		Step 2		Step 3		Step 4
	→		→		→	

Closed Circulatory Systems

Segmented worms, some mollusks, and all vertebrates have closed circulatory systems. In a closed circulatory system, blood always stays inside vessels and the heart. Large vessels lead away from the heart to the organs. In the organs, vessels called capillaries surround the cells. Capillaries are tiny, thin-walled blood vessels where the blood and body cells exchange substances. Digested food molecules and oxygen in the blood pass through the capillary walls into the cells. At the same time, carbon dioxide and other wastes pass from the cells into the capillaries. The capillaries merge and form large vessels that lead back to the heart. You can see an earthworm's closed circulatory system in **Figure 9**.

CHALLENGE Why is an earthworm's circulatory system more efficient than that of an insect?

_____

_____

_____

_____

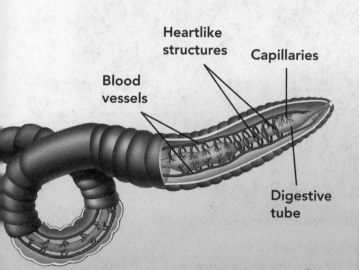

Heartlike structures

Capillaries

Blood vessels

Digestive tube

FIGURE 9 ....

A Closed Circulatory System

An earthworm's body is divided into more than 100 segments. The earthworm's circulatory system runs through all of the segments.

✎ **Compare and Contrast** On the notebook page, write how open and closed circulatory systems are alike and different.

Lab zone® Do the Quick Lab *Comparing Circulatory Systems.*

🔑 Assess Your Understanding

2a. Describe What are the parts of a circulatory system?

_____

_____

_____

b. Draw Conclusions What happens in a circulatory system if the heart stops functioning?

_____

_____

_____

got it? ....

○ **I get it!** Now I know that the two types of circulatory systems are _____

_____

○ I need extra help with _____

_____

Animal Reproduction and Fertilization

UNLOCK THE BIG Q?

🔑 **How Do Animals Reproduce?**

🔑 **How Do External and Internal Fertilization Differ?**

my planet diary

PROFILE

A Nutty Experiment

Did you know that moths have favorite foods? The navel orangeworm moth lays its eggs inside of nuts, such as pistachios, walnuts, and almonds. The young that hatch out of the eggs look like worms, and eat their way out of the nuts. This causes damage to crops on nut farms.

Navel orangeworm moths were thought to prefer almonds over other nuts—that is, until California middle school student Gabriel Leal found evidence to the contrary. Gabriel conducted a science project to investigate whether the young of navel orangeworm moths preferred pistachios, walnuts, or almonds. He put equal amounts of each type of nut into three different traps. A fourth trap was left empty. All four traps were placed into a cage with young navel orangeworms. Most worms went to the pistachio trap. No worms went to the empty trap. Gabriel's research could help scientists control worm damage to walnut and almond crops.

Control Variables Read the paragraphs and answer the questions below.

1. Write a one-sentence conclusion of Gabriel's research.

_____

_____

_____

2. What was the purpose of the empty trap in Gabriel's experiment?

_____

_____

_____

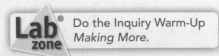

Lab zone® Do the Inquiry Warm-Up *Making More.*

Vocabulary
- larva • polyp • medusa • external fertilization
- internal fertilization • gestation period

Skills
- Reading: Compare and Contrast
- Inquiry: Calculate

How Do Animals Reproduce?

Whether they wiggle, hop, fly, or run, have backbones or no backbones—all animal species reproduce. Elephants make more elephants, grasshoppers make more grasshoppers, and sea stars make more sea stars. Some animals produce offspring that are identical to the parent. Most animals, including humans, produce offspring that are different from the parents.

Animals undergo either asexual or sexual reproduction to make more of their own kind or species. Because no animal lives forever, reproduction is essential to the survival of a species.

Asexual Reproduction Imagine you are digging in the soil with a shovel, and accidentally cut a worm into two pieces. Most animals wouldn't survive getting cut in two—but the worm might. Certain kinds of worms can form whole new worms from each cut piece. This is one form of asexual reproduction. Another example of asexual reproduction is called budding. In budding, a new animal grows out of the parent and breaks off. In asexual reproduction, one parent produces a new organism identical to itself. This new organism receives an exact copy of the parent's set of genetic material, or DNA. Some animals, including sponges, jellyfish, sea anemones, worms, and the hydra in **Figure 1,** can reproduce asexually.

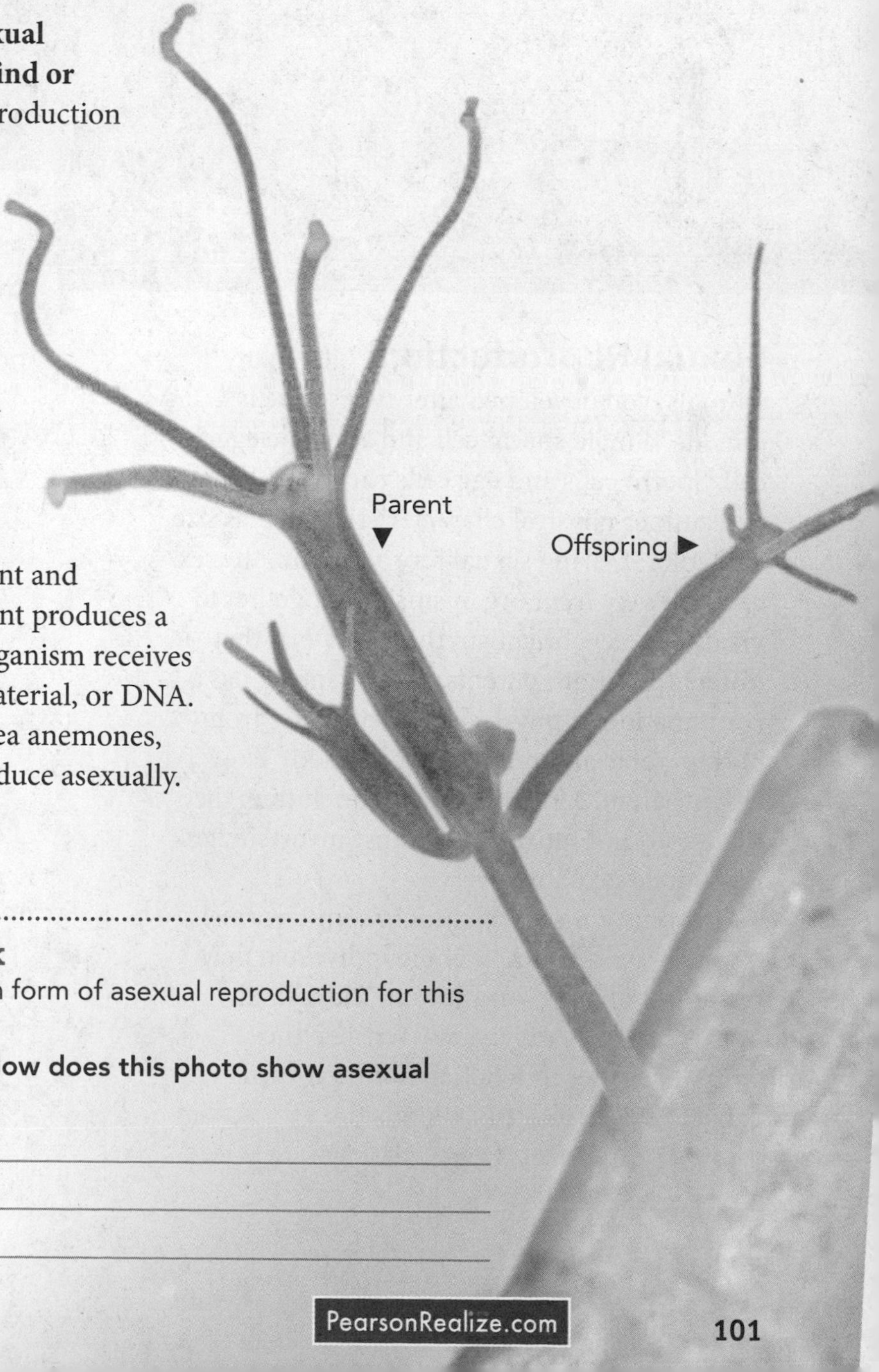

Parent ▼

Offspring ▶

FIGURE 1 ·······

A Chip off the Old Block
Budding is the most common form of asexual reproduction for this hydra, a type of cnidarian.

✎ **Relate Text to Visuals** How does this photo show asexual reproduction?

_____

_____

_____

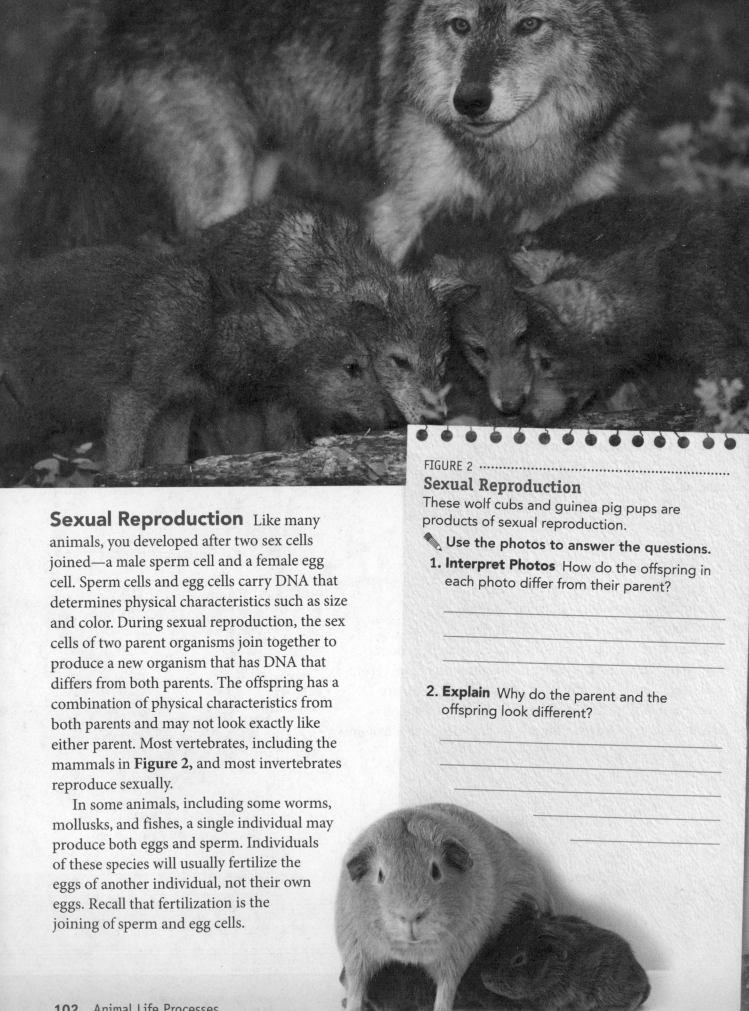

Sexual Reproduction

Like many animals, you developed after two sex cells joined—a male sperm cell and a female egg cell. Sperm cells and egg cells carry DNA that determines physical characteristics such as size and color. During sexual reproduction, the sex cells of two parent organisms join together to produce a new organism that has DNA that differs from both parents. The offspring has a combination of physical characteristics from both parents and may not look exactly like either parent. Most vertebrates, including the mammals in **Figure 2,** and most invertebrates reproduce sexually.

In some animals, including some worms, mollusks, and fishes, a single individual may produce both eggs and sperm. Individuals of these species will usually fertilize the eggs of another individual, not their own eggs. Recall that fertilization is the joining of sperm and egg cells.

FIGURE 2 ·····················

Sexual Reproduction

These wolf cubs and guinea pig pups are products of sexual reproduction.

✎ **Use the photos to answer the questions.**

1. **Interpret Photos** How do the offspring in each photo differ from their parent?

_____

_____

_____

2. **Explain** Why do the parent and the offspring look different?

_____

_____

_____

_____

_____

Comparing Asexual and Sexual Reproduction

Asexual and sexual reproduction are different survival methods. Each method has advantages and disadvantages. An advantage of asexual reproduction is that one parent can quickly produce many identical offspring. But a major disadvantage is that the offspring have the same DNA as the parent. The offspring have no variation from the parent and may not survive changes in the environment. In contrast, sexual reproduction has the advantage of producing offspring with new combinations of DNA. These offspring may have characteristics that help them adapt and survive changes in the environment. However, a disadvantage of sexual reproduction is that it requires finding a mate, and the development of offspring takes a longer time.

did you
know?

Some fishes, such as this anemone clownfish, can change from male to female during their lifetime!

FIGURE 3

Asexual and Sexual Reproduction

Compare and Contrast Write an advantage and a disadvantage of each type of reproduction in the table.

	Asexual Reproduction	Sexual Reproduction
Advantage		
Disadvantage		

These aphids can reproduce asexually and sexually. They reproduce asexually when environmental conditions are favorable. If conditions worsen, they reproduce sexually.

Reproductive Cycles Several aquatic invertebrates, such as sponges and cnidarians, have life cycles that alternate between asexual and sexual reproduction.

A Sponges

Sponges reproduce both asexually and sexually. Sponges reproduce asexually through budding. Small new sponges grow, or bud, from the sides of an adult sponge. Eventually, the buds break free and begin life on their own. Sponges reproduce sexually, too, but they do not have separate sexes. A sponge can produce both sperm cells and egg cells. After a sponge egg is fertilized by a sperm, a larva develops. A **larva** (plural *larvae*) is an immature form of an animal that looks very different from the adult. **Figure 4** shows sponge reproduction.

B Cnidarians

Many cnidarians alternate between two body forms: a **polyp** (PAHL ip) that looks like an upright vase and a **medusa** (muh DOO suh) that looks like an open umbrella. Some polyps reproduce asexually by budding. Other polyps just pull apart, forming two new polyps. Both kinds of asexual reproduction rapidly increase the number of polyps in a short time. Cnidarians reproduce sexually when in the medusa stage. The medusas release sperm and eggs into the water. A fertilized egg develops into a swimming larva. In time, the larva attaches to a hard surface and develops into a polyp that may continue the cycle. The moon jelly in **Figure 5** undergoes both asexual and sexual reproduction.

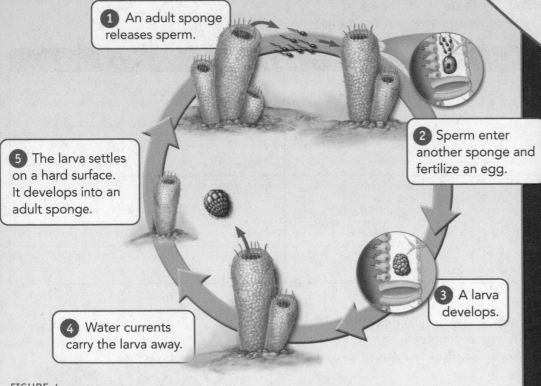

1 An adult sponge releases sperm.

2 Sperm enter another sponge and fertilize an egg.

3 A larva develops.

4 Water currents carry the larva away.

5 The larva settles on a hard surface. It develops into an adult sponge.

FIGURE 4 ···
Reproduction of a Sponge
These sponges are reproducing sexually. ✏ **Complete these tasks.**

1. **Identify** A budded sponge is a product of (asexual/sexual) reproduction and a larva is a product of (asexual/sexual) reproduction.

2. **Interpret Diagrams** How do the sponge larva and adult differ?

_____

_____

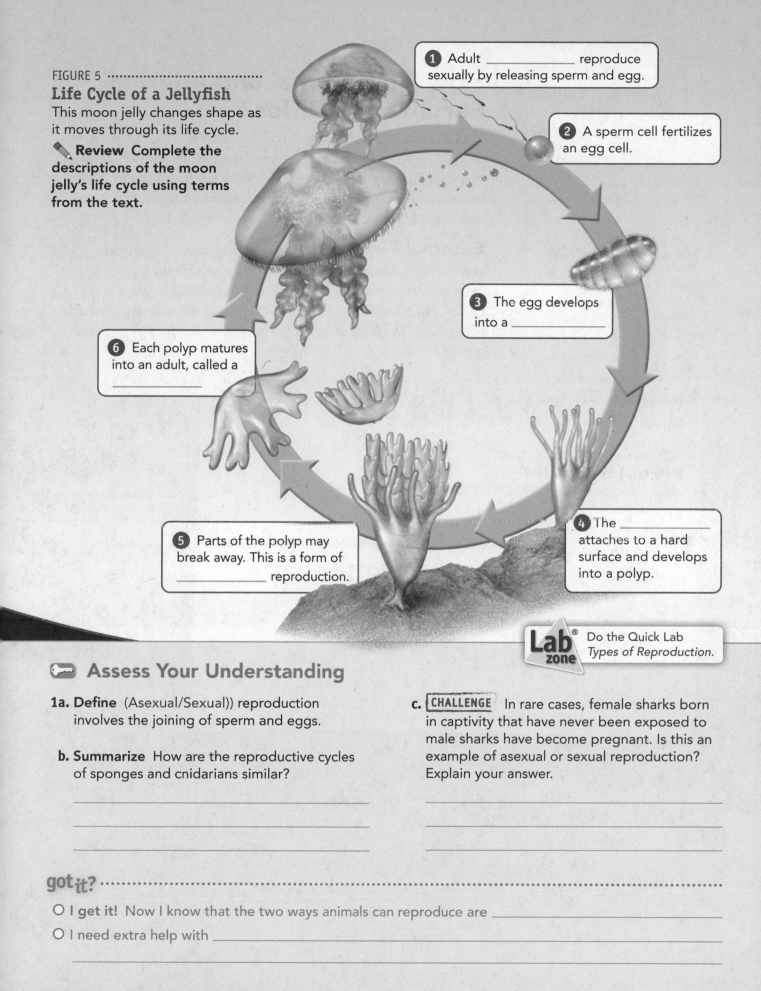

FIGURE 5 ·················

Life Cycle of a Jellyfish

This moon jelly changes shape as it moves through its life cycle.

✎ **Review** Complete the descriptions of the moon jelly's life cycle using terms from the text.

1 Adult _____ reproduce sexually by releasing sperm and egg.

2 A sperm cell fertilizes an egg cell.

3 The egg develops into a _____

4 The _____ attaches to a hard surface and develops into a polyp.

5 Parts of the polyp may break away. This is a form of _____ reproduction.

6 Each polyp matures into an adult, called a _____

Lab® zone Do the Quick Lab *Types of Reproduction.*

🔑 Assess Your Understanding

1a. Define (Asexual/Sexual)) reproduction involves the joining of sperm and eggs.

b. Summarize How are the reproductive cycles of sponges and cnidarians similar?

_____

_____

_____

c. **CHALLENGE** In rare cases, female sharks born in captivity that have never been exposed to male sharks have become pregnant. Is this an example of asexual or sexual reproduction? Explain your answer.

_____

_____

_____

got**it?** ···

○ **I get it!** Now I know that the two ways animals can reproduce are _____

○ **I need extra help with** _____

_____

How Do External and Internal Fertilization Differ?

Sexual reproduction involves fertilization, or the joining of a sperm cell and an egg cell. Fertilization may occur either outside or inside of the female organism's body. **External fertilization occurs outside of the female's body, and internal fertilization occurs inside the female's body.**

External Fertilization For many fishes, amphibians, and aquatic invertebrates, fertilization occurs outside the body. Usually external fertilization must take place in water to prevent the eggs and sperm from drying out. First, the female releases eggs into the water. Then the male releases sperm nearby. **Figure 6** shows trout fertilization.

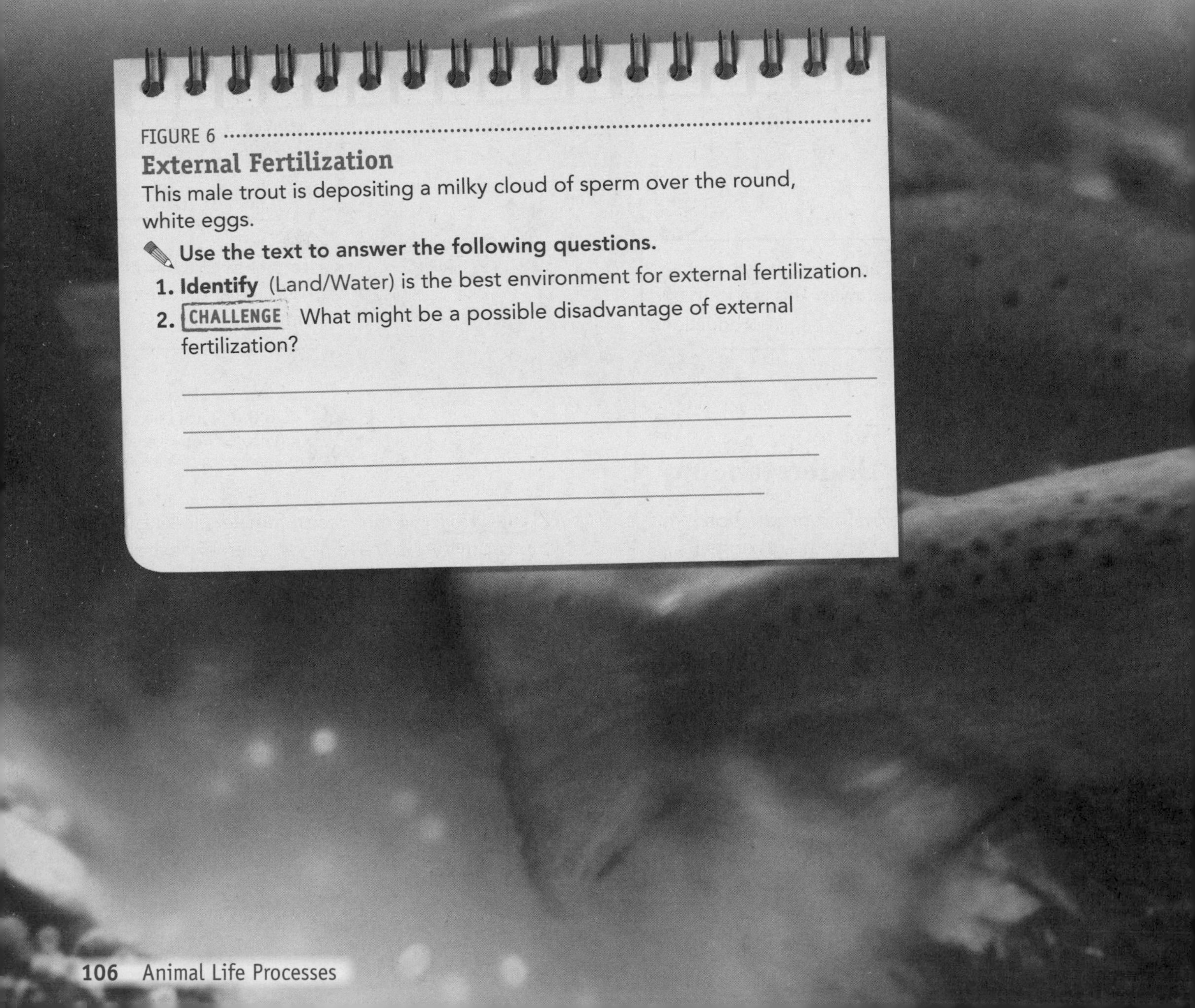

FIGURE 6 ....
External Fertilization
This male trout is depositing a milky cloud of sperm over the round, white eggs.

✎ **Use the text to answer the following questions.**

1. **Identify** (Land/Water) is the best environment for external fertilization.

2. CHALLENGE What might be a possible disadvantage of external fertilization?

_____

_____

_____

_____

Internal Fertilization Fertilization occurs inside the body in many aquatic animals and all land animals. The male releases sperm directly into the female's body, where the eggs are located.

Most invertebrates and many fishes, amphibians, reptiles, and birds lay eggs outside the parent's body. The offspring continue to develop inside the eggs. For other animals, including most mammals, fertilized eggs develop inside the female animal. The female then gives birth to live young. The length of time between fertilization and birth is called the **gestation period.** Opossums have the shortest gestation period—around 13 days. African elephants have the longest gestation period—up to 22 months.

⟲ **Compare and Contrast**
Describe how external and internal fertilization are alike and different. .

_____
_____
_____
_____
_____
_____
_____

do the math!

Study the graph and answer the questions below.

1 Calculate About how many days longer is the giraffe's gestation period than the fox's?

_____

2 Make Generalizations How do you think an animal's size relates to the length of its gestation period?

_____
_____
_____

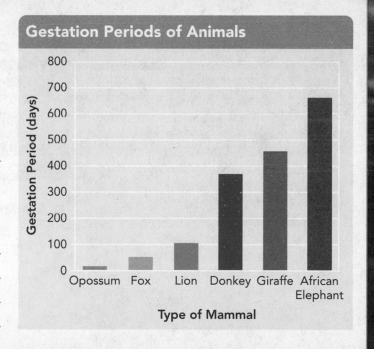

Gestation Periods of Animals

Graph: Gestation Period (days) vs. Type of Mammal. Y-axis 0 to 800. Opossum ~13, Fox ~50, Lion ~110, Donkey ~370, Giraffe ~450, African Elephant ~660.

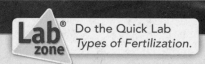

Do the Quick Lab
Types of Fertilization.

🔑 Assess Your Understanding

got it? ....

○ **I get it!** Now I know that external fertilization occurs _____

   and internal fertilization occurs _____

○ **I need extra help with** _____

Development and Growth

🔑 **Where Do Embryos Develop?**

🔑 **How Do Young Animals Develop?**

🔑 **How Do Animals Care for Their Young?**

my plaɴeт DiaRY

DISCOVERY

Beware of Glass

Is that a beetle or a bottle? Australian jewel beetles seem to have trouble figuring out the difference. These large insects live in certain dry regions of Australia. Male beetles can fly, but the larger females cannot. As males fly around, they look for females. Males recognize females by the color and pattern of the female beetle's body. Researchers have discovered that male beetles are also attracted to something else with a similar color and pattern: glass bottles. Many beetles have been seen trying to mate with discarded glass bottles. Scientists are concerned that the jewel beetle population may be harmed—because mating with bottles does not produce jewel beetle offspring!

Read the paragraph and answer the questions below.

1. Why would the male's attempt to mate with bottles harm the jewel beetle population?

_____

_____

_____

_____

2. What is one way that this problem could be prevented?

_____

_____

Lab zone® Do the Inquiry Warm-Up "Eggs-amination."

Vocabulary
- amniotic egg
- placenta
- metamorphosis
- complete metamorphosis
- pupa
- incomplete metamorphosis
- nymph
- tadpole

Skills
- Reading: Summarize
- Inquiry: Interpret Data

Where Do Embryos Develop?

Turtles, sharks, and mice all reproduce sexually. But after fertilization occurs, the offspring of these animals develop in different ways. **The growing offspring, or embryo, may develop outside or inside of the parent's body.**

Egg-Laying Animals The offspring of some animals develop inside an egg laid outside of the parent's body. Most animals without backbones, including worms and insects, lay eggs. Many fishes, reptiles, and birds lay eggs, too. The contents of the egg provide all the nutrients that the developing embryo needs. The eggs of land vertebrates, such as reptiles and birds, are called **amniotic eggs.** Amniotic eggs are covered with membranes and a leathery shell while still inside the parent's body. **Figure 1** shows some of the structures of an amniotic egg.

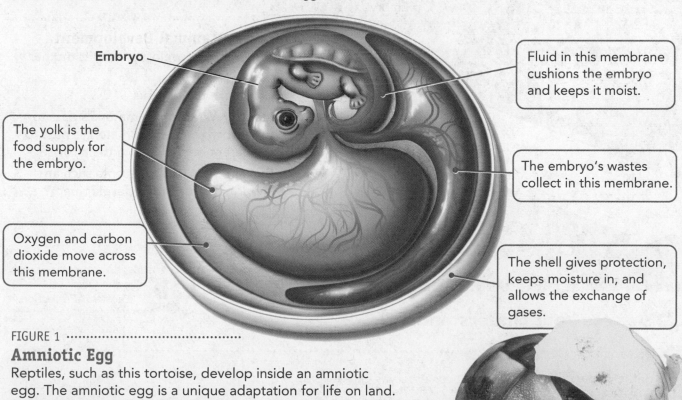

Embryo

Fluid in this membrane cushions the embryo and keeps it moist.

The yolk is the food supply for the embryo.

The embryo's wastes collect in this membrane.

Oxygen and carbon dioxide move across this membrane.

The shell gives protection, keeps moisture in, and allows the exchange of gases.

FIGURE 1 ·····························

Amniotic Egg
Reptiles, such as this tortoise, develop inside an amniotic egg. The amniotic egg is a unique adaptation for life on land.

✎ **Relate Text to Visuals** Circle the descriptions of the structures that keep the embryo from drying out.

✏️ **Summarize** Read the text about egg-retaining animals. Then summarize how the embryo develops in these animals.

_____

_____

_____

_____

Egg-Retaining Animals In certain animals, an embryo develops inside an egg that is kept, or retained, within the parent's body. The developing embryo gets all its nutrients from the egg's yolk, just like the offspring of egg-laying animals. The young do not receive any extra nutrients from the parent. The egg hatches either before or after being released from the parent's body. This type of development is found in fishes, amphibians, and reptiles.

Placental Mammals In dogs, horses, humans, and other placental mammals, the embryo develops inside the mother's body. The mother provides the embryo with everything it needs during development. Materials are exchanged between the embryo and the mother through an organ called the **placenta,** shown in **Figure 2.** Blood carrying food and oxygen from the mother flows to the placenta and then to the embryo. Blood carrying wastes and carbon dioxide from the embryo flows to the placenta and then to the mother. The mother's blood does not mix with the embryo's blood. A placental mammal develops inside its mother's body until its body systems can function on their own.

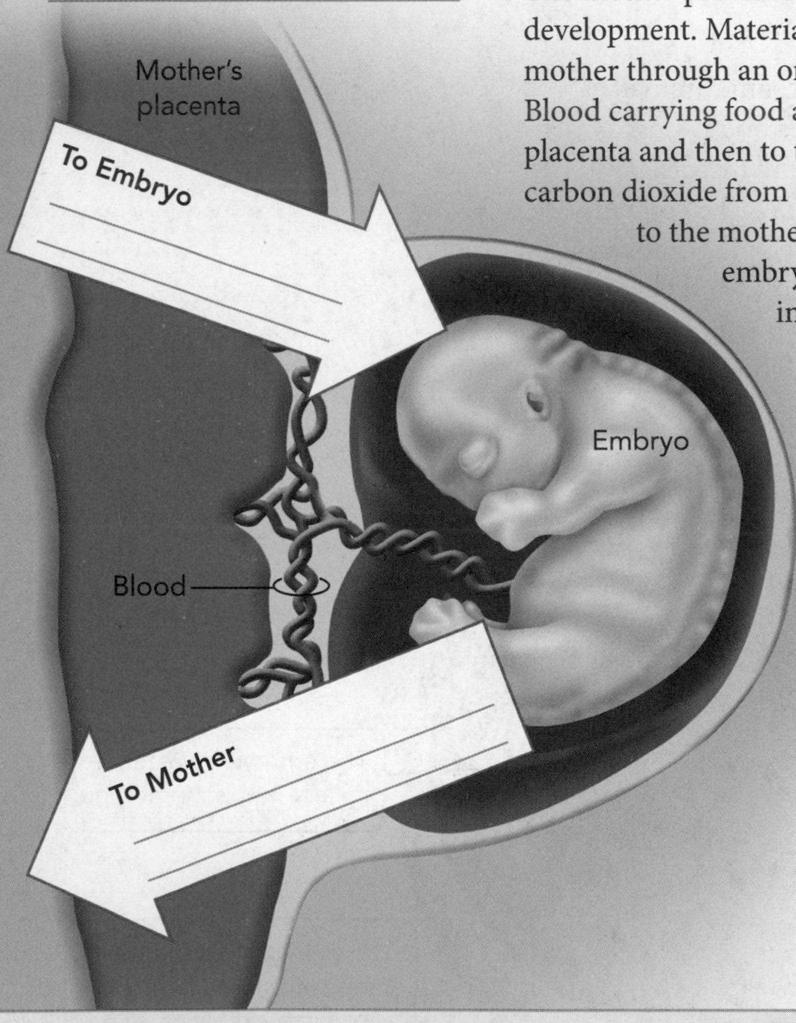

Mother's placenta

To Embryo

Embryo

Blood

To Mother

FIGURE 2 ··
Placental Mammal Development
This cat embryo develops inside its mother for about two months.

✏️ **Complete these tasks.**

1. **Identify** Write which materials pass to the embryo and which materials pass to the parent on the lines in the arrows.

2. **Explain** Why is the placenta such an important structure in development?

_____

_____

Lab ® Do the Quick Lab
zone "Eggs-tra" Protection.

🔑 **Assess Your Understanding**

got it? ··

○ I get it! Now I know that the places embryos can develop are _____

_____

○ I need extra help with _____

_____

_____

How Do Young Animals Develop?

Living things grow, change, and reproduce during their lifetimes. Some young animals, including most vertebrates, look like small versions of adults. Other animals go through the process of **metamorphosis,** or major body changes, as they develop from young organisms into adults. 🔑 **Young animals undergo changes in their bodies between birth and maturity, when they are able to reproduce.** As you read, notice the similarities and differences among the life cycles of crustaceans, insects, and amphibians.

Crustaceans Most crustaceans, such as lobsters, crabs, and shrimp, begin their lives as tiny, swimming larvae. The bodies of these larvae do not resemble those of adults. Larvae may swim or drift in the water as they grow and change. Eventually, through metamorphosis, crustacean larvae develop into adults. **Figure 3** shows three stages of a lobster's life cycle.

FIGURE 3 ·····································

Lobster Metamorphosis

Lobster larvae are only 8 millimeters long. Adults can reach lengths of 1 meter!

✎ **Use the photos to help you complete the tasks.**

1. **Sequence** Write the correct order of the lobster's development in the circles above each photo.

2. **Interpret Photos** Which structures changed as the lobster developed and grew?

_____

_____

_____

111

Insects

Insects Have you ever seen an insect egg? You might find one on the underside of a leaf. After an insect hatches from the egg, it begins metamorphosis as it develops into an adult. Insects such as butterflies, beetles, and grasshoppers undergo complete metamorphosis or incomplete metamorphosis.

Complete Metamorphosis The cycle to the right shows a ladybug going through **complete metamorphosis,** which has four different stages: egg, larva, pupa, and adult. An egg hatches into a larva. A larva usually looks something like a worm. It is specialized for eating and growing. After a time, a larva enters the next stage of the process and becomes a **pupa** (PYOO puh). As a pupa, the insect is enclosed in a protective covering. Although the pupa does not eat and moves very little, it is not resting. Major changes in body structure take place in this stage, as the pupa becomes an adult.

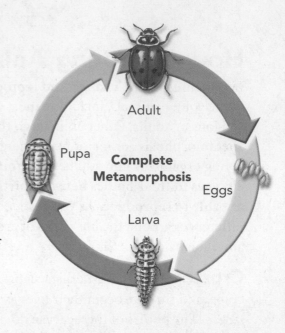

Adult

Pupa

Complete Metamorphosis

Eggs

Larva

A monarch butterfly egg develops on a milkweed plant.

A larva, or a caterpillar, hatches from the egg. The caterpillar grows larger as it feeds on plants. Then it enters the pupa stage.

Inside the pupa case, adult structures such as wings, antennae, and legs form.

Incomplete Metamorphosis In contrast, a second type of metamorphosis, called **incomplete metamorphosis,** has no distinct larval stage. Incomplete metamorphosis has three stages: egg, nymph, and adult. An egg hatches into a stage called a **nymph** (nimf), which usually looks like the adult insect without wings. As the nymph grows, it may shed its outgrown exoskeleton several times before becoming an adult. The chinch bug to the right is going through incomplete metamorphosis.

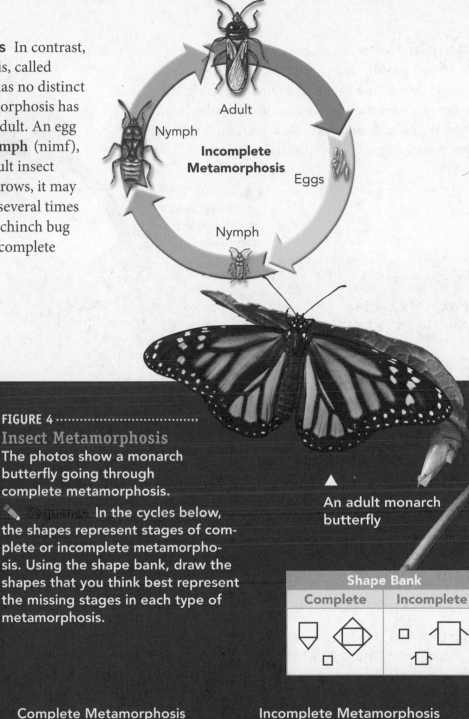

Adult

Nymph

Incomplete Metamorphosis

Eggs

Nymph

An adult monarch butterfly

FIGURE 4 ·····················

Insect Metamorphosis
The photos show a monarch butterfly going through complete metamorphosis.

✎ Sequence In the cycles below, the shapes represent stages of complete or incomplete metamorphosis. Using the shape bank, draw the shapes that you think best represent the missing stages in each type of metamorphosis.

Shape Bank	
Complete	**Incomplete**

The adult butterfly comes out of the pupa case and the butterfly's wings expand as the blood flows into them.

Complete Metamorphosis

Adult

Pupa

Egg

Larva

Incomplete Metamorphosis

Adult

Nymph

Egg

Nymph

Amphibians Frogs begin their life cycle as fertilized eggs in water. After a few days, larvae wriggle out of the eggs and begin swimming. The larva of a frog is called a **tadpole.** Tadpoles look very different from adult frogs. You can follow the process of frog metamorphosis in **Figure 5.**

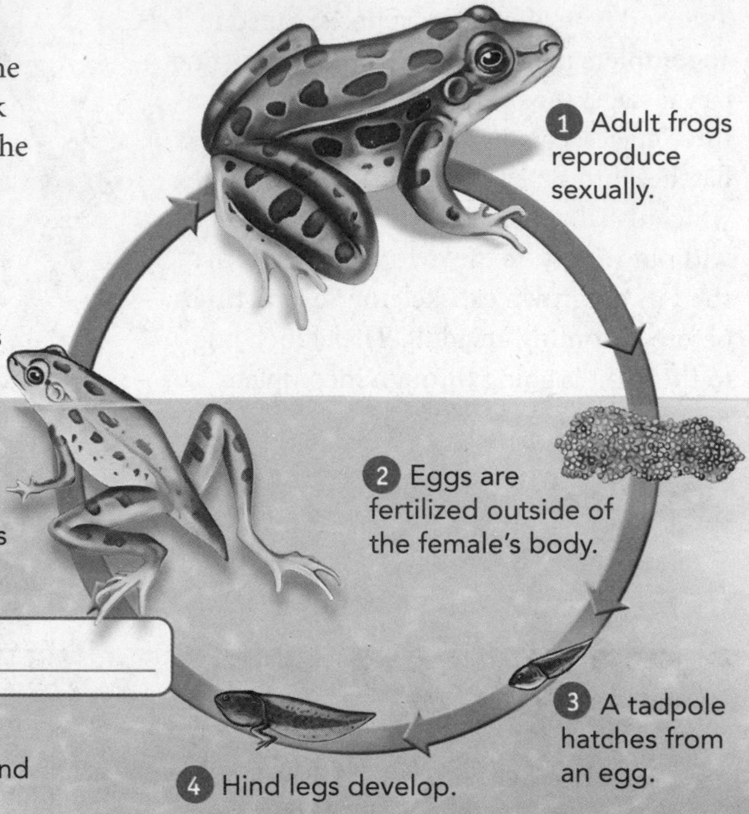

1 Adult frogs reproduce sexually.

6 The tail is absorbed, and development is completed.

2 Eggs are fertilized outside of the female's body.

3 A tadpole hatches from an egg.

4 Hind legs develop.

5 _____

FIGURE 5 ·····················
Frog Life Cycle
Important structures form during metamorphosis that help the frog live in water and on land.

✏ **Use the frog life cycle diagram to complete each task.**

1. **Name** In the space provided, write the structures that grew at stage 5.

2. **Infer** How do the structures in stages 3, 4, and 5 help the frog live in water and on land?

_____

_____

_____

Lab ® Do the Quick Lab
zone *Cycles of Life.*

🔑 **Assess Your Understanding**

1a. Define (Complete/Incomplete) metamorphosis has three stages: egg, nymph, and adult.

b. Apply Concepts Why is a nymph more likely than a larva to eat the same food as an adult?

_____

_____

_____

c. Compare and Contrast How are the life cycles of crustaceans and amphibians similar?

_____

_____

_____

_____

_____

got**it?** ···

O **I get it!** Now I know that as young animals develop they _____

_____

O **I need extra help with** _____

_____

How Do Animals Care for Their Young?

Have you seen a caterpillar, tadpole, puppy, duckling, or other baby animal recently? You may have noticed that different animals care for their offspring in different ways. **Most amphibians and reptiles do not provide parental care, while most birds and mammals typically care for their offspring.**

No Parental Care Not all animals take care of their young. Most aquatic invertebrates, fishes, and amphibians release many eggs into water and then completely ignore them! Most amphibian larvae, or tadpoles, develop into adults without parental help. Similarly, the offspring of most reptiles, such as the snakes in **Figure 6,** are independent from the time they hatch. Offspring that do not receive parental care must be able to care for themselves from the time of birth.

FIGURE 6 ....
Checklist for Survival
These hognose snakes have just hatched from their eggs. They may stay inside the shell for several days for safety.

✎ **List** Make a list of what you think these snakes must be able to do to survive their first few days of life.

_____

_____

_____

_____

_____

_____

Parental Care You've probably never seen a duckling walking by itself. That's because most birds and all mammals typically spend weeks to years under the care and protection of a parent.

Birds Most bird species lay their eggs in nests that one or both parents build. Then one or both parents sit on the eggs, keeping them warm until they hatch. Some species of birds can move around and find food right after they hatch. Others are helpless and must be fed by the parent, as shown in **Figure 7**. Most parent birds feed and protect their young until they are able to care for themselves.

Mammals Whether a monotreme, a marsupial, or a placental mammal, young mammals are usually quite helpless for a long time after they are born. After birth, all young mammals are fed with milk from the mother's body. One or both parents may continue caring for their offspring until the young animals are independent.

FIGURE 7 ···

Parental Care
The parent bird shown above cares for its hungry offspring until they are ready to fly. The mother polar bear at the right stays with her cubs for up to two years.

✎ Answer each question.

1. **Interpret Photos** How are the parents in these two photos caring for their young?

_____

_____

_____

_____

2. **Communicate** What is one way that a family member cares for you?

_____

_____

_____

do the math! Analyzing Data

Suppose that you are a scientist researching how many fox and turtle offspring survive the first year of life. Foxes provide parental care, but turtles do not.

1 Calculate Using the information in the second and fourth columns of the table, calculate the number of offspring that survive the first year. Put your answer in the third column of the table.

2 Graph Use the data from the table to construct a double bar graph in the space provided. Label the vertical axis. Then provide a key for the data in the graph.

3 ⚠ Interpret Data How do you think parental care is related to the percentage of offspring that survive the first year of life?

_____
_____
_____
_____

4 [CHALLENGE] Why do you think animals that provide parental care have fewer offspring?

_____
_____
_____
_____

Type of Animal	Number of Offspring	Number That Survive the First Year	Percentage That Survive the First Year
Fox	5	_____	60%
Turtle	20	_____	20%

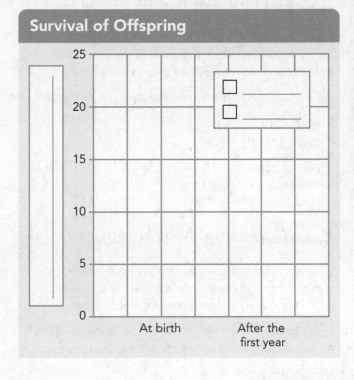

Survival of Offspring

At birth   After the first year

🔑 Assess Your Understanding

got it? ....

○ **I get it!** Now I know that parental care occurs _____
_____

○ **I need extra help with** _____
_____
_____

2 Study Guide

An animal's _____, _____, and _____ work together to help the animal move.

LESSON 1 Skeletons and Muscles

🔑 A skeleton is a framework that shapes and supports an animal, protects its internal organs, and allows it to move in its environment.

🔑 Muscles help animals move their body parts.

Vocabulary
• molting
• cartilage
• joint
• muscle

LESSON 2 The Nervous System

🔑 A nervous system allows animals to detect, process, and react to environmental signals.

🔑 The simplest nervous systems are a netlike arrangement of neurons throughout the body. Complex systems have a nerve cord and a brain.

Vocabulary
• nervous system • stimulus • response • neuron
• impulse • sensory neuron • interneuron
• motor neuron • brain

LESSON 3 Animal Movement

🔑 An animal moves about when its nervous system, muscular system, and skeletal system work together to make movement happen.

🔑 Animals that live in water, on land, or in the air have different adaptations for movement.

Vocabulary
• water vascular system
• swim bladder

LESSON 4 Obtaining Energy

🔑 The different ways that an animal obtains energy depends on what and how it eats.

🔑 Animal cells exchange oxygen and carbon dioxide with their surroundings by diffusion.

🔑 Complex animals have one of two types of circulatory systems: open or closed.

Vocabulary
• carnivore • herbivore • omnivore • filter feeder
• digestion • digestive system • cellular respiration
• diffusion • respiratory system • circulatory system

LESSON 5 Animal Reproduction and Fertilization

🔑 Animals undergo either asexual or sexual reproduction to make more of their own kind.

🔑 External fertilization occurs outside of the female's body, and internal fertilization occurs inside the female's body.

Vocabulary
• larva • polyp • medusa
• external fertilization • internal fertilization
• gestation period

LESSON 6 Development and Growth

🔑 The growing offspring, or embryo, may develop outside or inside of the parent's body.

🔑 Young animals undergo changes in their bodies between birth and maturity.

🔑 Most amphibians and reptiles do not provide parental care. Most birds and mammals do.

Vocabulary
• amniotic egg • placenta • metamorphosis
• complete metamorphosis • pupa
• incomplete metamorphosis • nymph • tadpole

Review and Assessment

LESSON 1 **Skeletons and Muscles**

1. A _____ is a place where two or more parts of a skeleton meet.

2. **Relate Cause and Effect** How might an endoskeleton affect the size of an animal?

_____

_____

_____

3. **Sequence** Describe how your muscles work to help you kick a ball.

_____

_____

_____

_____

_____

LESSON 2 **The Nervous System**

4. A signal that causes an animal to react in some way is called a

   a. response.   b. neuron.

   c. stimulus.   d. impulse.

5. The most complex nervous systems have

   a nerve cord and a _____

Use the diagrams below to answer Question 6.

A   B

6. **Interpret Diagrams** Explain the stimulus in diagram A and the response in diagram B.

_____

_____

_____

LESSON 3 **Animal Movement**

7. An animal that moves using a water vascular system is a

   a. sea star.   b. penguin.

   c. squid.   d. shark.

8. **Draw Conclusions** What are three reasons why an animal might need to move about?

_____

_____

_____

_____

_____

_____

_____

9. **Write About It** Write a paragraph in which you describe a different adaptation that rabbits, bats, and snakes each have that enables them to move as they do.

LESSON 4 **Obtaining Energy**

10. Animals that eat only plant material are

    a. omnivores.   b. filter feeders.

    c. carnivores.   d. herbivores.

11. The process of breaking down food into small

    molecules is called _____

12. **Make Generalizations** What type of teeth would you expect an omnivore to have? How do they help the animal eat its food?

_____

_____

_____

_____

_____

_____

13. The process in which an animal's cells use oxygen and digested food molecules to release the energy in food is

    a. breathing.
    b. cellular respiration.
    c. diffusion.
    d. gas exchange.

14. **Write About It** Describe three structures that an animal's respiratory system may have. Name one animal that has each structure.

LESSON 5 Animal Reproduction and Fertilization

15. External fertilization is common for organisms that live in

    a. trees.
    b. water.
    c. deserts.
    d. open fields.

16. The _____ is an immature form of an organism that looks very different from the adult.

17. **Write About It** Consider the following statement: *Organisms that reproduce asexually are at a higher risk of extinction than organisms that reproduce sexually.* Do you agree or disagree? Explain your answer.

LESSON 6 Development and Growth

18. Which of the following organisms lays amniotic eggs?

    a. fish
    b. insect
    c. turtle
    d. rabbit

19. **Compare and Contrast** How is the development of an embryo in an amniotic egg and in a placental mammal different?

20. **Make Generalizations** Why is parental care so important for newborn birds and mammals?

APPLY THE BIG ？ How do animals move?

21. Suppose this ostrich's nervous system was not receiving signals properly. How might it be dangerous for the ostrich?

Standardized Test Prep

Read each question and choose the best answer.

1. Which is true of the endoskeleton of a mammal?

   A It grows with the animal.

   B It molts as the animal grows.

   C It does not have hard parts.

   D It is mostly cartilage.

2. The larval form of the frog shown in stage 3 is called a(n)

   A nymph.   **B** pupa.

   C tadpole.   **D** adult.

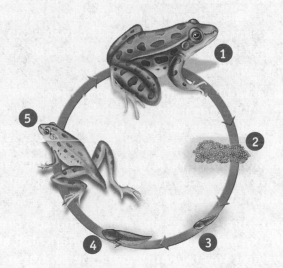

3. An amniotic egg is the result of _____ and _____.

   A asexual reproduction; external fertilization

   B asexual reproduction; internal fertilization

   C sexual reproduction; external fertilization

   D sexual reproduction; internal fertilization

4. Based on the type of teeth you see in the diagram below, make an inference about what type of animal it is.

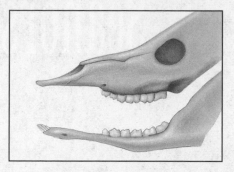

   A omnivore   **B** herbivore

   C carnivore   **D** filter feeder

5. Animals with nerve nets have

   A no specialized neurons.

   B sensory neurons, but no interneurons.

   C interneurons, but no sensory neurons.

   D only motor neurons.

Constructed Response

Use the diagram below and your knowledge of science to help you answer Question 6. Write your answer on a separate sheet of paper.

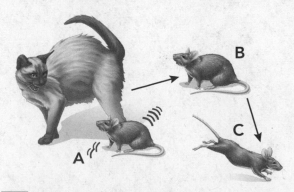

6. Describe how the mouse's nervous system is functioning in this diagram. Include the roles of the sensory neurons, interneurons, and motor neurons.

SPECIAL DELIVERY!

Seahorse Reproduction

In warm, coastal waters all over the world, just after sunrise every day, a dance-like scene takes place. Tails intertwined, pairs of seahorses spin and twirl under water. Some use their long tails to hold onto strands of seaweed. These long tails that are adapted for grabbing and holding things aren't seahorses' only unusual feature. Seahorses also have some unusual reproductive habits!

Seahorses practice sexual reproduction, like other fish do. Unlike fish—or any other vertebrate for that matter—it's the male seahorse that carries fertilized eggs, provides the eggs with oxygen and nutrients, and gives birth. The males can do this because they have pouches, called brood pouches, in their abdomens.

When mating, the female seahorse deposits about 2,000 eggs inside the male's pouch each time, and he does the rest. He fertilizes the eggs, which become embedded in his pouch wall, and carries them for several weeks. During this time, the eggs receive oxygen and nutrients through a network of tiny blood vessels.

In about three weeks, the male seahorse's brood pouch expands until it is almost spherical. It stays this way for several hours, until the seahorse suddenly gives birth to between eight and 200 baby seahorses. These tiny seahorses can swim and feed by themselves, although they will not be ready to mate with their own partners for many months. About an hour after giving birth, the male is ready to mate again.

▲ The male seahorse's brood pouch expands as the baby seahorses grow.

Design It Pipefish are another species with unusual reproductive habits. Find out about their reproductive cycles. Create a Venn diagram to compare and contrast the pipefish cycle and the seahorse cycle.

"feet" of engineering

Geckos are tiny lizards that live in warm climates all over the world, including the southwestern United States. If you've ever seen one, you've probably watched it scale a wall in about the time it takes for you to blink. Or you may have seen a gecko hang from one foot.

How do geckos hang from one foot? The answer is their hair! The gecko's feet are covered in millions of tiny hairs. Molecules in the hairs are attracted to molecules in the wall or on any other surface. These forces of attraction, called van der Waals forces, affect every form of matter, but they are usually so weak that you can't feel them. However, there are so many tiny hairs on a gecko's feet that geckos can cling to nearly any surface!

Gecko feet have inspired scientists to design artificial super-sticky materials that use the same principle. Maybe someday these materials could be used for surgical bandages, wall-crawling robots, or even shoes with incredible grip. For now, scientists will have to see which designs stick!

Design It Technological design inspired by biology is called biomimetic design. Research a few other examples of biomimetic design, and choose a simple problem that one of your examples could solve. Make or draw a model of your solution.

Why Do Clownfish Play With Poison?

THE BIG

How do living things affect one another?

Clownfish live among the poisonous and stinging tentacles of sea anemones to avoid being eaten by larger fish. Amazingly, the clownfish do not get stung! This is because a fluid called mucus protects the skin of the fish. △Develop Hypotheses How might a sea anemone benefit from having clownfish around?

_____

_____

_____

_____

_____

_____

Watch the **Untamed Science** video to learn more about interactions between organisms.

Populations and Communities

Getting Started

Check Your Understanding

1. **Background** Read the paragraph below and then answer the question.

Raquel planted a garden in a sunny area near her home. First, she loosened the **soil,** so the plant roots could easily grow. If days passed with no **precipitation,** she watered the plants. That was all she had to do—the rest of what the plants needed came from the **atmosphere!**

> **Soil** is made up of rock fragments, water, air, and decaying plant and animal matter.
>
> Rain, hail, sleet, and snow are all types of **precipitation.**
>
> Earth's **atmosphere** contains oxygen, carbon dioxide, nitrogen, and other gases.

• How do soil, precipitation, and the atmosphere help a plant grow?

_____

_____

Vocabulary Skill

Latin Word Origins Some key terms in this chapter contain word parts with Latin origins. The table below lists two of the Latin words that key terms come from.

Latin Word	Meaning of Latin Word	Example
aptare	to fit	adaptation, *n.* a characteristic that allows an organism to live successfully in its environment
migrare	to move	immigration, *n.* movement into a population

2. **Quick Check** The terms *immigration* and *emigration* both come from the Latin word *migrare*. Circle the meaning of *migrare* in the table above.

organism

immigration

adaptation

predation

Chapter Preview

LESSON 1
- organism • habitat
- biotic factor • abiotic factor
- species • population
- community • ecosystem
- ecology

↻ **Compare and Contrast**
△ **Draw Conclusions**

LESSON 2
- birth rate • death rate
- immigration • emigration
- population density
- limiting factor
- carrying capacity

↻ **Relate Cause and Effect**
△ **Infer**

LESSON 3
- natural selection • adaptation
- niche • competition • predation
- predator • prey • symbiosis
- mutualism • commensalism
- parasitism • parasite • host

↻ **Relate Text and Visuals**
△ **Classify**

For extra help with vocabulary, visit **Vocab Flash Cards** and type in *Populations and Communities.*

That Can't Possibly Work!

Purpose   To investigate the accuracy of the Mark and Recapture population estimating method

Materials
- 15 plastic zipper storage bags
- felt-tip marker
- small items to fill the bags (dried beans, uncooked macaroni, etc.)

Scenario

You have just learned about a method for estimating the size of a population called "Mark and Recapture." Ecologists use Mark and Recapture when it isn't practical for them to count all the individuals in a population. Mark and Recapture involves estimating the size of a population by capturing, marking, and then recapturing some members of the population. This technique can yield a very accurate estimate. Perhaps you are skeptical? You need to see for yourself that this can work.

Mark and Recapture

1. To estimate the size of a population, a researcher visits the study area and uses traps to capture a group of individuals. Each individual is marked with a numbered tag or band and then released unharmed back into the environment.

2. The researcher goes away to allow time for the marked individuals to mix back into the population.

3. When the researcher returns, he or she captures another sample of individuals.

Some of the individuals in this second sample will already be marked. The rest will not be marked.

4. The researcher records the number of marked and unmarked individuals in each sample. The researcher then uses a mathematical formula to calculate the size of the population. The researcher can estimate population size from as few as two visits to the study area, but more visits provide a more accurate estimate.

Scientists Are Skeptical

Scientists like to see evidence. When they read or hear about a new claim, their first reaction is to examine the evidence to see if the facts support the claim. When scientists read about a new way of doing something, they are skeptical about that, too. They ask, "Does the new way work as well as the older way of doing the same thing? Is the new way better?"

Procedure

☑ **1. The Population** Your teacher will give you a bag filled with small objects. The objects represent a population of lively animals.

☑ **2. The Capture and Mark** Capture 10 animals by reaching into the bag and removing them one at a time. (It's okay to look during this step.)

☑ **3. The Mark** Mark the captured animals with the marker and return them to the bag.

☑ **4. The Mix** Allow the population to mix. Stir them or shake them to get them to move.

☑ **5. The Recapture** With your eyes closed, reach into the bag and remove 15 animals.

Procedure *(continued)*

☑ **6. Recording the Data** Record on the data table the number of the recaptured animals that already have a mark.

☑ **7. Return and Repeat** Return the animals to the bag and repeat Steps 4 and 5. Complete a total of 10 recaptures.

☑ **8. Total the Results** After you have entered the counts from the 10 recaptures, add them and record the total number of recaptured animals that had a mark on them.

☑ **9. Calculate and Count** Use the formula below to calculate your estimate of the population size, and then check your estimate by counting the actual number of animals in the bag:

Trial Number	Total Recaptured	Number Recaptured with a mark
1	15	
2	15	
3	15	
4	15	
5	15	
6	15	
7	15	
8	15	
9	15	
10	15	
Total:	150	

Estimate of Total Population = $\dfrac{\text{(total number recaptured)} \times \text{(number originally marked)}}{\text{(total number recaptured with a mark)}}$

Estimated size: _____   Actual size: _____

Conclusion

Let's see what you learned about estimating the size of a population using the Mark and Recapture method. Compare the actual size to the estimated size and answer the following questions.

☑ **1.** How close was your estimate? _____

☑ **2.** Was your estimate too high or too low? _____

☑ **3.** Explain how you could make the estimate more accurate. _____

_____

☑ **4.** Are you still skeptical? Explain. _____

A friend of yours is using the Mark and Recapture technique to study the butterfly population in the area around his school. He first marked and released 50 butterflies. For four weeks, he checked his traps daily, counted the butterflies in the traps, and then released them. He caught a total of 300 butterflies, and 25 of them were marked. He determined that the total population of butterflies is 150. Is he correct? If not, what is the size of the butterfly population he is studying, and what mistake did he make? Prepare a brief answer to send to your friend by e-mail. Show all calculations.

Living Things and the Environment

UNLOCK THE BIG

🔑 **What Does an Organism Get From Its Environment?**

🔑 **What Are the Two Parts of an Organism's Habitat?**

🔑 **How Is an Ecosystem Organized?**

my planet DiaRY

DISCOVERY

Love Song

The gray, golden brown, and Goodman's mouse lemurs are some of the world's smallest primates. These three lemurs look similar. Looking so similar makes it difficult for the lemurs to find members of their own kind or species during mating season. However, it seems that the lemurs can identify their own species by song. Scientists recorded the mating calls of the three species of lemurs. They discovered that the lemurs reacted more to the calls from their own species. This allows the lemurs to pick the right mate, even at night.

Communicate Answer these questions. Discuss your answers with a partner.

1. If you were looking for your sneakers among several pairs that looked just like yours, what characteristics would make it easier for you to find them?

   _____

   _____

2. What do you think would happen if a lemur mated with a different kind of lemur?

   _____

   _____

Lab zone® Do the Inquiry Warm-Up *What's in the Scene?*

Goodman's mouse lemur

Golden brown mouse lemur

Gray mouse lemur

Vocabulary

- organism • habitat • biotic factor • abiotic factor
- species • population • community • ecosystem
- ecology

Skills

↻ Reading: Compare and Contrast
△ Inquiry: Draw Conclusions

What Does an Organism Get From Its Environment?

If you were to visit Alaska, you might see a bald eagle fly by. A bald eagle is one type of **organism,** or living thing. Different types of organisms live in different types of surroundings, or environments. **An organism gets food, water, shelter, and other things it needs to live, grow, and reproduce from its environment.** An environment that provides the things a specific organism needs to live, grow, and reproduce is called its **habitat.**

In a forest habitat, mushrooms grow in the damp soil and woodpeckers build nests in tree trunks. Organisms live in different habitats because they have different requirements for survival and reproduction. Some organisms live on a prairie, with its flat terrain, tall grasses, and low rainfall amounts. A prairie dog, like the one shown in **Figure 1,** obtains the food and shelter it needs from a prairie habitat. It could not survive on this rocky ocean shore. Likewise, the prairie would not meet the needs of a sea star.

FIGURE 1 ....

What's Wrong With This Picture?
Most people would never expect to see a prairie dog at the beach.

✏ **List** Give three reasons why this prairie dog would not survive in this habitat.

_____

_____

_____

_____

Lab zone® Do the Quick Lab
Organisms and Their Habitats.

⌕ Assess Your Understanding

got it? ....

○ **I get it!** Now I know that an organism's environment provides _____

_____

○ **I need extra help with** _____

_____

What Are the Two Parts of an Organism's Habitat?

To meet its needs, a prairie dog must interact with more than just the other prairie dogs around it. 🔑 **An organism interacts with both the living and nonliving parts of its habitat.**

Biotic Factors What living things can you see in the prairie dog's habitat shown in **Figure 2**? The parts of a habitat that are living, or were once living, and which interact with an organism are called **biotic factors** (by AHT ik). The plants that provide seeds and berries, the ferrets and eagles that hunt the prairie dog, and the worms and bacteria that live in the soil are all biotic factors. Prairie dog scat, owl pellets, and decomposing plant matter are also biotic factors.

Abiotic Factors Not all of the factors that organisms interact with are living. **Abiotic factors** (ay by AHT ik) are the nonliving parts of an organism's habitat. These factors, as shown in **Figure 2**, include sunlight, soil, temperature, oxygen, and water.

✏️ **Compare and Contrast** In the paragraphs at the right, circle how biotic and abiotic factors are similar and underline how they are different.

Sunlight Because sunlight is needed for plants to make their own food, it is an important abiotic factor for most living things.

Soil Soil consists of varying amounts of rock fragments, nutrients, air, water, and the decaying remains of living things. The soil in an area influences the kinds of plants and animals that can live and grow there.

Temperature The temperatures that are typical in an area determine the types of organisms that can live there.

Oxygen Most living things require oxygen to carry out their life processes. Organisms on land obtain oxygen from air. Aquatic organisms obtain oxygen that is dissolved in the water around them.

Water All living things require water to carry out their life processes. Plants and algae need water along with sunlight and carbon dioxide to make their own food. Other living things depend on plants and algae for food.

FIGURE 2 ··········

Factors in a Prairie Habitat

A prairie dog interacts with many biotic and abiotic factors in the prairie habitat.

✏️ **Relate Text and Visuals** Add another biotic factor to the picture. For each abiotic factor, draw a line from the text box to an example in the picture.

apply it!

Salt is an abiotic factor found in some environments. To see how the amount of salt affects the hatching of brine shrimp eggs, varying amounts of salt were added to four different 500-mL beakers.

1 **Observe** In which beaker(s) did the eggs, shown as purple circles, hatch? _____

2 **Infer** The manipulated variable was _____

3 **Infer** The responding variable was _____

_____

4 CHALLENGE Beaker _____ was the control.

5 Draw Conclusions What can you conclude about the amount of salt in the shrimps' natural habitat?

_____

_____

_____

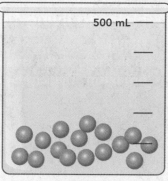

Beaker A
500 mL spring water

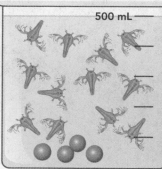

Beaker B
500 mL spring water
+ 2.5 g salt

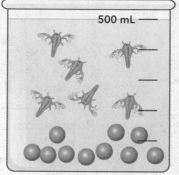

Beaker C
500 mL spring water
+ 7.5 g salt

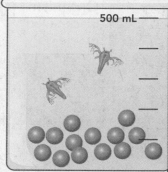

Beaker D
500 mL spring water
+ 15 g salt

Lab® zone Do the Lab Investigation
World in a Bottle.

🔑 Assess Your Understanding

1a. Interpret Diagrams List two biotic and two abiotic factors in **Figure 2.**

_____

_____

_____

_____

_____

b. Draw Conclusions Name two abiotic factors in your habitat and explain how your life would be different without them.

_____

_____

_____

_____

got it? ···

○ **I get it!** Now I know that the two parts of an organism's habitat are _____

_____

○ I need extra help with _____

_____

133

Ecological Organization

EXPLORE THE BIG ?

How do living things affect one another?

FIGURE 3 ··
In this figure, the smallest level of organization is the organism. The largest is the entire ecosystem.

Organism
Black-tailed prairie dog

Population
Prairie dog town

Community
All the living things that interact on the prairie

How Is an Ecosystem Organized?

Most organisms do not live all alone in their habitat. Instead, organisms live together in populations and communities that interact with abiotic factors in their ecosystems.

Organisms Black-tailed prairie dogs that live in prairie dog towns on the Nebraska plains are all members of one species. A **species** (SPEE sheez) is a group of organisms that can mate with each other and produce offspring that can also mate and reproduce.

Populations All the members of one species living in a particular area are referred to as a **population.** The prairie dogs in the Nebraska town are one example of a population.

Communities A particular area contains more than one species of organism. The prairie, for instance, includes prairie dogs, hawks, snakes, and grasses. All the different populations that live together in an area make up a **community.**

Apply Concepts Draw or write how an ecosystem of your choice is organized. Identify each level. Include biotic and abiotic examples.

Ecosystem
All the living and nonliving things that interact on the prairie

Ecosystems

The community of organisms that live in a particular area, along with their nonliving environment, make up an **ecosystem.** A prairie is just one of the many different ecosystems found on Earth. Other ecosystems are deserts, oceans, ponds, and forests.

Figure 3 shows the levels of organization in a prairie ecosystem. **The smallest level of organization is a single organism, which belongs to a population that includes other members of its species. The population belongs to a community of different species. The community and abiotic factors together form an ecosystem.**

The atoms that make up the organisms in an ecosystem are cycled repeatedly between the living and nonliving parts of the ecosystem. Because the populations in an ecosystem interact with one another, any change affects all the different populations that live there. The study of how organisms interact with each other and with their environment is called **ecology.**

Lab zone® Do the Quick-Lab *Organizing an Ecosystem.*

Assess Your Understanding

2a. Classify All of the different kinds of organisms in a forest are a (community/ population).

b. ANSWER THE BIG ? How do living things affect one another?

_____

_____

_____

got it? ....

○ **I get it!** Now I know that ecosystems are

organized into _____

_____

_____

○ I need extra help with_____

_____

_____

135

Populations

UNLOCK THE BIG ?

🔑 **How Do Populations Change in Size?**

🔑 **What Factors Limit Population Growth?**

my planeT DiaRY

Prairie Dog Picker-Upper

Did you know that vacuum cleaners do more than just clean carpets? Across the Great Plains, farmers are using specially designed vacuum cleaners to help them remove black-tailed prairie dogs from the farm land. Prairie dogs can eat crops, cause soil erosion, and endanger cattle and farm machinery. The prairie dog vacuum uses a 4-in. plastic hose to suck prairie dogs out of the ground at 483 km/h! The prairie dogs end up in a padded tank, usually unharmed. They are then relocated or donated to the U.S. Fish and Wildlife Service to be fed to endangered eagles, hawks, and black-footed ferrets.

Prairie dogs

TECHNOLOGY

Communicate Discuss these questions with a group of classmates. Write your answers below.

1. If all of the prairie dogs were removed, how do you think the prairie ecosystem would be affected?

_____

_____

_____

2. Should prairie dogs be used as food for endangered species? Explain.

_____

_____

_____

Lab zone ® Do the Inquiry Warm-Up *Populations.*

How Do Populations Change in Size?

Ecologists are scientists who study biotic and abiotic factors of an ecosystem and the interactions between them. Some ecologists study populations and monitor the sizes of populations over time. 🔑 **Populations can change in size when new members join the population or when members leave the population.**

Vocabulary

- birth rate • death rate • immigration
- emigration • population density
- limiting factor • carrying capacity

Skills

↪ Reading: Relate Cause and Effect
△ Inquiry: Infer

Births and Deaths The most common way in which new individuals join a population is by being born into it. If more individuals are born into a population than die in any period of time, a population can grow. So when the **birth rate,** the number of births per 1,000 individuals for a given time period, is greater than its **death rate,** the number of deaths per 1,000 individuals for a given time period, the population may increase. The main way that individuals leave a population is by dying. If the birth rate is the same as the death rate, then the population may stay the same. In situations where the death rate is higher than the birth rate, then the population may decrease.

do the math!

Depending on the size and age of the female, an American Alligator can lay between 10 and 50 eggs per year.

1. **Graph** Using the data table and colored pencils, create a double bar graph showing alligator births and deaths for four years.
2. Label the x-axis and y-axis.
3. Write a title for the graph.
4. Fill in the graph using the colors shown.
5. **Develop Hypotheses** What factors might explain the number of births and deaths in Year 3?

_____

_____

_____

_____

_____

_____

Data Table		
Year	Births	Deaths
1	32	8
2	28	13
3	47	21
4	33	16

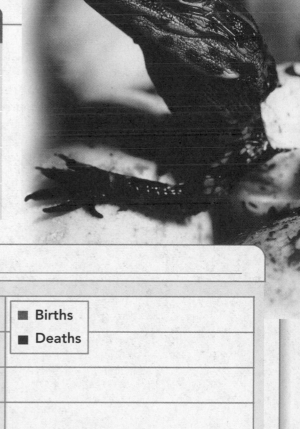

Legend:
- ■ Births
- ■ Deaths

The Population Statement

When the birth rate in a population is greater than the death rate, the population will generally increase. This can be written as a mathematical statement using the "is greater than" sign:

If birth rate > death rate, population size increases.

However, if the death rate in a population is greater than the birth rate, the population size will generally decrease. This can also be written as a mathematical statement:

If death rate > birth rate, population size decreases.

Immigration and Emigration

The size of a population also can change when individuals move into or out of the population. **Immigration** (im ih GRAY shun) means moving into a population. **Emigration** (em ih GRAY shun) means leaving a population. For instance, if food is scarce, some members of an antelope herd may wander off in search of better grassland. If they become permanently separated from the original herd, they will no longer be part of that population.

FIGURE 1

Immigration

In 1898, white-tailed deer were almost extinct in Iowa due to over-hunting. The deer population was reestablished as animals from Minnesota, Wisconsin, and Missouri immigrated into Iowa.

✎ **Apply Concepts** Using your classroom, describe an example of each of the following.

Immigration: _____

_____

Emigration: _____

_____

Graphing Changes in Population Changes in a population's size can be displayed on a line graph. Figure 2 shows a graph of the changes in a rabbit population. The vertical axis identifies the number of rabbits in the population, while the horizontal axis shows time. The graph represents the size of the rabbit population over a ten-year period.

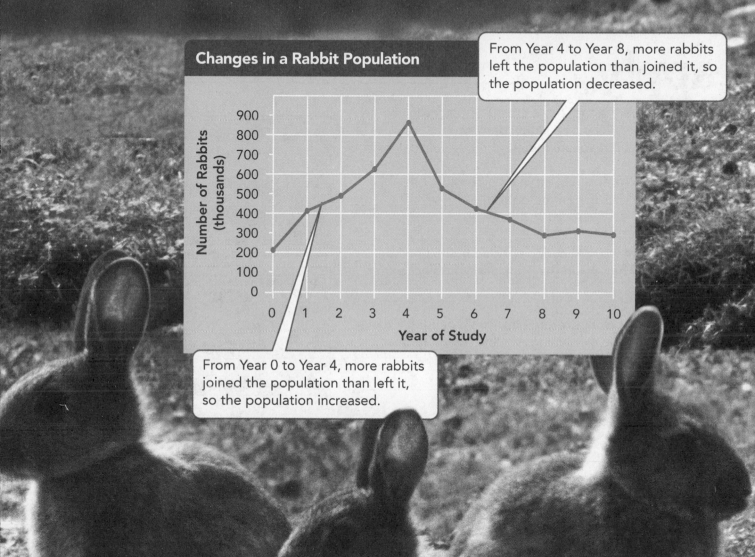

Changes in a Rabbit Population

From Year 4 to Year 8, more rabbits left the population than joined it, so the population decreased.

From Year 0 to Year 4, more rabbits joined the population than left it, so the population increased.

FIGURE 2 ·······

Changes in a Rabbit Population

✎ This graph shows how the size of a rabbit population changed over ten years.

1. **Interpret Data** In Year _____, the rabbit population reached its highest point.

2. **Read Graphs** What was the size of the rabbit population in that year? _____

3. CHALLENGE How do you think the rabbit population affected the fox population over the same ten-year period? Explain your reasoning.

_____

_____

_____

_____

_____

_____

Population Density Sometimes an ecologist needs to know more than just the total size of a population. In many situations, it is helpful to know the **population density**—the number of individuals in an area of a specific size. Population density can be written as an equation:

$$\text{Population density} = \frac{\text{Number of individuals}}{\text{Unit area}}$$

For example, suppose you counted 20 butterflies in a garden measuring 10 square meters. The population density would be 20 butterflies per 10 square meters, or 2 butterflies per square meter.

apply it!

In the pond on the top, there are 10 flamingos in 8 square meters. The population density is 1.25 flamingos per square meter.

❶ Calculate What is the population density of the flamingos in the pond on the bottom?

_____

❷ ⚠ Infer If 14 more flamingos landed in the pond on the bottom, what would the population density be then?

_____

❸ CHALLENGE What do you think would happen if the population density of flamingos in the pond on the bottom became too great?

_____

_____

_____

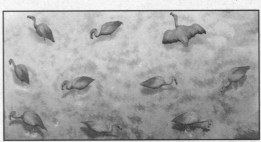

← 4 meters →

2 meters

2 meters

Lab zone Do the Quick Lab *Growing and Shrinking.*

🔑 Assess Your Understanding

1a. Review Two ways to join a population are _____ and _____.

Two ways to leave a population are _____ and _____.

b. Calculate Suppose a population of 8 wolves has produced 20 young in a year. If 7 wolves have died, how many wolves are in the population now? (Assume no wolves have moved into or out of the population for other reasons.)

_____

_____

got it?

○ **I get it!** Now I know that population size changes due to _____

_____

○ **I need extra help with** _____

What Factors Limit Population Growth?

When the living conditions in an area are good, a population will generally grow. But eventually some environmental factor will cause the population to stop growing. A **limiting factor** is an environmental factor that causes a population to stop growing or decrease in size. 🔑 **Some limiting factors for populations are weather conditions, space, food, and water.**

Climate Changes in climate conditions, such as temperature and the amount of rainfall, can limit population growth. A cold spring season can kill the young of many species of organisms, including birds and mammals. Unusual events like floods, hurricanes, and the tornado shown in **Figure 3** can also have long-lasting effects on population size.

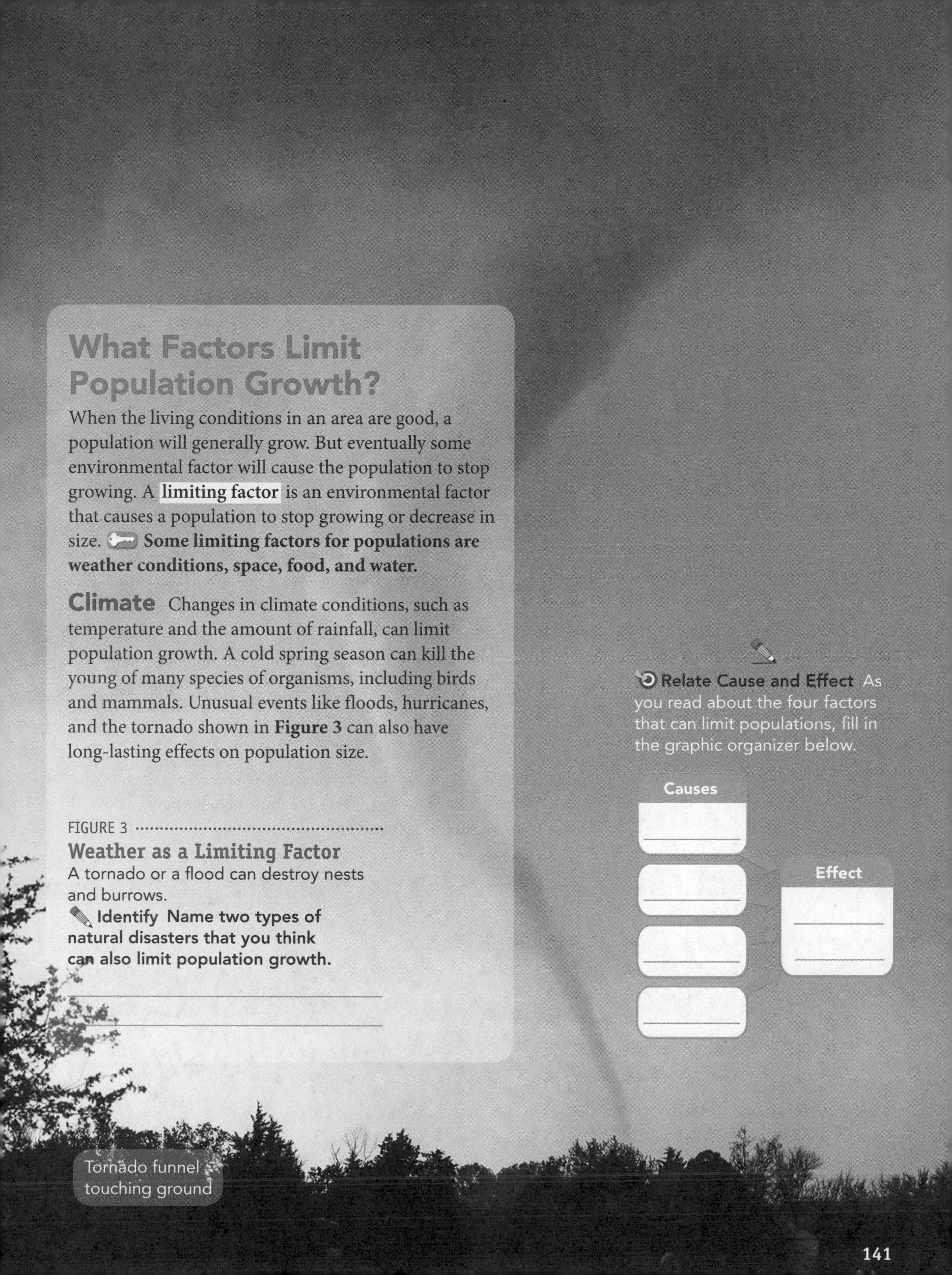

FIGURE 3 ···························

Weather as a Limiting Factor

A tornado or a flood can destroy nests and burrows.

✎ **Identify** Name two types of natural disasters that you think can also limit population growth.

_____

_____

↻ **Relate Cause and Effect** As you read about the four factors that can limit populations, fill in the graphic organizer below.

Causes

Effect

Tornado funnel touching ground

141

Space

Space is another limiting factor for populations. Gannets are seabirds that are usually seen flying over the ocean. They come to land only to nest on rocky shores. But the nesting shores get very crowded. If a pair does not find room to nest, they will not be able to add any offspring to the gannet population. So nesting space on the shore is a limiting factor for gannets. If there were more nesting space, more gannets would be able to nest. The population could increase.

Figure 4 shows how space is also a limiting factor for plants. The amount of space in which a plant grows determines whether the plant can obtain the sunlight, water, and soil nutrients it needs. For example, many pine seedlings sprout each year in forests. But as the seedlings grow, the roots of those that are too close together run out of space. Branches from other trees may block the sunlight the seedlings need. Some of the seedlings then die, limiting the size of the pine population.

Food and Water

Organisms require food and water to survive. When food and water are in limited supply, they can be limiting factors. Suppose a giraffe must eat 10 kilograms of leaves each day to survive. The trees in an area can provide 100 kilograms of leaves a day while remaining healthy. Five giraffes could live easily in this area, because they would need just 50 kilograms of food a day. But 15 giraffes could not all survive—there would not be enough food. No matter how much shelter, water, and other resources there were, the population would not grow much larger than 10 giraffes. The largest population that an area can support is called its carrying capacity. The carrying capacity of this giraffe habitat would be 10 giraffes. The size of a population can vary, but usually stays near its carrying capacity because of the limiting factors in its habitat.

FIGURE 4

Space as a Limiting Factor

If no more tulip plants can grow in this field, the field has reached its carrying capacity for tulips.

✎ List Name three things a plant needs to survive.

apply it!

Giant pandas live in the mountains of south central China. Most (99 percent) of the pandas' diet is made up of the bamboo plant. Bamboo is not nutrient rich. Pandas spend 55 percent of their day eating between 9 and 38 kilograms of bamboo. Getting enough bamboo to eat can be a challenge. Farming and the timber industry have destroyed the pandas' habitat and bamboo forests. In addition, when a bamboo plant flowers, the plant dies and does not regrow for several years. It is difficult for scientists to know exactly how many giant pandas exist in the wild. The best estimate is that there are about 1,600 of them. Due to the small population size, this species is classified as endangered.

✎ **Communicate** Write a letter to the editor that describes how food and space may be limiting factors for the giant panda species. Add a headline to your letter.

_____
_____
_____
_____
_____
_____
_____
_____

Lab zone® Do the Quick Lab *Elbow Room.*

🔑 Assess Your Understanding

2a. Summarize When the climate changes or there is not enough _____ or _____ or _____, a population can (begin/stop) growing in size.

b. Relate Cause and Effect Choose a limiting factor and describe the factor's effect on population growth.

_____
_____
_____
_____

got it? ....

○ I get it! Now I know that populations can be limited when_____

_____

○ I need extra help with _____

_____

Interactions Among Living Things

UNLOCK THE BIG ?

🔑 **How Do Adaptations Help an Organism Survive?**

🔑 **What Are Competition and Predation?**

🔑 **What Are the Three Types of Symbiosis?**

MY PLANET DiARY

Predator Power

What predator can close its jaws the fastest? You might think it is a lion or a shark, but you would be wrong. It is the trap-jaw ant that has the fastest strike in the animal kingdom. The trap-jaw ant closes its mouth around its prey in 0.13 milliseconds at speeds of 35 to 64 meters per second! The force created when its jaw snaps shut also helps the ant escape danger by either jumping up to 8.3 centimeters high or 39.6 centimeters sideways.

A trap-jaw ant stalks its prey.

FUN FACT

Communicate Answer the questions below. Discuss your answers with a partner.

1. How does the trap-jaw ant's adaptation help it avoid becoming the prey of another organism?

_____

_____

_____

2. What are some adaptations that other predators have to capture prey?

_____

_____

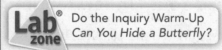 **Lab zone®** Do the Inquiry Warm-Up *Can You Hide a Butterfly?*

How Do Adaptations Help an Organism Survive?

As day breaks, a sound comes from a nest tucked in the branch of a saguaro cactus. Two young red-tailed hawks are preparing to fly. Farther down the stem, a tiny elf owl peeks out of its nest in a small hole. A rattlesnake slithers around the base of the saguaro, looking for breakfast. Spying a shrew, the snake strikes it with needle-like fangs. The shrew dies instantly.

Vocabulary
- natural selection • adaptation • niche • competition
- predation • predator • prey • symbiosis • mutualism
- commensalism • parasitism • parasite • host

Skills
- Reading: Relate Text and Visuals
- Inquiry: Classify

Figure 1 shows some organisms that live in, on, and around the saguaro cactus. Each organism has unique characteristics. These characteristics affect the individual's ability to survive and reproduce in its environment.

Natural Selection A characteristic that makes an individual better suited to a specific environment may eventually become common in that species through a process called **natural selection.** Natural selection works like this: Individuals whose unique characteristics are well-suited for an environment tend to survive and produce more offspring. Offspring that inherit these characteristics also live to reproduce. In this way, natural selection results in **adaptations,** the behaviors and physical characteristics that allow organisms to live successfully in their environments. For example, the arctic hare has fur that turns from gray to white in the winter which helps camouflage the hare against the snow.

Individuals with characteristics poorly suited to a particular environment are less likely to survive and reproduce. Over time, poorly suited characteristics may disappear from the species. If a species cannot adapt to changes in its environment, the entire species can disappear from Earth and become extinct.

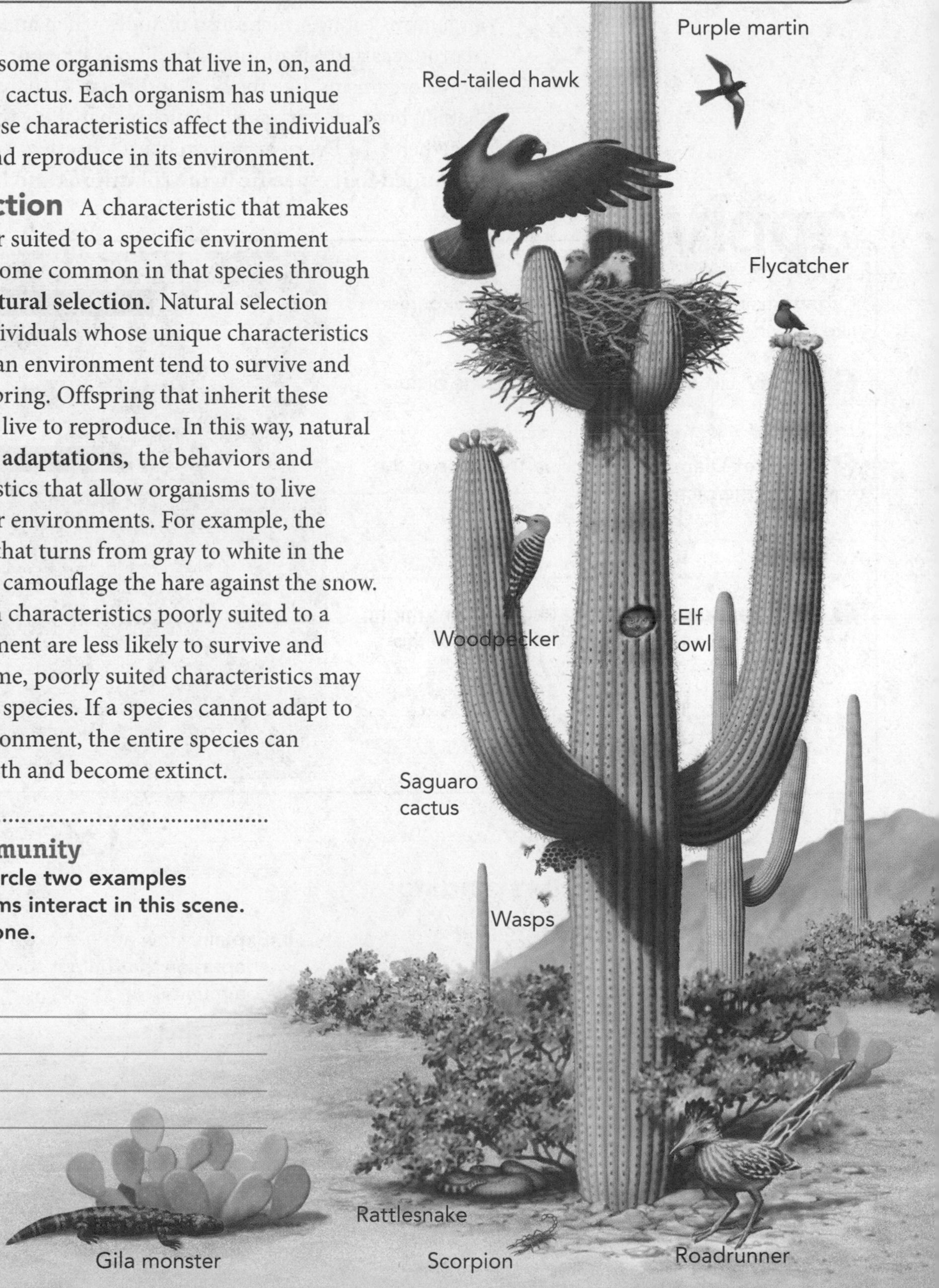

FIGURE 1 ·······························

Saguaro Community
✎ **Describe** Circle two examples of how organisms interact in this scene. Describe each one.

_____

_____

_____

_____

_____

Red-tailed hawk

Purple martin

Flycatcher

Woodpecker

Elf owl

Saguaro cactus

Wasps

Gila monster

Rattlesnake

Scorpion

Roadrunner

Niche The organisms in the saguaro community have adaptations that result in specific roles. The role of an organism in its habitat is called its **niche.** A niche includes what type of food the organism eats, how it obtains this food, and what other organisms eat it. A niche also includes when and how the organism reproduces and the physical conditions it requires to survive. Some organisms, like the birds in **Figure 2,** share the same habitat but have very specific niches that allow them to live together. 🔑 **Every organism has a variety of adaptations that are suited to its specific living conditions and help it survive.**

apply it!

Organisms occupy many niches in an environment like the one in this picture.

❶ Identify List two abiotic factors in the picture.

_____

❷ Interpret Diagrams Describe the niche of the squirrel in the picture.

_____

_____

❸ Make Generalizations What adaptations might the squirrel have that make it able to live in this environment?

_____

_____

Lab zone® Do the Quick Lab
Adaptations for Survival.

🔑 Assess Your Understanding

1a. Define Adaptations are the _____ and _____ characteristics that allow organisms to live successfully in their environments.

b. Explain How are a snake's sharp fangs an adaptation that help it survive in the saguaro community?

_____

_____

got it? . . . .

○ **I get it!** Now I know that adaptations are_____

_____

○ I need extra help with _____

_____

What Are Competition and Predation?

During a typical day in the saguaro community, a range of interactions takes place among organisms. ⬤ **Two major types of interactions among organisms are competition and predation.**

Competition Different species can share the same habitat and food requirements. For example, the flycatcher and the elf owl both live on the saguaro and eat insects. However, these two species do not occupy exactly the same niche. The flycatcher is active during the day, while the owl is active mostly at night. If two species occupy the same niche, one of the species might eventually die off. The reason for this is **competition.** The struggle between organisms to survive as they attempt to use the same limited resources is called competition. For example, weeds in a garden compete with vegetable crops for soil nutrients, water, and sunlight.

In any ecosystem, there are limited amounts of food, water, and shelter. Organisms that share the same habitat often have adaptations that enable them to reduce competition. For example, the three species of warblers in **Figure 2** specialize in feeding only in a certain part of the spruce tree.

Cape May Warbler
This species feeds at the tips of branches near the top of the tree.

Bay-Breasted Warbler
This species feeds in the middle part of the tree.

Yellow-Rumped Warbler
This species feeds in the lower part of the tree and at the bases of the middle branches.

FIGURE 2 ··

Niche and Competition

🖉 Each of these warbler species occupies a very specific location in its habitat. By feeding on insects in different areas of the tree, the birds avoid competing for food and are able to live together.

1. **Predict** What could happen if these warbler species fed in the same location on the tree?

_____

_____

_____

_____

2. **List** For what resources do the tree and the grass compete?

_____

_____

_____

_____

FIGURE 3 ·····························

Predation
This tiger shark and this albatross are involved in a predator-prey interaction.

✏️ **Interpret Photos**
Label the predator and the prey in the photo.

Predation   In **Figure 3**, a tiger shark bursts through the water to seize an albatross in its powerful jaws. An interaction in which one organism kills another for food or nutrients is called **predation**. The organism that does the killing is the **predator**. The organism that is killed is the **prey**. Even though they do not kill their prey, organisms like cows and giraffes are also considered predators because they eat plants.

Predation can have a major effect on a prey population size. Recall that when the death rate exceeds the birth rate in a population, the population size can decrease. So, if there are too many predators in an area, the result is often a decrease in the size of the prey population. But a decrease in the number of prey results in less food for their predators. Without adequate food, the predator population can decline. Generally, populations of predators and their prey rise and fall in related cycles.

Remember that predators are part of a food chain. Predators are consumers, which are organisms that obtain energy by feeding on other organisms. Sometimes consumers eat other consumers, and sometimes they eat plants, which are producers, or organisms that can make their own food. To complete the food chain, decomposers break down dead organisms and return the raw materials to the ecosystem.

FIGURE 4 ·····························

Predator Adaptations
A jellyfish's tentacles contain a poisonous substance that paralyzes tiny water animals. The sundew is a plant that is covered with sticky bulbs on stalks. When a fly lands on a bulb, it remains snared in the sticky goo while the plant digests it.

✏️ **Make Models** Imagine an ideal predator to prey upon a porcupine. Draw or describe your predator below and label its adaptations.

Predator Adaptations Predators, such as those in **Figure 4**, have adaptations that help them catch and kill their prey. A cheetah can run very fast for a short time, enabling it to catch its prey. Some predators, such as owls and bats, have adaptations that enable them to hunt at night when their prey, small mammals and insects, are active.

Prey Adaptations How do organisms avoid being killed by effective predators? The smelly spray of a skunk and the sharp quills of a porcupine help keep predators at a distance. As you can see in **Figure 5**, organisms have many kinds of adaptations that help them avoid becoming prey.

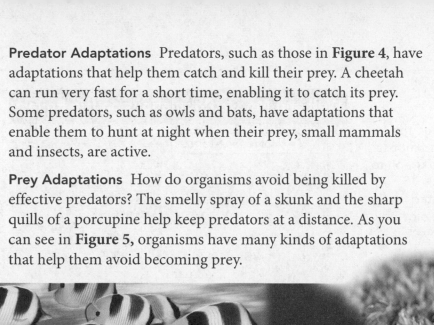

Warning Coloring Like many brightly colored animals, this frog is poisonous. Its bright blue and yellow colors warn predators not to eat it.

False Coloring Predators may be confused by a false eyespot and attack the wrong end of the fish. This allows the fish to swim safely away in the opposite direction.

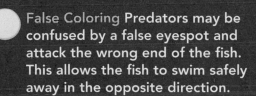

Mimicry The mimic octopus (top) imitates the coloring, shape, and swimming style of the venomous sole fish (bottom) to discourage predators.

Protective Covering Have you ever seen a pinecone with a face? This is a pangolin, a small African mammal. When threatened, the pangolin protects itself by rolling up into a scaly ball.

Camouflage Is it a leaf? Actually, it's a walking leaf insect. But if you were a predator, you might be fooled into looking elsewhere for a meal.

FIGURE 5 ··
Defense Strategies
Organisms display a wide range of adaptations that help them avoid becoming prey. ✏ **Communicate** In a group, rate each prey adaptation from 1 (best) to 5 (worst) in the circles. Explain your best choice.

_____

_____

_____

do the math!

Predator-Prey Interactions

On Isle Royale, an island in Lake Superior, the populations of wolves (the predator) and moose (the prey) rise and fall in cycles. Use the graph to answer the questions.

1 **Read Graphs** What variable is plotted on the horizontal axis? What two variables are plotted on the vertical axis?

_____

2 **Interpret Data** How did the moose population change between 2002 and 2007? What happened to the wolf population from 2003 through 2006?

_____

_____

_____

3 **Draw Conclusions** How might the change in moose population have led to the change in the wolf population?

_____

_____

_____

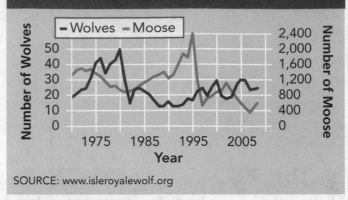

Wolf and Moose Populations on Isle Royale

SOURCE: www.isleroyalewolf.org

4 **Explain** What adaptations does a wolf have that make it a successful predator?

_____

_____

5 **Predict** How might disease in the wolf population one year affect the moose population the next year?

_____

_____

_____

_____

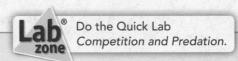
Do the Quick Lab
Competition and Predation.

🔑 Assess Your Understanding

2a. Review Two main ways in which organisms

interact are_____

and _____ .

b. Describe Give an example of competition. Explain your answer.

_____

_____

c. Apply Concepts Owls often prey on mice. What adaptations do you think the mice have that help them avoid becoming prey?

_____

_____

_____

_____

got it? ....

○ **I get it!** Now I know that competition and predation_____

_____

○ **I need extra help with** _____

_____

What Are the Three Types of Symbiosis?

In addition to competition and predation, symbiosis is a third type of interaction among organisms. **Symbiosis** (sim bee OH sis) is any relationship in which two species live closely together and at least one of the species benefits. 🔑 **The three main types of symbiotic relationships are mutualism, commensalism, and parasitism.**

Mutualism In some relationships, two species may depend on one another. This is true for some species of acacia trees and stinging ants in South America. The stinging ants nest only in the acacia tree, whose thorns discourage the ants' predators. The tree also provides the ants' only food. The ants, in turn, attack other animals that approach the tree and clear competing plants away from the base of the tree. This relationship is an example of **mutualism** (MYOO choo uh liz um). A relationship in which both species benefit is called mutualism. Other examples of mutualism can be seen in **Figure 6.**

FIGURE 6 ···
Mutualism
✎ An oxpecker rides and snacks aboard an impala. The oxpecker eat ticks living on the impala's ears. This interaction is an example of mutualism because both organisms benefit.

1. Infer How does the oxpecker benefit?

_____

2. Infer How does the impala benefit?

_____

3. CHALLENGE Explain how the relationship between the hummingbird and the flower is an example of mutualism.

_____

_____

Commensalism

Have you ever seen a bird build a nest in a tree? The bird gets a place to live while the tree is unharmed. This relationship is an example of commensalism. **Commensalism** (kuh MEN suh liz um) is a relationship in which one species benefits and the other species is neither helped nor harmed. In nature, commensalism is not very common because two species are usually either helped or harmed a little by any interaction.

Parasitism

Many family pets get treated with medication to prevent tick and flea bites. Without treatment, pets can suffer from severe health problems as a result of these bites. A relationship that involves one organism living with, on, or inside another organism and harming it is called **parasitism** (PA ruh sit iz um). The organism that benefits is called a **parasite.** The organism it lives on or in is called a **host.** The parasite is usually smaller than the host. In a parasitic relationship, the parasite benefits while the host is harmed. Unlike a predator, a parasite does not usually kill the organism it feeds on. If the host dies, the parasite could lose its source of food or shelter.

Some parasites, like fleas and ticks, have adaptations that enable them to attach to their host and feed on its blood. Other examples of parasitism are shown in **Figure 7.**

✏ **Relate Text and Visuals** List the names of the parasites and the hosts in **Figure 7**.

Parasites	Hosts
_____	_____
_____	_____
_____	_____
_____	_____

A parasitic cowbird laid its eggs in a yellow warbler's nest. The cowbird chick is outcompeting the warbler chicks for space and food.

Fish lice feed on the blood and other internal fluids of fish.

Dwarf mistletoe is a small parasitic flowering plant that grows into the bark of trees to obtain water and nutrients.

FIGURE 7 ··
Parasitism
There are many examples of parasitic relationships. Besides fleas, ticks, and tapeworms, some plants and birds are parasites. ✏ **Explain** Why doesn't a parasite usually kill its host?

_____

_____

_____

apply it!

⚠ **Classify** Each photograph on the right represents a different type of symbiosis. Classify each interaction as mutualism, commensalism, or parasitism. Explain your answers.

Interaction 1: A remora fish attaches itself to the underside of a shark without harming the shark, and eats leftover bits of food from the shark's meals.

Interaction 2: A vampire bat drinks the blood of horses.

Interaction 3: A bee pollinates a flower.

❶ Interaction 1

_____
_____

❷ Interaction 2

_____
_____

❸ Interaction 3

_____
_____

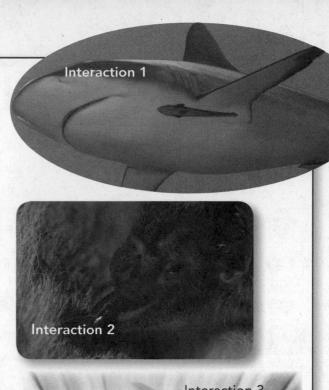

Interaction 1

Interaction 2

Interaction 3

Lab zone® Do the Quick Lab *Type of Symbiosis.*

🔑 Assess Your Understanding

3a. Identify The three types of symbiosis are

_____, _____,

and _____ .

b. ⚠ **Classify** Microscopic mites live at the base of human eyelashes, where they feed on tiny bits of dead skin. What type of symbiosis could this be? Explain your answer.

_____
_____
_____

c. Compare and Contrast Name each type of symbiosis and explain how the two species are affected.

_____
_____
_____
_____
_____
_____
_____

got it? ....

○ **I get it!** Now I know that the three types of symbiosis differ in _____

_____

○ **I need extra help with** _____

_____

3 Study Guide

Living things interact in many ways, including competition and _____, as well as through symbiotic relationships such as mutualism, commensalism, and _____.

LESSON 1 Living Things and the Environment

🔑 An organism gets the things it needs to live, grow, and reproduce from its environment.

🔑 Biotic and abiotic factors make up a habitat.

🔑 The levels of organization in an ecosystem are organism, population, and community.

Vocabulary
- organism • habitat • biotic factor
- abiotic factor • species • population
- community • ecosystem • ecology

LESSON 2 Populations

🔑 Populations can change in size when new members join the population or when members leave the population.

🔑 Some limiting factors for populations are weather conditions, space, food, and water.

Vocabulary
- birth rate • death rate • immigration
- emigration • population density
- limiting factor • carrying capacity

LESSON 3 Interactions Among Living Things

🔑 Every organism has a variety of adaptations that are suited to its specific living conditions to help it survive.

🔑 Two major types of interactions among organisms are competition and predation.

🔑 The three main types of symbiotic relationships are mutualism, commensalism, and parasitism.

Vocabulary
- natural selection • adaptation • niche • competition
- predation • predator • prey • symbiosis • mutualism
- commensalism • parasitism • parasite • host

Review and Assessment

LESSON 1 Living Things and the Environment

1. A prairie dog, a hawk, and a snake are all members of the same

　a. niche. 　　　**b.** community.

　c. species. 　　**d.** population.

2. Grass is an example of a(n) _____ in a habitat.

3. Sequence Put these levels in order from the smallest to the largest: population, organism, ecosystem, community.

_____

_____

4. Apply Concepts Name two biotic and two abiotic factors you might find in a forest ecosystem.

_____

_____

5. Draw Conclusions In 1815, Mount Tambora, a volcano in Indonesia, erupted. So much volcanic ash and dust filled the atmosphere that 1816 is referred to as the "Year Without a Summer." How might a volcanic eruption affect the abiotic factors in an organism's habitat?

_____

_____

_____

_____

_____

6. **Write About It** Write at least one paragraph describing your habitat. Describe how you get the food, water, and shelter you need from your habitat. How does this habitat meet your needs in ways that another would not?

LESSON 2 Populations

7. All of the following are limiting factors for populations except

　a. space. 　　　**b.** food.

　c. time. 　　　**d.** weather.

8. _____ occurs when individuals leave a population.

Use the data table to answer the questions below. Ecologists monitoring a deer population collect data during a 30-year study.

Year	0	5	10	15	20	25	30
Population (thousands)	15	30	65	100	40	25	10

9. Graph Use the data to make a line graph.

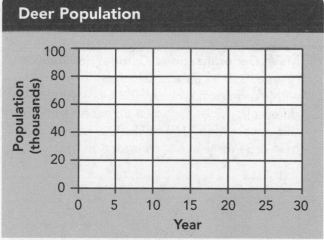

Deer Population

10. Interpret Data In which year was the deer population the highest? The lowest?

_____

11. Develop Hypotheses In Year 16 of the study, this region experienced a severe winter. How might this have affected the deer population?

_____

_____

_____

LESSON 3 Interactions Among Living Things

12. In which type of interaction do both species benefit?

   a. predation   **b.** mutualism

   c. commensalism   **d.** parasitism

13. A parasite lives on or inside its _____.

14. Relate Cause and Effect Name two prey adaptations. How does each adaptation protect the organism?

_____

_____

_____

_____

_____

_____

15. Make Generalizations Competition for resources in an area is usually more intense within a single species than between two different species. Suggest an explanation for this observation. (*Hint:* Consider how niches help organisms avoid competition.)

_____

_____

_____

_____

_____

16. **Write About It** Some scientists think that the relationship between clownfish and sea anemones is an example of commensalism. Other scientists think that the relationship is mutualism. If this relationship is actually mutualism, how might both the clownfish and sea anemone benefit?

How do living things affect one another?

17. In Lesson 3, you learned that fleas are parasites that live on family pets. Are humans also affected by parasites? Using at least three vocabulary terms from this chapter, describe one or more parasites that interact with humans and the effect the parasites have on humans.

_____

_____

_____

_____

_____

_____

_____

_____

_____

_____

_____

Standardized Test Prep

Read each question and choose the best answer.

1. Symbiotic relationships include mutualism, commensalism, and parasitism. Which of the images below shows mutualism?

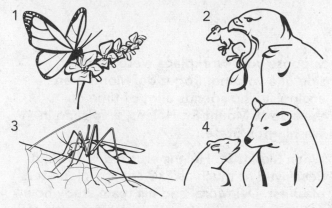

A Image 1	**B** Image 2
C Image 3	**D** Image 4

2. In general, which of the following is a true statement about population size?

A If birth rate < death rate, population size increases.

B If death rate < birth rate, population size decreases.

C If birth rate > death rate, population size increases.

D If death rate > birth rate, population size increases.

3. Ecosystems have different levels of organization. A group of similar organisms makes up a _____, which, along with other types of organisms, makes up a(n) _____.

A species, population

B habitat, ecosystem

C population, community

D population, habitat

4. Three different bird species all live in the same trees in an area, but competition between the birds rarely occurs. Which of the following is a likely explanation for this lack of competition?

A The three species occupy different niches.

B The three species eat the same food.

C The three species have a limited supply of food.

D The three species live in the same part of the trees.

5. There are 100 squirrels living in a forest that is 5 square miles. What is the population density of the squirrels living in the forest?

A 10 squirrels per square mile

B 20 squirrels per square mile

C 50 squirrels per square mile

D 500 squirrels per square mile

Constructed Response

Use the diagram below and your knowledge of science to help you answer Question 6. Write your answer on a separate piece of paper.

6. An organism interacts with both the biotic and abiotic factors in its habitat. List three biotic factors and three abiotic factors shown in the drawing above.

ECOLOGIST

These lupine plants are growing out of the volcanic ash on Mount St. Helens, 20 years after its last eruption.

Suppose your workplace were on the side of a volcano! Roger del Moral is an ecologist who spends a lot of time on the side of Mount St. Helens, a volcano in Washington State.

When Mount St. Helens erupted in 1980, it destroyed as much as 518 square kilometers of forest. Del Moral and his team study how plant communities form in the aftermath of volcanic eruptions. They visit the volcano regularly to identify plants and estimate the remaining populations of plants to describe how the plant communities are recovering. This work enables researchers to develop more effective ways to help areas recover from human-caused environmental changes.

Del Moral loves his work and says, "My work on Mount St. Helens allows me to follow my passion, train students, and contribute to a better understanding of how the world works."

If you are interested in ecology, try volunteering or interning at a local park or field museum. National parks also have Junior Naturalist programs designed to give you experience in the field.

Compare It Find a park in your neighborhood or town and describe the kinds of plants you find. Make a table in which you list each kind of plant, describe it, describe where it grew, and draw conclusions about the reasons why it might have grown there.

BINOCULAR BOOT CAMP

▼ Populations of common and rare birds can be estimated based on input from students like you!

Scientists need all the help they can get estimating large populations! Binocular Boot Camp, a program for kids in Sonoma Valley, California, trains kids to identify the songs, calls, and flight patterns of birds. Participants form teams and identify and count as many birds as they can in one afternoon. The information they gather gets entered into a huge database of bird observations.

You don't have to go to Binocular Boot Camp to help, though. For four days in February, schools, clubs, and individuals in the United States and Canada take part in the Great Backyard Bird Count (GBBC). All you need to do is count birds for 15 minutes, then fill out a form to help scientists learn how climate change, habitat change, and other factors affect bird populations.

Research It Find out more about the GBBC. Design a poster or use presentation software to create a presentation to convince your school to participate.

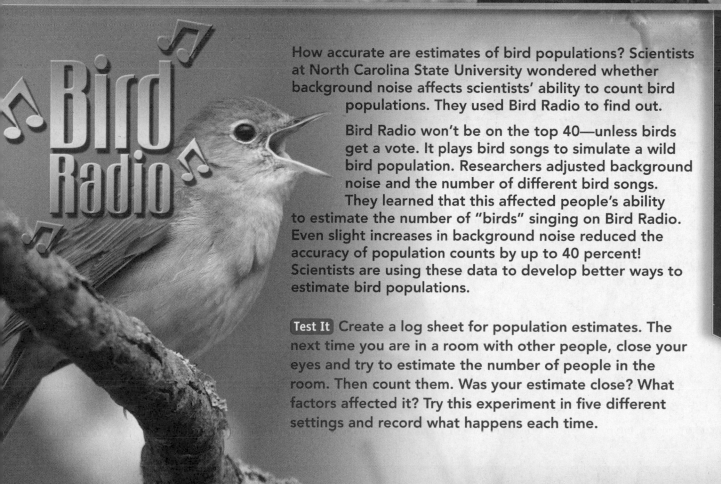

Bird Radio

How accurate are estimates of bird populations? Scientists at North Carolina State University wondered whether background noise affects scientists' ability to count bird populations. They used Bird Radio to find out.

Bird Radio won't be on the top 40—unless birds get a vote. It plays bird songs to simulate a wild bird population. Researchers adjusted background noise and the number of different bird songs. They learned that this affected people's ability to estimate the number of "birds" singing on Bird Radio. Even slight increases in background noise reduced the accuracy of population counts by up to 40 percent! Scientists are using these data to develop better ways to estimate bird populations.

Test It Create a log sheet for population estimates. The next time you are in a room with other people, close your eyes and try to estimate the number of people in the room. Then count them. Was your estimate close? What factors affected it? Try this experiment in five different settings and record what happens each time.

WHERE DOES FOOD COME FROM?

THE BIG ?

How do energy and matter move through ecosystems?

Flying around hunting for food, this barn owl spots a mouse for dinner. But what did the mouse eat? Perhaps it nibbled on seeds or a caterpillar. Then you might ask, where did the seeds and caterpillar get their food?

△ Develop Hypotheses Where do living things get their food?

_____

_____

_____

_____

_____

_____

Watch the **Untamed Science** video to learn more about ecosystems and biomes.

Ecosystems and Biomes

4 Getting Started

Check Your Understanding

1. Background Read the paragraph below and then answer the question.

One morning, Han walks to the park and sits by the pond. He has just studied **ecosystems** in class, and now, looking at the pond, he realizes he sees things in a new way. He notices a turtle sunning itself on a rock, and knows that the sun and rock are **abiotic factors,** while the turtle, and other living things, are **biotic factors.**

> The community of organisms that live in a particular area, along with their nonliving environment, make up an **ecosystem.**
>
> **Abiotic factors** are the nonliving parts of an organism's habitat.
>
> **Biotic factors** are the living parts of an organism's habitat.

- Name one more biotic factor and one more abiotic factor that Han might see at the pond.

_____

_____

Vocabulary Skill

Prefixes Some words can be divided into parts. A root is the part of the word that carries the basic meaning. A prefix is a word part that is placed in front of the root to change the word's meaning. The prefixes below will help you understand some vocabulary in this chapter.

Prefix	Meaning	Example
inter-	between	intertidal, *adj.* ocean zone between the highest high-tide line and the lowest low-tide line

2. Quick Check Circle the prefix in each boldface word below.

- There was an **intermission** between the acts of the play.
- The **biosphere** is the area where life exists.

consumer

precipitation

desert

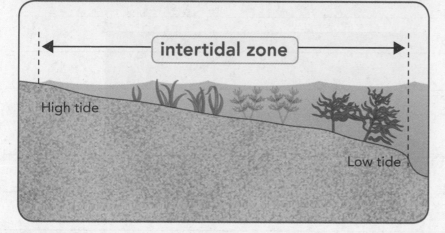
intertidal zone

High tide

Low tide

Chapter Preview

LESSON 1
- producer • consumer
- herbivore • carnivore • omnivore
- scavenger • decomposer
- food chain • food web
- energy pyramid • desertification

↻ **Relate Text and Visuals**
△ **Classify**

LESSON 2
- evaporation • condensation
- precipitation • nitrogen fixation

↻ **Sequence**
△ **Infer**

LESSON 3
- biome • climate • desert
- rain forest • emergent layer
- canopy • understory • grassland
- savanna • deciduous tree
- boreal forest • coniferous tree
- tundra • permafrost

↻ **Compare and Contrast**
△ **Draw Conclusions**

LESSON 4
- estuary
- intertidal zone
- neritic zone

↻ **Outline**
△ **Communicate**

River Works

Moving water on Earth's surface causes erosion and deposition of sediment. This process shapes various land features. The steepness of a hill and the amount of water running down it affect the speed and path of moving water. The materials the water flows over and around also affect its speed and path. These factors determine how land features are formed. Erosion caused by rivers can produce many features, including waterfalls, floodplains, meanders, and oxbow lakes. Deposition of sediments forms features such as deltas and alluvial fans.

In this activity, you will design, build, and test a river model that shows how water erosion and deposition lead to various land features. You will construct your river model on a stream table, as shown in the picture.

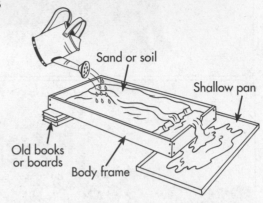

Sand or soil

Shallow pan

Old books or boards

Body frame

Identify the Problem

1. Suppose you want to build a home along a river. Why would it be useful to learn about how a river shapes the land? What problem will your design help solve, and how would it apply to site selection for a home?

_____

_____

_____

_____

Do Research

2. Examine the photos of the six land features produced by rivers: waterfalls, flood plains, meanders, oxbow lakes, deltas, and alluvial fans. On a separate sheet of paper, explain how moving water produces these features. _____

_____

_____

3. What variables in a working river model can affect the movement of sediment?

_____

_____

_____

Go to the materials station(s). Examine the materials. Think about how each one may or may not be useful for your river model. Leave the materials where they are.

☑ **4.** What are your design constraints? _____

_____

_____

Develop Possible Solutions

☑ **5.** On a separate sheet of paper, describe ways you could use the materials to build a working river model. Identify at least two variables you could control in your model. Explain how the variables would affect the moving water. Then explain how this could form land features.

_____

_____

_____

_____

Choose One Solution

Answer the following questions on a separate sheet of paper.

☑ **6.** List the material(s) you will use for your river model.

_____

_____

☑ **7.** Draw your design and label all the parts. Describe how you will build your river model.

_____

_____

☑ **8.** Describe how your model will show river erosion and deposition processes.

_____

_____

Design and Construct a Prototype

Have your teacher review and approve your design. Then, gather the materials you need to build your river model. Build a prototype, the first working version of your design. Wear goggles as you build and test your prototype. Measure the dimensions of your prototype, and note the placement of fixed features that you put into position. If you can, document your construction process by taking photos or recording video.

9. On a separate sheet of paper, record the design details of your prototype. Include measurements and quantities for the materials you use.

_____

10. On a separate sheet of paper, draw a detailed diagram of your prototype under the heading Before the Test. Label the features and measurements.

_____

Test the Prototype

Test your prototype. Produce a flow of water on the stream table across the land surface that you have designed. Observe what effects the moving water has on sediment. Identify any land features that the moving water produces.

11. Answer yes or no to the following:

I could observe the water eroding sediment.	
I could observe the water depositing sediment.	
Moving water changed the land surface in my prototype.	

12. Underline the features below that you built in your prototype. Circle the features that were formed by the moving water during your test.

Waterfall   Floodplain   Meander
Oxbow lake   Delta   Alluvial fan

13. On a separate sheet of paper, draw a detailed diagram of your prototype under the heading After the Test. Label the features and measurements.

_____

_____

_____

Communicate Results

14. Collect the materials that document the design, construction, and testing of your prototype. Assemble a portfolio that includes the before and after diagrams of your river, your photographs or video of the process, and a record of your test results. Use at least one chart, graph, or data table to show your test results. Write a short summary of how your process and results could solve the problem of site selection for construction of a new home.

15. Prepare a storyboard or computer slide show that shows how your river and land features changed over time. A storyboard is a series of sketches, similar to a comic strip, that shows a progression of steps over time. Number your sketches and display the storyboard in your class.

Evaluate and Redesign

16. Evaluate your prototype using the following rubric. Check one answer for each question.

Does the prototype...	Very Much	Somewhat	Not At All
fit onto the stream table?			
show visible changes to the "land" from the movement of sediment?			
function without overflowing the stream table?			

17. Compare your results with your classmates. Did your prototypes function in similar ways? Explain.

_____

_____

18. What changes could you make to your prototype to make it more accurately show how rivers produce land features?

_____

_____

_____

Energy Flow in Ecosystems

🔑 **What Are the Energy Roles in an Ecosystem?**

🔑 **How Does Energy Move Through an Ecosystem?**

🔑 **How Do Human Activities Affect Ecosystems?**

my planet diary

I'll Have the Fish

Scientists have noticed something fishy going on with the wolves in British Columbia, Canada. During autumn, the wolves ignore their typical food of deer and moose and feast on salmon instead. Salmon are very nutritious and lack the big horns and hoofs that can injure or kill wolves. Plus, there are plenty of fish in a small area, making them easier to find and catch.

Many animals, including the wolves, depend upon the salmon's annual mating trip upstream. Losing this important food source to overfishing would hurt the populations of bears, wolves, birds, and many other animals.

DISCOVERY

Communicate Discuss these questions with a classmate. Write your answers below.

1. What are two reasons the wolves may eat fish in autumn instead of deer or moose?

_____

_____

2. What effect could overfishing salmon have on an ecosystem?

_____

_____

_____

_____

Lab zone® Do the Inquiry Warm-Up *Where Did Your Dinner Come From?*

Vocabulary

- producer • consumer • herbivore • carnivore
- omnivore • scavenger • decomposer • food chain
- food web • energy pyramid • desertification

Skills

🔄 Reading: Relate Text and Visuals

△ Inquiry: Classify

What Are the Energy Roles in an Ecosystem?

Do you play an instrument in your school band? If so, you know that each instrument has a role in a piece of music. Similar to instruments in a band, each organism has a role in the movement of energy through its ecosystem.

An organism's energy role is determined by how it obtains food and how it interacts with other organisms. 🔑 **Each of the organisms in an ecosystem fills the energy role of producer, consumer, or decomposer.**

Producers Energy enters most ecosystems as sunlight. Some organisms, like the plants and algae shown in **Figure 1,** and some types of bacteria, capture the energy of sunlight and store it as food energy. These organisms use the sun's energy to turn water and carbon dioxide into food molecules in a process called photosynthesis.

An organism that can make its own food is a **producer.** Producers are the source of all the food in an ecosystem. In a few ecosystems, producers obtain energy from a source other than sunlight. One such ecosystem is found in rocks deep beneath the ground. Certain bacteria in this ecosystem produce their own food using the energy in hydrogen sulfide, a gas that is present in their environment.

FIGURE 1 ·····················

Producers

Producers are organisms that can make their own food.

✎ **Identify** Complete the shopping list below to identify the producers that are part of your diet.

- ⭘ wheat
- ⭘ corn
- ⭘ banana
- ⭘
- ⭘
- ⭘
- ⭘
- ⭘
- ⭘
- ⭘

Tape grass and water milfoil

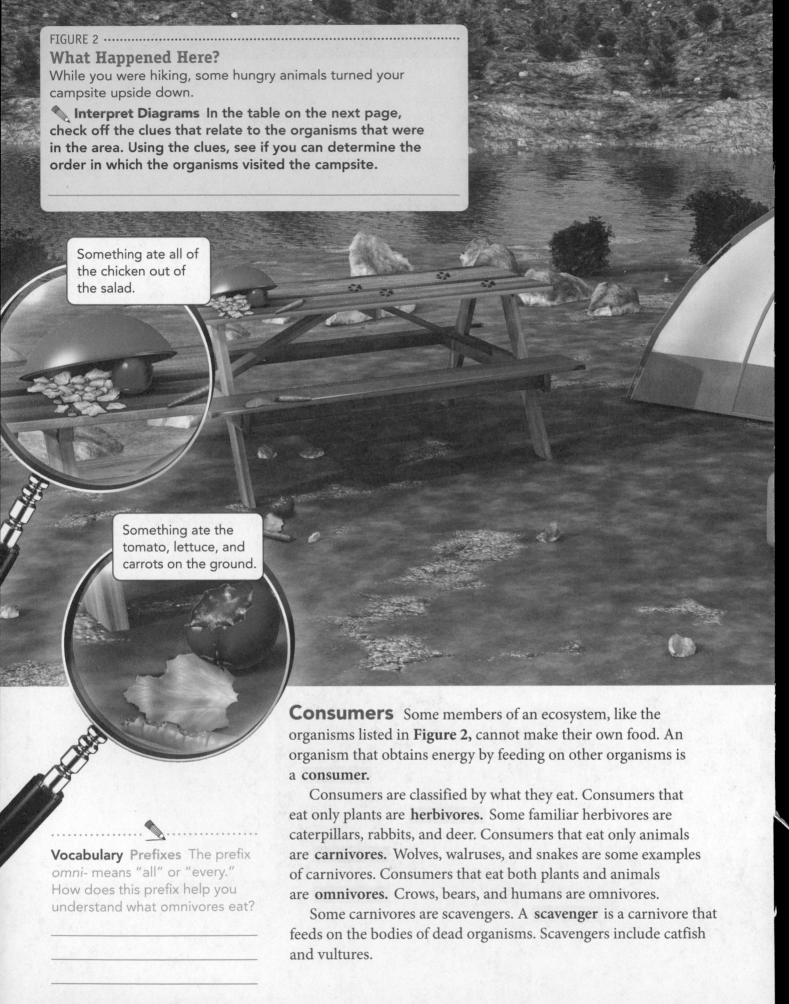

FIGURE 2 ....

What Happened Here?
While you were hiking, some hungry animals turned your campsite upside down.

✎ **Interpret Diagrams** In the table on the next page, check off the clues that relate to the organisms that were in the area. Using the clues, see if you can determine the order in which the organisms visited the campsite.

Something ate all of the chicken out of the salad.

Something ate the tomato, lettuce, and carrots on the ground.

Vocabulary Prefixes The prefix *omni-* means "all" or "every." How does this prefix help you understand what omnivores eat?

Consumers Some members of an ecosystem, like the organisms listed in **Figure 2,** cannot make their own food. An organism that obtains energy by feeding on other organisms is a **consumer.**

Consumers are classified by what they eat. Consumers that eat only plants are **herbivores.** Some familiar herbivores are caterpillars, rabbits, and deer. Consumers that eat only animals are **carnivores.** Wolves, walruses, and snakes are some examples of carnivores. Consumers that eat both plants and animals are **omnivores.** Crows, bears, and humans are omnivores.

Some carnivores are scavengers. A **scavenger** is a carnivore that feeds on the bodies of dead organisms. Scavengers include catfish and vultures.

Clues	Bear	Mold	Rabbit	Wolf
Can easily reach the table top				
Grows on food and breaks it down				
Small enough to enter and exit tent				
Gets energy from meat				
Strong enough to open cooler				
Not a picky eater				
Gets energy from plants				

Something ate the apples and beef jerky from inside the tent.

Something ate strawberries, even some of the moldy ones.

Decomposers If an ecosystem had only producers and consumers, the raw materials of life, such as carbon and nitrogen, would stay locked up in wastes and the bodies of dead organisms. However, there are organisms in ecosystems that prevent this from happening. **Decomposers** break down biotic wastes and dead organisms and return the raw materials to the ecosystem.

You can think of decomposers as nature's recyclers. While obtaining energy for their own needs, decomposers return simple molecules to the environment. These molecules can be used again by other organisms. Mushrooms, bacteria, and mold are common decomposers.

Lab ® Do the Quick Lab
zone *Observing Decomposition.*

🔑 Assess Your Understanding

1a. Describe An organism's energy role is determined by how it obtains

_____ and how it _____

with other organisms.

b. Apply Concepts What is the main source of energy for all three energy roles? Why?

_____

_____

_____

_____

_____

_____

_____

_____

got it? ··

○ **I get it!** Now I know that the energy roles in

an ecosystem are _____

_____

_____

○ **I need extra help with** _____

_____

_____

_____

How Does Energy Move Through an Ecosystem?

As you have read, energy enters most ecosystems as sunlight and is converted into food by producers. This energy is transferred to the organisms that eat the producers, and then to other organisms that feed on the consumers. **Energy moves through an ecosystem when one organism eats another.** This movement of energy can be shown as food chains, food webs, and energy pyramids.

Food Chains One way to show how energy moves in an ecosystem is with a food chain. A **food chain** is a series of events in which one organism eats another and obtains energy. You can follow one example of a food chain in **Figure 3.**

Food Webs A food chain shows only one possible path along which energy can move through an ecosystem. Most producers and consumers are part of many food chains. A more realistic way to show the flow of energy through an ecosystem is with a food web. As shown in **Figure 4,** a **food web** consists of many overlapping food chains in an ecosystem.

Organisms may play more than one role in an ecosystem. Look at the crayfish in **Figure 4.** A crayfish is an omnivore that is a first-level consumer when it eats plants. But when a crayfish eats a snail, it is a second-level consumer.

Just as food chains overlap and connect, food webs interconnect as well. A gull might eat a fish at the ocean, but it might also eat a mouse at a landfill. The gull, then, is part of two food webs—an ocean food web and a land food web. All the world's food webs interconnect in what can be thought of as a global food web.

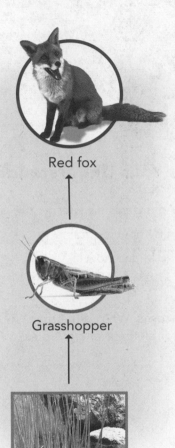

Red fox

Grasshopper

Plants

FIGURE 3 ······································
Food Chain
In this food chain, you can see how energy moves from plants, to a grasshopper, to the fox. The arrows show how energy moves up the food chain, from one organism to the next.

apply it!

Classify Using what you have learned about food chains, draw or describe a food chain from your local ecosystem. Show at least three organisms in your food chain. Name each organism and label it as a producer, consumer, or decomposer.

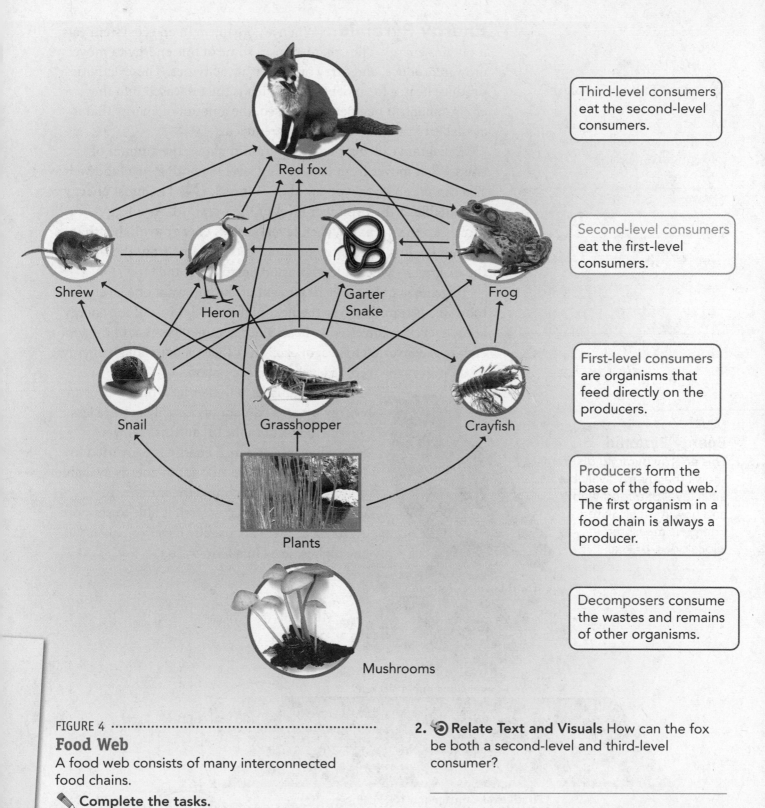

Third-level consumers eat the second-level consumers.

Second-level consumers eat the first-level consumers.

First-level consumers are organisms that feed directly on the producers.

Producers form the base of the food web. The first organism in a food chain is always a producer.

Decomposers consume the wastes and remains of other organisms.

FIGURE 4 ···

Food Web

A food web consists of many interconnected food chains.

✏ **Complete the tasks.**

1. **Interpret Diagrams** Pick two organisms from the food web. Draw arrows connecting them to the decomposers.

2. 🔄 **Relate Text and Visuals** How can the fox be both a second-level and third-level consumer?

_____

_____

_____

_____

_____

_____

Energy Pyramids

Energy Pyramids When an organism in an ecosystem eats, it obtains energy. The organism uses some of this energy to move, grow, reproduce, and carry out other life activities. These activities produce heat, a form of energy, which is then released into the environment. When heat is released, the amount of energy that is available to the next consumer is reduced.

A diagram called an **energy pyramid** shows the amount of energy that moves from one feeding level to another in a food web. You can see an energy pyramid in **Figure 5**. 🔑 **The most energy is available at the producer level of the pyramid. As energy moves up the pyramid, each level has less energy available than the level below.** An energy pyramid gets its name from the shape of the diagram—wider at the base and narrower at the top.

In general, only about 10 percent of the energy at one level of a food web is transferred to the next higher level. Most of the energy at each level is converted to heat. Since about 90 percent of the food energy is converted to heat at each step, there is not enough energy to support many feeding levels in an ecosystem.

The organisms at higher feeding levels of an energy pyramid do not necessarily require less energy to live than the organisms at lower levels. Because so much energy is converted to heat at each level, the amount of energy available at the producer level limits the number of consumers that the ecosystem is able to support. As a result, there are usually fewer organisms at the highest level in a food web.

↩ Relate Text and Visuals

Look at the energy pyramid. Why is a pyramid the best shape to show how energy moves through an ecosystem?

_____

_____

_____

_____

_____

_____

_____

FIGURE 5 ·····················

Energy Pyramid

This energy pyramid diagram shows the energy available at each level of a food web and how it is calculated. Energy is measured in kilocalories, or kcal.

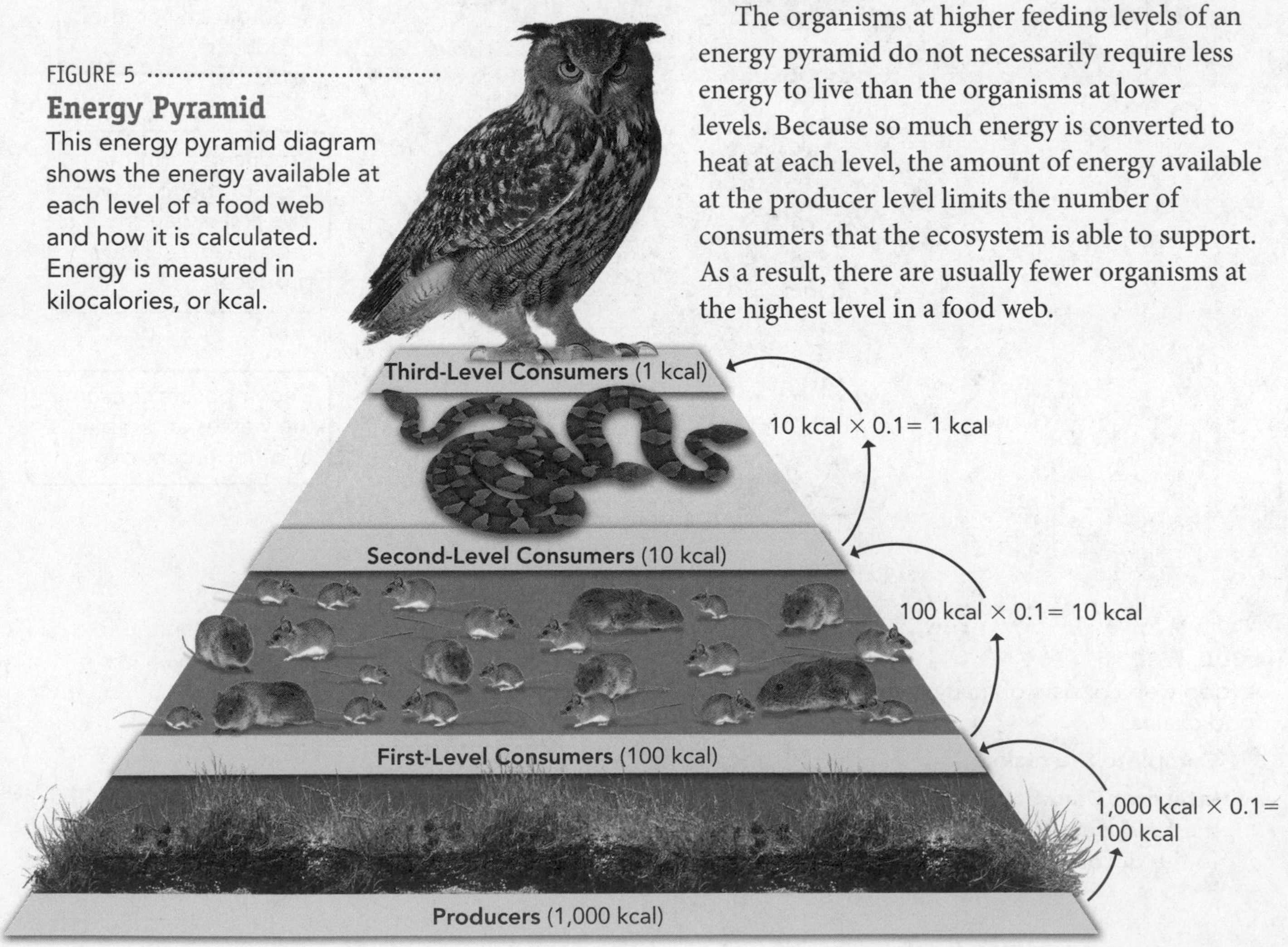

Third-Level Consumers (1 kcal)

10 kcal × 0.1 = 1 kcal

Second-Level Consumers (10 kcal)

100 kcal × 0.1 = 10 kcal

First-Level Consumers (100 kcal)

1,000 kcal × 0.1 = 100 kcal

Producers (1,000 kcal)

do the math!

Energy Pyramids

Suppose that the producers at the base of an energy pyramid contain 330,000 kilocalories.

Calculate Using **Figure 5** as a guide, label how much energy would be available at each level of the pyramid based on the questions below.

1 If mice ate all of the plants, how much energy would be available to them as first-level consumers?

2 If all of the mice were eaten by snakes, how much energy would the snakes receive?

3 If all of the snakes were eaten by the owl, how much energy would the owl receive?

4 CHALLENGE About how much energy would the owl use for its life processes or lose as heat? _____

5 CHALLENGE How much energy would be stored in the owl's body? _____

Third-Level Consumers

Second-Level Consumers

First-Level Consumers

330,000 kcal
Producers

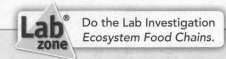

Do the Lab Investigation
Ecosystem Food Chains.

🔑 Assess Your Understanding

2a. Define A food (web/chain) is a series of events in which one organism eats another and obtains energy. A food (web/chain) consists of many overlapping food (webs/chains).

b. Compare and Contrast Why is a food web a more realistic way of portraying an ecosystem than a food chain?

_____
_____
_____

c. Relate Cause and Effect Why are there usually fewer organisms at the top of an energy pyramid?

_____
_____
_____
_____
_____
_____
_____

got it? ....

○ **I get it!** Now I know that energy moves through an ecosystem when_____
_____

○ **I need extra help with** _____

How Do Human Activities Affect Ecosystems?

Human activities can affect the environment. 🔑 **Human activities may affect the balance in an ecosystem and thereby change the ecosystem.** Some examples of human activities include overusing resources and using technology in agriculture.

Agriculture Billions of people live on Earth, and they all need food. Many technologies have been developed to increase the amount of food produced. However, these technologies often have negative effects on the environment. For example, technologies that allow people to clear large tracts of forests for new farmland affect the amount of carbon dioxide in the atmosphere in two ways. First, the equipment used to remove the trees burns oil. Second, trees use carbon dioxide during photosynthesis. With fewer trees to take in carbon dioxide, more carbon dioxide remains in the atmosphere.

Farmers may use different types of chemicals to increase their crop yields. Insecticides kill insect pests that damage crops. Herbicides kill weeds. Both chemicals can enter the soil, where they can be absorbed by plant roots. They might also wash into streams and lakes, poisoning the organisms that live there. Farmers may also use chemicals called fertilizers, which put nutrients back into the soil. Like insecticides and herbicides, fertilizers may enter streams and lakes. Once there, the fertilizers may increase plant and algae growth. This overgrowth can kill animals living in the water.

◈ Relate Cause and Effect
Underline the effects of fertilizers on the environment.

do the math!

DDT in the Environment

DDT is an artificial insecticide that was commonly used in the mid-1900s. DDT washed into soil and eventually into streams and rivers. DDT was absorbed by plants and, as a result, entered the food supply of animals. DDT affected the ability of animals such as bald eagles to produce young.

① ◬ **Interpret Data** What is the relationship between DDT use and bald eagle reproduction?

_____

_____

_____

② **CHALLENGE** DDT was banned in 1972. In 1974, the mean number of young fell sharply. What might explain this decrease?

_____

_____

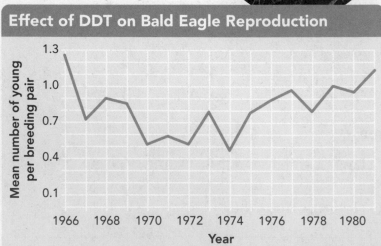

Effect of DDT on Bald Eagle Reproduction

Mean number of young per breeding pair (y-axis: 0.1, 0.4, 0.7, 1.0, 1.3)

Year (x-axis: 1966, 1968, 1970, 1972, 1974, 1976, 1978, 1980)

Overuse of Resources When humans overuse the resources in an ecosystem, the plants and animals living there can be affected. Marine ecosystems provide much of the world's food, especially fish. If people catch most of the fish in an ecosystem, the fish populations may not recover. It is estimated that about 70 percent of the world's fish species are overfished.

In the plains, people use grassland ecosystems to raise farm animals. These animals may eat the grasses more quickly than the grasses grow, or they may eat the grasses entirely so they do not grow back. Without the roots of grasses to hold the soil, winds can blow away fertile topsoil that supports plant growth. The grasslands may then become desert-likc, as in **Figure 6**. The advance of desert-like conditions in an area once fertile is called **desertification.**

FIGURE 6 ···

Overgrazing
Overusing resources can greatly change an ecosystem.

✎ **Relate Text and Visuals** Write a caption for each picture.

 Do the Quick Lab Consequences of Human Activity.

🔑 **Assess Your Understanding**

got͟it?···

○ I get it! Now I know that human activities_____

_____

○ I need extra help with _____

_____

Cycles of Matter

UNLOCK THE BIG ?

🔑 **What Processes Are Involved in the Water Cycle?**

🔑 **How Are the Carbon and Oxygen Cycles Related?**

🔑 **How Does Nitrogen Cycle Through Ecosystems?**

MY PLANET DIARY

DISASTER

Canaries and Coal

Have you ever stopped to listen to a bird sing? If you were a coal miner in the early 1900s, your life may have depended on it! Sometimes miners stumbled upon pockets of carbon monoxide, a toxic, odorless gas that makes it difficult for the body to get enough oxygen. Without fresh air circulating in the mineshafts, the miners would fall asleep and eventually die. To prevent this disaster from happening, canaries were used to monitor the air quality. A singing canary indicated that all was well. If the canary stopped singing and died, the miners knew that they needed to quickly leave the mine.

Answer the question below.

Do you think it was ethical, or fair, to use canaries this way? Explain.

_____

_____

_____

_____

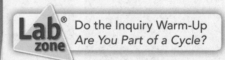

Lab® zone   Do the Inquiry Warm-Up
Are You Part of a Cycle?

What Processes Are Involved in the Water Cycle?

Recycling is important for ecosystems because matter is limited. To understand how matter cycles through an ecosystem, you need to know a few terms that describe the structure of matter. Matter is made up of tiny particles called atoms. Two or more atoms that are joined and act as a unit make up a molecule. For example, a water molecule consists of two hydrogen atoms and one oxygen atom.

Water is essential for life. The water cycle is the continuous process by which water moves from Earth's surface to the atmosphere and back. 🔑 **The processes of evaporation, condensation, and precipitation make up the water cycle.**

Vocabulary
- evaporation
- condensation
- precipitation
- nitrogen fixation

Skills
- Reading: Sequence
- Inquiry: Infer

FIGURE 1 ·······································

Water Cycle
In the water cycle, water moves continuously from Earth's surface to the atmosphere and back.

 Identify As you read, label the three processes of the water cycle in the diagram.

Evaporation
How does water from the ground get into the air? The process by which molecules of liquid water absorb energy and change to a gas is called **evaporation.** The energy for evaporation comes from the heat of the sun. In the water cycle, liquid water evaporates from oceans, lakes, and other sources and forms water vapor, a gas, in the atmosphere. Smaller amounts of water also evaporate from living things. Plants release water vapor from their leaves. You release liquid water in your wastes and water vapor when you exhale.

Condensation As water vapor rises higher in the atmosphere, it cools down. The cooled vapor then turns back into tiny drops of liquid water. The process by which a gas changes to a liquid is called **condensation.** The water droplets collect around dust particles and form clouds.

Precipitation As more water vapor condenses, the drops of water in the clouds grow larger. Eventually the heavy drops fall to Earth as **precipitation**—rain, snow, sleet, or hail. Precipitation may fall into oceans, lakes, or rivers. The precipitation that falls on land may soak into the soil and become groundwater, or run off the land, flowing back into a river or ocean.

Lab Do the Quick Lab
zone *Following Water.*

Assess Your Understanding
got**it**? ·····································

O **I get it!** Now I know that the processes of the water cycle are _____

_____

_____

O **I need extra help with** _____

_____

_____

_____

How Are the Carbon and Oxygen Cycles Related?

Carbon and oxygen are also necessary for life. Carbon is an essential building block in the bodies of living things. For example, carbon is a major component of bones and the proteins that build muscles. And most organisms use oxygen for their life processes. 🔑 **In ecosystems, the processes by which carbon and oxygen are recycled are linked. Producers, consumers, and decomposers all play roles in recycling carbon and oxygen.**

The Carbon Cycle Most producers take in carbon dioxide gas from the air during food-making or photosynthesis. They use carbon from the carbon dioxide to make food—carbon-containing molecules such as sugars and starches. As consumers eat producers, they take in the carbon-containing molecules. Both producers and consumers then break down the food to obtain energy during a process called cellular respiration. As the food is broken down, producers and consumers release carbon dioxide and water into the environment. When producers and consumers die, decomposers break down their remains and return carbon molecules to the soil. Some decomposers also release carbon dioxide into the air.

The Oxygen Cycle Look at **Figure 2**. Like carbon, oxygen cycles through ecosystems. Producers release oxygen as a result of photosynthesis. In fact, photosynthesis is responsible for most of the oxygen in Earth's atmosphere. Most organisms take in oxygen from the air or water and use it to carry out their life processes.

Human Impact Human activities also affect the levels of carbon and oxygen in the atmosphere. When humans burn oil and other plant-based fuels, carbon dioxide is released into the atmosphere. Carbon dioxide levels can also rise when humans clear forests for lumber, fuel, and farmland. Increasing levels of carbon dioxide are a major factor in global warming.

As you know, producers take in carbon dioxide during photosynthesis. When trees are removed from the ecosystem, there are fewer producers to absorb carbon dioxide. There is an even greater effect if trees are burned down to clear a forest. When trees are burned down, additional carbon dioxide is released during the burning process.

apply it!

Producers, consumers, and decomposers all play a role in recycling carbon and oxygen.

⚠ **Infer** On the lines below, describe how you think a cow eating grass is part of both the carbon and oxygen cycles.

_____

_____

_____

_____

_____

_____

_____

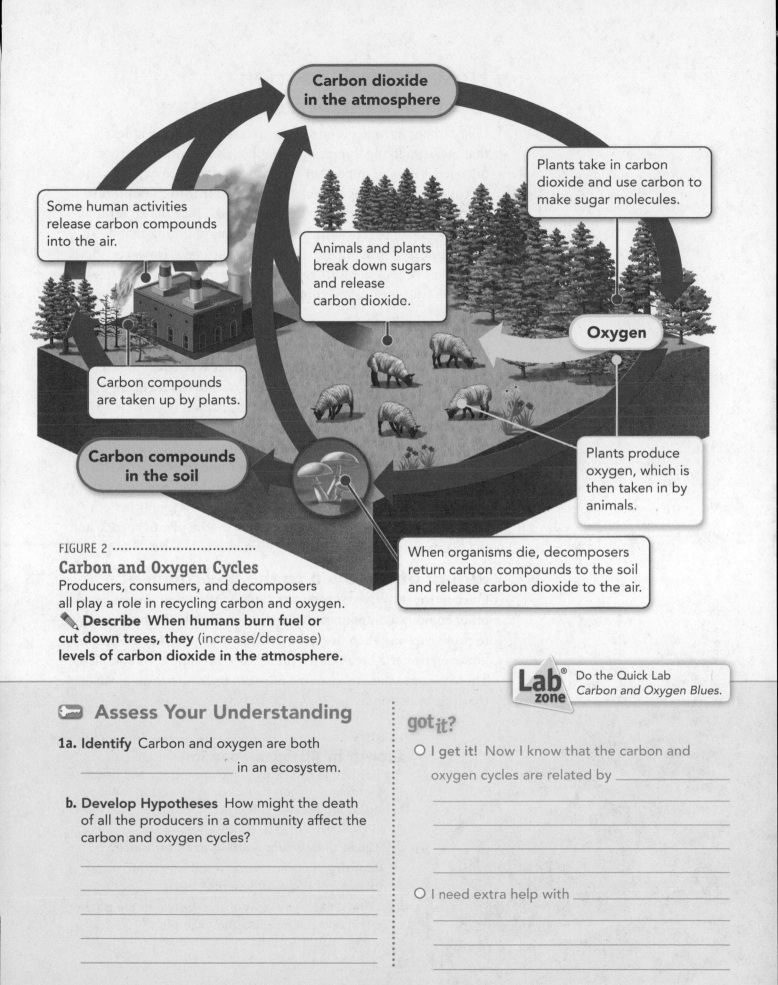

Carbon dioxide in the atmosphere

Plants take in carbon dioxide and use carbon to make sugar molecules.

Some human activities release carbon compounds into the air.

Animals and plants break down sugars and release carbon dioxide.

Oxygen

Carbon compounds are taken up by plants.

Carbon compounds in the soil

Plants produce oxygen, which is then taken in by animals.

When organisms die, decomposers return carbon compounds to the soil and release carbon dioxide to the air.

FIGURE 2 ....

Carbon and Oxygen Cycles
Producers, consumers, and decomposers all play a role in recycling carbon and oxygen.
✎ **Describe When humans burn fuel or cut down trees, they** (increase/decrease) **levels of carbon dioxide in the atmosphere.**

Lab® zone
Do the Quick Lab
Carbon and Oxygen Blues.

🔑 **Assess Your Understanding**

1a. Identify Carbon and oxygen are both

_____ in an ecosystem.

b. Develop Hypotheses How might the death of all the producers in a community affect the carbon and oxygen cycles?

_____

_____

_____

_____

got it?

○ **I get it!** Now I know that the carbon and

oxygen cycles are related by _____

_____

_____

_____

○ **I need extra help with** _____

_____

_____

_____

How Does Nitrogen Cycle Through Ecosystems?

Like carbon, nitrogen is one of the necessary building blocks that make up living things. For example, in addition to carbon, nitrogen is also an important component of proteins. **In the nitrogen cycle, nitrogen moves from the air into the soil, into living things, and back into the air or soil.** Since the air around you is about 78 percent nitrogen gas, you might think that it would be easy for living things to obtain nitrogen. However, most organisms cannot use nitrogen gas. Nitrogen gas is called "free" nitrogen because it is not combined with other kinds of atoms.

Nitrogen Fixation Most organisms can use nitrogen only after it has been "fixed," or combined with other elements to form nitrogen-containing compounds. The process of changing free nitrogen into a usable form of nitrogen, as shown in **Figure 4,** is called **nitrogen fixation.** Most nitrogen fixation is performed by certain kinds of bacteria. These bacteria live in bumps called nodules (NAHJ oolz) on the roots of legumes. These plants include clover, beans, peas, alfalfa, peanuts, and some trees.

The relationship between the bacteria and the legumes is an example of mutualism. Both the bacteria and the plants benefit from this relationship: The bacteria feed on the plants' sugars, and the plants are supplied with nitrogen in a usable form.

Return of Nitrogen to the Environment

Once nitrogen is fixed, producers can use it to build proteins and other complex compounds. Nitrogen can cycle from the soil to producers and then to consumers many times. At some point, however, bacteria break down the nitrogen compounds completely. These bacteria then release free nitrogen back into the air, causing the cycle to continue.

FIGURE 3 ·······································

Growth in Nitrogen-Poor Soil

Pitcher plants can grow in nitrogen-poor soil because they obtain nitrogen by trapping insects in their tube-shaped leaves. The plants then digest the insects and use their nitrogen compounds.

✎ **Circle the correct word in each sentence.**

1. **Identify** If nitrogen in the soil isn't (fixed/free), then most organisms cannot use it.

2. **CHALLENGE** The relationship between the pitcher plant and the insects is an example of (competition/predation/symbiosis).

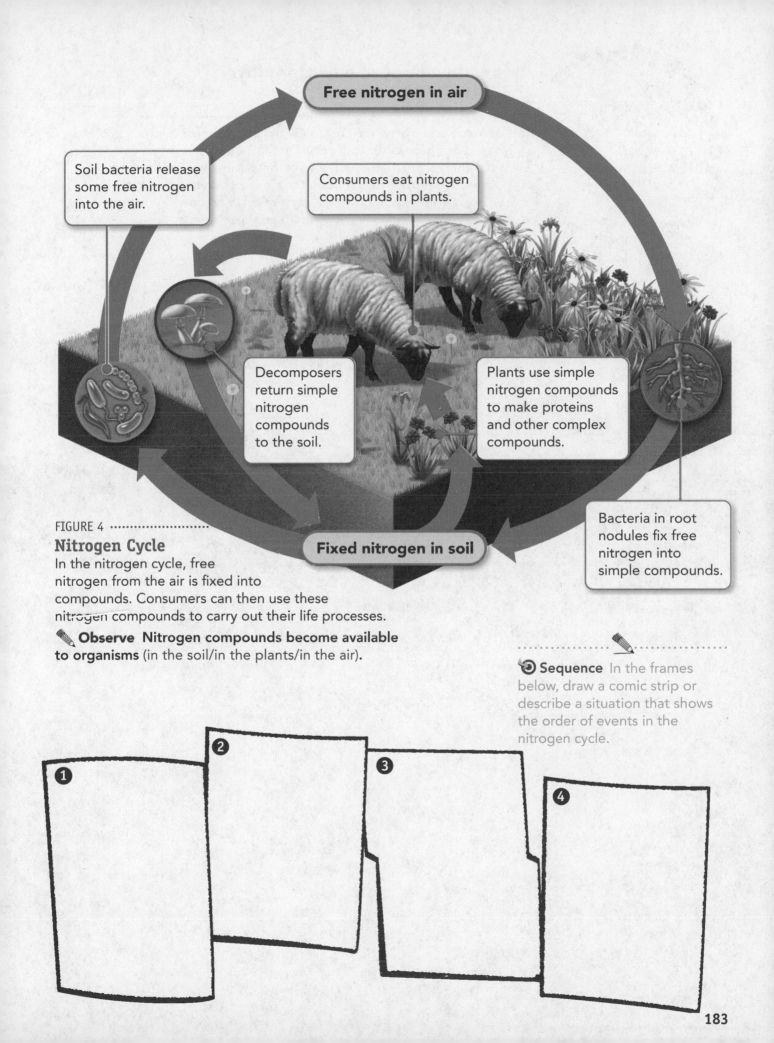

Free nitrogen in air

Soil bacteria release some free nitrogen into the air.

Consumers eat nitrogen compounds in plants.

Decomposers return simple nitrogen compounds to the soil.

Plants use simple nitrogen compounds to make proteins and other complex compounds.

Bacteria in root nodules fix free nitrogen into simple compounds.

Fixed nitrogen in soil

FIGURE 4 ·····················

Nitrogen Cycle

In the nitrogen cycle, free nitrogen from the air is fixed into compounds. Consumers can then use these nitrogen compounds to carry out their life processes.

✎ **Observe** Nitrogen compounds become available **to organisms** (in the soil/in the plants/in the air).

🔄 **Sequence** In the frames below, draw a comic strip or describe a situation that shows the order of events in the nitrogen cycle.

❶

❷

❸

❹

How do energy and matter move through ecosystems?

FIGURE 5 ••

Energy and matter are constantly being cycled through an ecosystem. These cycles can occur at the same time.

✎ **Interpret Diagrams** Using colored pencils, draw arrows to represent the following in the figure below: water cycle (blue), carbon cycle (purple), oxygen cycle (yellow), nitrogen cycle (orange), food chain (green). Label each cycle.

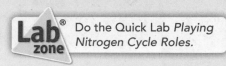
 Do the Quick Lab *Playing Nitrogen Cycle Roles.*

🔑 Assess Your Understanding

2a. Describe (Fixed/Free) nitrogen is not combined with other kinds of atoms.

b. Predict What might happen in a community if farmers did not plant legume crops?

_____

_____

_____

_____

_____

_____

_____

c. ANSWER THE BIG **?** How do energy and matter move through ecosystems?

_____

_____

_____

_____

_____

_____

_____

_____

_____

got **it?** ....

O I get it! Now I know that the nitrogen cycle

_____

_____

_____

O I need extra help with _____

_____

_____

_____

Biomes

UNLOCK
THE BIG

🔑 What Are the Six Major Biomes?

my planet Diary

That's Super Cool!

Misconception: It is always fatal when body temperatures drop below freezing.

Fact: In the tundra, arctic ground squirrels hibernate up to eight months a year. During this time, a squirrel's body temperature drops below freezing! This is called supercooling and gives the squirrel the lowest body temperature of any mammal. Without waking, a squirrel will shiver for several hours every couple of weeks to increase its body temperature.

MISCONCEPTION

Answer the question below.

What do you think are the advantages of supercooling?

_____

_____

_____

_____

_____

_____

Lab
zone ® Do the Inquiry Warm-Up
How Much Rain Is That?

What Are the Six Major Biomes?

Imagine that you are taking part in an around-the-world scientific expedition. On this expedition you will collect data on the typical climate and organisms of each of Earth's biomes. A **biome** is a group of ecosystems with similar climates and organisms.

🔑 **The six major biomes are desert, rain forest, grassland, deciduous forest, boreal forest, and tundra.** It is mostly the **climate**—the average annual temperature and amount of precipitation—in an area that determines its biome. Climate limits the species of plants that can grow in an area. In turn, the species of plants determine the kinds of animals that live there.

Vocabulary
- biome • climate • desert • rain forest
- emergent layer • canopy • understory • grassland
- savanna • deciduous tree • boreal forest
- coniferous tree • tundra • permafrost

Skills
⟳ Reading: Compare and Contrast
△ Inquiry: Draw Conclusions

Desert Biomes The first stop on your expedition is a desert. You step off the bus into the searing heat. A **desert** is an area that receives less than 25 centimeters of rain per year. Some of the driest deserts may not receive any precipitation in a year! Deserts often undergo large shifts in temperature during the course of a day. A scorching hot desert like the Namib Desert in Africa cools rapidly each night when the sun goes down. Other deserts, such as the Gobi in central Asia, have a yearly average temperature that is below freezing.

Organisms that live in the desert, like the fennec in **Figure 1**, must be adapted to little or no rain and to extreme temperatures. For example, the stem of a saguaro cactus has folds that are similar to the pleats in an accordion. The stem expands to store water when it is raining. Gila monsters can spend weeks at a time in their cool underground burrows. Many other desert animals are most active at night when the temperatures are cooler.

FIGURE 1 ··
Desert
Organisms must be adapted to live in the desert.

✎ **Complete these tasks.**

1. CHALLENGE How do you think the fennec's ears and fur are adaptations to the desert's extreme temperatures?

_____

_____

_____

2. **List** Write five things you'll need to be well adapted to desert conditions. Pack carefully!

Supply List
- ○ wide-brimmed hat
- ○
- ○
- ○
- ○
- ○

Equator

Desert Biomes
☐ Desert

Compare and Contrast As
you read about temperate and
tropical rain forests, fill in the
Venn diagram.

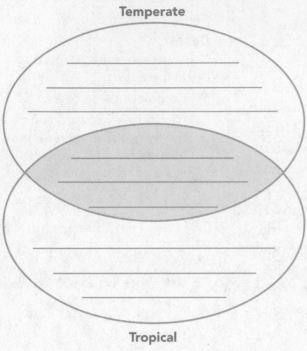

Temperate

Tropical

Rain-Forest Biomes
The second stop on your expedition is a rain forest. **Rain forests** are forests in which large amounts of rain fall year-round. This biome is living up to its name—it's pouring! After a short shower, the sun reappears. However, very little sunlight reaches the ground.

Plants are everywhere in the rain forest. Some plants, like the vines hanging from tree limbs, even grow on other plants! And animals are flying, creeping, and slithering all around you.

Temperate Rain Forests
You may think that a rain forest is a warm, humid "jungle" in the tropics. But there is another type of rain forest. The Pacific Northwest of the United States receives more than 300 centimeters of rain a year. Huge trees grow there, including redwoods, cedars, and firs. Many ecologists refer to this ecosystem as a temperate rain forest. The term *temperate* means "having moderate temperatures."

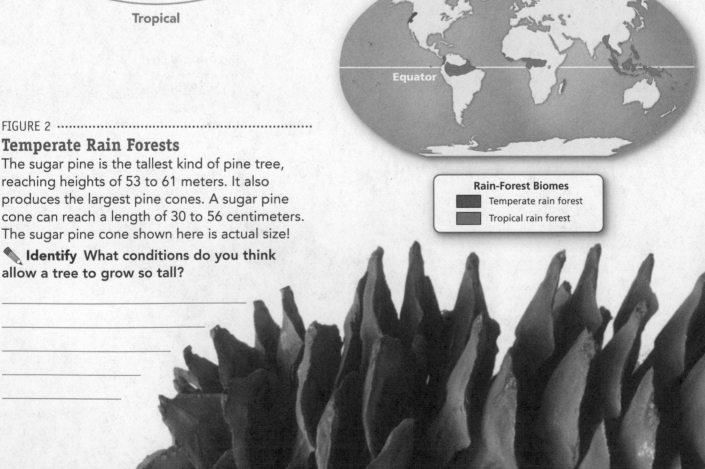

Equator

Rain-Forest Biomes
Temperate rain forest
Tropical rain forest

FIGURE 2

Temperate Rain Forests
The sugar pine is the tallest kind of pine tree, reaching heights of 53 to 61 meters. It also produces the largest pine cones. A sugar pine cone can reach a length of 30 to 56 centimeters. The sugar pine cone shown here is actual size!

✎ **Identify** What conditions do you think allow a tree to grow so tall?

_____

_____

_____

_____

Tropical Rain Forests As you can see on the map, tropical rain forests are found in regions close to the equator. The climate is warm and humid all year long, and there is a lot of rain. Because of these climate conditions, an amazing variety of plants grow in tropical rain forests.

Trees in the rain forest form several distinct layers. The tallest layer of the rain forest which receives the most sunlight and can reach up to 70 meters, is the **emergent layer.** Underneath, trees up to 50 meters tall form a leafy roof called the **canopy.** Below the canopy, a layer of shorter trees and vines, around 15 meters high, form an **understory.** Understory plants grow well in the shade formed by the canopy. The forest floor is nearly dark, so only a few plants live there. Look at the tree layers in **Figure 3.**

The abundant plant life in tropical rain forests provides habitats for many species of animals. Ecologists estimate that millions of species of insects live in tropical rain forests. These insects serve as a source of food for many reptiles, birds, and mammals. Many of these animals, in turn, are food sources for other animals. Although tropical rain forests cover only a small part of the planet, they probably contain more species of plants and animals than all the other biomes combined.

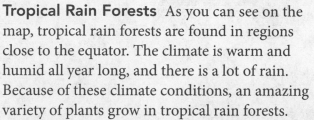

FIGURE 3 ·····································

Tropical Rain Forests
On the edge of this tropical rain forest, an amazing variety of organisms can be found in the different layers.

✎ **Relate Text and Visuals** Based on your reading, label the four distinct layers of the tropical rain forest in the boxes above.

FIGURE 4 ·····················

Grasslands
The rhea, cassowary, and ostrich are grassland birds that live on different continents.

✏️ **Interpret Maps** On the world map, identify the continents in which these three birds are located. List three characteristics that these grassland birds all share.

_____

_____

_____

_____

_____

Grassland Biomes The third stop on the expedition is a grassy plain called a prairie. Temperatures are more comfortable here than they were in the desert. The breeze carries the scent of soil warmed by the sun. This rich soil supports grasses as tall as you. Startled by your approach, sparrows dart into hiding places among the waving grass stems.

Although the prairie receives more rain than a desert, you may notice only a few scattered areas of trees and shrubs. Ecologists classify prairies, which are generally found in the middle latitudes, as grasslands. A **grassland** is an area that is populated mostly by grasses and other nonwoody plants. Most grasslands receive 25 to 75 centimeters of rain each year. Fires and droughts are common in this biome. Grasslands that are located closer to the equator than prairies are known as savannas. A **savanna** receives as much as 120 centimeters of rain each year. Scattered shrubs and small trees grow on savannas, along with grass.

Grasslands are home to many of the largest animals on Earth—herbivores such as elephants, bison, antelopes, zebras, giraffes, kangaroos, and rhinoceroses. Grazing by these large herbivores maintains the grasslands. Their grazing keeps young trees and bushes from sprouting and competing with the grass for water and sunlight. You can see some grassland birds in **Figure 4**.

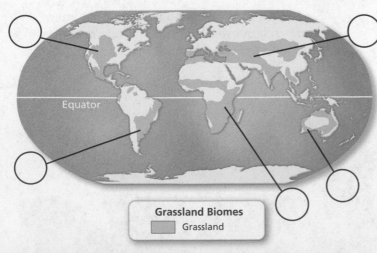

Equator

Grassland Biomes
Grassland

Deciduous Forest Biomes

Your trip to the fourth biome takes you to another forest. It is now late summer. Cool mornings here give way to warm days. Several members of the expedition are busy recording the numerous plant species. Others are looking through binoculars, trying to identify the songbirds.

You are now visiting a deciduous forest biome. Many of the trees in this forest are **deciduous trees** (dee SIJ oo us), trees that shed their leaves and grow new ones each year. Oaks and maples are examples of deciduous trees. Deciduous forests receive enough rain to support the growth of trees and other plants, at least 50 centimeters of rain per year. Temperatures can vary greatly during the year. The growing season usually lasts five to six months.

The variety of plants in a deciduous forest creates many different habitats. Many species of birds live in different parts of the forest, eating the insects and fruits in their specific areas. Mammals such as chipmunks and skunks live in deciduous forests. In a North American deciduous forest you might also see wood thrushes and white-tailed deer.

If you were to return to this biome in the winter, you would not see much wildlife. Many of the bird species migrate, or fly great distances, to warmer areas. Some of the mammals hibernate, or enter a state of greatly reduced body activity similar to sleep. Look at **Figure 5.** During the winter months, animals that hibernate get energy from fat stored in their bodies.

did you know?

How far would you be willing to migrate? The bobolink has one of the longest songbird migration routes. The birds travel south from southern Canada and the northern United States to northern Argentina. This migration route is approximately 20,000 kilometers round trip!

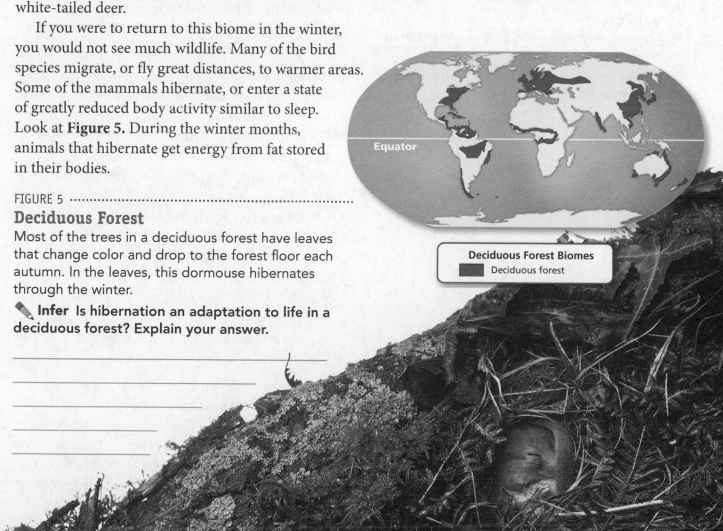

Equator

Deciduous Forest Biomes
■ Deciduous forest

FIGURE 5 ···
Deciduous Forest

Most of the trees in a deciduous forest have leaves that change color and drop to the forest floor each autumn. In the leaves, this dormouse hibernates through the winter.

✎ **Infer** Is hibernation an adaptation to life in a deciduous forest? Explain your answer.

_____

_____

_____

_____

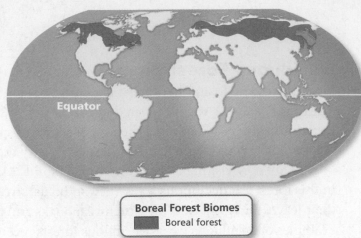

Boreal Forest Biomes
Boreal forest

FIGURE 6 ······························
Boreal Forest
✎ This lynx and snowshoe hare are adapted to life in the boreal forest.

1. **Infer** Choose the best answer. The feet of each animal are an adaptation to its

   ○ food.   ○ climate.
   ○ predators.   ○ all of the above

2. **Explain** Defend your answer.

_____

_____

_____

_____

Boreal Forest Biomes Now the expedition heads north to a colder biome, the boreal forest. The term *boreal* means "northern," and **boreal forests** are dense forests found in upper regions of the Northern Hemisphere. The expedition leaders claim they can identify a boreal forest by its smell. When you arrive, you catch a whiff of the spruce and fir trees that blanket the hillsides. Feeling the chilly early fall air, you pull a jacket and hat out of your bag.

Boreal Forest Plants Most of the trees in the boreal forest are **coniferous trees** (koh NIF ur us), trees that produce their seeds in cones and have leaves shaped like needles. The boreal forest is sometimes referred to by its Russian name, the *taiga* (TY guh). Winters in these forests are very cold. The snow can reach heights well over your head! Even so, the summers are rainy and warm enough to melt all the snow.

Tree species in the boreal forest are well adapted to the cold climate. Since water is frozen for much of the year, trees must have adaptations that prevent water loss. Coniferous trees, such as firs and hemlocks, all have thick, waxy needles that prevent water from evaporating.

Boreal Forest Animals Many of the animals of the boreal forest eat the seeds produced by the coniferous trees. These animals include red squirrels, insects, and birds such as finches. Some herbivores, such as moose and beavers, eat tree bark and new shoots. The variety of herbivores in the boreal forest supports many predators, including lynx, otters, and great horned owls. **Figure 6** shows an herbivore and its predator.

Tundra Biomes

As you arrive at your last stop, the driving wind gives you an immediate feel for this biome. The **tundra** is extremely cold and dry. Expecting deep snow, many are surprised to learn that the tundra may receive no more precipitation than a desert.

Most of the soil in the tundra is frozen all year. This frozen soil is called **permafrost.** During the short summer, the top layer of soil thaws, but the underlying soil remains frozen. Because rainwater cannot soak into the permafrost, shallow ponds and marshy areas appear in the summer.

Tundra Plants Mosses, grasses, and dwarf forms of a few trees can be found in the tundra. Most of the plant growth takes place during the long days of the short summer season. North of the Arctic Circle, the sun does not set during midsummer.

Tundra Animals In summer, the insects are abundant. Insect-eating birds take advantage of the plentiful food by eating as much as they can. But when winter approaches, these birds migrate south. Mammals of the tundra include caribou, foxes, and wolves. The mammals that remain on the tundra during the winter grow thick fur coats. What can these animals find to eat on the tundra in winter? The caribou scrape snow away to find lichens. Wolves follow the caribou and look for weak members of the herd to prey upon.

FIGURE 7

Tundra

Although the ground is frozen for most of the year, mosses, grasses, and dwarf willow trees grow here.

✏ **Communicate** Discuss with a partner why there are no tall trees on the tundra. Describe two factors that you think may influence tree growth.

_____

_____

_____

_____

_____

_____

_____

_____

_____

Equator

Tundra Biomes

☐ Tundra

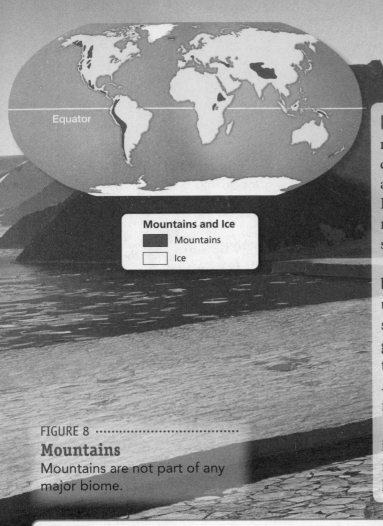

Mountains and Ice
■ Mountains
□ Ice

FIGURE 8 ·························
Mountains
Mountains are not part of any major biome.

Mountains and Ice

Some land areas are not classified as biomes. Recall that biomes are defined by abiotic factors such as climate and soil, and by biotic factors such as plant and animal life. Because the organisms that live in these areas vary, mountain ranges and land covered with thick ice sheets are not considered biomes.

The climate of a mountain changes from its base to its summit. If you were to hike all the way up a tall mountain, you would pass through a series of biomes. At the base, you might find grasslands. As you climbed, you might pass through deciduous forest and then boreal forest. As you neared the top, your surroundings would resemble the cold, dry tundra.

Other places are covered year-round with thick ice sheets. Most of Greenland and Antarctica fall into this category. Organisms that are adapted to life on ice include leopard seals and polar bears.

do the math!

Biome Climates

An ecologist collected climate data from two locations. The graph shows the monthly average temperatures in the two locations. The total yearly precipitation in Location A is 250 centimeters. In Location B, the total yearly precipitation is 14 centimeters.

1 Read Graphs Provide a title for the graph. What variable is plotted on the horizontal axis? On the vertical axis?

_____

2 Interpret Data Study the graph. How would you describe the temperature over the course of a year in Location A? In Location B?

_____
_____
_____

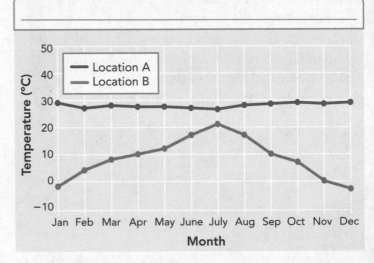

3 Draw Conclusions Given the precipitation and temperature data for these locations, in which biome would you expect each to be located?

_____
_____
_____

apply it!

Key of Earth Biomes
- ☐ Desert
- ☐ Temperate rain forest
- ☐ Tropical rain forest
- ☐ Grassland
- ☐ Deciduous rain forest
- ☐ Boreal forest
- ☐ Tundra

1 Interpret Maps Using the colors shown in the biome maps throughout this lesson, color in the key above. Use the key to color in the areas on the map of North America.

2 Draw Conclusions Where are most of the boreal forests located? Why are there no boreal forests in the Southern Hemisphere?

_____
_____
_____
_____
_____

3 Describe Mark the area in which you live with an X on the map. What is the climate like where you live? How do you think your climate affects which organisms live there?

_____
_____
_____
_____
_____
_____
_____

Lab zone® Do the Quick Lab
Inferring Forest Climates.

🔑 Assess Your Understanding

1a. Review _____ and _____ are the two main factors that determine an area's biome.

b. Infer What biome might you be in if you were standing on a bitterly cold, dry plain with only a few, short trees scattered around?

_____
_____

got it? ·

○ **I get it!** Now I know that the six major biomes are _____
_____

○ **I need extra help with** _____
_____

Aquatic Ecosystems

What Are the Two Major Aquatic Ecosystems?

my PLaneT DiaRY

TECHNOLOGY

Underwater *Alvin*

Meet *Alvin*, an HOV (Human-Occupied Vehicle). Equipped with propulsion jets, cameras, and robotic arms, *Alvin* helps scientists gather data and discover ecosystems that exist deep in the ocean. Built in 1964, *Alvin* was one of the world's first deep-ocean submersibles and has made more than 4,500 dives. *Alvin* is credited with finding a lost hydrogen bomb, exploring the first known hydrothermal vents, and surveying the wreck of the *Titanic*.

Calculate Suppose that on each of the 4,500 dives *Alvin* has made, a new pilot and two new scientists were on board. How many scientists have seen the deep ocean through *Alvin's* windows? How many people, in total, traveled in *Alvin*?

_____

_____

 Do the Inquiry Warm-Up *Where Does It Live?*

What Are the Two Major Aquatic Ecosystems?

Since almost three quarters of Earth's surface is covered with water, many living things make their homes in and near water. **There are two types of aquatic, or water-based, ecosystems: freshwater ecosystems and marine (or saltwater) ecosystems.** All aquatic ecosystems are affected by the same abiotic, or nonliving, factors: sunlight, temperature, oxygen, and salt content. Sunlight is an important factor in aquatic ecosystems because it is necessary for photosynthesis in the water just as it is on land. Half of all oxygen produced on Earth comes from floating algae called phytoplankton. Because water absorbs sunlight, there is only enough light for photosynthesis to occur near the surface or in shallow water.

Vocabulary
- estuary
- intertidal zone
- neritic zone

Skills
- Reading: Outline
- Inquiry: Communicate

Freshwater Ecosystems No worldwide expedition would be complete without exploring Earth's waters. Even though most of Earth's surface is covered with water, only 3 percent of the volume is fresh water. Freshwater ecosystems include streams, rivers, ponds, and lakes. On this part of your expedition, you'll find that freshwater biomes provide habitats for a variety of organisms.

Streams and Rivers At the source of a mountain stream, the water flows slowly. Plants take root on the bottom, providing food for insects and homes for frogs. These consumers then provide food for larger consumers. Stream currents increase as streams come together to make larger streams, often called rivers. Animals here are adapted to strong currents. For example, trout have streamlined bodies to swim in the rushing water. As the current speeds up, it can become cloudy with sediment. Few plants or algae grow in this fast-moving water. Consumers such as snails feed on leaves and seeds that fall into the stream. At lower elevations, streams are warmer and often contain less oxygen, affecting the organisms that can live in them.

Ponds and Lakes Ponds and lakes are bodies of still, or standing, fresh water. Lakes are generally larger and deeper than ponds. Ponds are often shallow enough that sunlight can reach the bottom, allowing plants to grow there. In large ponds and most lakes, however, algae floating at the surface are the major producers. Many animals are adapted for life in still water. Dragonflies, snails, and frogs live along the shores of ponds. In the open water, sunfish feed on insects and algae close to the surface. Scavengers such as catfish live near the bottoms of ponds. Bacteria and other decomposers also feed on the remains of other organisms.

Outline As you read, make an outline on a separate sheet of paper that includes the different types of aquatic ecosystems. Use the red headings for the main ideas and the black headings for the supporting details.

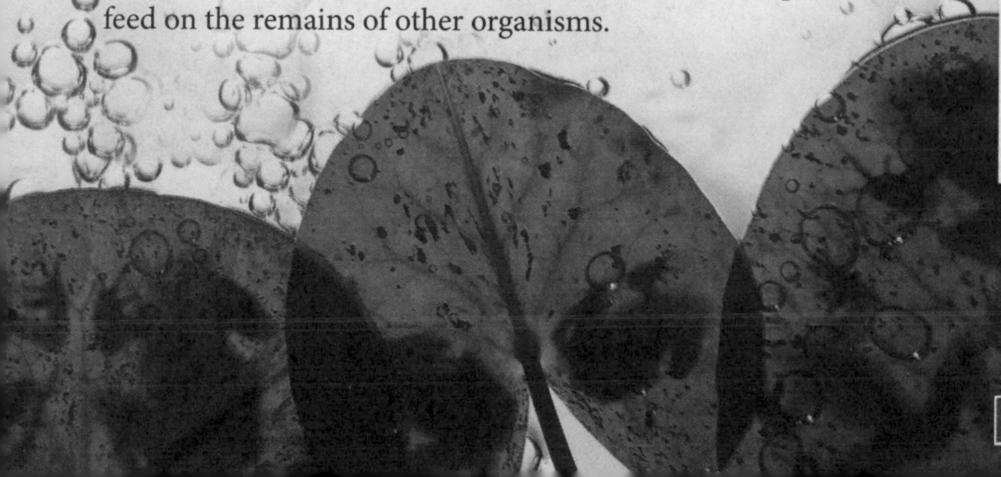

FIGURE 1

Freshwater Ecosystems

Water lilies live in ponds and lakes.

Answer the questions.

1. **Identify** What are two abiotic factors that can affect water lilies?

_____

_____

_____

_____

2. CHALLENGE What adaptations do fish have that allow them to live in water?

_____

_____

_____

_____

_____

_____

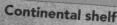

Intertidal zone

Neritic zone

High tide

Low tide

Continental shelf

Marine Ecosystems
The expedition now heads to the coast to explore some marine biomes. On your way, you'll pass through an estuary. An **estuary** (ES choo ehr ee), is found where the fresh water of a river meets the salt water of an ocean. Algae and plants provide food and shelter for animals, including crabs and fish. Many animals use the calm waters of estuaries for breeding grounds. Last, you explore the different ocean zones as described in **Figure 2.**

Ocean Zones		
Zone	Location	Inhabitants
Intertidal zone	Located on the shore between the highest high-tide line and the lowest low-tide line	Organisms must be able to survive pounding waves and the sudden changes in water levels and temperature that occur with high and low tides. For example, barnacles and sea stars cling to the rocks while clams and crabs burrow in the sand.
Neritic zone	Region of shallow water found below the low-tide line and extending over the continental shelf	Sunlight passes through shallow water, allowing photosynthesis to occur. Many living things, such as algae and schools of fish, live here. Coral reefs can also be found here in warmer waters.
Surface zone, open ocean	Located beyond the neritic zone and extending from the water's surface to about 200 meters deep	Sunlight penetrates this zone, allowing photosynthesis to occur in floating phytoplankton and other algae. Tuna, swordfish, and some whales depend on the algae for food.
Deep zone, open ocean	Located beneath the surface zone to the ocean floor	Little, if any, sunlight passes through. Animals feed on the remains of organisms that sink down. Organisms, like the giant squid and anglerfish, are adapted to life in the dark.

FIGURE 2 ·······················

Marine Ecosystems
The ocean is home to a number of different ecosystems.

✎ **Classify** Using the clues, determine at which depth each organism belongs. In the circles in the ocean, write the letter for each organism in the correct zone.

Ⓒ

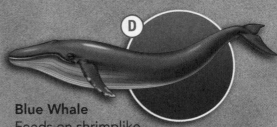

Yellowfin Tuna
Found in open waters and has been known to eat squid

Ⓓ

Blue Whale
Feeds on shrimplike creatures at depths of more than 100 meters during the day

Ⓐ

Anglerfish
Females have a lighted lure to help them attract prey in the dark.

Ⓑ

Tripod Fish
This fish has three elongated fins to help it stand.

Ⓔ

Swordfish
Often seen jumping out of the water to stun smaller fish

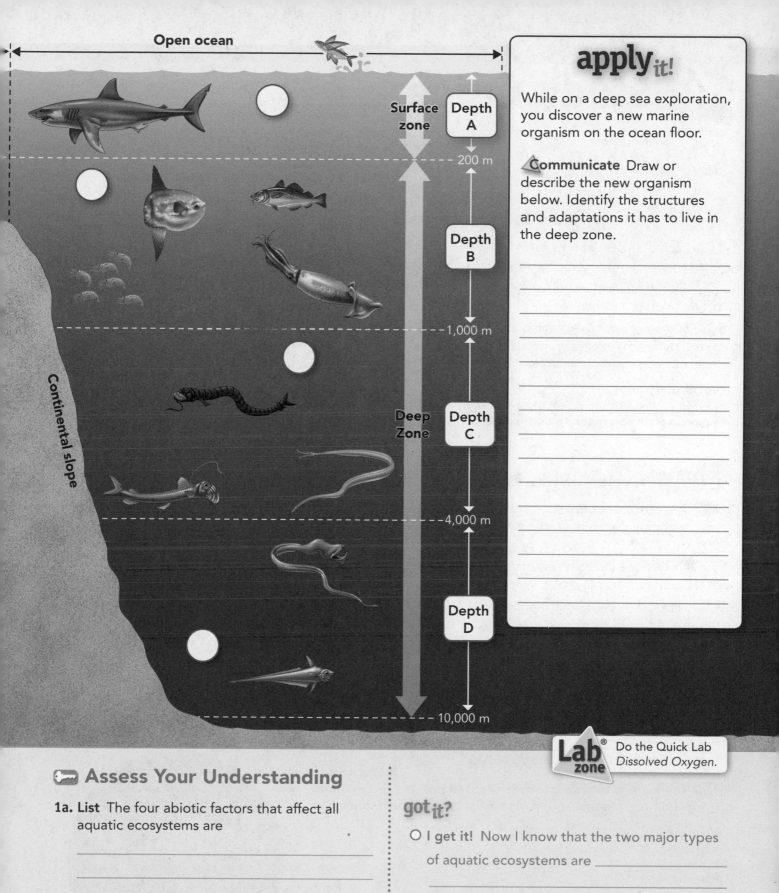

Open ocean

Surface zone

Depth A

— 200 m

Depth B

— 1,000 m

Deep Zone

Depth C

— 4,000 m

Depth D

— 10,000 m

Continental slope

apply it!

While on a deep sea exploration, you discover a new marine organism on the ocean floor.

▲ **Communicate** Draw or describe the new organism below. Identify the structures and adaptations it has to live in the deep zone.

_____

_____

_____

_____

_____

_____

_____

_____

_____

_____

_____

_____

_____

_____

Lab zone ® Do the Quick Lab *Dissolved Oxygen.*

🔑 Assess Your Understanding

1a. List The four abiotic factors that affect all aquatic ecosystems are

_____

_____

b. Make Generalizations Why is sunlight important to all aquatic ecosystems?

_____

_____

got it?

○ **I get it!** Now I know that the two major types of aquatic ecosystems are _____

_____

○ I need extra help with _____

_____

4 Study Guide

Producers, _____, and _____ help to cycle energy through ecosystems.

LESSON 1 **Energy Flow in Ecosystems**

🔑 Each of the organisms in an ecosystem fills the energy role of producer, consumer, or decomposer.

🔑 Energy moves through an ecosystem when one organism eats another.

🔑 The most energy is available at the producer level of the pyramid. As energy moves up the pyramid, each level has less energy available than the level below.

Vocabulary
- producer • consumer • herbivore • carnivore
- omnivore • scavenger • decomposer • food chain • food web • energy pyramid • desertification

---

LESSON 2 **Cycles of Matter**

🔑 The processes of evaporation, condensation, and precipitation make up the water cycle.

🔑 The processes by which carbon and oxygen are recycled are linked. Producers, consumers, and decomposers play roles in recycling both.

🔑 Nitrogen moves from the air into the soil, into living things, and back into the air or soil.

Vocabulary
- evaporation • condensation
- precipitation • nitrogen fixation

LESSON 3 **Biomes**

🔑 The six major biomes are desert, rain forest, grassland, deciduous forest, boreal forest, and tundra.

Vocabulary
- biome • climate • desert • rain forest
- emergent layer • canopy • understory
- grassland • savanna • deciduous tree
- boreal forest • coniferous tree • tundra
- permafrost

LESSON 4 **Aquatic Ecosystems**

🔑 There are two types of aquatic, or water-based, ecosystems: freshwater ecosystems and marine (or saltwater) ecosystems.

Vocabulary
- estuary
- intertidal zone
- neritic zone

Review and Assessment

Energy Flow in Ecosystems

1. A diagram that shows how much energy is available at each feeding level in an ecosystem is a(n)

   a. food web.　　**b.** food chain.

   c. water cycle.　　**d.** energy pyramid.

2. A(n) _____ is a consumer that eats only plants.

3. **Interpret Diagrams** Which organisms in the illustration are producers? Consumers?

   _____
   _____
   _____
   _____
   _____
   _____
   _____

4. **Compare and Contrast** How are food chains and food webs different?

   _____
   _____
   _____
   _____

5. **Write About It** Think about your own food web. Name the producers and consumers that make up your diet.

   _____
   _____
   _____
   _____
   _____
   _____

Cycles of Matter

6. When drops of water in a cloud become heavy enough, they fall to Earth as

   a. permafrost.　　**b.** evaporation.

   c. precipitation.　　**d.** condensation.

7. Evaporation, condensation, and precipitation are the three main processes in the

   _____

8. **Infer** Which process is responsible for the droplets visible on the glass below? Explain.

   _____
   _____
   _____
   _____

9. **Classify** Which group of organisms is the source of oxygen in the oxygen cycle? Explain.

   _____
   _____

10. **Make Generalizations** Describe the roles of producers and consumers in the carbon cycle.

    _____
    _____
    _____
    _____
    _____
    _____
    _____

11. **Draw Conclusions** What would happen if all the nitrogen-fixing bacteria disappeared?

    _____
    _____
    _____
    _____

4 Review and Assessment

LESSON 3 Biomes

12. Little precipitation and extreme temperatures are main characteristics of which biome?

   a. desert   **b.** grassland

   c. boreal forest   **d.** deciduous forest

13. A _____ is a group of

ecosystems with similar climates and

organisms.

14. Compare and Contrast How are the tundra and desert similar? How are they different?

_____

_____

_____

_____

_____

_____

_____

_____

_____

LESSON 4 Aquatic Ecosystems

15. In which ocean zone would you find barnacles, sea stars, and other organisms tightly attached to rocks?

   a. neritic zone   **b.** intertidal zone

   c. estuary ecosystem   **d.** freshwater ecosystem

16. Coral reefs are found in the shallow, sunny

waters of the _____

17. Compare and Contrast How are a pond and lake similar? How do they differ?

_____

_____

_____

_____

_____

_____

_____

_____

_____

_____

_____

APPLY THE BIG ? How do energy and matter cycle through ecosystems?

18. Many acres of the Amazon rain forest have been destroyed to create farmland. Describe how the amount of energy in the food web for this area might be affected. How might the carbon and oxygen cycle also be affected?

_____

_____

_____

_____

_____

_____

_____

_____

_____

_____

Standardized Test Prep

Read each question and choose the best answer.

1. At which level of this energy pyramid is the <u>least</u> energy available?

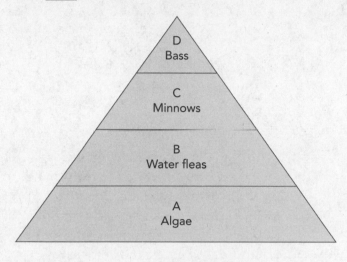

D
Bass

C
Minnows

B
Water fleas

A
Algae

A Level A   **B** Level B
C Level C   **D** Level D

2. You are in an area in Maryland where the fresh water of the Chesapeake Bay meets the Atlantic Ocean. Which of the following terms describes where you are?

A tundra   **B** estuary
C neritic zone   **D** intertidal zone

3. Which pair of terms could apply to the same organism?

A carnivore and producer
B consumer and carnivore
C scavenger and herbivore
D producer and omnivore

4. The use of chemicals in agriculture, such as herbicides, insecticides, and fertilizer, can negatively impact the environment by

A putting nutrients back into soil.
B poisoning organisms in streams and rivers that the chemicals enter.
C destroying weeds that keep crops from growing.
D killing insects and pests that damage crops.

Constructed Response

Write your answer to Question 5 on the lines below.

5. Describe the process of desertification and the impact it has on an ecosystem.

_____

_____

_____

_____

_____

_____

Use the diagram below and your knowledge of science to help you answer Question 6. Write your answer on a separate piece of paper.

Nitrogen Cycle

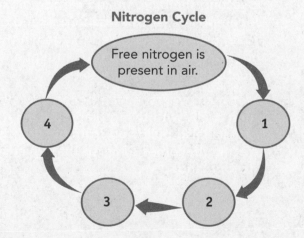

Free nitrogen is present in air.

4

1

3

2

6. Describe each numbered part of the cycle shown in the diagram above.

A lake Can't last forever

Much like living things, lakes change over time and even have life spans. Scientists call this change "lake succession". One way this occurs is through eutrophication.

Eutrophication refers to the addition of nutrients to bodies of water. It occurs naturally, but human activity can speed up the process. Nutrients—especially phosphorus and nitrogen—are necessary for algae and plants to grow in lakes. However, too many nutrients, such as those from fertilizers and sewage, can lead to excessive algae growth or "blooms."

These blooms often kill plant and animal life by upsetting the oxygen and carbon dioxide cycles. Decomposers, such as bacteria, feed off the algae, using up dissolved oxygen in the water in the process. This limits the amount and kinds of aquatic life that can live there.

Over many years, a lake becomes shallower when it fills with dying plant and animal matter. Material also builds up from outside the lake. The lake becomes a marsh that, over time, turns into dry land.

Research It With your classmates, analyze a body of water to determine its ability to support life. To study biotic factors, obtain and identify samples of organisms. Find information about how to count the kinds and numbers of invertebrates to judge pollution levels. Then look at abiotic factors. Use thermometers, probeware, and water chemistry kits to determine temperature, dissolved oxygen, and pH levels. Research information about how these factors affect the survival of organisms. Compile findings in a table and graph data. Pass records on to future classes to interpret and predict changes over time.

Trees: Environmental Factories

Some of the most important members of your community don't volunteer. They consume huge amounts of water and they make a mess. Despite these drawbacks, these long-standing community members do their share. Who are these individuals? They're trees!

Keeping it clean: Trees remove pollutants from the air. Some researchers have calculated the value of the environmental cleaning services that trees provide. One study valued the air-cleaning service that trees in the Chicago area provide at more than $9 million every year.

Keeping it cool: Trees provide shade and lower air temperature by the process of transpiration. Pollutants, like ozone and smog, form more easily when air temperatures are high, so by keeping the air cool, trees also keep it clean.

Acting locally and globally: Trees help fight global environmental problems such as climate change. Trees remove carbon dioxide from the air and store the carbon as they grow. Experts estimate that urban trees in the United States remove more than 700 million tons of carbon from the air every year.

Helping the local economy: Trees are also good for business. One study found that shoppers spend more money in urban areas where trees are planted than they do in similar areas that don't have trees!

Research It Examine a topographical map of the area where you live. Compare it to an aerial photograph from a library or local archive. Identify areas with a lot of trees, and areas that you think could benefit from more trees. Create a proposal to plant trees in one of the areas you identified. What kinds of trees will you plant? What do those trees need in order to grow well?

Schools, clubs, and civic groups all over the United States volunteer to plant trees in their communities. ▶

HOW MIGHT A BAYOU CHANGE OVER TIME?

How do natural and human activities change ecosystems?

Louisiana's Atchafalaya Basin covers about 5665.5 square kilometers. The basin contains hardwood forest, swamp, bayou, and marsh ecosystems. Many organisms listed on state and federal threatened and endangered species lists, such as the pallid sturgeon and ivory-billed woodpecker, live here. Storms, oil exploration, and logging all threaten the basin.

Infer What other events might affect wetlands?

_____

_____

_____

_____

_____

Watch the **Untamed Science** video to learn more about ecosystems.

Balance Within Ecosystems

5 Getting Started

Check Your Understanding

1. **Background** Read the paragraph below, then answer the question.

Lavar's science class was having its yearly bird count. The class was going to a nearby marsh, where there was a population of snowy egrets. The class might also see another egret species, the great egret. When the class arrived at the marsh, they discovered that it had a large community of birds, including egrets and other birds.

> All the members of one species living in a particular area is a population.
>
> A species is a group of organisms that can mate with each other and produce offspring that also mate and reproduce.
>
> All the different populations that live in an area make up a community.

• What other populations might make up the marsh community?

_____

_____

Vocabulary Skill

Latin Word Origins Some key terms in this chapter contain word parts with Latin origins. The table below lists two of the Latin words that key terms come from.

Latin Word	Meaning	Example
habitare	to dwell	habitat, *n.* the place where an organism lives
extinguere	to wipe out	extinction, *n.* the disappearance of all members of a species from Earth

2. **Quick Check** The terms *habitat destruction* and *habitat fragmentation* both come from the Latin word *habitare*. Circle the meaning of *habitare* in the table above.

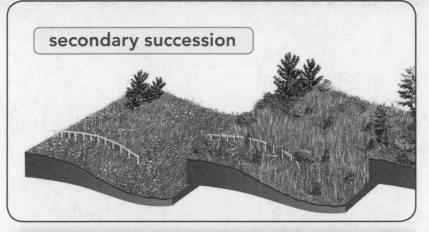

secondary succession

resources

keystone species

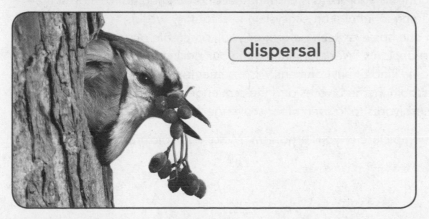

dispersal

Chapter Preview

Scenario Investigation

Fantasy Food Chain

Purpose To investigate the roles of different organisms in a food chain

Materials
- colored index cards (4 different colors)
- colored pencils or markers
- white index cards
- poster board or newsprint
- white copier paper

Scenario

You are an ecologist. Your specialty is ecosystems. Normally that means investigating relationships among the plants and animals that live together in an area. Your work involves food chains and food webs.

Today, you and three of your colleagues were given a different kind of job to do. You have been asked to create three imaginary animals and one imaginary plant for a new children's book.

Stories by Curtis Larking in *The Adventures of Henry Porter* are all set in a fantasy world that the author creates in his mind. After writing fourteen novels, he is looking for some original ideas. That's where you come in. Larking plans to use the three animals and one plant that you invent as he writes about a fictional food chain in his new book.

Larking needs a fictional plant to be the producer and three levels of animal consumers—one species of herbivore, one species of carnivore, and one species of scavenger. Although these organisms are fictional, Larking wants the food chain to be scientifically accurate.

That means the largest amount of available energy should be at the producer level. It also means that as you move up the food chain, the available energy must decrease, so consumer populations will get smaller.

Procedure

☑ **1. Forming Your Fantasy Team** Your teacher has given each student in your class a card. The cards come in four colors. When your teacher tells you, form a team in which each person on your team has a different color card.

☑ **2. Who's Inventing What?** Your teacher will tell you which color card represents which organism (plant, herbivore, carnivore, and scavenger).

☑ **3. Creating an Organism** The organisms your team is creating need to be imaginative—even the plant. (After all, the organisms are going to inhabit an ecosystem in a fantasy world.)
You can create an organism that no one has ever seen before, or you can create an organism by combining parts of real animals or real plants. Work together with your partners to make sure your organisms can live together in the same kind of environment. Also, remember that the herbivores will eat the plants, the carnivores will eat both the herbivores and the scavengers, and the scavengers will eat any dead animals (carnivores, herbivores, and even other scavengers).

☑ **4. Drawing Your Organism** Draw a picture of your organism. Make each picture large enough to fill a sheet of copier paper.

Conclusion

Let's see what you learned about food chains.

☑ **1.** What role do producers play in an ecosystem?

_____

☑ **2.** Which level in a food chain has the most available energy?

_____

☑ **3.** Which level in a food chain has the least available energy?

_____

☑ **4.** If Curtis Larking asks you to suggest decomposers, what will their role be?

_____

Now mount your group's four organisms on a poster to show the food chain. Arrange them so that producers are on the bottom, carnivores and scavengers are at the top, and herbivores are in the middle. Leave room for labels and arrows to show the relationships that exist in the food chain.

Next to each organism, Larking wants an index card with the following information:

- role in the food chain
- population size (make sure it is appropriate for the role in the food chain)
- litter size (for plants, give the number of germinated seeds it produces)
- life expectancy
- any strange behaviors it exhibits

Once you have added all of the index cards to your poster, add arrows to show the flow of energy through your food chain.

Changing Ecosystems

UNLOCK
THE BIG
?

🗝 **How Do Ecosystems Change Over Time?**

🗝 **How Do Changes in Ecosystems Affect the Survival of Organisms?**

my planet DiaRY

Fighting Fire With Fire

Wildfires are often reported in the national news. The images associated with these reports show how damaging these fires can be to property and to some ecosystems. What you may not know is that fire can actually help fight wildfires! Controlled burns, or prescribed burns, are fires that are purposely and carefully set by professional foresters. Prescribed burns are used to remove materials such as dead, dry branches and leaves that can fuel wildfires. A wildfire that occurs in an area that has previously been burned would cause less damage and be easier for firefighters to control.

This forester is carefully igniting a controlled burn.

MISCONCEPTION

Communicate Discuss these questions with a classmate. Write your answers below.

1. Why should only professional foresters set prescribed fires?

_____

_____

_____

2. What do you think could be some other benefits to using prescribed burns in an ecosystem?

_____

_____

_____

 Lab ® Do the Inquiry Warm-Up
zone *How Communities Change.*

How Do Ecosystems Change Over Time?

Natural disasters can change communities in an ecosystem quickly. Even without a disaster, communities change. The series of predictable changes that occur in a community over time is called **succession**. 🗝 **Primary succession and secondary succession are two types of succession.**

Vocabulary
- succession • primary succession
- pioneer species • secondary succession

Skills
- Reading: Compare and Contrast
- Inquiry: Observe

Primary Succession When a new island is formed by the eruption of an undersea volcano or an area of rock is uncovered by a melting sheet of ice, no living things are present. Over time, living things will inhabit these areas. **Primary succession** is the series of changes that occurs in an area where no soil or organisms exist.

Figure 1 shows how an area might change following a volcanic eruption. Just like the pioneers that first settled new frontiers, the first species to populate an area are called **pioneer species.** They are often carried to the area by wind or water. Typical pioneer species are mosses and lichens. Lichens are fungi and algae growing in a symbiotic relationship. As pioneer species grow, they help break up the rocks and form soil. When organisms die, they provide nutrients that enrich the layer of soil forming on the rocks.

As plant seeds land in the new soil, they begin to grow. The specific plants that grow depend on the climate of the area. For example, in a cool, northern area, early seedlings might include alder and cottonwood trees. Eventually, succession may lead to a community of organisms that does not change unless the ecosystem is disturbed. Reaching this mature community can take centuries.

FIGURE 1 ·····························

Primary Succession
Primary succession occurs in an area where no soil and no organisms exist.

✎ **Sequence** In the circles, number the stage of primary succession to show the correct order of events.

Soil Creation
As pioneer species grow and die, soil forms. Some plants grow in this new soil.

Pioneer Species
The first species to grow are pioneer species such as mosses and lichens.

Volcanic Eruption
Shortly after a volcanic eruption, there is no soil, only ash and rock.

Fertile Soil and Maturing Plants
As more plants die, they decompose and make the soil more fertile. New plants grow and existing plants mature in the fertile soil.

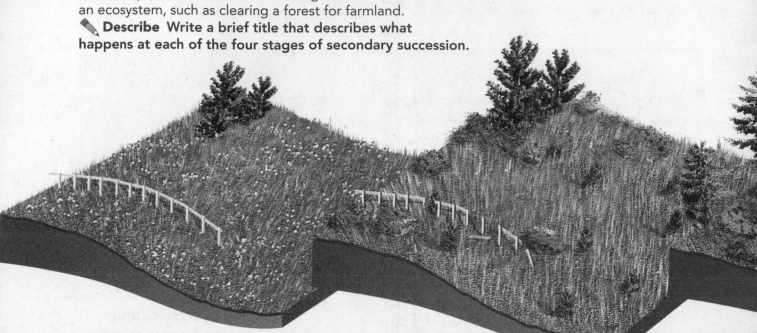

FIGURE 2

Secondary Succession

Secondary succession occurs following a disturbance to an ecosystem, such as clearing a forest for farmland.

✏️ **Describe** Write a brief title that describes what happens at each of the four stages of secondary succession.

Increasing time

Title: _____

Grasses and wildflowers have taken over this abandoned field.

Title: _____

After a few years, pine seedlings and other trees replace some of the grasses and wildflowers.

apply *it!*

↻ **Compare and Contrast** Based on your reading, complete the table below.

Factors in Succession	Primary Succession	Secondary Succession
Possible Cause	Volcanic eruption	_____
Type of Area	_____ _____	_____ _____ _____ _____
Existing Ecosystem?	_____	_____

Secondary Succession In October 2007, huge wildfires raged across southern California. The changes following the California fires are an example of secondary succession. **Secondary succession** is the series of changes that occurs in an area where the ecosystem has been disturbed, but where soil and organisms still exist. Natural disturbances that have this effect include fires, hurricanes, and tornadoes. Human activities, such as farming, logging, or mining, may also disturb an ecosystem and cause secondary succession to begin.

Unlike primary succession, secondary succession occurs in a place where an ecosystem currently exists. Secondary succession usually occurs more rapidly than primary succession because soil already exists and seeds from some plants remain in the soil. You can follow the process of succession in an abandoned field in **Figure 2**. After a century, a forest develops. This forest community may remain for a long time.

Title: _____
As tree growth continues, the trees begin to crowd out the grasses and wildflowers.

Title: _____
Eventually, a forest of mostly oak, hickory, and some pine dominates the landscape.

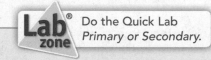
Do the Quick Lab
Primary or Secondary.

🔑 Assess Your Understanding

1a. Define _____ succession is the series of changes that occurs where no soil or organisms exist.

b. Observe Is grass poking through a sidewalk crack primary or secondary succession?

_____

_____

_____

c. [CHALLENGE] Why are the changes during succession predictable?

_____

_____

_____

_____

got it? ....

○ **I get it!** Now I know that ecosystems can change through _____

_____

○ I need extra help with _____

_____

How Do Changes in Ecosystems Affect the Survival of Organisms?

Organisms in an ecosystem experience day-to-day changes in their surroundings that do not affect them much. But when changes occur that are long lasting or extreme, most organisms in the ecosystem do not survive. However, some organisms may survive these changes. ⬤ **Organisms that survive a changing ecosystem have adaptations that help them survive in the new conditions.**

Figure 3 shows an ecosystem called the longleaf pine forest. Longleaf pine trees dominate this ecosystem. These trees grow in a pattern that allows plenty of sunlight to shine on the forest floor. The abundant sunlight allows many grasses and other small plants to grow below the trees. However, invasive plants such as oak trees eventually start to grow among the small plants. Without extreme change, the invasive plants crowd out the grasses and pine trees, and eventually dominate the forest.

Wildfires from lightning strikes occur frequently in the longleaf pine forests and change the ecosystem quickly. Although many of the organisms disappear during a wildfire, they reappear a short time after the fires. Most organisms return because they have adaptations that help them survive fire. You can read about these adaptations in **Figure 3.** However, invasive plants such as oak trees are not adapted to survive fire. The seeds of these trees must be carried into the ecosystem before they can grow there again. So, the populations of invasive plants disappear from the longleaf pine forest. The populations of longleaf pine trees, grasses, and other organisms survive the change and again dominate the ecosystem.

FIGURE 3 ·······················

Adapted to Fire

In the longleaf pine ecosystem, a variety of plants and animals are adapted to survive fire.

✎ **Complete these tasks.**

1. **Classify** In each box, write whether the organism's adaptation is a structural or behavioral adaptation.

2. **Explain** How does a wildfire impact the survival of the population of oak trees?

_____

_____

_____

_____

3. **Infer** How might a wildfire help the longleaf pine population survive a deadly fungal infection on the needles of seedlings?

_____

_____

_____

_____

Fire burns the blades of bluestem grass, but its underground roots remain unharmed. After the fire new shoots sprout from the roots.

_____

_____

A pine snake escapes fire by seeking shelter in a gopher burrow.

_____

_____

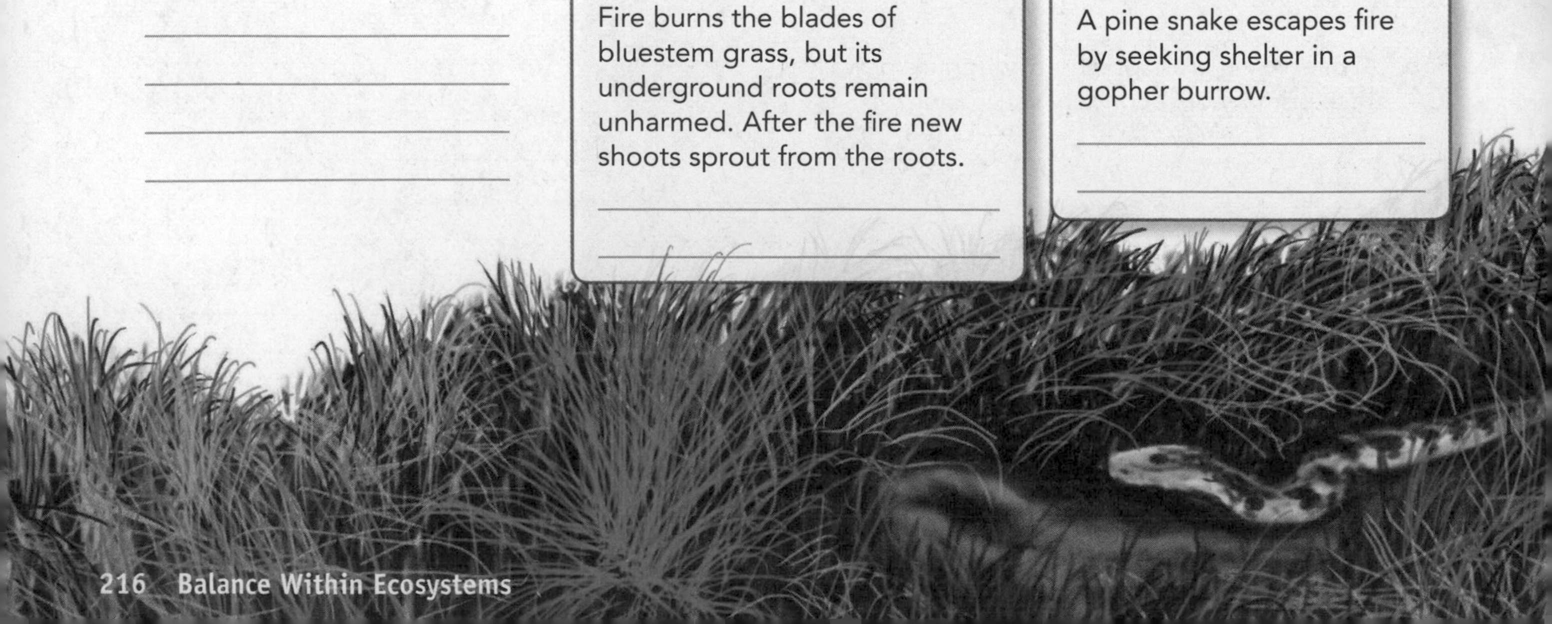

The red-cockaded woodpecker flies away from the fire to safety.

_____

As the thick, scaly bark burns, flakes fall off and take the heat with them.

_____

_____

A longleaf pine seedling is topped with a moist tuft of needles. As fire burns the needles, they produce steam that moves the heat away from the plant and extinguishes the fire. If the needles burn off entirely, the seedling can regrow from its root.

_____

_____

Lab zone® Do the Lab Investigation *How Is Survival Dependent on the Ecosystem?*

🔑 **Assess Your Understanding**

got it? •••

O **I get it!** Now I know that organisms can survive changes in ecosystems if _____

_____

_____

_____

_____

O **I need extra help with** _____

_____

_____

217

Humans and the Environment

🔑 **What Resources Do Humans Obtain From Ecosystems?**

🔑 **How Do Human Activities Affect Ecosystems?**

MY PLANET DiARY

DISCOVERY

The Grass That Invaded Louisiana

In April of 1990, an invader was discovered in a pasture in southeastern Louisiana. This invader had entered the United States in crates shipped from Asia to Alabama back in 1912. Used as packing material, this invader, a grassy weed called cogongrass, began spreading. Today, cogongrass has negatively affected ecosystems in many parts of Louisiana. It is a hardy grass that grows quickly and thickly, preventing the seedlings of native plants such as pine trees to grow. However, scientists have found that ryegrass can compete successfully with cogongrass. So, pastures dominated by cogongrass are being plowed under and planted with ryegrass to control the spread of this invasive grass.

Answer the questions.

1. Why do you think grass was used as a packing material in Asia in 1912?

_____

_____

2. How has modern transportation spread foreign organisms?

_____

_____

_____

_____

Lab zone® Do the Inquiry Warm-Up How Do You Interact With Your Environment?

What Resources Do Humans Obtain From Ecosystems?

You live in an ecosystem. The ecosystem provides you with resources. **Resources** are anything in an ecosystem that you need to live. 🔑 **The resources that humans obtain from ecosystems include abiotic resources and biotic resources.**

Abiotic Resources Abiotic resources, or nonliving resources, are found in the air, on Earth's surface, in soil, and beneath Earth's surface. The abiotic resources that humans obtain from ecosystems include water, sunlight, oxygen, and minerals.

How do you and others obtain these abiotic resources? Sources of freshwater provide most of the water that you need. Foods provide some of it, too. You absorb sunlight through your skin. Your body uses it to produce vitamin D, which helps build bones. When you breathe, you take in oxygen from the air. You need oxygen to release the energy from the foods you eat. You get minerals such as iron and calcium, which your body needs to stay healthy, when you eat plants. Plants absorb these minerals from the soil. Other minerals that make up objects you use, such as coins and jewelry, are mined. Use **Figure 1** to identify some abiotic resources you use.

FIGURE 1 ·······························
Abiotic Resources
This girl is helping the plants in this garden to grow.

✎ **Interpret Photos** In the chart, write from where in the photo you might get each abiotic resource.

Sunlight	
Oxygen	
Water	
Minerals	

Biotic Resources The living things in an ecosystem are important biotic resources. They provide humans with food, materials to build shelter, and fuels. Food is found in many ecosystems. For example, marine ecosystems are a source of fish, aquatic plants, and invertebrates such as clams and mussels. The trees in forests provide lumber for building homes and other structures. **Figure 2** shows another way trees are used. Oil, coal, and natural gas are commonly used fuels. They were formed from the remains of organisms that lived millions of years ago. People use fuels for transportation, heating, cooking, manufacturing, and the production of electricity.

Decomposers are also biotic resources. Decomposers are animals, bacteria, and fungi that break down and recycle the remains of dead organisms. Their activities provide important things that people need, such as a part of soil called humus. Humus is the decayed parts of organisms. It contains nutrients that plants need to grow. Decomposers recycle nutrients from dead plant and animal matter back to the soil in land ecosystems and to the water in aquatic ecosystems.

FIGURE 2 ··

Trees as Resources
Trees provide food for people. Many fruits, seeds, and nuts grow on trees. People also collect the sap from maple trees to produce maple syrup.

✎ **List** On the notebook paper, list three foods you like to eat that come from trees.

Lab zone Do the Quick Lab *How Do Humans Impact Ecosystems?*

⚷ Assess Your Understanding

1a. Identify A _____ is anything in an ecosystem that you need to live.

b. Apply Concepts Give an example of an abiotic and a biotic resource you used today.

_____

_____

got it?

○ I get it! Now I know that the resources humans obtain from ecosystems are _____

_____

○ I need extra help with _____

_____

How Do Human Activities Affect Ecosystems?

Human activities can cause changes in ecosystems. **Human activities may affect the balance in an ecosystem and thereby change the ecosystem.** Some examples of human activities include the introduction of nonnative species, the process of energy production, and the use of resources for habitation and transportation.

Nonnative Species Humans can harm an ecosystem when they introduce a species into it. A species brought to an ecosystem where it is not native is a nonnative species. In the United States, cogongrass is a nonnative plant species.

Animals may also be nonnative species. Animals called nutrias live in the United States. However, nutrias are not native to North America. They are a rodent species from South America. These animals were brought to the United States for their fur and later released into ecosystems to control weeds. But the animals also ate many other types of native wetland plants. As a result, the populations of the native plants have decreased. These native plants are important because their roots hold the soil in place. **Figure 3** shows the damage nutrias can do to a wetland ecosystem.

FIGURE 3 ·······························

Damage by Nutrias

Damage by nutrias in an ecosystem is sometimes irreversible.

✎ **Observe** In the chart, write three observations about the healthy and damaged ecosystem pictured.

Healthy Wetland	Damaged Wetland

Nutria

Nutrias have not damaged this wetland ecosystem.

Nutrias have damaged this wetland ecosystem.

221

Energy Production Technologies have been developed to obtain and process energy resources such as coal and oil. However, these technologies have affected the environment. One mining method involves stripping the rock and soil off mountaintops to obtain coal. During this process, some of the removed material may be deposited in nearby valleys, covering streams and destroying forests. Heavy rains can wash minerals from this material downstream, where they can poison aquatic animals.

Drilling for oil in oceans and transporting oil have resulted in large oil spills. These spills affect the ecosystems where they occur, as shown in **Figure 4.** Processing oil into fuels such as gasoline and burning these fuels add carbon dioxide to the air. Too much carbon dioxide affects the temperature of the atmosphere.

FIGURE 4 ··················

Oil Spill

On July 25, 2008, the oil tanker *Tintomara* and a barge collided on the Mississippi River in New Orleans, spilling nearly 1.5 million liters of oil into the water. These workers are using absorption mops to contain the oil spill.

Infer Identify organisms that would be most affected by an oil spill in water.

_____

_____

_____

_____

_____

Human Habitation and Transportation

Building homes, towns, and transportation systems requires resources. Forests are an important source of wood for building. To obtain this resource, loggers may clear-cut forests, which damages the ecosystem. Organisms that lived in the forest no longer have food or shelter. Many people also use wood to heat their homes. Trees use carbon dioxide during photosynthesis. With fewer trees to take in carbon dioxide, more carbon dioxide remains in the atmosphere. Also, as wood burns, it releases carbon dioxide into the atmosphere.

Millions of people travel in cars, trains, and airplanes. Most of these vehicles burn gasoline. As gasoline is burned, it releases gases such as carbon dioxide into the air. Some scientists think carbon dioxide is contributing to global warming through the greenhouse effect. The **greenhouse effect** is the process in which certain gases trap the sun's energy in Earth's atmosphere as heat. Look at **Figure 5.**

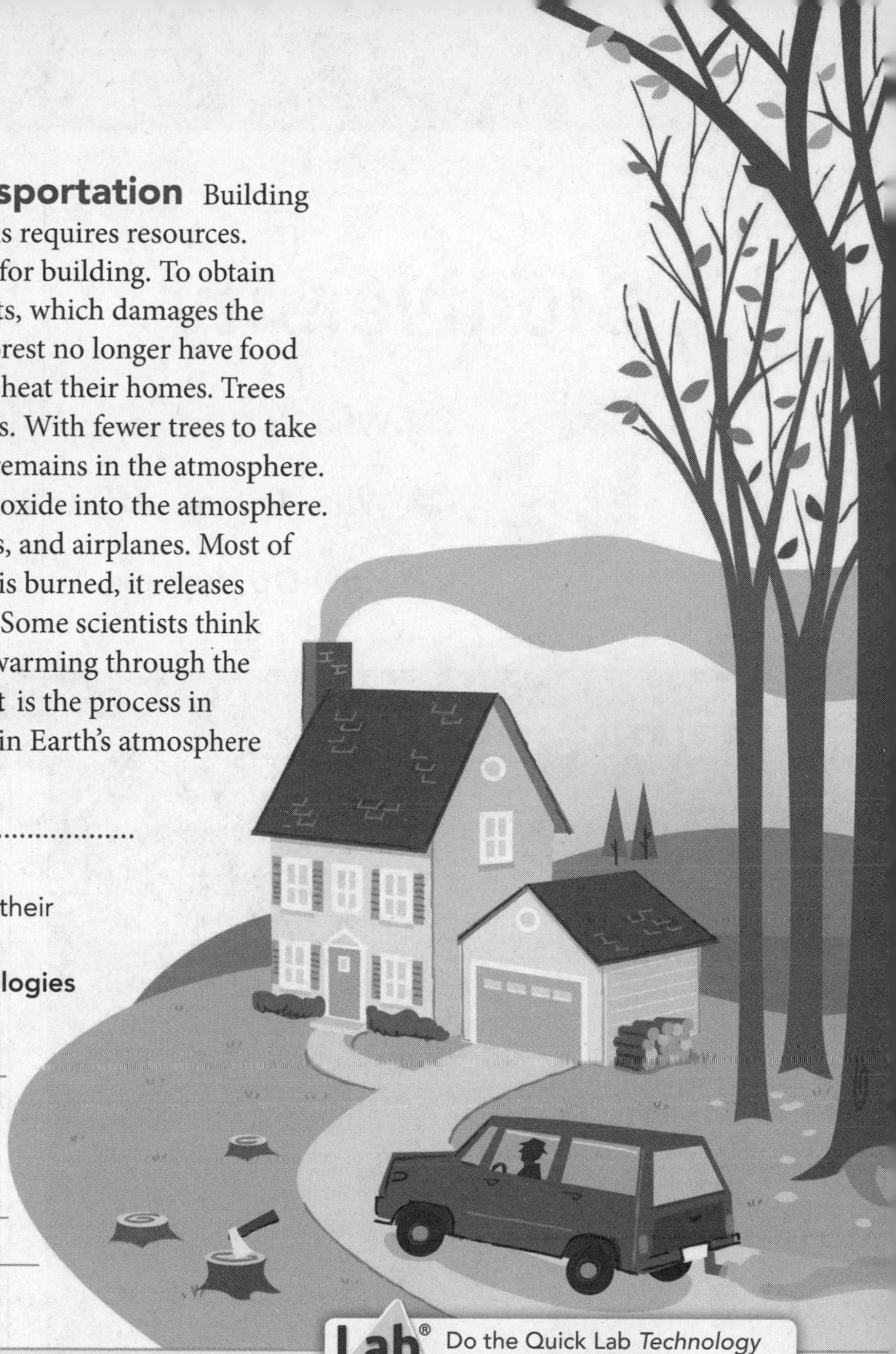

FIGURE 5 ....
Technology at Home
Different technologies that people use at their homes can impact the environment.

✏️ **Identify** Write two ways that technologies in the picture affect the environment.

_____

_____

_____

_____

Lab ® Do the Quick Lab *Technology*
zone *and the Environment.*

🔑 Assess Your Understanding

2. **Summarize** How does the burning of fuels affect the amount of carbon dioxide in the atmosphere?

_____

_____

_____

got it? ....

○ **I get it!** Now I know that technologies such as _____

_____

○ **I need extra help with** _____

_____

Biodiversity

UNLOCK
THE BIG
?

🔑 **What Is Biodiversity's Value?**

🔑 **What Factors Affect Biodiversity?**

🔑 **How Do Humans Affect Biodiversity?**

MY PLANET DIARY

BLOG

Posted by: Max

Location: Hagerstown, Maryland

I went to summer camp to learn about wildlife and how to protect it. One of the activities that I liked the most was making "bat boxes." These are wooden homes for brown bats, which often need places to nest. Making these houses is important, because without brown bats, there would be too many mosquitoes. I hope the bats like their new homes as much as I loved making them.

Communicate Discuss the question with a group of classmates. Then write your answers below.

How do you think helping the bats in an area helps other species nearby?

_____

_____

_____

_____

_____

_____

_____

Lab zone® Do the Inquiry Warm-Up
How Much Variety Is There?

What Is Biodiversity's Value?

No one knows exactly how many species live on Earth. As you can see in **Figure 1,** scientists have identified more than 1.6 million species so far. The number of different species in an area is called the area's **biodiversity.** It is difficult to estimate the total biodiversity on Earth because many areas have not been thoroughly studied.

Vocabulary

- biodiversity • keystone species • extinction
- endangered species • threatened species
- habitat destruction • habitat fragmentation
- poaching • captive breeding

Skills

- ↻ Reading: Compare and Contrast
- △ Inquiry: Calculate

There are many reasons why preserving biodiversity is important. One reason to preserve biodiversity is that wild organisms and ecosystems are a source of beauty and recreation. 🔑 **In addition, biodiversity has both economic value and ecological value within an ecosystem.**

Economic Value Many plants, animals, and other organisms are economically valuable for humans. These organisms provide people with food and supply raw materials for clothing, medicine, and other products. No one knows how many other useful species have not yet been identified. Ecosystems are economically valuable, too. Many companies now run wildlife tours to rain forests, savannas, mountains, and other places. This ecosystem tourism, or ecotourism, is an important source of jobs and money for such nations as Brazil, Costa Rica, and Kenya.

Ecological Value All the species in an ecosystem are connected to one another. Species may depend on each other for food and shelter. A change that affects one species can affect all the others.

Some species play a particularly important role in their ecosystems. A **keystone species** is a species that influences the survival of many other species in an ecosystem. Sea otters, as shown in **Figure 2,** are one example of a keystone species.

FIGURE 1 ·······························
Species Diversity
There are many more species of insects than plant or other animal species on Earth!

✎ △Calculate What percentage of species shown on the pie graph do insects represent? Round your answer to the nearest tenth.

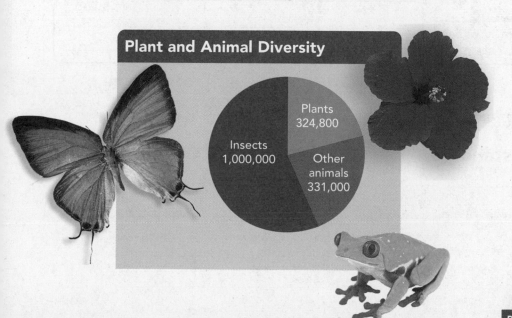

Plant and Animal Diversity

Plants
324,800

Insects
1,000,000

Other animals
331,000

FIGURE 2 ·····················

Keystone Otters

Sea otters are a keystone species in the kelp forest ecosystem.

✏ **Describe** Read the comic. In the empty panel, draw or explain what happened to the kelp forest when the otters returned. Write a caption for your panel.

The sea otter is a keystone species in a kelp forest ecosystem.

In the 1800s, many otters were killed for their fur.

Without otters preying on them, the population of kelp-eating sea urchins exploded, destroying kelp forests.

Under new laws that banned the hunting of sea otters, the sea otter population grew again.

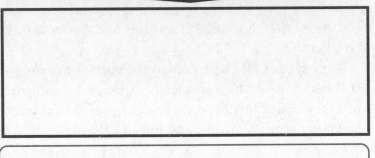

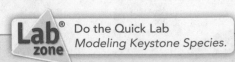

Do the Quick Lab
Modeling Keystone Species.

🗝 Assess Your Understanding

got it? ·····························

○ I get it! Now I know that biodiversity has _____

_____

○ I need extra help with _____

_____

What Factors Affect Biodiversity?

Biodiversity varies from place to place on Earth.  **Factors that affect biodiversity in an ecosystem include climate, area, niche diversity, genetic diversity, and extinction.**

Climate
The tropical rain forests of Latin America, southeast Asia, and central Africa are the most diverse ecosystems in the world. The reason for the great biodiversity in the tropics is not fully understood. Many scientists hypothesize that it has to do with climate. For example, tropical rain forests have fairly constant temperatures and large amounts of rainfall throughout the year. Many plants grow year-round. This continuous growing season means that food is always available for other organisms.

Area
See **Figure 3.** Within an ecosystem, a large area will usually contain more species than a small area. For example, you would usually find more species in a 100-square-meter area than in a 10-square-meter area.

FIGURE 3 ⋯⋯⋯⋯⋯⋯⋯⋯⋯⋯⋯⋯
Park Size
A park manager has received three park plans. The dark green area represents the park.

✏️ **Complete each task.**

1. **Identify** Circle the plan the manager should choose to support the most biodiversity.

2. **Calculate** Suppose that 15 square meters of the park could support seven species of large mammals. About how many species could the park you circled support?

10 m
10 m

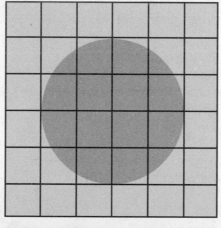

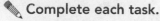

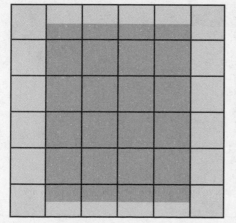

227

Niche Diversity Coral reefs are the second most diverse ecosystems in the world. Found only in shallow, warm waters, coral reefs are often called the rain forests of the sea. A coral reef supports many different niches. Recall that a niche is the role of an organism in its habitat, or how it makes its living. A coral reef enables a greater number of species to live in it than a more uniform habitat, such as a flat sandbar, does.

Genetic Diversity Diversity is very important within a species. The greatest genetic diversity exists among species of unicellular organisms. Organisms in a healthy population have diverse traits such as color and size. Genes are located within cells and carry the hereditary information that determines an organism's traits. Organisms inherit genes from their parents.

The organisms in one species share many genes. But each organism also has some genes that differ from those of other individuals. Both the shared genes and the genes that differ among individuals make up the total gene pool of that species. Species that lack a diverse gene pool are less able to adapt to and survive changes in the environment.

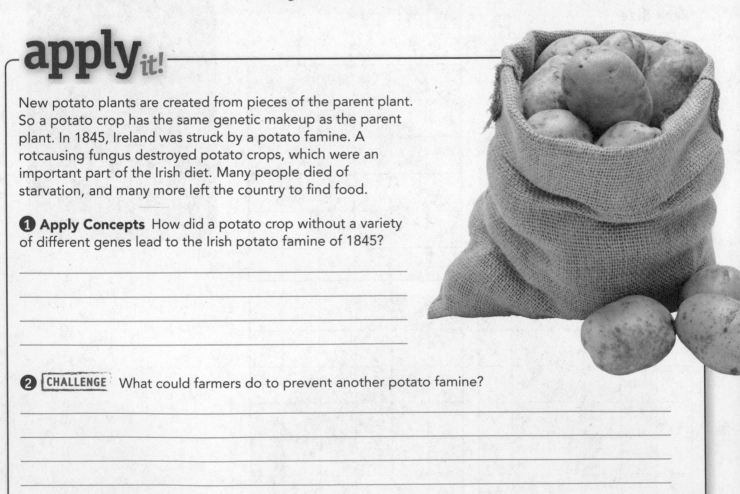

apply it!

New potato plants are created from pieces of the parent plant. So a potato crop has the same genetic makeup as the parent plant. In 1845, Ireland was struck by a potato famine. A rotcausing fungus destroyed potato crops, which were an important part of the Irish diet. Many people died of starvation, and many more left the country to find food.

❶ **Apply Concepts** How did a potato crop without a variety of different genes lead to the Irish potato famine of 1845?

_____

_____

_____

_____

❷ [CHALLENGE] What could farmers do to prevent another potato famine?

_____

_____

_____

_____

Extinction of Species

Extinction of Species Many species that once lived on Earth, from dinosaurs to dodo birds, have disappeared. The disappearance of all members of a species from Earth is called **extinction**. Extinction is a natural process that occurs when organisms do not adapt to changes in their environment. Environmental factors such as climate change, disease, and volcanic eruptions may result in extinction. **Figure 4** shows the effects of environmental factors on two populations. Once a population drops below a certain level, the species may not recover. Also, human habitat destruction, hunting, or other activities affect the survival of populations, which can lead to extinction.

Species in danger of becoming extinct in the near future are called **endangered species**. Species that could become endangered in the near future are called **threatened species**. Endangered and threatened species are found everywhere on earth.

FIGURE 4 ·····················

Environmental Factors

Environmental factors affect populations.

✎ **Read the boxes and answer the questions.**

1. **Identify** In each box, underline the environmental factor affecting the population.

2. **CHALLENGE** Why did the blocking out of sunlight affect dinosaurs?

_____

_____

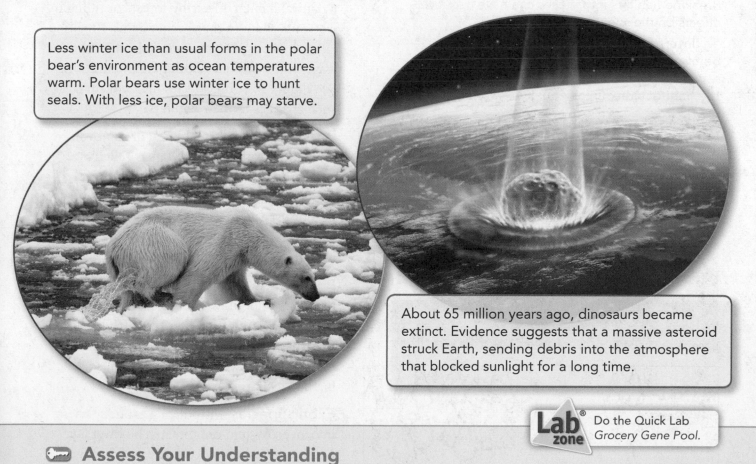

Less winter ice than usual forms in the polar bear's environment as ocean temperatures warm. Polar bears use winter ice to hunt seals. With less ice, polar bears may starve.

About 65 million years ago, dinosaurs became extinct. Evidence suggests that a massive asteroid struck Earth, sending debris into the atmosphere that blocked sunlight for a long time.

Lab zone ® Do the Quick Lab *Grocery Gene Pool.*

🔑 Assess Your Understanding

got it? ··

○ **I get it!** Now I know that the factors that affect biodiversity include _____

_____

○ **I need extra help with** _____

_____

How Do Humans Affect Biodiversity?

Humans interact with their surroundings every day. The many choices people make impact the environment and affect species. 🔑 **Biodiversity can be negatively or positively affected by the actions of humans.**

Damaging Biodiversity

A natural event, such as a hurricane, can damage an ecosystem, wiping out populations or even entire species. Human activities can also threaten biodiversity and cause extinction. These activities include habitat destruction, poaching, pollution, and the introduction of exotic species.

Habitat Destruction The major cause of extinction is **habitat destruction,** the loss of a natural habitat. Clearing forests or filling in wetlands changes those ecosystems. Breaking larger habitats into smaller, isolated pieces, or fragments, is called **habitat fragmentation.** See **Figure 5.** Some species may not survive such changes to their habitats.

Poaching The illegal killing or removal of wildlife from their habitats is called **poaching.** Some endangered species are valuable to poachers. Animals can be sold as pets or used to make jewelry, coats, belts, or shoes. Plants can be sold as houseplants or used to make medicines.

Pollution Some species are endangered because of pollution. Pollution may reach animals through the water they drink, the air they breathe, or the food they eat. Pollutants may kill or weaken organisms or cause birth defects.

Exotic Species Introducing exotic species into an ecosystem can threaten biodiversity. Exotic species can outcompete and damage native species. The gypsy moth was introduced into the United States in 1869 to increase silk production. Gypsy moth larvae have eaten the leaves off of millions of acres of trees in the northeastern United States.

FIGURE 5 ···

Habitat Fragmentation

Breaking habitats into pieces can have negative effects on the species that live there.

✏️ **Interpret Diagrams** In the first diagram below, a road divides a habitat in two. On the second diagram, redraw the road so it divides the habitat's resources equally.

Protecting Biodiversity Some people who preserve biodiversity focus on protecting individual endangered species. Others try to protect entire ecosystems. Three methods of protecting biodiversity are captive breeding, laws and treaties, and habitat preservation.

Captive Breeding Captive breeding is the mating of animals in zoos or on wildlife preserves. Scientists care for the young, and then release them into the wild. Much of the sandhill crane habitat in the United States has been destroyed. To help the population, some cranes have been taken into captivity. The young are raised and trained by volunteers to learn the correct behaviors, such as knowing how and where to migrate. They are then released into the wild.

✎

↻ Compare and Contrast
The photos on top show young sandhill cranes being raised by their parents. The photos on the bottom show humans copying this process to increase the crane population. What is a possible disadvantage of the human approach?

_____

_____

_____

_____

231

Life in a Coral Reef

EXPLORE THE BIG ?

How do natural and human activities change ecosystems?

FIGURE 6 ··

This photo shows the diversity of the organisms in a coral reef ecosystem. The coral and sponges provide living space for algae and shelter for crabs, fishes, and other animals. Some fishes eat the algae.

✏ Predict Answer the questions in the boxes.

> Suppose many more orange fish immigrate to this ecosystem, doubling the species' population. How might the increased numbers of orange fish impact other populations in the ecosystem? Explain.
>
> _____
>
> _____
>
> _____

Laws and Treaties In the United States, the Endangered Species Act prohibits trade of products made from threatened or endangered species. This law also requires the development of plans to save endangered species. The Convention on International Trade in Endangered Species is an international treaty that lists more than 800 threatened and endangered species that cannot be traded for profit or other reasons anywhere in the world.

Habitat Preservation The most effective way to preserve biodiversity is to protect whole ecosystems. Protecting whole ecosystems saves endangered species, the species they depend upon, and those that depend upon them. Many countries have set aside wildlife habitats as parks and refuges. Today, there are about 7,000 nature parks, preserves, and refuges in the world.

Scientists monitor the biodiversity of a variety of ecosystems, including preserved habitats. Generally, ecosystems with high biodiversity are considered healthier than ecosystems with low biodiversity. The completeness of an ecosystem's biodiversity is one measure of its health.

Suppose people start to overfish this area. How might this change the ecosystem? Explain.

_____

_____

_____

_____

_____

_____

Suppose a tsunami, a huge ocean wave, were to hit this ecosystem, destroying much of the reef. Do you think the ecosystem would come back after the tsunami? Explain.

_____

_____

_____

_____

_____

_____

_____

Lab zone® Do the Quick Lab
Humans and Biodiversity.

🔑 Assess Your Understanding

1a. Define What is poaching?

_____

_____

_____

_____

b. ANSWER THE BIG **❓** How do natural and human activities change ecosystems?

_____

_____

_____

_____

_____

got it? ....

○ **I get it!** Now I know that humans affect biodiversity_____

_____

○ **I need extra help with** _____

_____

_____

_____

_____

_____

233

Biogeography

🔑 **What Factors Affect Species Dispersal?**

my planet diary

FUN FACT

Australia's Animals

When you think of Australia, what animal comes to mind? Most likely, you think of a kangaroo or a koala. Did you know that these animals are marsupials, mammals that carry their young in a pouch? You might be surprised to learn that most marsupials exist only in Australia. Now, can you name any monotremes, or mammals that lay eggs? The only monotremes that exist are platypuses and echidnas, both native to Australia. Lots of unique animals are native to Australia because it is completely surrounded by water.

Communicate Answer the following questions with a classmate.

1. What are two types of mammals that are common in Australia?

   _____

2. Would you ever expect a platypus to move from Australia to the United States? Explain.

   _____

   _____

   _____

   _____

Lab zone® Do the Inquiry Warm-Up
How Can You Move a Seed?

Vocabulary
- biogeography
- continental drift
- dispersal
- exotic species

Skills
- Reading: Relate Cause and Effect
- Inquiry: Predict

What Factors Affect Species Dispersal?

Do you think all of the people who live in your hometown were born there? Some of them may have come from different cities, states, or countries. Just as humans do, different plants and animals live in different parts of the world. The study of where organisms live and how they got there is called **biogeography.** Biogeographers also study factors that have led to the worldwide distribution of species that exist today.

The movement of the Earth's continents is one factor that has affected how species are distributed. The continents are parts of huge blocks of solid rock, called plates, that make up Earth's surface. These plates have been moving very slowly for millions of years. As the plates move, the continents move with them in a process called **continental drift. Figure 1** shows how the continents have moved over time. Notice that about 225 million years ago, all of the continents were part of one huge landmass, called Pangaea.

Continental drift has had a great impact on species distribution. For example, Australia drifted away from the other landmasses millions of years ago. Organisms from other parts of the world could not reach the isolated island and unique Australian species developed in this isolation.

🔑 **Continental drift, wind, water, and living things are all means of distributing species. Other factors, such as physical barriers, competition, and climate, can limit species dispersal.**

225 Million Years Ago

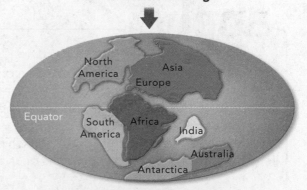

115 Million Years Ago

Earth Today

FIGURE 1 ·······································

Continental Drift

The movement of landmasses is one factor affecting the distribution of organisms.

✏️ **Observe** How has Australia's location changed over time?

_____

_____

_____

Means of Dispersal

Means of Dispersal The movement of organisms from one place to another is called **dispersal**. Dispersal can be caused by gravity, wind, water, or living things, such as the blue jay in **Figure 2**.

Wind and Water Many animals move into new areas on their own. But plants and small organisms need help in moving from place to place. Wind can disperse seeds, fungi spores, tiny spiders, and other small, light organisms. Birds use the wind to fly to new locations. Similarly, water transports objects that float, such as coconuts and leaves. Small animals, such as insects or snails, may get a ride to a new home on top of these floating rafts. Water also transports organisms like fish and marine mammals.

FIGURE 2 ·······························
Means of Dispersal
Seeds can be dispersed by the wind or by organisms like this blue jay.

Other Living Things Organisms can also be dispersed by other living things. If your dog or cat has ever come home covered with sticky plant burs, you have seen an example of dispersal. Humans have sped up the dispersal of organisms, both intentionally and unintentionally, as they travel around the world. An **exotic species** is an organism that is carried into a new location by people. Exotic species have contributed to the decline or elimination of native species.

apply it!

In 1780, a Japanese ship ran aground on one of Alaska's uninhabited Aleutian Islands. Rats from the ship swam to the island. Since then, the rats on this island, now called Rat Island, have preyed upon and destroyed seabird populations and the overall ecosystem. "Rat spills" from ships are one of the leading causes of seabird extinctions on islands worldwide.

❶ Communicate With a partner, identify ways in which sailors can control rats on board their ships and prevent them from going ashore.

_____
_____
_____
_____
_____

❷ Predict Do you think the role of humans in the dispersal of species will increase or decrease in the next 50 years? Defend your answer.

_____
_____
_____
_____
_____

Limits to Dispersal With all these means of dispersal, you might expect to find the same species in many places around the world. Of course, that's not so. Three factors that limit distribution of a species are physical barriers, competition, and climate.

Physical Barriers Water and mountains form barriers that are hard to cross. These features can limit the movement of organisms. For example, once Australia became separated from the other continents, organisms could not easily move to or from Australia.

Competition When an organism enters a new area, it must compete for resources with the species that already live there. To survive, the organism must find a unique niche, or role. Existing species may outcompete the new species. In this case, competition is a barrier to dispersal. Sometimes, in certain situations, new species outcompete and displace the existing species.

Climate The typical weather pattern in an area over a long period of time is the area's climate. Climate differences can limit dispersal. For example, the climate changes greatly as you climb a tall mountain. The warm, dry mountain base, the cooler and wetter areas higher up, and the cold, windy top all support different species. Those species that thrive at the base may not survive at the top.

FIGURE 3 ·······
Limits to Dispersal
Physical barriers, like the Grand Canyon and the Colorado River, can make it difficult for species to move around.

✎ **Relate Cause and Effect**
In the paragraphs at the left, circle the factors that can limit dispersal. Then underline the effects of these limits.

Lab zone Do the Quick Lab
Relating Continental Drift to Dispersal.

🔑 **Assess Your Understanding**

1a. Explain What role do humans play in the dispersal of species?

_____
_____
_____
_____
_____

b. [CHALLENGE] Suppose that a new species of insect were introduced to your area. Explain how competition might limit its dispersal.

_____
_____
_____
_____

got it? ···

○ **I get it!** Now I know that species dispersal is affected by _____
_____

○ **I need extra help with** _____
_____

237

A species that cannot adapt to natural or human activities

can become _____.

LESSON 1 Changing Ecosystems

🔑 Primary succession and secondary succession are two types of succession.

🔑 Organisms that survive a changing ecosystem have adaptations that help them survive in the new conditions.

Vocabulary
• succession   • primary succession
• pioneer species   • secondary succession

LESSON 2 Humans and the Environment

🔑 The resources that humans obtain from ecosystems include abiotic resources and biotic resources.

🔑 Human activities may affect the balance in an ecosystem and thereby change the ecosystem.

Vocabulary
• resources   • greenhouse effect

LESSON 3 Biodiversity

🔑 Biodiversity has both economic value and ecological value within an ecosystem.

🔑 Factors that affect biodiversity in an ecosystem include climate, area, niche diversity, genetic diversity, and extinction.

🔑 Biodiversity can be negatively or positively affected by the actions of humans.

Vocabulary
• biodiversity   • keystone species   • extinction   • endangered species
• threatened species   • habitat destruction   • habitat fragmentation
• poaching   • captive breeding

LESSON 4 Biogeography

🔑 Continental drift, wind, water, and living things are all means of distributing species. Other factors, such as physical barriers, competition, and climate, can limit species dispersal.

Vocabulary
• biogeography   • continental drift
• dispersal   • exotic species

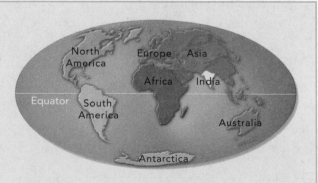

Review and Assessment

Changing Ecosystems

1. The series of predictable changes that occur in a community over time is called

   a. natural selection.   **b.** ecology.

   c. adaptations.   **d.** succession.

2. _____ are the first species to populate an area.

3. **Analyze Cost and Benefits** How do wildfires affect the ability of longleaf pine trees to survive?

   _____

   _____

   _____

   _____

   _____

   _____

   _____

   _____

4. **Compare and Contrast** Describe one scenario that would result in primary succession and one scenario that would result in secondary succession. Explain your reasoning.

   _____

   _____

   _____

   _____

   _____

   _____

   _____

   _____

   _____

   _____

   _____

Humans and Ecosystems

5. An example of a biotic resource that people obtain from ecosystems is

   a. oxygen.   **b.** sunlight.

   c. wood.   **d.** minerals.

6. An example of an abiotic resource that people obtain from ecosystems is

   a. bacteria.   **b.** fish.

   c. water.   **d.** trees.

7. **Relate Cause and Effect** What impact might nutria have on the native animals living in an ecosystem?

   _____

   _____

   _____

   _____

   _____

   _____

   _____

8. **Predict** Students living in a heavily deforested area are working to plant new trees. What effect might this program have on the atmosphere?

   _____

   _____

   _____

   _____

   _____

   _____

   _____

   _____

LESSON 3 Biodiversity

9. The most effective way to preserve biodiversity is through

    a. captive breeding.   **b.** habitat preservation.

    c. habitat destruction.   **d.** habitat fragmentation.

10. Environmental factors such as climate change and disease can cause a species to become

_____ .

11. **[Write About It]** When people transport agricultural products such as plants to other countries, exotic insects living on or in the products may be shipped accidentally. What steps might people take to prevent these exotic insects from harming the native ecosystems? Is it always possible to prevent the introduction of exotic species into ecosystems?

12. A species that has disappeared from Earth is

    a. threatened.   **b.** extinct.

    c. endangered.   **d.** diverse.

13. **Relate Cause and Effect** What is the relationship between genetic diversity and biodiversity?

_____

_____

_____

_____

_____

_____

_____

_____

_____

_____

LESSON 4 Biogeography

14. What is a likely method of dispersal for seeds that are contained within a small berry?

    a. wind   **b.** water

    c. an animal   **d.** continental drift

15. The study of where organisms live and how they got there is called _____ .

16. **Predict** When might seed dispersal not be beneficial?

_____

_____

_____

_____

_____

_____

_____

_____

_____

How do natural and human activities change ecosystems?

17. People regularly set controlled fires in some ecosystems to prevent the growth of invasive plants. What impact do the fires have on these ecosystems? On the atmosphere?

_____

_____

_____

_____

_____

_____

_____

_____

_____

_____

Standardized Test Prep

Read each question and choose the best answer.

1. How does primary succession differ from secondary succession?

   A Primary succession occurs where no soil exists.

   B Primary succession follows a disturbance in an ecosystem.

   C Primary succession is a natural process.

   D Primary succession takes a short amount of time.

2. Which organism introduced to the United States has caused populations of native wetland plants to decrease?

   A gypsy moth

   B nutria

   C cogongrass

   D ryegrass

3. Which of the following are biotic resources that humans obtain from marine ecosystems?

   A fish, shells, aquatic plants

   B shells, sand, invertebrates

   C fish, water, clams

   D clams, mussels, aquatic plants

4. Organisms can be dispersed in all of the following ways <u>except</u> by

   A wind.

   B water.

   C temperature.

   D other organisms.

Short Answer

Write your answers to questions 5 and 6 on another sheet of paper.

5. Why are decomposers useful to people?

   _____

   _____

   _____

   _____

Use the table below to answer Question 6.

Reasons Mammals and Birds Become Endangered or Threatened		
Reason	**Mammals**	**Birds**
Poaching	31%	20%
Habitat loss	32%	60%
Exotic species	17%	12%
Other	20%	8%

6. Make a bar graph comparing the reasons why mammals and birds become endangered or threatened. Show reasons on the horizontal axis and percentages of animal groups on the vertical axis. Then suggest two explanations for the differences between the data for mammals and birds.

ENDANGERED NO MORE

Brown pelicans are now thriving thanks to a ban on DDT in 1972 and strong conservation efforts over the years. ▶

In 1970, the brown pelican was placed on the endangered species list. Today, it is officially off the list and flying high.

What endangered the brown pelican? Scientists learned that a chemical pesticide called DDT caused the number of pelicans to decrease. DDT was widely used from the mid-1940s through the late 1960s to kill insects that destroyed crops. After being sprayed on crops, DDT washed into the soil. Plant roots absorbed DDT from the soil. Then, fish fed on contaminated plants growing in waterways and along their banks. So, when brown pelicans ate fish, they also took in DDT.

DDT affected the way pelicans absorbed calcium, which is a mineral in their eggshells. As a result, pelicans laid eggs with weak shells. When they sat on their eggs, the eggs broke. So birthrates dropped dramatically.

Banning DDT use was the first step in protecting brown pelicans. Recovery efforts involved protecting their habitats and releasing 1,276 pelicans from Florida into Louisiana. Since recovery efforts began, more than 24,000 young birds have been born in Louisiana. That's enough to keep the state's brown pelican population thriving for many years.

Research It Identify an endangered species and write about the environmental factors affecting its survival. Include information on changes that could help the species survive. Present your ideas to a classmate, family member, or friend.

Recovering from the Dust Bowl

Today the Kiowa National Grasslands, located in northeast New Mexico, is one of 20 National Grasslands that are protected by the federal government. These lands are managed to protect the native plant and animal species. In the late 1920s, however, this area was part of the southwestern Great Plains, an area that was devastated by the Dust Bowl.

The plant species native to the grasslands can survive with little rain and can endure droughts. In the late 1800s, however, settlers began farming the grasslands. They plowed up the soil and replaced the grasses with crops that needed more water to thrive. When a severe drought hit, the crops could not survive, and there were no grasses to hold the topsoil in place. Winds blew away the soil, creating massive dust storms. The farmers experienced great hardship, and the ecosystem was in ruins.

The key to restoring this habitat is the native grasses. They are well suited to the soil, range of temperatures, and available rainfall. These grasses hold the soil in place. Rain can soak into the soil and drain into streams without taking the soil with it. As a result, more ground water is available to support the plants, and the streams can provide clean water for wildlife and cattle. The grasses also help to cycle nutrients, such as carbon and nitrogen, through the ecosystems as they grow and decompose. In doing so, the grasses make energy and other resources available to the animals in the grasslands.

The large areas of healthy native habitat allow multiple uses. With proper management, crops and cattle can be raised while native plant and animal populations thrive.

Library of Congress

► Without grass to hold the soil in place, large dust clouds blew across the Great Plains.

Research It The key to the success of the Kiowa National Grasslands is proper management of the available resources. Research the management practices used by the National Grasslands. Write a short report describing how resources and physical factors, such as water and soil, are managed to protect the grasslands. Describe also how water, carbon, and nitrogen cycles contribute to a healthy ecosystem.

George H.H. Huey

WHY WON'T THIS ACROBAT LAND ON HER HEAD?

How do objects react to forces?

This teen is part of a traveling youth circus that performs in New England. As a circus trouper, she may do stunts such as tumbling and swinging on a trapeze. These stunts often appear to be gravity-defying and dangerous, but the troupers know how to perform in a way that lets them land safely.

Develop Hypotheses How does this athlete land on her feet?

_____

_____

_____

_____

_____

Watch the **Untamed Science** video to learn more about forces.

CHAPTER

Forces 6

CHAPTER 6 Getting Started

Check Your Understanding

1. **Background** Read the paragraph below and then answer the question.

The dashboard of a car displays your **speed** so that you know how fast you're going. Since this reading doesn't change when you turn, you don't know the car's **velocity.** If the car did show you your change in velocity, you could calculate the car's **acceleration.**

> **Speed** is the distance an object travels per unit of time.
>
> **Velocity** is speed in a given direction.
>
> **Acceleration** is the rate at which velocity changes with time.

- What are three ways to accelerate (change velocity)?

_____

_____

Vocabulary Skill

Latin Word Origins Many science words in English come from Latin. For example, the word *solar*, which means "of the sun," comes from the Latin *sol*, which means "sun."

Latin Word	Meaning of Latin Word	Example
fortis	strong	force, *n.* a push or pull exerted on an object
iners	inactivity	inertia, *n.* the tendency of an object to resist any change in its motion
centrum	center	centripetal force, *n.* a force that causes an object to move in a circle

2. **Quick Check** Choose the word that best completes the sentence.

- A _____ always points toward the center of a circle.

force

friction

gravity

inertia

Chapter Preview

Sail Away

When you think of boating, you might think of enjoying a breezy day sitting in a sail boat that is powered by wind. However, wind also can power wheeled vehicles on land. In both cases, wind applies a force to the sail, which sets the vehicle in motion. Factors that affect how quickly and how far the vehicle will move include the force of the wind on the sail and the size and shape of the vehicle and the sail. Another factor is the condition of the surface over which the vehicle is moving. As the force of the wind pushing on the sail moves the vehicle forward, other forces work against this motion to slow or stop the vehicle.

In this activity, you will build an air-powered, wheeled vehicle—a sail car—designed to achieve a fast speed over a set distance.

Identify the Problem

1. You are an engineer looking for alternative ways to power land vehicles. Your goal is to design a car that does not run on fossil fuels. You decide to build a prototype of an experimental sail car to explore how wind will make cars move. What problem(s) will your design help solve?

_____

_____

Do Research

Review the information about forces and motion provided by your teacher.

2. On a separate sheet of paper, explain the following concepts: force, motion, gravity, friction, speed, velocity, average acceleration. Include formulas where appropriate.

3. What factors that are not parts of the sail car itself will affect the motion of the car? Describe how.

_____

_____

_____

Go to the materials station(s). Examine the materials. Think about how each one may or may not be useful for building your sail car.

☑ **4.** What are your design constraints? _____

_____

_____

☑ **5.** Identify the variables that will affect the speed of your sail car. Include both factors that you control in the car's design and outside factors. _____

_____

_____

Develop Possible Solutions

☑ **6.** Describe how you could use the materials to build a wind-powered wheeled vehicle. Identify at least two types of car bodies and wind-catching sails.

_____

_____

_____

_____

Choose One Solution

Answer the following on a separate sheet of paper.

☑ **7.** List the material(s) you will use to build your sail car.

☑ **8.** Draw your design and label all the parts. Describe how you will build your sail car prototype.

☑ **9.** Describe how your sail car prototype will function.

Inquiry STEM Activity

Design and Construct a Prototype

Have your teacher review and approve your design. Then, gather the materials you need to build your sail car. Build a prototype, the first working version of your design. Wear goggles as you build, and later test, your prototype. If you can, document your process by taking photos or recording video as you go.

☑ **10.** Record the design details of your finished prototype. Draw your sail car prototype to scale on graph paper. Label the parts and identify the scale.

Test the Prototype

Use wind from a fan to power your sail car prototype along a four-meter distance. Use a stopwatch to time the test for three different trials.

☑ **11.** Record your results in the table below. You will need to calculate the average speed and the final speed. To convert average speed from m/s to km/h, remember that 1 km = 1,000 m and 1 hr = 3,600 s. In the last row, you will calculate the average values for the average speed and final speed for all three trials.

Trial	Time in s	Average Speed in m/s	Average Speed in km/h	Final Speed in m/s (Average Speed × 2)
1				
2				
3				
Average values for all three trials				

☑ **12.** Calculate the sail car prototype's average rate of acceleration. Use the equation shown and the final speed you calculated in the last row of the above table. Remember that the initial speed of your car was 0 m/s.

$$a = \frac{v_f - v_i}{t}$$

250

Communicate Results

13. Collect the materials that document the design, construction, and testing of your sail car prototype. Assemble a portfolio that includes your diagrams, your photographs or video of the process, and your records of your test results. Graph the motion of your sail car prototype. Set up a single time/distance grid, and graph each of the three trials in a different color.

14. Prepare a presentation (poster, video, or computer slide show) showing how you built your sail car prototype and how it performed during the test. Discuss the pros and cons of your design as if it were to be manufactured for use by the public as an alternative to cars that use fossil fuels. Share your presentation with the class.

Evaluate and Redesign

15. Compare your results with your classmates. What were the characteristics of the fastest prototypes in the class? _____

_____

_____

_____

16. Evaluate your prototype. Check one answer for each question.

Does the prototype...	Very Much	Somewhat	Not At All
have a vehicle body with a top surface area of at least 300 cm²?			
move solely on wind power?			
travel at least four meters?			

17. What changes could you make to your sail car prototype to make it move faster with the same wind and surface?

_____

_____

Scenario Investigation

Please Drop In

Purpose To investigate falling objects and design a safe parachute ride for an amusement park

Materials
- paper clip
- large metal washers
- string
- stopwatch
- plastic bag
- scissors

Scenario

A famous amusement park company has hired your engineering company to design a parachute ride for their newest park. They want the ride to be fun, but they also want it to be safe and reliable. The parachute should drop quickly, but not so quickly that it injures the riders. Also, the parachute must land in a small area directly below the release point. If the parachute drifts too far from the target, it could crash into other rides or people.

Before you can send the amusement park your design, you have to do some experimenting. How will you find the perfect balance of accuracy and speed?

Procedure

☑ **1. Fall for Accuracy** Slide some washers onto a paper clip. Your teacher will demonstrate how you can safely drop this mass from a high place. Measure the drop height in meters from the bottom of the washers. The height should be at least two meters.

_____

☑ **2. Timing the Fall** Use a stopwatch to measure the free-fall time for the mass. Repeat for a total of five trials. Calculate and record the average free-fall time.

_____

☑ **3. Gravity and Acceleration** Find your drop height on the table to the right. Your drop time should be close to the time on the table. If it is not, check your height measurement and try again. Notice that the free-fall time for a drop height of four meters is less than twice the free-fall time for a drop height of two meters. This means that objects do not fall at a constant velocity. The velocity of an object increases as the object falls. This acceleration is caused by the force of gravity.

Drop Height (m)	Free-Fall Time (s)
2.00	0.639
2.10	0.655
2.20	0.670
2.30	0.685
2.40	0.700
2.50	0.714
2.60	0.728
2.70	0.742
2.80	0.756
2.90	0.769
3.00	0.782
3.10	0.795
3.20	0.808
3.30	0.821
3.40	0.833
3.50	0.845
3.60	0.857
3.70	0.869
3.80	0.881
3.90	0.892
4.00	0.904

Procedure *(continued)*

☑ **4. Adding a Parachute** Make a parachute out of a plastic bag. Fasten it to the washers using string. Start the parachute at the same drop height as you did for the free-fall trials (measured from the bottom of the washers). Measure and record the parachute drop times. Repeat for five trials. Calculate and record the average drop time.

_____

☑ **5. Perfecting Your Parachute** You may redesign your parachute in any way. Your goal is to have the longest drop time possible and still have an accurate landing.

☑ **6. My Parachute Worked Best!** When all groups have demonstrated their parachute drops, notice which designs worked best. Infer why some designs worked better than others.

_____

_____

Conclusion

Let's see what you learned about falling objects.

☑ **1.** Compare the free-fall time of the free-falling washers to the free-fall time of washers hanging from the parachute. Use these times to fi gure out which washers had the greater acceleration. Explain your reasoning.

_____

_____

☑ **2.** Recall that Newton's second law states that the net force on an object is equal to the mass of the object multiplied by the acceleration of the object. Which set of washers was acted upon by the greater net force?

_____

_____

☑ **3.** The gravitational force that Earth exerts on an object, also called weight, depends on the mass of the object. Did the weight of the washers ever change during your experiment? Explain what caused the change in net force when you added the parachute. (Hint: Remember the diff erent types of friction.)

_____

_____

Now write a report that explains your results and makes a recommendation to the amusement park company. Describe the parachute you designed and the results of your tests. Include your data in a table. Based on your own results and what you observed for other teams' designs, recommend the best parachute design for the ride. Be sure to discuss both the speed and accuracy of the ride design.

The Nature of Force

UNLOCK THE BIG **?** Q

🗝 **What Is Acceleration?**

🗝 **How Are Forces Described?**

🗝 **How Do Forces Affect Motion?**

my planet Diary

MISCONCEPTIONS

Forced to Change

Misconception: Any object that is set in motion will slow down on its own.

Fact: A force is needed to change an object's state of motion.

A soccer ball sits at rest. You come along and kick it, sending it flying across the field. It eventually slows to a stop. You applied a force to start it moving, and then it stopped all on its own, right?

No! Forces cause *all* changes in motion. Just as you applied a force to the ball to speed it up from rest, the ground applied a force to slow it down to a stop. If the ground didn't apply a force to the ball, it would keep rolling forever without slowing down or stopping.

Answer the questions below.

1. Give an example of a force you apply to slow something down.

_____

_____

2. Where might it be possible to kick a soccer ball and have it never slow down?

_____

_____

_____

 Do the Inquiry Warm-Up
Is the Force With You?

Vocabulary
• acceleration • force
• newton • net force

Skills
↻ Reading: Relate Text and Visuals
△ Inquiry: Make Models

What Is Acceleration?

Suppose you are a passenger in a car stopped at a red light. When the light changes to green, the driver steps on the accelerator. As a result, the car speeds up, or accelerates. In everyday language, acceleration means "the process of speeding up."

Acceleration has a more precise definition in science. Scientists define **acceleration** as the rate at which velocity changes. Velocity describes both the speed and direction of an object. A change in velocity can involve a change in either speed or direction—or both. 🔑 **In science, acceleration refers to increasing speed, decreasing speed, or changing direction.**

Changing Speed Whenever an object's speed changes, the object accelerates. A car that begins to move from a stopped position or speeds up to pass another car is accelerating. People can accelerate too. For example, you accelerate when you coast down a hill on your bike.

Just as objects can speed up, they can also slow down. This change in speed is sometimes called deceleration, or negative acceleration. A car decelerates as it comes to a stop at a red light. A water skier decelerates as the boat slows down.

Changing Direction Even an object that is traveling at a constant speed can be accelerating. Recall that acceleration can be a change in direction as well as a change in speed. Therefore, a car accelerates as it follows a gentle curve in the road or changes lanes. Runners accelerate as they round the curve in a track. A softball accelerates when it changes direction as it is hit.

Many objects continuously change direction without changing speed. The simplest example of this type of motion is circular motion, or motion along a circular path. For example, the seats on a Ferris wheel accelerate because they move in a circle.

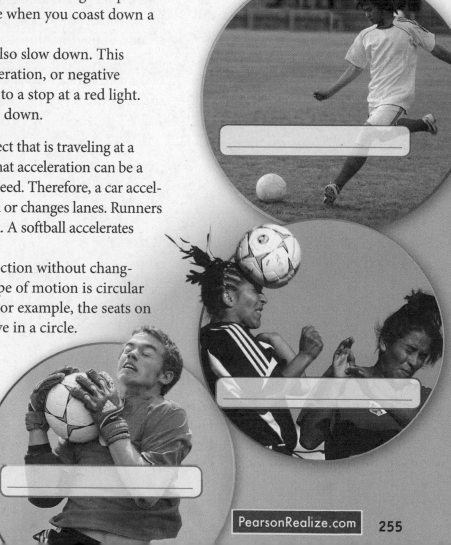

FIGURE 1 ···

Acceleration
During the game of soccer, a soccer ball can show three types of acceleration—increasing speed, decreasing speed, and changing direction.

✎ **Interpret Photos** Label the type of acceleration that is occurring in each of the photos.

0.0s   1.0s   2.0s   3.0s

0 m/s   8 m/s   16 m/s   24 m/s

FIGURE 2

Acceleration

The airplane is accelerating at a rate of 8 m/s².

✎ **Predict** Determine the speed of the airplane at 4.0 s and 5.0 s. Write your answers in the boxes next to each airplane.

Calculating Acceleration Acceleration describes the rate at which velocity changes. If an object is not changing direction, you can describe its acceleration as the rate at which its speed changes. To determine the acceleration of an object moving in a straight line, you calculate the change in speed per unit of time. This is summarized by the following equation.

$$\text{Acceleration} = \frac{\text{Final Speed} - \text{Initial Speed}}{\text{Time}}$$

If speed is measured in meters per second (m/s) and time is measured in seconds, the SI unit of acceleration is meters per second per second, or m/s². Suppose speed is measured in kilometers per hour and time is measured in hours. Then the unit for acceleration is kilometers per hour per hour, or km/h².

To understand acceleration, imagine a small airplane moving down a runway. **Figure 2** shows the airplane's speed after each second of the first three seconds of its acceleration. To calculate the acceleration of the airplane, you must first subtract the initial speed of 0 m/s from its final speed of 24 m/s. Then divide the change in speed by the time, 3 seconds.

$$\text{Acceleration} = \frac{24 \text{ m/s} - 0 \text{ m/s}}{3 \text{ s}}$$

$$\text{Acceleration} = 8 \text{ m/s}^2$$

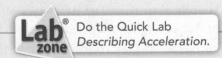

Lab zone ® Do the Quick Lab *Describing Acceleration.*

🔑 Assess Your Understanding

1a. Define The rate at which velocity changes is

called _____

b. Infer A softball has a (positive/negative) acceleration when it is thrown. A softball has a (positive/negative) acceleration when it is caught.

c. Explain A girl skates around the perimeter of a circular ice rink at a constant speed of 2 m/s. Is the girl accelerating? Explain.

_____

_____

got it?

○ **I get it!** Now I know that in science

acceleration refers to _____

_____

_____

_____

○ **I need extra help with** _____

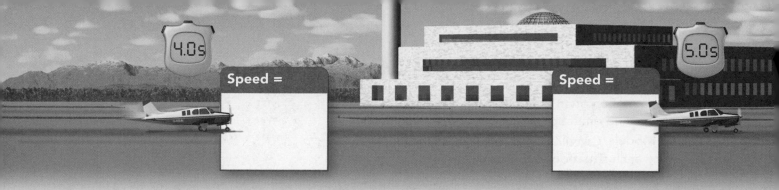

Speed =

Speed =

How Are Forces Described?

In science, the word *force* has a simple and specific meaning. A **force** is a push or a pull. When one object pushes or pulls another object, the first object exerts a force on the second object. You exert a force on a computer key when you push it. You exert a force on a chair when you pull it away from a table.

🔑 **Like velocity and acceleration, a force is described by its strength and by the direction in which it acts.** Pushing to the left is a different force from pushing to the right. The direction and strength of a force can be represented by an arrow. The arrow points in the direction of the force, as shown in **Figure 3.** The length of the arrow tells you the strength of the force—the longer the arrow, the greater the force. The strength of a force is measured in the SI unit called the **newton** (N), after scientist Sir Isaac Newton.

FIGURE 3 ··

Describing Forces

Forces act on you whenever your motion changes. In the photos at the right, two men are celebrating an Olympic victory. Forces cause them to pull each other in for a hug, lean over, and fall into the pool.

✏️ **Identify** In the box within each photo, draw an arrow that represents the force acting on the person on the right. The first one is done as an example.

Do the Quick Lab
What Is Force?

🔑 **Assess Your Understanding**

got it? ···

○ **I get it!** Now I know that forces are described by _____

_____

○ **I need extra help with** _____

_____

257

FIGURE 4 ·····

Net Force

The change in motion of an object is determined by
the net force acting on the object.

✎ **Make Models** Calculate and draw an arrow for the
net force for each situation in the boxes below.

a Net force _____

b Net force _____

How Do Forces Affect Motion?

Often more than one force acts on an object at the same time. The combination of all the forces on an object is called the **net force.** The net force determines if and how an object will accelerate.

You can find the net force on an object by adding together the strengths of all the individual forces acting on the object. Look at **Figure 4a.** The big dog pushes on the box with a force of 16 N to the right. The small dog pushes on the box with a force of 10 N to the right. The net force on the box is the sum of these forces. The box will accelerate to the right. In this situation, there is a nonzero net force. 🔑 **A nonzero net force causes a change in the object's motion.**

What if the forces on an object aren't acting in the same direction? In **Figure 4b,** the big dog pushes with a force of 20 N. The small dog still pushes with a force of 10 N, but now they're pushing against each other. When forces on an object act in opposite directions, the strength of the net force is found by subtracting the strength of the smaller force from the strength of the larger force. You can still think of this as *adding* the forces together if you think of all forces that act to the right as positive forces and all forces that act to the left as negative forces. The box will accelerate to the right. When forces act in opposite directions, the net force is in the same direction as the larger force.

✎ **Relate Text and Visuals** Use the information in the text to determine the net force of these two force arrows.

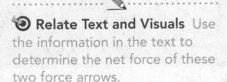

Circle the net force below.

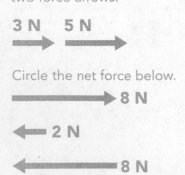

258 Forces

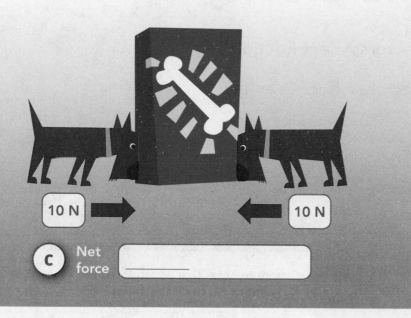

10 N ➡️   ⬅️ 10 N

c Net force [_____]

apply it!

1 You pull on your dog's leash to the right with a 12 N force. Your dog pulls to the left with a 6 N force. Sketch this situation, including labeled force arrows, below.

Use what you know about net force to describe the motion of the box in **Figure 4c.** Assume that the box starts at rest.

_____
_____
_____
_____

2 What is the net force on the leash? Calculate it. Draw and label it in the space above.

_____

 Do the Quick Lab
Modeling Unbalanced Forces.

🔑 Assess Your Understanding

2a. Calculate You push on a desk with a force of 120 N to the right. Your friend pushes on the same desk with a force of 90 N to the left. What is the net force on the desk?

_____
_____

b. Predict Your friend increases her force on the desk by 30 N. She doesn't change the direction of her push. What happens to the net force on the desk? Will the desk accelerate?

_____
_____
_____

got it? ....

○ **I get it!** Now I know that changes in motion are caused by _____
_____

○ **I need extra help with** _____
_____

Friction and Gravity

UNLOCK THE BIG
?

🔑 **What Factors Affect Friction?**

🔑 **What Factors Affect Gravity?**

my planet diary

CAREERS

Space Athletes

Have you ever seen pictures of astronauts playing golf on the moon or playing catch in a space station? Golf balls and baseballs can float or fly farther in space, where gravitational forces are weaker than they are on Earth. Imagine what professional sports would be like in reduced gravity!

You may not have to imagine much longer. At least one company specializes in airplane flights that simulate a reduced gravity environment. Similar to NASA training flights that astronauts use when preparing to go into space, these flights allow passengers to fly around the cabin. In environments with reduced gravity, athletes can perform jumps and stunts that would be impossible on Earth. As technology improves, permanent stadiums could be built in space for a whole new generation of athletes.

Communicate Discuss these questions with a partner and then answer them below.

1. Sports can be more fun in reduced gravity. What jobs could be harder or less fun to do in space? Why?

_____

_____

_____

2. What kinds of sports do you think could be more fun in space? Why?

_____

_____

_____

Lab zone Do the Inquiry Warm-Up *Observing Friction.*

Vocabulary

- friction • sliding friction • static friction
- fluid friction • rolling friction • gravity
- mass • weight

What Factors Affect Friction?

If you slide a book across a table, the surface of the book rubs against the surface of the table. The force that two surfaces exert on each other when they rub against each other is called **friction.**

🔑 **Two factors that affect the force of friction are the types of surfaces involved and how hard the surfaces are pushed together.** The football player in **Figure 1** is pushing on a blocking sled. If his coach wanted to make it harder to move the sled, the coach could change the surface of the sled. Covering the bottom of the sled with rubber would increase friction and make the sled harder to move. In general, smooth surfaces produce less friction than rough surfaces.

What would happen if the football player switched to a much heavier sled? He would find the heavier sled harder to push because it pushes down harder against the ground. Similarly, if you rubbed your hands together forcefully, there would be more friction than if you rubbed your hands together lightly. Friction increases when surfaces push harder against each other.

Friction acts in a direction opposite to the direction of the object's motion. Without friction, a moving object will not stop until it strikes another object.

Vocabulary Latin Word Origins
Friction comes from the Latin word *fricare*. Based on the definition of *friction*, what do you think *fricare* means?
- ○ to burn
- ○ to rub
- ○ to melt

FIGURE 1 ·········
Friction and Different Surfaces
The strength of friction depends on the types of surfaces involved. ✏ **Sequence** Rank the surfaces above by how hard it would be to push a sled over them, from easiest (1) to hardest (3). (Each surface is flat.) What does this ranking tell you about the amount of friction over these surfaces?

_____

_____

Sliding Friction

Sliding friction occurs when two solid surfaces slide over each other. Sliding friction is what makes moving objects slow down and stop. Without sliding friction, a penguin that slid down a hill wouldn't stop until he hit a wall!

✎ **Classify** Label five examples of sliding friction and compare with a classmate.

Friction acts opposite the direction of motion.

Direction of motion ⟶

⟵ Friction

Static Friction

Static friction acts between objects that aren't moving. Think about trying to push a couch across the room. If you don't push hard enough, it won't move. The force that's keeping you from moving it is static friction. Once you push hard enough to overcome static friction, the couch starts moving and there is no more static friction. However, there is sliding friction.

✎ **Classify** Label five examples of static friction and compare with a classmate.

Draw an arrow representing the frictional force at work.

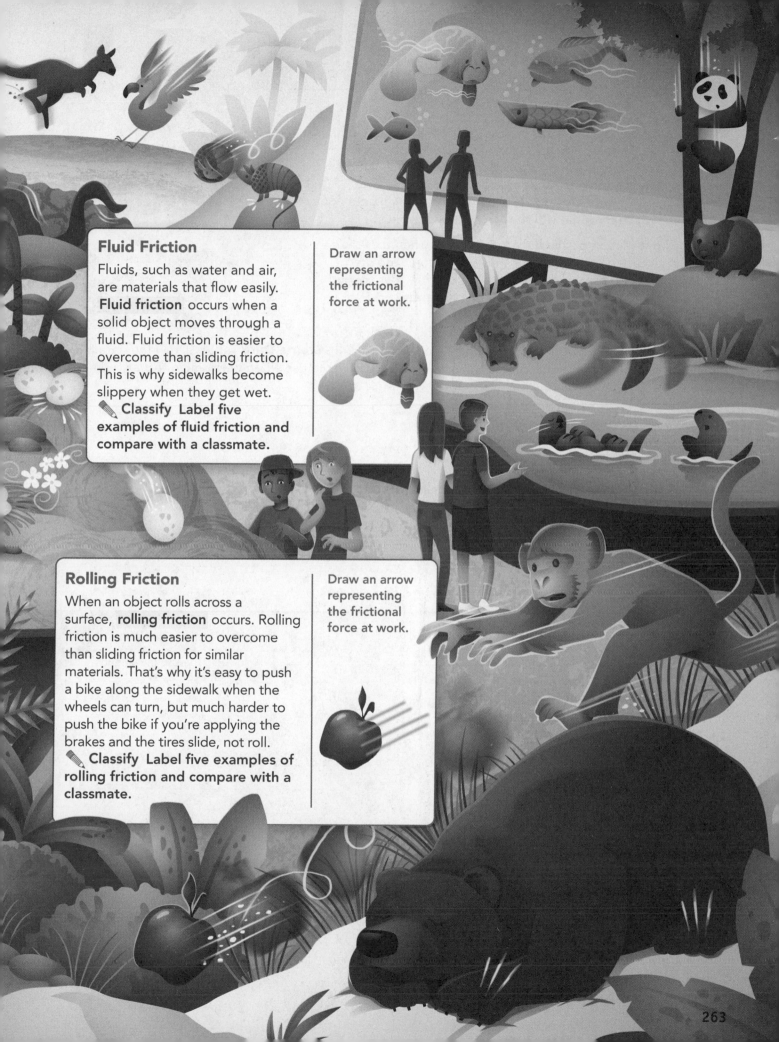

Fluid Friction

Fluids, such as water and air, are materials that flow easily. **Fluid friction** occurs when a solid object moves through a fluid. Fluid friction is easier to overcome than sliding friction. This is why sidewalks become slippery when they get wet.

✏️ **Classify** Label five examples of fluid friction and compare with a classmate.

Draw an arrow representing the frictional force at work.

Rolling Friction

When an object rolls across a surface, **rolling friction** occurs. Rolling friction is much easier to overcome than sliding friction for similar materials. That's why it's easy to push a bike along the sidewalk when the wheels can turn, but much harder to push the bike if you're applying the brakes and the tires slide, not roll.

✏️ **Classify** Label five examples of rolling friction and compare with a classmate.

Draw an arrow representing the frictional force at work.

263

apply it!

Your family is moving and isn't sure how to best overcome friction while moving furniture. You have a spring scale, wood blocks to represent your furniture, and sandpaper, aluminum foil, marbles, and olive oil as possible surfaces to slide your furniture over.

⚠️ **Design Experiments** **Design an experiment that will help you determine which material will reduce friction the most.**

You know that friction occurs between surfaces when they slide against each other. If you measure the applied force required to push something across a surface, you know that your applied force would (increase/decrease) as friction increased.

STEP 1 **Measure** How would you determine your applied force in this experiment?

_____

_____

_____

STEP 2 **Control Variables** What variables would you have to control to keep your results accurate?

_____

_____

_____

STEP 3 **Create Data Tables** Draw the data table you would use when performing this experiment.

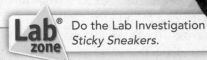
Do the Lab Investigation
Sticky Sneakers.

🔑 Assess Your Understanding

1a. List Name four types of friction and give an example of each.

_____

_____

_____

_____

_____

b. Classify What types of friction occur between your bike tires and the ground when you ride over cement, ride through a puddle, and apply your brakes?

_____

got it?

○ **I get it!** Now I know that friction is affected by

_____

_____

_____

○ **I need extra help with** _____

_____

_____

_____

What Factors Affect Gravity?

A skydiver would be surprised if she jumped out of a plane and did not fall. We are so used to objects falling that we may not have thought about why they fall. One person who thought about it was Sir Isaac Newton. He concluded that a force acts to pull objects straight down toward the center of Earth. **Gravity** is a force that pulls objects toward each other.

Universal Gravitation Newton realized that gravity acts everywhere in the universe, not just on Earth. It is the force that makes the skydivers in **Figure 2** fall to the ground. It is the force that keeps the moon orbiting around Earth. It is the force that keeps all the planets in our solar system orbiting around the sun.

What Newton realized is now called the law of universal gravitation. The law of universal gravitation states that the force of gravity acts between all objects in the universe that have mass. This means that any two objects in the universe that have mass attract each other. You are attracted not only to Earth but also to the moon, the other planets in the solar system, and all the objects around you. Earth and the objects around you are attracted to you as well. However, you do not notice the attraction among small objects because these forces are extremely small compared to the force of Earth's attraction.

FIGURE 2

Observing Gravity
Newton published his work on gravity in 1687.

✎ **Observe** What observations might you make today that would lead you to the same conclusions about gravity? Write down your ideas below.

_____

_____

_____

_____

_____

_____

Factors Affecting Gravity A gravitational force exists between any two objects in the universe. However, you don't see your pencil fly toward the wall the way you see it fall toward Earth. That's because the gravitational force between some objects is stronger than the force between others. You observe only the effects of the strongest gravitational forces. 🔑 **Two factors affect the gravitational attraction between objects: mass and distance.** **Mass** is a measure of the amount of matter in an object. The SI unit of mass is the kilogram.

The more mass an object has, the greater the gravitational force between it and other objects. Earth's gravitational force on nearby objects is strong because the mass of Earth is so large. The more massive planets in **Figure 3** interact with a greater gravitational force than the less massive planets. Gravitational force also depends on the distance between the objects' centers. As distance increases, gravitational force decreases. That's why Earth can exert a visible gravitational force on a pencil in your room and not on a pencil on the moon.

🖉 **Identify Supporting Evidence** Underline the factors that determine how strong the gravitational force is between two objects.

FIGURE 3 ···

Gravitational Attraction

Gravitational attraction depends on two factors: mass and distance. Suppose there was a solar system that looked like this.
🖉 **Interpret Diagrams** Use the diagram below to compare the gravitational force between different planets and their sun. Assume all planets are made of the same material, so bigger planets have more mass.

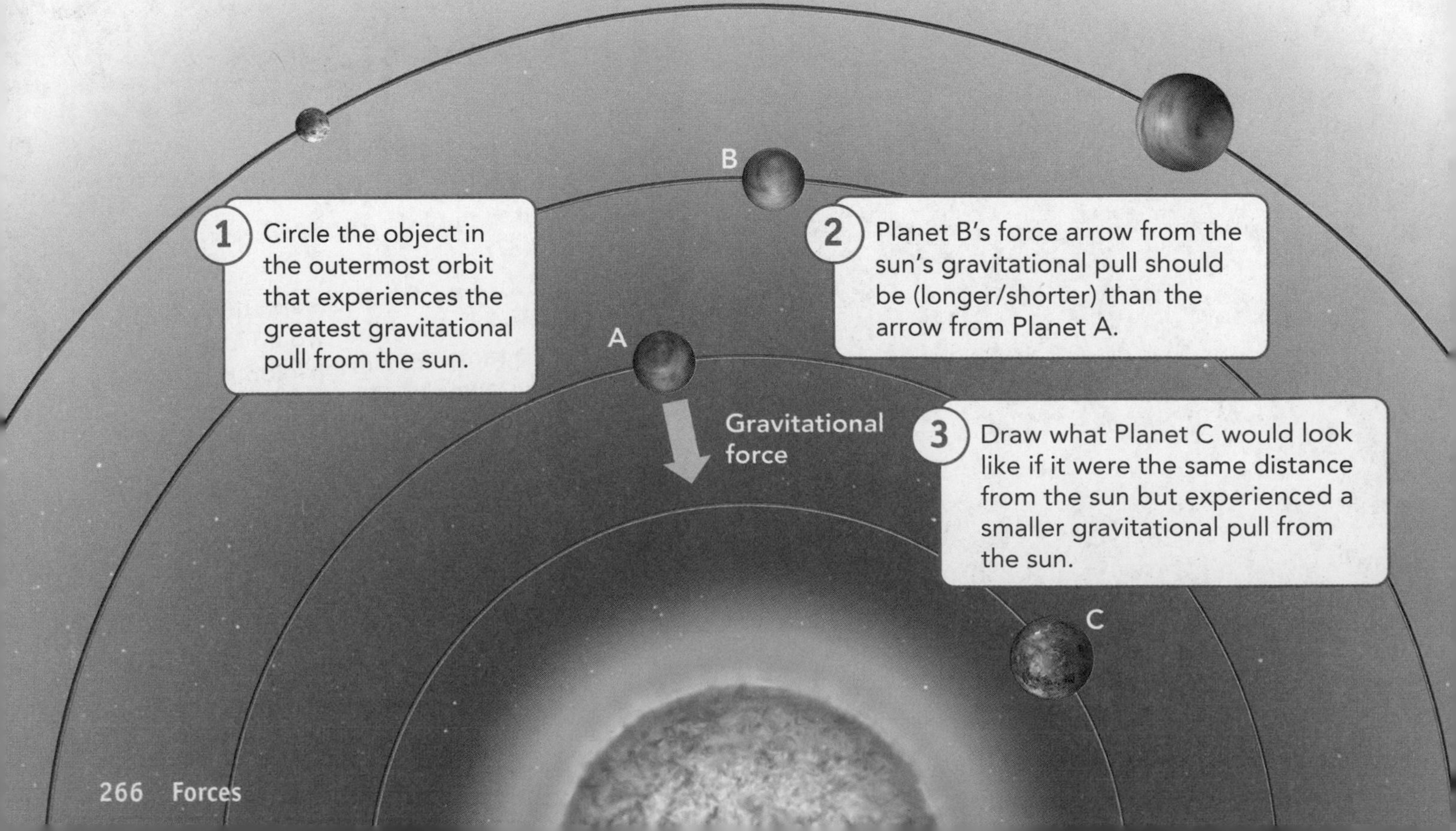

1. Circle the object in the outermost orbit that experiences the greatest gravitational pull from the sun.

2. Planet B's force arrow from the sun's gravitational pull should be (longer/shorter) than the arrow from Planet A.

3. Draw what Planet C would look like if it were the same distance from the sun but experienced a smaller gravitational pull from the sun.

Gravitational force

Earth
60 N

Moon
_____ N

Mars
_____ N

Weight and Mass Mass is sometimes confused with weight. Mass is a measure of the amount of matter in an object. **Weight** is a measure of the force of gravity on an object. When you stand on a bathroom scale, it displays the gravitational force Earth is exerting on you.

At any given time, your mass is the same on Earth as it would be on any other planet. But weight varies with the strength of the gravitational force. The dog in **Figure 4** has a different weight at different places in the solar system. On the moon, he would weigh about one sixth of what he does on Earth. On Mars, he would weigh just over a third of what he does on Earth.

FIGURE 4 ···
Weight and Mass
The Mars Phoenix Lander weighs about 3,400 N on Earth. It weighs about 1,300 N on Mars. ✎ Predict **The first scale shows the dog's weight on Earth. Predict its weight on the moon and on Mars. Enter those weights in the boxes on the other two scales.**

Lab ® Do the Quick Lab
zone *Calculating.*

🔑 **Assess Your Understanding**

2a. Describe What happens to the gravitational force between two objects when their masses are increased? What happens when the distance between the objects increases?

_____

_____

_____

b. Relate Cause and Effect If the mass of Earth increased, what would happen to your weight? What about your mass?

_____

_____

_____

got it? ··

○ **I get it!** Now I know that the factors that affect the gravitational force between objects are _____

_____

○ I need extra help with _____

_____

267

Newton's Laws of Motion

UNLOCK THE BIG Q?

🔑 **What Is Newton's First Law of Motion?**

🔑 **What Is Newton's Second Law of Motion?**

🔑 **What Is Newton's Third Law of Motion?**

MY PLANET DIARY

VOICES FROM HISTORY

Horse Force

"If a horse draws a stone tied to a rope, the horse (if I may so say) will be equally drawn back towards the stone...."

—Sir Isaac Newton

Scientists have used everyday examples to explain their ideas for hundreds of years. The quotation is from Newton's *Mathematical Principles of Natural Philosophy*, which was first published in the 1680s. Newton used this book to set down his laws of motion. These three simple laws describe much of the motion around you, and they continue to be studied today.

Answer the question below.
What current scientific discoveries might be taught in schools hundreds of years from now?

_____

_____

_____

_____

Lab zone® Do the Inquiry Warm-Up What Changes Motion?

What Is Newton's First Law of Motion?

You would be surprised if a rock started rolling on its own or a raindrop paused in midair. If an object is not moving, it will not start moving until a force acts on it. If an object is moving, it will continue at a constant velocity until a force acts to change its speed or its direction. 🔑 **Newton's first law of motion states that an object at rest will remain at rest unless acted upon by a nonzero net force. An object moving at a constant velocity will continue moving at a constant velocity unless acted upon by a nonzero net force.**

Inertia All objects, moving or not, resist changes in motion. Resistance to change in motion is called inertia (in UR shuh). Newton's first law of motion is also called the law of inertia. Inertia explains many common events, including why you move forward in your seat when the car you are in stops suddenly. You keep moving forward because of inertia. A force, such as the pull of a seat belt, is needed to pull you back. Roller coasters like the one in **Figure 1** have safety bars for the same reason.

Inertia Depends on Mass Some objects have more inertia than others. Suppose you need to move an empty backpack and a full backpack. The greater the mass of an object, the greater its inertia, and the greater the force required to change its motion. The full backpack is harder to move than the empty one because it has more mass and therefore more inertia.

FIGURE 1 ·······················
Inertia
A roller coaster is hard to stop because it has a lot of inertia. ✎ ⚠ **Infer** Use Newton's **first law of motion to explain why you feel tossed around whenever a roller coaster goes over a hill or through a loop.**

_____
_____
_____
_____
_____

Lab zone ® Do the Quick Lab
Around and Around.

⚷ **Assess Your Understanding**

got it? ···

○ **I get it!** Now I know that Newton's first law of motion states that _____
_____

○ **I need extra help with**
_____

What Is Newton's Second Law of Motion?

Which is harder to push, a full shopping cart or an empty one? Who can cause a greater acceleration on a shopping cart, a small child or a grown adult?

Changes in Force and Mass Suppose you increase the force on a cart without changing its mass. The acceleration of the cart will also increase. Your cart will also accelerate faster if something falls out. This reduces the mass of the cart, and you keep pushing just as hard. The acceleration of the sled in **Figure 2** will change depending on the mass of the people on it and the force the sled dogs apply. Newton realized these relationships and found a way to represent them mathematically.

Determining Acceleration Newton's second law of motion states that an object's acceleration depends on its mass and on the net force acting on it. This relationship can be written as follows.

$$\text{Acceleration} = \frac{\text{Net force}}{\text{Mass}}$$

This formula can be rearranged to show how much force must be applied to an object to get it to accelerate at a certain rate.

$$\text{Net force} = \text{Mass} \times \text{Acceleration}$$

FIGURE 2 ⋯⋯⋯⋯⋯⋯⋯⋯⋯⋯⋯
Newton's Second Law
Suppose that four dogs pull a sled carrying two people.
✎ **Explain** Use words and fill in the pictures to show how you can change the dog/person arrangement to change the sled's acceleration.

How could you increase the sled's acceleration?

_____
_____
_____
_____

How could you decrease the sled's acceleration?

_____
_____
_____
_____

Acceleration is measured in meters per second per second (m/s^2). Mass is measured in kilograms (kg). Newton's second law shows that force is measured in kilograms times meters per second per second ($kg \cdot m/s^2$). This unit is also called the newton (N), which is the SI unit of force. One newton is the force required to give a 1-kg mass an acceleration of $1\ m/s^2$.

do the math!

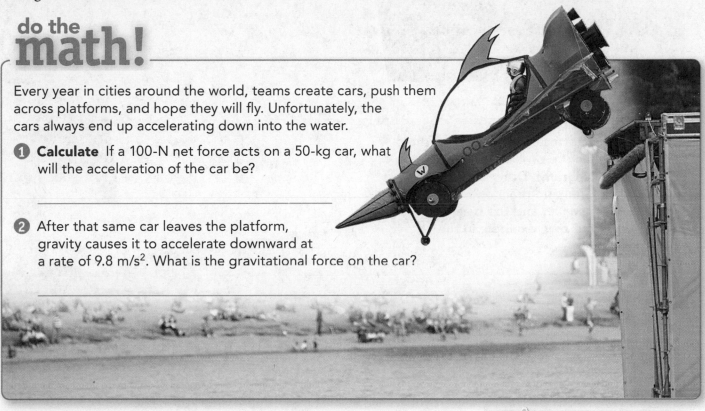

Every year in cities around the world, teams create cars, push them across platforms, and hope they will fly. Unfortunately, the cars always end up accelerating down into the water.

1 **Calculate** If a 100-N net force acts on a 50-kg car, what will the acceleration of the car be?

_____

2 After that same car leaves the platform, gravity causes it to accelerate downward at a rate of $9.8\ m/s^2$. What is the gravitational force on the car?

_____

Lab® Do the Quick Lab
zone *Newton's Second Law.*

🔑 Assess Your Understanding

1a. Review What equation allows you to calculate the force acting on an object?

_____

b. Calculate What is the net force on a 2-kg skateboard accelerating at a rate of $2\ m/s^2$?

c. Predict If the mass of the skateboard doubled but the net force on it remained constant, what would happen to the acceleration of the skateboard?

_____

_____

_____

got it?

○ **I get it!** Now I know that Newton's second law of motion describes the relationship _____

_____

○ I need extra help with _____

_____

FIGURE 3
Action-Reaction Pairs
A swimmer moves because the water pushes her forward when she pushes back on it.
✏ **Interpret Diagrams** Draw arrows to show the action and reaction forces between the gymnast and the balance beam. Draw your own example in the space provided.

Reaction force   Action force

What Is Newton's Third Law of Motion?

If you leaned against a wall and it didn't push back on you, you'd fall through. The force exerted by the wall is equal in strength and opposite in direction to the force you exert on the wall. 🔑 **Newton's third law of motion states that if one object exerts a force on another object, then the second object exerts a force of equal strength in the opposite direction on the first object.** Another way to state Newton's third law is that for every action there is an equal but opposite reaction.

Action-Reaction Pairs Pairs of action and reaction forces are all around you. When you walk, you push backward on the ground with your feet. Think of this as an action force. (It doesn't matter which force is called the "action" force and which is called the "reaction" force.) The ground pushes forward on your feet with an equal and opposite force. This is the reaction force. You can only walk because the ground pushes you forward! In a similar way, the swimmer in **Figure 3** moves forward by exerting an action force on the water with her hands. The water pushes on her hands with an equal reaction force that propels her body forward.

🔄 **Ask Questions** Action and reaction force pairs are all around you, but they aren't always obvious. Write down a question about a situation in which you can't identify what force pairs are at work.

_____
_____
_____
_____
_____
_____

Detecting Motion If you drop your pen, gravity pulls the pen downward. According to Newton's third law, the pen pulls Earth upward with an equal and opposite reaction force. You see the pen fall. You *don't* see Earth accelerate toward the pen. Remember Newton's second law. If mass increases and force stays the same, acceleration decreases. The same force acts on both Earth and your pen. Since Earth has such a large mass, its acceleration is so small that you don't notice it.

Do Action-Reaction Forces Cancel?

You have learned that two equal forces acting in opposite directions on an object cancel each other out and produce no change in motion. So why don't the action and reaction forces in Newton's third law of motion cancel out as well?

Action and reaction forces do not cancel out because they act on different objects. The swimmer in **Figure 3** exerts a backward action force on the water. The water exerts an equal but opposite forward reaction force on her hands. The action and reaction forces act on different objects—the action force acts on the water and the reaction force acts on her hands.

Unlike the swimmer and the water, the volleyball players in **Figure 4** both exert a force on the *same* object—the volleyball. Each player exerts a force on the ball equal in strength but opposite in direction. The forces on the volleyball are balanced. The ball does not move toward one player or the other.

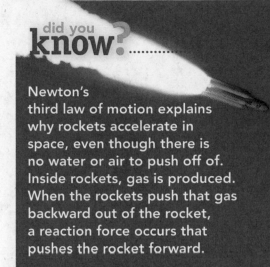

know?

Newton's third law of motion explains why rockets accelerate in space, even though there is no water or air to push off of. Inside rockets, gas is produced. When the rockets push that gas backward out of the rocket, a reaction force occurs that pushes the rocket forward.

Force on ball

Forces on hands

Force on ball

FIGURE 4 ·······································

Action-Reaction Forces
All the horizontal forces on the volleyball cancel out.

✎ **Apply Concepts** In the dog illustration above, use Newton's third law of motion to draw and label any missing force arrows for all the objects.

273

What Makes a Bug Go *Splat*?

How do objects react to forces?

FIGURE 5 ···

Splat! A bug has just flown into the windshield of an oncoming car. The car must have hit the bug much harder than the bug hit the car, right? ✎ **Apply Concepts** Use Newton's laws of motion to make sense of the situation and answer the questions.

10 - LG - SP

A

Buzz!

In order for the bug to fly through the air, a force has to push the bug forward. Identify this force. How does the bug produce it? (*Hint:* Think back to how a swimmer moves through the water.)

_____

_____

_____

_____

_____

The bug was at rest on a tree when it saw the car and decided to fly toward it. If the bug has a mass of 0.05 kg and accelerates at 2 m/s^2, what's the net force on the bug?

_____

B

Vroom!

The driver hates killing bugs. When she saw one coming toward the windshield, she braked suddenly and hoped it would get out of the way. (Sadly, it did not.) When she hit the brakes, she felt that she was thrown forward. Use one of Newton's laws to explain why.

_____

_____

_____

_____

_____

C

Splat!

The unfortunate bug hits the windshield with a force of 1 N. If you call this the action force, what is the reaction force? Does the car hit the bug any harder than the bug hits the car? Use one of Newton's laws to explain why or why not.

_____

_____

_____

_____

_____

Compare the forces on the bug and the car again. Use another one of Newton's laws to explain why the bug goes _splat_ and the car keeps going, without noticeably slowing down.

_____

_____

_____

_____

Lab zone® Do the Quick Lab
Interpreting Illustrations.

🔑 Assess Your Understanding

2a. Identify A dog pulls on his leash with a 10-N force to the left, but doesn't move. Identify the reaction force.

_____

_____

_____

_____

b. **ANSWER THE BIG ?** Using all three of Newton's laws, explain how objects react to forces.

_____

_____

_____

_____

_____

_____

_____

_____

_____

_____

_____

_____

_____

_____

got**it?** ....

○ **I get it!** Now I know that Newton's third law of motion states that _____

_____

_____

_____

○ **I need extra help with** _____

_____

_____

_____

Momentum

🔑 **What Is an Object's Momentum?**

my planet Diary

Air Hockey Science

Whoosh—you've just scored a goal! The puck is about to go back into play. How can you keep the puck out of your goal and get it back into your opponent's? One of the factors you have to consider is momentum. Momentum is a physical quantity that all moving objects have. If you know about momentum, you can predict how an object will act when it collides with other objects. With some quick scientific thinking, you can get the puck to bounce all over the table and back into your opponent's goal!

Answer the questions below.

1. Why might it be better to try to bounce a puck off the wall rather than shoot it straight into your opponent's goal?

   _____

   _____

   _____

2. Where else could it be helpful to know how objects act after colliding?

   _____

   _____

   _____

Lab zone ® Do the Inquiry Warm-Up *How Pushy Is a Straw?*

Vocabulary
• momentum
• law of conservation of momentum

Skills
⟳ Reading: Identify the Main Idea
△ Inquiry: Calculate

What Is an Object's Momentum?

Is it harder to stop a rolling bowling ball or a rolling marble? Does your answer depend on the velocities of the objects? All moving objects have what Newton called a "quantity of motion." Today it's called momentum. **Momentum** (moh MEN tum) is a characteristic of a moving object that is related to the mass and the velocity of the object. 🔑 **The momentum of a moving object can be determined by multiplying the object's mass by its velocity.**

$$\text{Momentum} = \text{Mass} \times \text{Velocity}$$

Since mass is measured in kilograms and velocity is measured in meters per second, the unit for momentum is kilograms times meters per second (kg·m/s). Like velocity, acceleration, and force, momentum is described by both a direction and a strength. The momentum of an object is in the same direction as its velocity.

The more momentum a moving object has, the harder it is to stop. For example, a 0.1-kg baseball moving at 40 m/s has a momentum of 4 kg·m/s in the direction it's moving.

$$\text{Momentum} = 0.1 \text{ kg} \times 40 \text{ m/s}$$

$$\text{Momentum} = 4 \text{ kg·m/s}$$

But a 1,200-kg car moving at the same speed as the baseball has a much greater momentum: 48,000 kg·m/s. The velocity of an object also affects the amount of momentum it has. For example, a tennis ball served by a professional tennis player has a large momentum. Although the ball has a small mass, it travels at a high velocity.

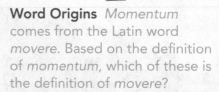

Word Origins *Momentum* comes from the Latin word *movere*. Based on the definition of *momentum*, which of these is the definition of *movere*?

○ to spin
○ to move
○ to sit

apply it!

△ **Calculate** In each question below, calculate the desired quantity.

❶ The lioness has a mass of 180 kg and a velocity of 16 m/s to the right. What is her momentum?

_____

_____

❷ The warthog has a mass of 100 kg. What does the warthog's speed have to be for it to have the same momentum as the lioness?

_____

⊙ Identify the Main Idea
Circle a sentence that relates the main idea of this section to two colliding cars. Then underline two supporting examples.

FIGURE 1 ··························

Conservation of Momentum
✏ ⊿Calculate Complete the equations describing the momentum of each collision. Identify the direction in each case.

Conservation of Momentum
Imagine you're driving a go-cart. If you ran into another go-cart that was at rest and got stuck to it, what do you think would happen to your momentum? Before you hit the other go-cart, your momentum was just your mass times your velocity. How has the additional mass changed that momentum? It actually hasn't changed it at all!

A quantity that is conserved is the same after an event as it was before. The **law of conservation of momentum** states that, in the absence of outside forces like friction, the total momentum of objects that interact does not change. The amount of momentum two cars have is the same before and after they interact.

🗝 **The total momentum of any group of objects remains the same, or is conserved, unless outside forces act on the objects.**

Before

→ 4 m/s

100 kg

Momentum = 400 kg·m/s to the right

Total momentum = _____ kg·m/s _____

→ 2 m/s

100 kg

Momentum = 200 kg·m/s to the right

After

→ 2 m/s

Momentum = _____ kg·m/s to the right

→ 4 m/s

Momentum = _____ kg·m/s to the right

Total momentum = _____ kg·m/s _____

"Non-Sticky" Collisions

Look at this example of a collision. When two objects of the same mass don't stick together and outside forces (such as friction) are negligible, the objects just trade velocities. The car that is going faster before the collision will end up slowing down, and the car that is going slower before the collision will end up speeding up.

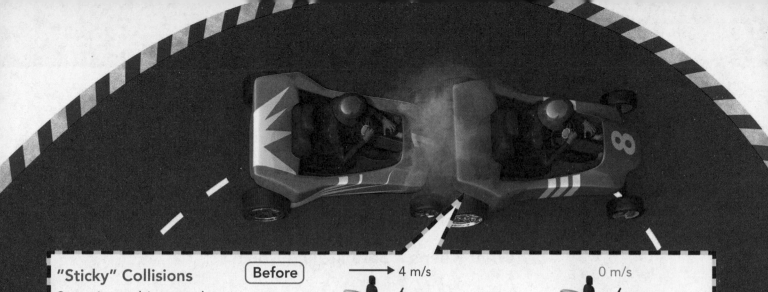

"Sticky" Collisions

Sometimes objects end up sticking together during a collision. These two cars, which have the same mass, got tangled together after they collided. Since the green car was at rest and had a momentum of zero, only the blue car had any momentum before the collision. After they collided and stuck together, the cars shared that momentum. The total momentum of the two cars stayed the same.

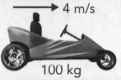

Before

4 m/s   0 m/s

100 kg   100 kg

Momentum = _____ kg·m/s to the right   Momentum = _____ kg·m/s

Total momentum = _____ kg·m/s _____

After

→ ?

Total mass = _____

Total momentum = _____ kg·m/s _____

What must the velocity be? _____

Lab zone® Do the Quick Lab *Colliding Cars.*

🔑 Assess Your Understanding

1a. Explain How can a heavy moving van have the same momentum as a small motorcycle?

_____

_____

_____

_____

_____

b. Calculate What is the momentum of a 750-kg car traveling at a velocity of 25 m/s?

_____

c. Infer The total momentum of two marbles before a collision is 0.06 kg·m/s. No outside forces act on the marbles. What is the total momentum of the marbles after the collision?

_____

got it? •••

○ **I get it!** Now I know that momentum is

conserved unless _____

_____

○ **I need extra help with** _____

_____

Free Fall and Circular Motion

🔑 **What Is Free Fall?**

🔑 **What Keeps a Satellite in Orbit?**

my planet diary

Finding Yourself

The GPS (Global Positioning System) is a "constellation" of satellites that orbit 10,600 miles above Earth. The GPS makes it possible for people with ground receivers to pinpoint their geographic location. The first GPS satellites were placed in orbit in 1978. These early satellites were expected to operate for approximately five years. Newer satellites have an expected lifespan of seven to eight years.

GPS Satellites in Orbit

Years	Number of GPS Satellites Launched	Number of Operating GPS Satellites
1978–1982	6	6
1983–1987	4	8
1988–1992	17	21
1993–1997	12	27
1998–2002	5	28
2003–2007	11	31

SCIENCE STATS

Interpret Data Use the data in the table to answer the questions below.

1. What is the total number of satellites launched from 1978 to 2007? How many were still operating as of 2007?

_____
_____
_____
_____

2. How many satellites stopped operating between 2003 and 2007?

_____
_____
_____
_____

Lab zone® Do the Inquiry Warm-Up *What Makes an Object Move in a Circle?*

Vocabulary
- free fall • satellite
- centripetal force

Skills
- Reading: Relate Cause and Effect
- Inquiry: Create Data Tables

What Is Free Fall?

When the only force acting on an object is gravity, the object is said to be in **free fall.** The force of gravity causes the object to accelerate. **Free fall is motion where the acceleration is caused by gravity.** When something falls on Earth, there is fluid friction from the air around it. This friction acts against gravity, reducing the acceleration of falling objects. Air friction increases as an object falls. If an object falls for long enough, increased air friction will reduce its acceleration to zero. The object will continue to fall, but it will fall at a constant velocity.

Near the surface of Earth, the acceleration due to gravity is 9.8 m/s^2. If there were no air friction, a falling object would have a velocity of 9.8 m/s after one second and 19.6 m/s after two seconds. Since air friction reduces acceleration, an object falling on Earth for one second will actually have a velocity that is less than 9.8 m/s.

FIGURE 1 ......

Free Fall

The photo shows a tennis ball and a crumpled piece of paper of different masses as they fall during a fraction of a second. If the only force acting on them were gravity, they would fall at exactly the same rate and line up perfectly. However, air friction is also present. Air friction has a greater effect on the paper's acceleration than on the tennis ball's acceleration. This causes the tennis ball to fall faster.

do the math!

✎ **Create Data Tables** Suppose you had a chamber with no air, eliminating the force of air friction. Complete the table below for an object that is dropped from rest. Remember the formula **Velocity = Acceleration × Time.** The acceleration due to gravity is 9.8 m/s^2.

Time (s)	Velocity (m/s)
0	_____
1	_____
2	_____
3	_____
4	_____

Lab zone Do the Quick Lab *Which Lands First?*

☞ Assess Your Understanding

got it?

○ I get it! Now I know that free fall is _____

_____

○ I need extra help with _____

_____

What Keeps a Satellite in Orbit?

Objects don't always fall down in straight lines. If you throw a ball horizontally, the ball will move away from you while gravity pulls the ball to the ground. The horizontal and vertical motions act independently, and the ball follows a curved path toward the ground. If you throw the ball faster, it will land even farther in front of you. The faster you throw an object, the farther it travels before it lands.

Satellite Motion This explains how **satellites,** which are objects that orbit around other objects in space, follow a curved path around Earth. What would happen if you were on a high mountain and could throw a ball as fast as you wanted? The faster you threw it, the farther away it would land. But, at a certain speed, the curved path of the ball would match the curved surface of Earth. Although the ball would keep falling due to gravity, Earth's surface would curve away from the ball at the same rate. The ball would fall around Earth in a circle, as shown in **Figure 2.**

↻ Relate Cause and Effect
On the next page, underline the effect a centripetal force has on an object's motion. Circle the effect of turning off a centripetal force.

FIGURE 2 ···

Satellite Motion

A satellite launched from Earth enters orbit because the curve of its path matches the curved surface of Earth.

✎ **Make Models** On the picture at the right, draw arrows representing the gravitational force on the ball at each point.

[CHALLENGE] Explain why Earth's atmosphere would prevent this baseball from ever actually being thrown into orbit. Why is this not a problem for satellites?

_____

_____

_____

🔑 **Satellites in orbit around Earth continuously fall toward Earth, but because Earth is curved they travel around it.** In other words, a satellite is a falling object that keeps missing the ground! It falls around Earth rather than onto it. Once it has entered a stable orbit, a satellite does not need fuel. It continues to move ahead due to its inertia. At the same time, gravity continuously changes the satellite's direction. Most satellites are launched at a speed of about 7,900 m/s. That's more than 17,000 miles per hour!

Centripetal Force Many manufactured satellites orbit Earth in an almost circular path. Recall that an object traveling in a circle is accelerating because it constantly changes direction. If an object is accelerating, a force must be acting on it. A force that causes an object to move in a circular path is a **centripetal force** (sen TRIP ih tul). The word *centripetal* means "center-seeking." Centripetal forces always point toward the center of the circle an object is moving in. If you could turn off a centripetal force, inertia would cause the object to fly off in a straight line. For example, the string of a yo-yo being swung in a circle provides a centripetal force. Cutting the string would cut off the centripetal force, and the yo-yo would fly off in a straight line.

apply it!

Identify What is creating the centripetal force in each situation below?

❶ A tetherball swinging around a pole

_____

❷ Mars orbiting around the sun

_____

❸ A child standing on a merry-go-round

_____

Lab zone ® Do the Quick Lab *Orbiting Earth.*

🔑 Assess Your Understanding

1a. Identify What is the force that causes objects to move in circles?

_____

_____

b. Predict If Earth's gravity could be turned off, what would happen to satellites that are currently in orbit? Explain your reasoning.

_____

_____

_____

_____

got it?

○ I get it! Now I know that satellites stay in orbit because _____

_____

_____

_____

○ I need extra help with _____

_____

_____

_____

_____

6 Study Guide

REVIEW
THE BIG
?

Changes in motion are caused by _____. _____ laws describe these changes in motion.

LESSON 1 The Nature of Force

🗝 In science, acceleration refers to increasing speed, decreasing speed, or changing direction.

🗝 Like velocity and acceleration, a force is described by its strength and by the direction in which it acts.

🗝 A nonzero net force causes a change in the object's motion.

Vocabulary
• acceleration • force • newton • net force

LESSON 2 Friction and Gravity

🗝 Two factors that affect the force of friction are the types of surfaces involved and how hard the surfaces are pushed together.

🗝 Two factors affect the gravitational attraction between objects: their masses and distance.

Vocabulary
• friction • sliding friction
• static friction • fluid friction
• rolling friction • gravity
• mass • weight

LESSON 3 Newton's Laws of Motion

🗝 Objects at rest will remain at rest and objects moving at a constant velocity will continue moving at a constant velocity unless they are acted upon by nonzero net forces.

🗝 The acceleration of an object depends on its mass and on the net force acting on it.

🗝 If one object exerts a force on another object, then the second object exerts a force of equal strength in the opposite direction on the first object.

Vocabulary
• inertia

LESSON 4 Momentum

🗝 The momentum of a moving object can be determined by multiplying the object's mass by its velocity.

🗝 The total momentum of any group of objects remains the same, or is conserved, unless outside forces act on the objects.

Vocabulary
• momentum
• law of conservation of momentum

LESSON 5 Free Fall and Circular Motion

🗝 Free fall is motion where the acceleration is caused by gravity.

🗝 Satellites in orbit around Earth continuously fall toward Earth, but because Earth is curved they travel around it.

Vocabulary
• free fall • satellite • centripetal force

Review and Assessment

The Nature of Force

1. When a nonzero net force acts on an object, the force

   a. changes the motion of the object.

   b. must be greater than the reaction force.

   c. does not change the motion of the object.

   d. is equal to the weight of the object.

2. The SI unit of force is the _____

3. **Calculate** What is the net force on the box? Be sure to specify direction.

15 N

10 N

Friction and Gravity

4. Friction always acts

   a. in the same direction as motion.

   b. opposite the direction of motion.

   c. perpendicular to the direction of motion.

   d. at a 30° angle to the direction of motion.

5. The factors that affect the gravitational force between two objects are _____

   _____

6. **List** What are two ways you can increase the frictional force between two objects?

   _____

   _____

7. **Write About It** Design a ride for an amusement park. Describe the ride and explain how friction and gravity will affect the ride's design.

Newton's Laws of Motion

8. Which of Newton's laws of motion is also called the law of inertia?

   a. First   **b.** Second

   c. Third   **d.** Fourth

9. Newton's second law states that force is equal

   to _____

10. **Interpret Diagrams** Look at the diagram below of two students pulling a bag of volleyball equipment. The friction force between the bag and the floor is 4 N. What is the net force acting on the bag? What is the acceleration of the bag?

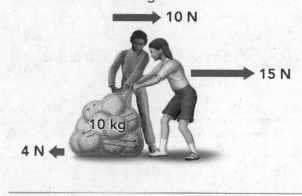

10 N

15 N

10 kg

4 N

   _____

   _____

   _____

   _____

   _____

11. **Apply Concepts** Suppose you are an astronaut making a space walk outside your space station and your jet pack runs out of fuel. How can you use your empty jet pack to get you back to the station?

   _____

   _____

   _____

   _____

   _____

   _____

   _____

   _____

6 Review and Assessment

LESSON 4 **Momentum**

12. Momentum is calculated by multiplying

    a. mass times velocity. **b.** weight times mass.

    c. force times speed.   **d.** inertia times force.

13. The SI unit of momentum is _____

14. **Explain** How can two objects of different masses have the same momentum?

    _____

    _____

    _____

    _____

    _____

LESSON 5 **Free Fall and Circular Motion**

15. Satellites remain in orbit around Earth because

    a. the moon's gravitational pull on them is equal to Earth's pull.

    b. no forces act on them.

    c. their motors keep them moving in circles.

    d. the curve of their paths as they fall matches the curve of Earth.

16. Centripetal forces always point _____

    _____

17. **Calculate** Determine the velocity of an object that started from rest and has been in free fall for 10 seconds. Assume there is no air resistance.

    _____

APPLY THE BIG ? How do objects react to forces?

18. Forces are all around you. Describe an example of each of Newton's laws of motion that you experience before you get to school in the morning.

    _____

    _____

    _____

    _____

    _____

    _____

    _____

    _____

    _____

    _____

    _____

    _____

    _____

    _____

    _____

    _____

    _____

    _____

    _____

    _____

Standardized Test Prep

Read each question and choose the best answer.

Force   Force   Motion

1. In the balloon diagram above, why don't the two forces cancel each other out?

    A   They are not equal.
    B   They both act on the air.
    C   They both act on the balloon.
    D   They act on different objects.

2. What force makes it less likely for a person to slip on a dry sidewalk than on an icy sidewalk?

    A   gravity
    B   friction
    C   inertia
    D   momentum

3. A satellite orbits Earth at a constant speed. What part of the satellite's motion is changing?

    A   speed
    B   friction
    C   inertia
    D   acceleration

4. Where would a 5-kg object experience the greatest gravitational force?

    A   on the moon
    B   at sea level
    C   at the top of a tall mountain
    D   at the bottom of the ocean

5. In a game of tug-of-war, you pull on the rope with a force of 100 N to the right and your friend pulls on the rope with a force of 100 N to the left. What is the net force on the rope?

    A   200 N to the right
    B   200 N to the left
    C   0 N
    D   100 N to the right

Constructed Response

Use your knowledge of science to help you answer Question 7. Write your answer on a separate sheet of paper.

6. Use all three of Newton's laws of motion to describe what happens when a car starts off at rest, is pushed across a platform, and then accelerates downward.

safety restraints

Did you wear your seat belt the last time you rode in a car? Seat belts are safety restraints designed to protect you from injury while you travel in a moving vehicle, whether you stop suddenly to avoid a crash or are stopped suddenly by a crash.

Without a seat belt, inertia would cause the driver and passengers in a car that suddenly stopped to continue traveling forward. Without a restraint, a 75-kilogram driver driving at 50 km/h would experience 12,000 newtons of force in a crash! A safety restraint prevents that forward motion and keeps the driver and passengers safe.

Safety harnesses and seat belts are available in many different designs. Most seat belts are three-point harnesses. Five- and seven-point harnesses are used in vehicles like race cars and fighter jets.

Race car drivers travel at higher speeds than most drivers experience. A five-point harness provides extra security at these high speeds. ▼

Debate It Most states have laws that require drivers and passengers to wear seat belts. Research the seat belt laws in your state, and participate in a class debate about whether the seat belt laws are strong enough.

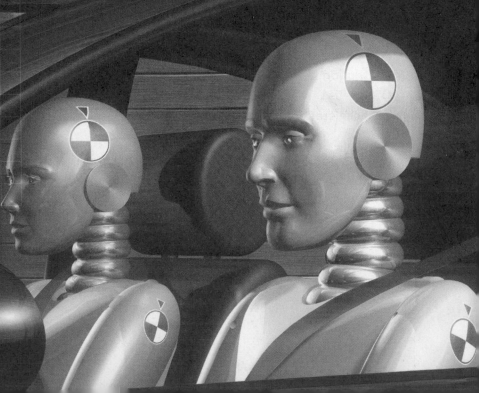

Forceful Fluids

Could you lift an elephant with water? It depends on the container the water is in! Suppose you have a sealed container completely full of water. If you apply pressure to one area of the container, that pressure is exerted equally in all parts of the fluid and on the inner surfaces of the container. This is Pascal's principle, named for Blaise Pascal, a French scientist who lived in the 1600s.

Hydraulic systems are based on Pascal's principle. In these systems, a force presses a piston against an enclosed fluid. The force transfers with the same pressure throughout the fluid and presses a second piston outward. If the two pistons are the same size, the inward force and the outward force are the same.

What if the surface areas of the two pistons differ? Suppose the output piston's surface area is four times greater than that of the input piston. Four times more fluid presses against the output piston, which applies four times the force. With a system like that, you could lift an elephant with water!

Design It Hydraulic car lifts and hydraulic brakes are two technologies that work because of Pascal's principle. Research another hydraulic device and diagram how it works. Share your diagram with your class.

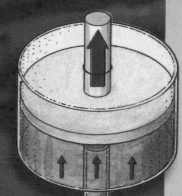

WHY ARE THE PEOPLE IN THIS BUILDING SAFE FROM LIGHTNING?

THE BIG ?

How does an electric circuit work?

Lightning strikes Earth more than 100 times every second. Buildings can be protected from lightning strikes with tall metal poles called lightning rods. When lightning strikes, it is more likely to hit the rod than the building. A lightning strike can flow through the rod and into metal wires that are connected to the ground. This prevents the building from being damaged and anyone inside from being injured.

Communicate How is a lightning bolt like the electricity that runs through power lines? Discuss this with a partner.

_____

_____

_____

_____

Watch the **Untamed Science** video to learn more about electricity.

CHAPTER 7

Electricity

Check Your Understanding

1. **Background** Read the paragraph below and then answer the question.

When you lift up a basketball, you apply a **force** to it. The **energy** you use to lift it gets transferred to the ball as gravitational **potential energy.** The higher you lift the ball, the more energy you use and the more gravitational potential energy the ball gains.

> A **force** is a push or pull exerted on an object.
>
> **Energy** is the ability to do work or cause change.
>
> **Potential energy** is the stored energy that results from the position or shape of an object.

- What happens to the ball's gravitational potential energy if it is dropped?

_____

Vocabulary Skill

Latin Word Origins Many science words in English come from Latin. For example, the word *solar*, which means "of the sun," comes from the Latin *sol*, which means "sun."

Latin Word	Meaning of Latin Word	Example
circuitus	going around	circuit, *n.* a complete, unbroken path
currere	to run	current, *n.* a continuous flow
insula	island	insulator, *n.* a material through which charges cannot flow

2. **Quick Check** Choose the word that best completes the sentence.

- An electric _____ is formed by the movement of electric charges from one place to another.

static electricity

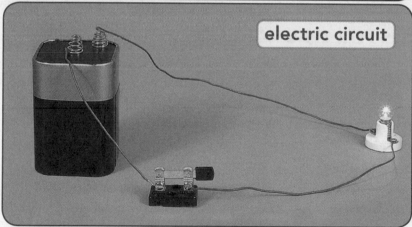

static discharge

electric circuit

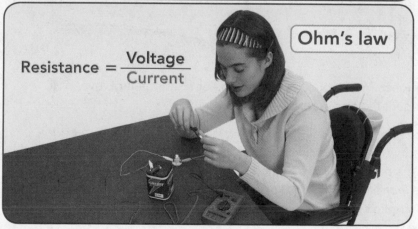

Ohm's law

$$Resistance = \frac{Voltage}{Current}$$

Chapter Preview

Scenario Investigation

My House Is Wired!

Purpose   To explore two types of electrical circuits

Materials
- three 1.5-V (D) batteries with holders
- three flashlight bulbs (2.47 volts, 0.3 amps) with sockets
- wire leads with alligator clips
- masking tape
- heavy cardboard

Scenario

Because of the recent focus on energy conservation, many people want to learn more about electricity. A toy company called That's My Toy (TMT) has made an electricity kit for use in elementary schools. TMT wants experts from your power company to check that the kits work. You and your partners at the power company will test the kits by following the directions written by TMT, and then provide feedback about how to improve the kits and simplify the directions to help fourth-graders understand them.

Procedure

☑ **1. I Can't Make This Work** Obtain a kit from your teacher. Read and follow the instructions provided by TMT. Do your best to make everything work, but remember that your job is to rewrite the instructions so that fourth-graders will understand them and be successful.

INSTRUCTIONS FOR WIRING A HOME

On the cardboard base, build a circuit that works just like the circuit in your house or apartment. You must obey the following guidelines:

   (a) make two flashlight bulbs light;

   (b) connect the wires so that when you remove one bulb the other bulb stays lit; and

   (c) after you succeed with goals (a) and (b), add a third bulb to the circuit.

The circuit may include up to three batteries (in series).

If bulbs go out when you disconnect another bulb, change the circuit.

Keep trying new arrangements until two bulbs are always lit, even when a third bulb is removed.

When everything works, draw a diagram of the circuit and label the parts.

☑ **2. Taking Notes** As you try different ideas, make accurate drawings of each attempt, even if it doesn't work. That way, you won't repeat the same design.

☑ **3. New Directions** Did the instructions from TMT easily lead you to success? If not, you need to rewrite them. Keep what worked, and write new instructions that describe what you actually did. Choose your words carefully. Make the new directions as clear and simple as you can. Add more steps where needed and change the wording to make it simpler. (Perhaps a numbered list of steps would help.) Also include a brief description of the difference between series and parallel circuits and a diagram of the correct circuit.

Conclusion

Let's see what you learned about electric circuits in your home.

1. There are two kinds of circuits. In one kind, all the bulbs go out when one bulb is removed. In the other kind, a bulb can be removed while all other bulbs remain lit. What are the names for these different circuits?

_____

_____

2. What will happen to the brightness of the first two bulbs if you add a third bulb in series? (If you aren't sure, try it.)

_____

_____

3. What will happen to the brightness of the first two bulbs if you add a third bulb in parallel?

_____

_____

4. Which type of circuit do you have in your home? How do you know?

_____

_____

Write a letter to the director of research and development at TMT. Tell the director what you liked about the kits and what you didn't like. (Try to be polite and constructive.) Include your new set of instructions with the letter.

Electric Charge and Static Electricity

UNLOCK THE BIG ?

🔑 **How Do Charges Interact?**

🔑 **How Does Charge Build Up?**

my planet diary

Force Fields

Misconception: Force fields exist only in science fiction stories.

Fact: Force fields are an important part of your everyday life.

You're actually sitting in a force field right now! A force field exists around any object that repels or attracts other objects. A giant gravitational force field surrounds Earth. This field keeps you from floating off into space. Earth's magnetic field makes compass needles point north. You make your own force field every time you get shocked when you reach for a doorknob!

MISCONCEPTIONS

Answer the questions below.

1. A gravitational field keeps you on Earth. What other uses might force fields have?

_____

_____

2. Describe how a different science fiction invention could be rooted in real science.

_____

_____

Do the Inquiry Warm-Up *Can You Move a Can Without Touching It?*

Vocabulary
- electric force
- electric field
- static electricity
- conservation of charge
- friction
- conduction
- induction
- polarization
- static discharge

Skills
- Reading: Relate Cause and Effect
- Inquiry: Draw Conclusions

How Do Charges Interact?

You're already late for school and one of your socks is missing! You finally find it sticking to the back of your blanket. How did that happen? The explanation has to do with electric charges.

Types of Charge Atoms contain charged particles called electrons and protons. If two electrons come close together, they push each other apart. In other words, they repel each other. Two protons behave the same way. If a proton and an electron come close together, they attract one another. Protons attract electrons because the two have opposite electric charges. The charge on a proton is positive (+). The charge on an electron is negative (−).

The two types of electric charges interact in specific ways, as you see in **Figure 1.** **Charges that are the same repel each other. Charges that are different attract each other.** The interaction between electric charges is called electricity. The force between charged objects is called **electric force.**

FIGURE 1 ···

Repel or Attract?

✎ △ Draw Conclusions On each sphere, write if it has a positive (+) or a negative (−) charge. Compare your answers with a group. Can you tell for sure which spheres are positively charged and which are negatively charged? What conclusions can you draw?

_____

_____

_____

_____

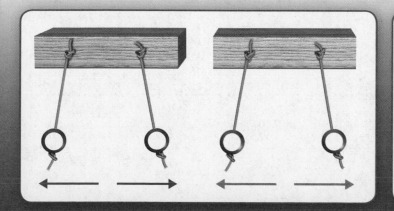

Electric Fields

You may have heard of a gravitational field, which is the space around an object (such as a planet) where the object's gravitational force is exerted. Similarly, an electric field extends around a charged object. An **electric field** is a region around a charged object where the object's electric force is exerted on other charged objects. Electric fields and forces get weaker the farther away they are from the charge.

An electric field is invisible. You can use field lines to represent it, as shown in **Figure 2**. A field line shows the force that would be exerted on a positive charge at any point along that line. Positive charges are repelled by positive charges and attracted to negative charges, so field lines point away from positive charges and toward negative charges. Single charges have straight field lines, since a positive charge will be repelled away from or attracted to it in a straight line. When multiple charges are present, each charge exerts a force. These forces combine to make more complicated field lines.

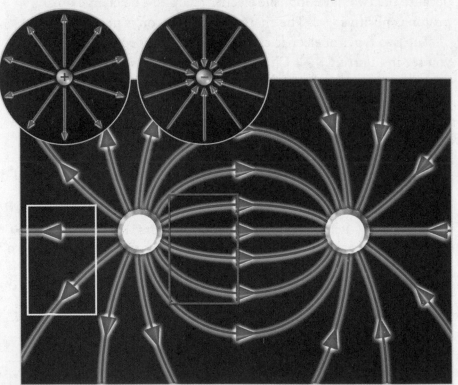

FIGURE 2 ······························

Electric Fields

Field lines show the direction of the force acting on a positive charge.

✎ **Answer the questions.**

1. **Identify** Identify which charge is positive and which charge is negative.

2. **Interpret Diagrams** The boxes on the electric field are the same size. How many field lines are inside the white box?

   _____

3. **Interpret Diagrams** The blue box is closer to the charges. How many field lines are in this box?

   _____

4. **Draw Conclusions** What is the relationship between the number of field lines in an area and the strength of the electric force?

   _____

   _____

   _____

Lab zone® Do the Quick Lab *Drawing Conclusions.*

Assess Your Understanding

got it? ···

O **I get it!** Now I know that the way electric charges interact depends on _____

_____

O **I need extra help with**_____

How Does Charge Build Up?

Most objects have no overall charge. An atom usually has as many electrons as it has protons, so each positive charge is balanced by a negative charge. This leaves the atom uncharged, or neutral.

An uncharged object can become charged by gaining or losing electrons. If an object loses electrons, it is left with more protons than electrons. It has an overall positive charge. If an object gains electrons, it will have an overall negative charge. The buildup of charges on an object is called **static electricity.** In static electricity, charges build up on an object, but they do not flow continuously.

FIGURE 3 ·······························

Charge Buildup
Rubbing two objects together can produce static electricity.

✎ **Interpret Photos** Circle the phrases that best complete the statements. Follow the directions to draw how the charges are arranged in each photo.

❶ The balloon is (positively/ negatively/not) charged. The balloon (attracts/repels/neither attracts nor repels) the girl's hair.

❷ Rubbing the balloon allows more electrons to move onto the balloon. The balloon is now (positively/negatively) charged. **Draw what the charges on the balloon look like now.**

❸ The (positive/negative) charges in the girl's hair are now attracted to the negative charges on the balloon. **Draw how the charges on the balloon are arranged now.**

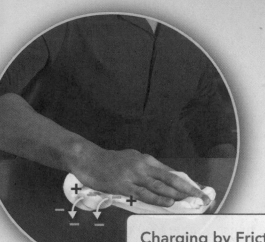

Charging Objects

Charges are neither created nor destroyed. This is a rule known as the law of **conservation of charge.** An object can't become charged by destroying or creating its own electrons. If one object loses electrons, another object must pick them up. 🔑 **There are four methods by which charges can redistribute themselves to build up static electricity: by friction, by conduction, by induction, and by polarization.**

Charging by Friction

When two uncharged objects are rubbed together, some electrons from one object can move onto the other object. The object that gains electrons becomes negatively charged. The object that loses electrons becomes positively charged. Charging by **friction** is the transfer of electrons from one uncharged object to another by rubbing the objects together.

Charging by Conduction

When a charged object touches another object, electrons can be transferred. Charging by **conduction** is the transfer of electrons from one object to another by direct contact. Electrons transfer from the object that has more negative charge to the object that has more positive charge. A positively charged object, like the metal ball, gains electrons when an uncharged person touches it. The girl starts out neutral, but electrons move from her hair, through her arm, to the ball. This leaves her hair positively charged, and the strands repel each other.

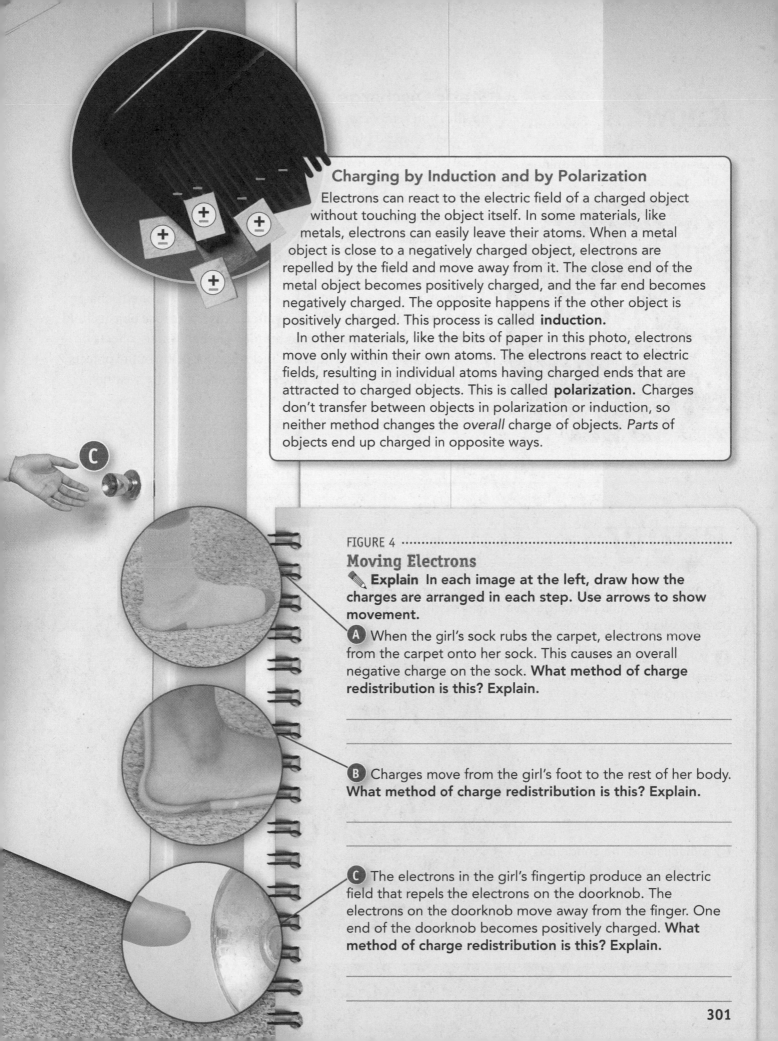

Charging by Induction and by Polarization

Electrons can react to the electric field of a charged object without touching the object itself. In some materials, like metals, electrons can easily leave their atoms. When a metal object is close to a negatively charged object, electrons are repelled by the field and move away from it. The close end of the metal object becomes positively charged, and the far end becomes negatively charged. The opposite happens if the other object is positively charged. This process is called **induction.**

In other materials, like the bits of paper in this photo, electrons move only within their own atoms. The electrons react to electric fields, resulting in individual atoms having charged ends that are attracted to charged objects. This is called **polarization.** Charges don't transfer between objects in polarization or induction, so neither method changes the *overall* charge of objects. *Parts* of objects end up charged in opposite ways.

FIGURE 4 ···

Moving Electrons

✎ **Explain** In each image at the left, draw how the charges are arranged in each step. Use arrows to show movement.

A When the girl's sock rubs the carpet, electrons move from the carpet onto her sock. This causes an overall negative charge on the sock. **What method of charge redistribution is this? Explain.**

_____

_____

B Charges move from the girl's foot to the rest of her body. **What method of charge redistribution is this? Explain.**

_____

_____

C The electrons in the girl's fingertip produce an electric field that repels the electrons on the doorknob. The electrons on the doorknob move away from the finger. One end of the doorknob becomes positively charged. **What method of charge redistribution is this? Explain.**

_____

_____

know? ....

Machines called Van de Graaff generators can create lightning bolts indoors!

Static Discharge If your hair becomes charged and sticks up after you remove a sweater, it doesn't stay that way forever. Positively charged objects gradually gain electrons from the air. Negatively charged objects gradually lose electrons to the air. The objects eventually become neutral again. The loss of static electricity as electric charges transfer from one object to another is called **static discharge.**

Static discharge often produces a spark. Moving electrons can heat the air around their path until it glows. The glowing air is the spark you see. The tiny spark you may have felt or seen when near a doorknob is an example of static discharge. Sparks from discharge happen more frequently during winter. This is because objects hold on to charge better in dry air. In humid weather, water collects on the surfaces of objects. The water picks up charge from the objects, so they don't stay charged as long as they would in dry weather.

apply it!

Draw Conclusions Anyone who works with computers has to be aware of static discharge. Even small discharges can damage electrical equipment.

1 What activities should you avoid to prevent static discharge while working on a computer?

_____

_____

_____

_____

2 What should the conditions of the room you are in be like?

_____

_____

_____

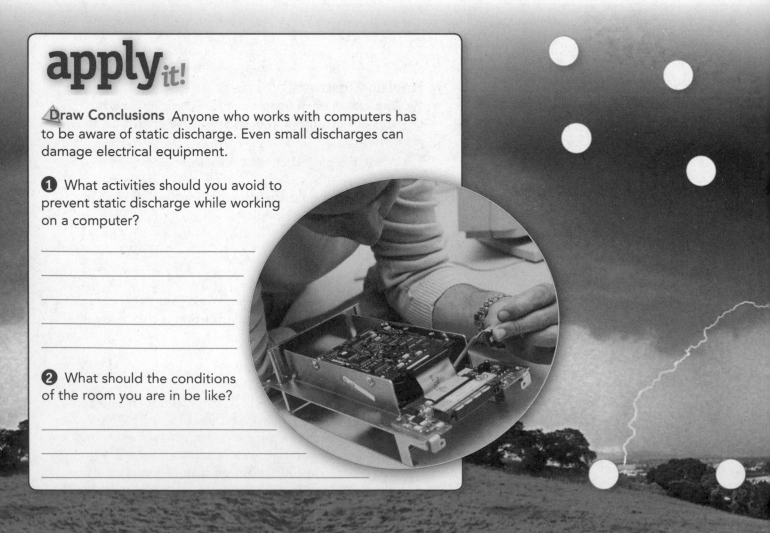

Lightning bolts are an example of static discharge. During thunderstorms, air swirls violently. Water droplets within the clouds become charged. Electrons move from areas of negative charge to areas of positive charge, producing an intense spark. That spark is lightning.

Some lightning reaches Earth. Negative charges at the bottoms of storm clouds create an electric field. This causes Earth's surface to become positively charged through induction. Electrons jump between the clouds and Earth's surface, producing a giant spark of lightning as they travel through the air.

Relate Cause and Effect
Pick one example of cause and effect in this section. Underline the cause, and then circle the effect that results.

FIGURE 5 ....

Static Discharge
Lightning is just a much bigger version of the sparks you feel when you shock yourself on a doorknob.

✎ **Relate Text and Visuals** In the white circles, draw how positive and negative charges are arranged during a lightning strike.

Do the Quick Lab
Sparks Are Flying.

🔑 **Assess Your Understanding**

1a. Describe What happens to an object's atoms when the object becomes positively charged?

_____

_____

b. [CHALLENGE] Explain how you could use a piece of silk and a glass rod to attract a stream of tap water.

_____

_____

_____

_____

got it? ....

○ **I get it!** Now I know that the four methods of building up static electricity are _____

_____

_____

○ **I need extra help with** _____

Electric Current

UNLOCK THE BIG ?

🔑 **How Is Electric Current Made?**

🔑 **How Do Conductors Differ From Insulators?**

🔑 **What Affects Current Flow?**

MY PLANET DIARY

CAREERS

Be a Superconductor—of Science!

John Vander Sande wants your city to run more efficiently. A company he cofounded is working to replace old power lines with materials that let electric current flow more efficiently. These materials are called superconductors. Superconductors are often found in lab equipment, as shown at the left, but companies like Vander Sande's are finding other uses for them. Vander Sande didn't start his career working with power lines. He began his work in materials science as a professor at the Massachusetts Institute of Technology (MIT). He got into superconducting by chance after hearing about discoveries at a lecture by one of his colleagues. He encourages everyone to stay open to opportunities in science, because they can pop up anywhere at any time.

Answer the question below.

Describe an instance in your life when hearing something by chance led to a new opportunity.

_____

_____

_____

_____

_____

_____

Lab zone® Do the Inquiry Warm-Up *How Can Current Be Measured?*

How Is Electric Current Made?

Dozens of sushi dishes ride along a conveyor belt in **Figure 1.** The conveyer belt carries full dishes past customers and carries empty plates back to the kitchen. You might be wondering what a conveyer belt of rice, vegetables, and fish could possibly have to do with electricity. Like the sushi plates, electric charges can be made to move in a confined path.

Vocabulary

- electric current
- conductor
- voltage
- electric circuit
- insulator
- resistance

Skills

- Reading: Ask Questions
- Inquiry: Classify

Flow of Electric Charges Lightning releases a large amount of electrical energy. However, the electric charge from lightning doesn't last long enough to power your radio or your TV. These devices need electric charges that flow continuously. They require electric current.

Recall that static electric charges do not flow continuously. **When electric charges are made to flow through a material, they produce an electric current.** Electric current is the continuous flow of electric charges through a material. The amount of charge that passes through a wire in a given period of time is the rate of electric current. The unit for the rate of current is the ampere, named for André Marie Ampère, an early investigator of electricity. The name of the unit is often shortened to amp or A. The number of amps describes the amount of charge flowing past a given point each second.

FIGURE 1 ·····

Electric Current

The conveyor belt represents a current. If it represented a greater current, more plates would pass by you in the same amount of time. One way for this to occur would be for the belt to go faster.

✏ **Make Models** Suppose the belt couldn't go faster. Draw a different way a greater current could be represented.

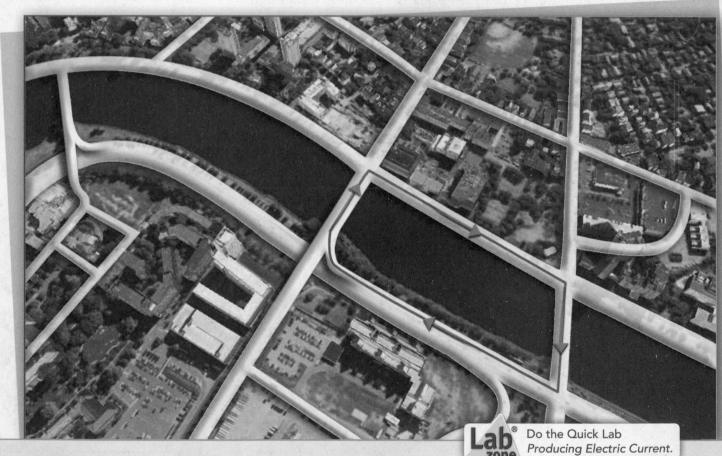

FIGURE 2 ·······························

Circuits

Just like charges in a wire, people can move around in circuits. One possible jogging circuit is outlined in this photo.

✎ **Interpret Photos** Trace another possible circuit. What could break this circuit?

_____

_____

_____

_____

Current in a Circuit The electric currents that power your computer and music player need very specific paths to work. In order to maintain an electric current, charges must be able to flow continuously in a loop. A complete, unbroken path that charges can flow through is called an **electric circuit.**

Someone jogging along the roads in **Figure 2** is moving like a charge in an electric circuit. If the road forms a complete loop, the jogger can move in a continuous path. However, the jogger cannot continue if any section of the road is closed. Similarly, if an electric circuit is complete, charges can flow continuously. If an electric circuit is broken, charges will not flow.

Electric circuits are all around you. All electrical devices, from toasters to televisions, contain electric circuits.

Lab zone® Do the Quick Lab *Producing Electric Current.*

🔑 Assess Your Understanding

1a. Review What is the unit of current?

_____

b. Predict What could break the circuit between your home and an electric power plant?

_____

got it?

○ **I get it!** Now I know that electric current is made of _____

_____

○ **I need extra help with** _____

How Do Conductors Differ From Insulators?

You can safely touch the rubber coating on an appliance cord. If you touched the wire inside, you'd get shocked. That's because charges can flow more easily through some materials than others.

A **conductor** is a material through which charge can flow easily. Electrons can move freely, allowing conductors to be charged by induction. Metals, such as copper, are good conductors. This is why current-carrying wires are usually made out of metal.

Wires are surrounded by insulators. **Insulators** are materials, such as rubber, that do not allow charges to flow. However, electrons can move around within their own atoms, allowing for polarization. They can also be stripped off when charging by friction.

The difference between conductors and insulators comes from how strongly electrons are attached to atoms. 🔑 **The atoms in conductors have loosely bound electrons that can move freely. Electrons in insulators cannot move freely among atoms.**

✍️ **Ask Questions** Current, conductors, and insulators all show up in your daily life. Write down a question about one of these topics that you would like answered.

_____

_____

_____

apply it!

All objects are made up of conductors or insulators, not just the ones you usually see in electronic devices.

❶ **Identify** The gloves that electricians wear when working on power lines should be made out of (insulating/conducting) materials.

❷ **Classify** Circle the conductors in these photos. Be careful—only parts of some items are conductors!

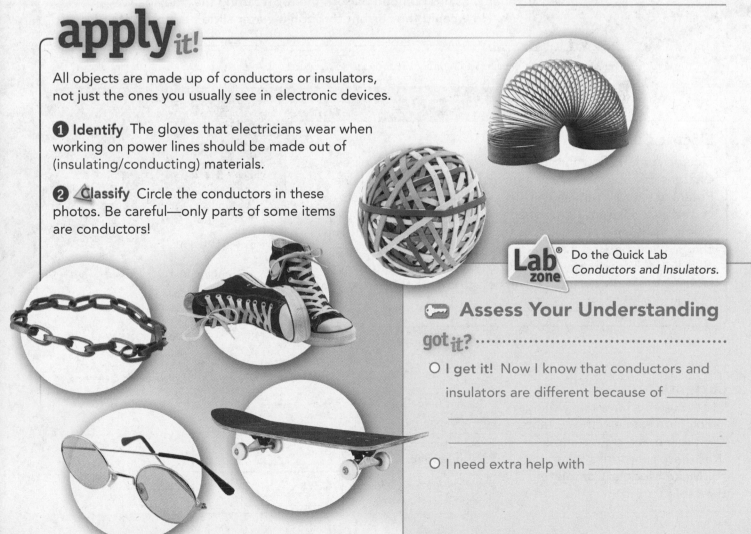

Lab zone® Do the Quick Lab *Conductors and Insulators.*

🔑 **Assess Your Understanding**

got it? ....

○ **I get it!** Now I know that conductors and insulators are different because of _____

_____

○ **I need extra help with** _____

307

What Affects Current Flow?

Suppose you are on a water slide at an amusement park. You climb the steps, sit down, and whoosh! The water current carries you down the slide. Electric charges flow in much the same way water moves down the slide. 🔑 **Current flow is affected by the energy of the charges and the properties of the objects that the charges flow through.**

Water Currents

A completely horizontal water slide wouldn't be much fun. A water slide that was only a few centimeters tall wouldn't be much better. Water slides are exciting because of gravitational potential energy. (Remember that gravitational potential energy is the energy an object has because of its height above the ground.) As the water falls down the slide, its potential energy is converted into kinetic energy. The water speeds up, since speed increases as kinetic energy increases. The higher the slide, the more potential energy the water starts with and the faster it will end up moving. At the bottom of the slide, the water has no potential energy. It has all been converted to kinetic energy. The water gains potential energy as it is pumped back to the top, starting the ride again.

✏️ **How could the current through a water slide be interrupted?**

_____

_____

Electric Currents

Electric currents flow through wires like water through pipes. Charges flow because of differences in electric potential energy. Potential energy from an energy source (like a battery) gets converted into different forms of energy. If a circuit contains a light bulb, its potential energy is converted into light and heat. The charges flow back to the energy source and the process restarts.

✏️ **Slides convert gravitational potential energy into kinetic energy. What do circuits convert electric potential energy into?**

_____

FIGURE 3 ·······························

Currents

Water currents have many things in common with electric currents. The table at the right summarizes these similarities.

✏️ **Make Models** Complete the table.

	Water Current	Electric Current
Current is made up of moving	water	charges
Potential energy is converted into		heat, light
The energy source for the circuit is a		battery

Voltage

The *V* on a battery stands for volts, which is the unit of voltage. **Voltage** is the difference in electric potential energy *per charge* between two points in a circuit. (Electric potential energy per charge is also called electric potential.) This energy difference causes charges to flow. Because the voltage of a battery is related to energy per charge, it doesn't tell you how much total energy the battery supplies. A car battery and eight watch batteries both supply 12 volts, but eight watch batteries can't run a car. Each charge has the same amount of energy, but the car battery can provide that energy to many more charges. This results in a higher *total* energy. You can compare voltage to gravitational potential energy *per kilogram*. **Figure 4** shows the difference between total energy and energy per kilogram.

FIGURE 4 ······································

Voltage

The total electric potential energy a charge has depends on voltage, just as the gravitational potential energy a person has depends on his or her height above the ground. Total gravitational potential energy is the energy per kilogram times the number of kilograms, and total electric potential energy is the energy per charge times the number of charges.

 Interpret Diagrams Answer the questions.

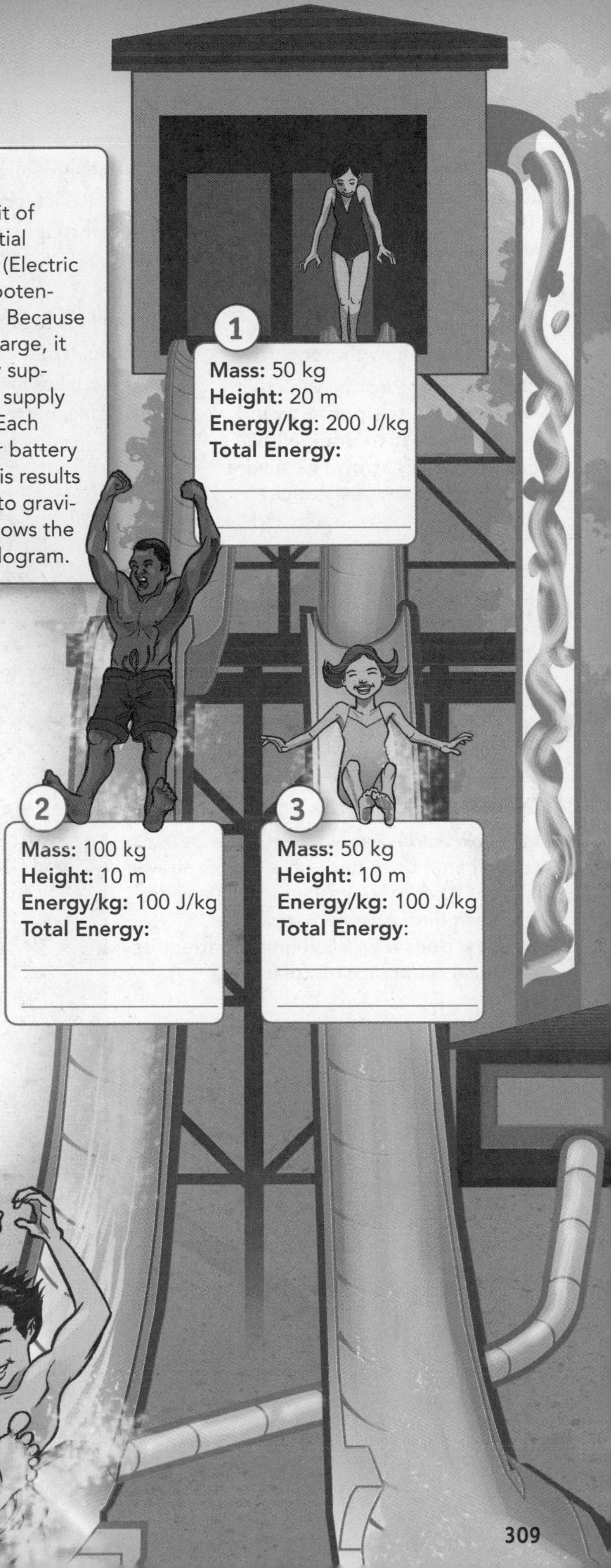

1. In the boxes, calculate the amount of gravitational potential energy each person has.

2. Which two people represent batteries with the same voltage?

_____

3. Draw boxes around the two people who represent batteries that supply the same total amount of energy.

4. Gravitational potential energy per kilogram decreases as you go down the slide. This is like decreasing (voltage/total potential energy).

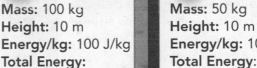

1
Mass: 50 kg
Height: 20 m
Energy/kg: 200 J/kg
Total Energy:
_____
_____

2
Mass: 100 kg
Height: 10 m
Energy/kg: 100 J/kg
Total Energy:
_____
_____

3
Mass: 50 kg
Height: 10 m
Energy/kg: 100 J/kg
Total Energy:
_____
_____

FIGURE 5 ··················

Dimensions and Resistance

The length and diameter of a straw determine how difficult it is to drink through it. Similarly, the length and diameter of a wire determine how difficult it is for charge to flow through it.

✎ **Interpret Photos** Which of the straws in the photo would be the hardest to drink with? Explain. Is this straw like a wire with high or low resistance?

_____
_____
_____
_____
_____
_____

Diameter

Milk flows more easily through a wide straw than it does through a narrow straw. Current flows more easily through a wide wire than through a narrow wire.

✎ **How does a wire's diameter affect its electrical resistance? Explain.**

_____
_____
_____
_____
_____

Resistance The amount of current in a circuit depends on more than voltage. Current also depends on the resistance of the circuit. **Resistance** is the measure of how difficult it is for charges to flow through an object. The greater the resistance, the less current there is for a given voltage. The unit of measure of resistance is the ohm (Ω).

The four factors that determine the resistance of an object are diameter, length, material, and temperature. Objects with different characteristics have different resistances. If more than one path is available, more current will flow through the path that has the lower resistance.

Length

You may have noticed that it is easier to drink milk through a short straw than through a long straw. Similarly, short wires have less resistance than long wires.

✎ **How does an object's length affect its electrical resistance?**

_____
_____
_____
_____

FIGURE 6

Materials and Resistance

When power lines fall down during storms, the workers repairing them must be careful to avoid electric shocks.

✏ **Solve Problems** What should workers wear while doing the job? What should they avoid wearing?

_____

_____

_____

_____

Material

Some materials have electrons that are tightly held to their atoms. They have a high resistance because it is difficult for charges to move. Other materials have electrons that are loosely held to their atoms. They have a low resistance because charges can move through them easily.

✏ **Do conductors or insulators have a lower resistance? Explain.**

_____

_____

_____

_____

Word Origins *Resistance* comes from the word *resist*, which comes from the Latin word *resistere*. What do you think *resistere* means?

○ to be opposed to

○ to run

○ to speed up

Temperature

The electrical resistance of most materials increases as temperature increases. As the temperature of most materials decreases, resistance decreases as well.

✏ **Why would it be useful to keep power lines cool in the summer?**

_____

_____

_____

_____

Lab zone Do the Quick Lab *Modeling Potential Difference.*

🔑 Assess Your Understanding

2a. List List the four factors that determine the resistance of an object.

_____

_____

b. **CHALLENGE** Battery A supplies 500 charges. Each charge has 2 J of energy. Battery B supplies 50 charges, each of which has 4 J of energy. Which battery supplies more total energy? Which has a higher voltage?

_____

got it?

○ **I get it!** Now I know that current is affected by _____

○ **I need extra help with** _____

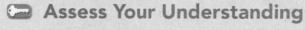

311

Electric Circuits

UNLOCK THE BIG ?

🔑 **What Did Ohm Discover?**

🔑 **What Is a Circuit Made Of?**

my planet DiaRY

Lights Out

One winter night, a string of bright lights adorning a store window catches your eye. As you look, one bulb suddenly goes out, yet the others stay on! How can that be?

Normally, when a light bulb burns out, it breaks the flow of current through a circuit. But many holiday lights are on circuits that provide more than one possible path for the electric current to follow. This type of circuit provides a path for the current to flow even if one component goes bad. So if one light bulb burns out, the rest of the lights remain lit.

FUN FACTS

Communicate Discuss these questions with a partner and then answer them below.

1. What other devices have you used that can keep working even if one part stops working?

   _____

   _____

   _____

2. When could it be useful to have a device turn off completely if one part breaks?

   _____

   _____

   _____

 Do the Inquiry Warm-Up *Do the Lights Keep Shining?*

Vocabulary
- Ohm's law
- series circuit
- parallel circuit

Skills
- Reading: Compare and Contrast
- Inquiry: Make Models

What Did Ohm Discover?

In the 1800s, Georg Ohm performed many experiments on electrical resistance. **Ohm found that the current, voltage, and resistance in a circuit are always related in the same way.**

Ohm's Observations Ohm set up a circuit with a voltage between two points on a conductor. He measured the resistance of the conductor and the current between those points. Then he changed the voltage and took new measurements.

Ohm found that if the factors that affect resistance are held constant, the resistance of most conductors does not depend on the voltage across them. Changing the voltage in a circuit changes the current but does not change the resistance. Ohm concluded that conductors and most other devices have a constant resistance regardless of the applied voltage.

FIGURE 1 ···

Circuit Relationships

The work Ohm did on circuits in the 1800s still applies to almost all electric circuits today. The mathematical relationship he found between the components in a circuit holds true for circuits in everyday devices such as cell phones.

✎ **Interpret Data** Suppose you use various cell phone parts to perform experiments similar to Ohm's. You come up with the following data table. Use the data to predict the relationship that Ohm found.

Voltage (V)	Current (A)	Resistance (Ω)
6.0	2.0	3.0
6.0	1.5	4.0
6.0	1.0	6.0
4.2	2.0	2.1
4.2	0.7	6.0
4.2	1.4	3.0

Ohm's Law Ohm created a law that describes how voltage, current, and resistance are related. **Ohm's law** says that resistance in a circuit is equal to voltage divided by current. This relationship can be represented by an equation.

$$\text{Resistance} = \frac{\text{Voltage}}{\text{Current}}$$

The units are ohms (Ω) = volts (V) ÷ amps (A). One ohm is equal to one volt per amp. You can rearrange Ohm's law to solve for voltage when you know current and resistance.

$$\textbf{Voltage} = \textbf{Current} \times \textbf{Resistance}$$

You can use the formula to see how changes in resistance, voltage, and current are related. For example, what happens to current if voltage is doubled without changing the resistance? For a constant resistance, if voltage is doubled, current doubles as well.

do the
math!

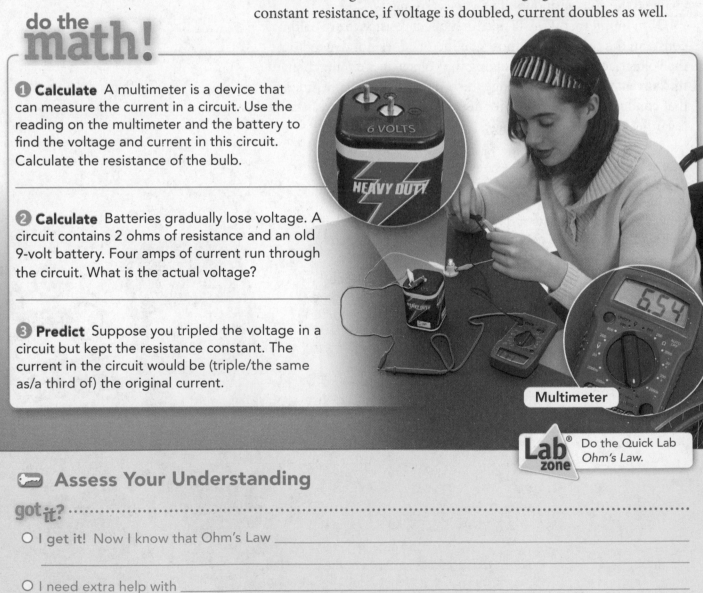

❶ **Calculate** A multimeter is a device that can measure the current in a circuit. Use the reading on the multimeter and the battery to find the voltage and current in this circuit. Calculate the resistance of the bulb.

_____

❷ **Calculate** Batteries gradually lose voltage. A circuit contains 2 ohms of resistance and an old 9-volt battery. Four amps of current run through the circuit. What is the actual voltage?

_____

❸ **Predict** Suppose you tripled the voltage in a circuit but kept the resistance constant. The current in the circuit would be (triple/the same as/a third of) the original current.

Multimeter

Lab zone® Do the Quick Lab
Ohm's Law.

🔑 Assess Your Understanding

got it? ....

O **I get it!** Now I know that Ohm's Law _____

_____

O **I need extra help with** _____

What Is a Circuit Made Of?

Objects that use electricity contain circuits. 🔑 **All electric circuits have these basic features: devices that run on electrical energy, sources of electrical energy, and conducting wires.**

- Batteries and power plants are examples of energy sources. They supply the voltage that causes current to flow. When the energy source is a battery, current flows from the positive end to the negative end.
- Energy is always conserved in a circuit. Electrical energy doesn't get used up. It gets transformed into other forms of energy, such as heat, light, mechanical, and sound energy. Appliances such as toasters transform electrical energy. These devices resist current, so they are represented in a circuit as resistors.
- Electric circuits are connected by conducting wires. The conducting wires complete the path of the current. They allow charges to flow from the energy source to the device that runs on electric current and back to the energy source.
- A switch is often included to control the current. Opening a switch breaks the circuit, which shuts off the device.

All the parts of a circuit are shown in **Figure 2**. Each part in the photograph is represented in the diagram by a simple symbol.

FIGURE 2 ·······························
Circuit Diagrams
A symbol in a circuit diagram represents a part of the circuit.

✏️ 🔺 **Make Models** Draw the circuit diagram for a circuit with two resistors, two batteries, and a switch.

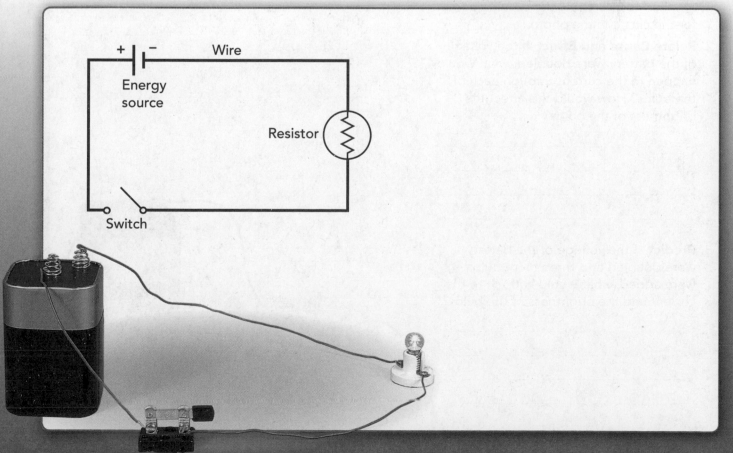

Compare and Contrast On these two pages, underline differences between series and parallel circuits. Below, list their similarities.

_____

_____

_____

_____

_____

Series Circuits

If all the parts of an electric circuit are connected one after another along one path, the circuit is called a **series circuit.** A series circuit has only one path for the current to take.

A series circuit is very simple to design and build, but it has some disadvantages. What happens if a light bulb in a series circuit burns out? A burned-out bulb is a break in the circuit, and there is no other path for the current to take. So if one light goes out, the other lights go out as well.

Another disadvantage of a series circuit is that the light bulbs in the circuit become dimmer as more bulbs are added. Think about what happens to the overall resistance of a series circuit as you add more bulbs. The resistance increases. Remember that for a constant voltage, if resistance increases, current decreases. If you add light bulbs to a series circuit without changing the voltage, the current decreases. The bulbs burn less brightly.

FIGURE 3 ····················

Series Circuits

The number of bulbs in a series circuit affects each bulb's brightness. Remember that voltage = current × resistance.

Answer the questions below.

1. **Make Models** Draw the circuit diagram for the circuit in the photo.

2. **Relate Cause and Effect** If the voltage of the battery were doubled, what would happen to the current through each of the bulbs? How would this affect the brightness of the bulbs?

_____

_____

_____

_____

3. **Predict** If the voltage of the battery were doubled **and** three more bulbs were added, what would happen to the current and the brightness of the bulbs?

_____

_____

_____

_____

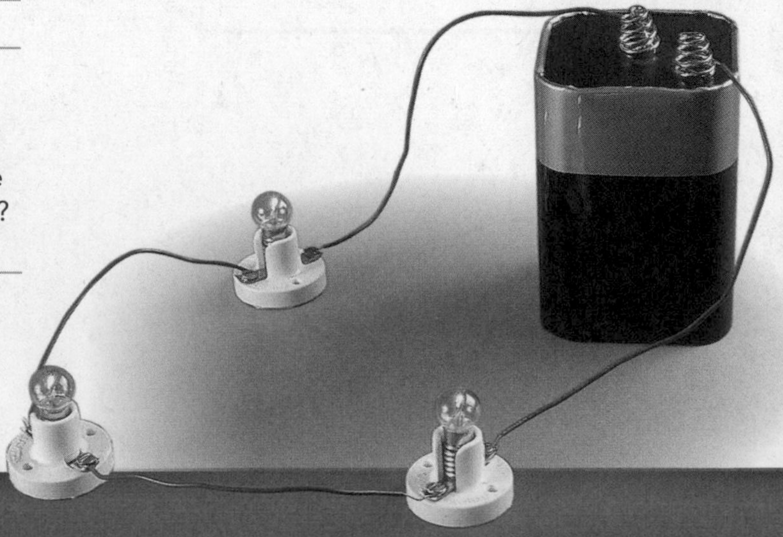

Parallel Circuits In a **parallel circuit,** different parts of the circuit are on separate branches. There are several paths for current to take. Each bulb is connected by a separate path from the battery and back to the battery.

What happens if a light burns out in a parallel circuit? If there is a break in one branch, charges can still move through the other branches. So if one bulb goes out, the others remain lit. Switches can be added to each branch to turn lights on and off without affecting the other branches.

What happens to the resistance of a parallel circuit when you add a branch? The overall resistance actually *decreases*. As new branches are added to a parallel circuit, the electric current has more paths to follow, so the overall resistance decreases. Remember that for a given voltage, if resistance decreases, current increases. The additional current travels along each new branch without affecting the original branches. So as you add branches to a parallel circuit, the brightness of the light bulbs does not change.

FIGURE 4 ·····································

Parallel Circuits
A floor lamp with multiple bulbs can be represented with the same circuit diagram as the circuit at the left. You can turn each bulb on and off individually.

✎ **Make Models** On the circuit diagram, draw where the switches must be for a lamp like this. If the lamp is lit as it is in the photo below, trace the path(s) in the circuit through which current flows.

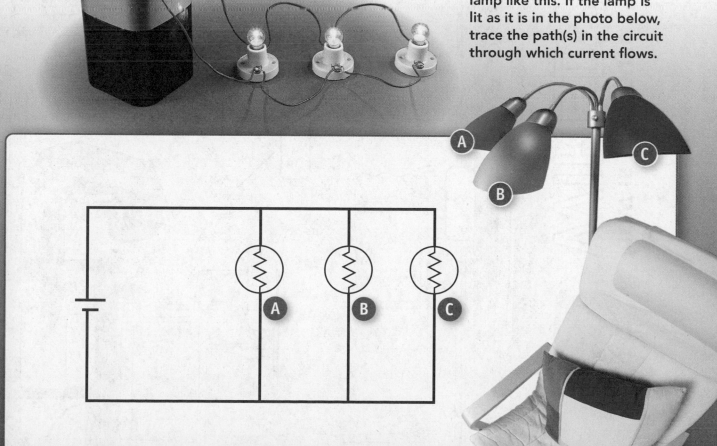

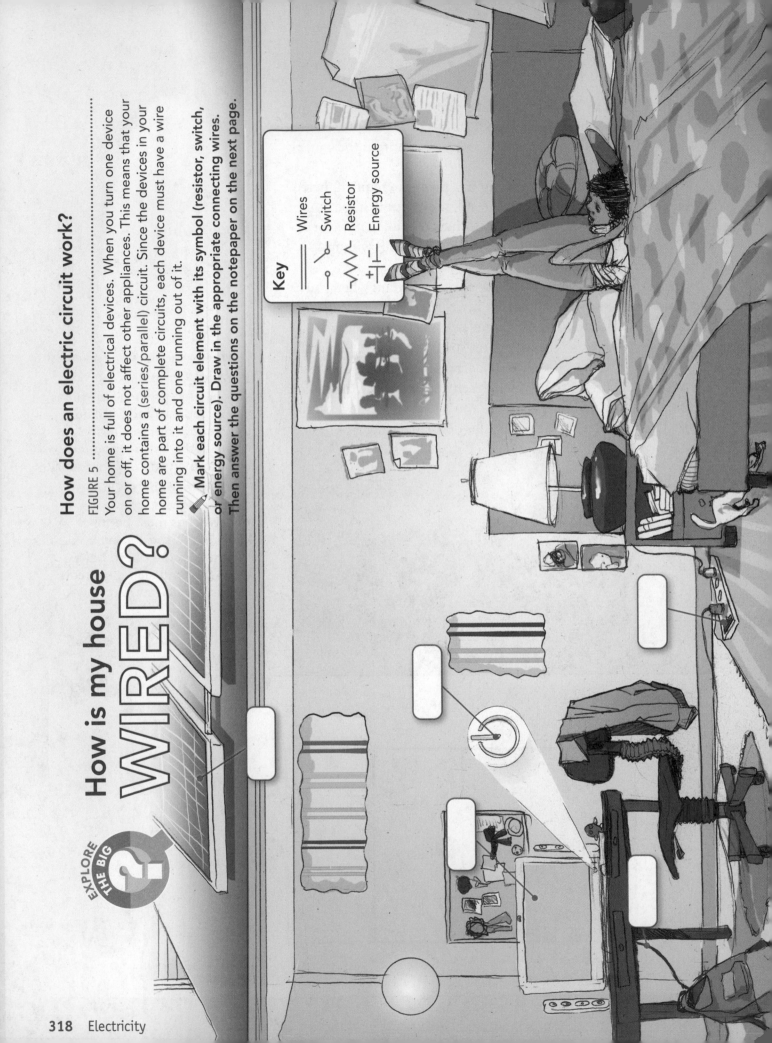

How is my house WIRED?

How does an electric circuit work?

FIGURE 5 .... Your home is full of electrical devices. When you turn one device on or off, it does not affect other appliances. This means that your home contains a (series/parallel) circuit. Since the devices in your home are part of complete circuits, each device must have a wire running into it and one running out of it.

✎ Mark each circuit element with its symbol (resistor, switch, or energy source). Draw in the appropriate connecting wires. Then answer the questions on the notepaper on the next page.

Key
- Wires
- Switch
- Resistor
- Energy source

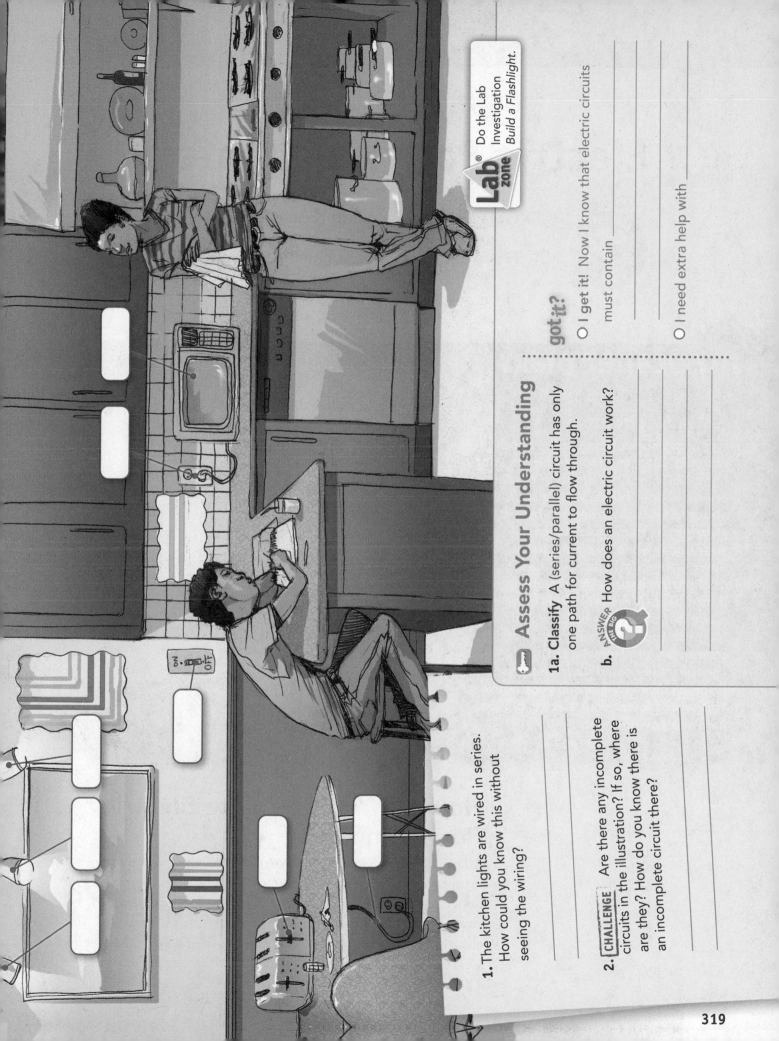

Lab
zone®

Do the Lab
Investigation
Build a Flashlight.

1. The kitchen lights are wired in series. How could you know this without seeing the wiring?

_____

2. **CHALLENGE** Are there any incomplete circuits in the illustration? If so, where are they? How do you know there is an incomplete circuit there?

_____

_____

Assess Your Understanding

1a. Classify A (series/parallel) circuit has only one path for current to flow through.

b. **ANSWER** How does an electric circuit work?

_____

_____

got it?

○ I get it! Now I know that electric circuits must contain _____

_____

○ I need extra help with _____

319

Electric Power and Safety

🔑 **How Do You Calculate Electric Power and Energy?**

🔑 **How Can Electric Shocks Be Prevented?**

my planeT DiaRY

DISCOVERY

A Bright Idea

Forget about being *in* the spotlight—with LED clothing you can *be* the spotlight! LEDs, or light-emitting diodes, are small light bulbs. What's special about LEDs is that they can be just as bright as the regular bulbs in your home while using much less energy. Regular bulbs waste a lot of electrical energy by converting it into heat. A dress like this one made out of regular bulbs would be much too hot to wear! As scientists work to make LEDs cheaper, they could go from dresses in fashion shows to lamps in your house. This would lower your electric bill and help the environment.

Answer the question below.

What other electrical devices could be made more efficient with LEDs?

_____

_____

_____

_____

 Do the Inquiry Warm-Up *How Can You Make a Bulb Burn More Brightly?*

How Do You Calculate Electric Power and Energy?

All electrical appliances transform electrical energy into other forms. Hair dryers transform electrical energy into thermal energy to dry your hair. An amplifier that a guitar player uses transforms electrical energy into sound. A washing machine transforms electrical energy into mechanical energy. The rate at which energy is transformed from one form to another is known as **power**. The unit of power is the watt (W).

Vocabulary
- power • short circuit
- third prong • grounded
- fuse • circuit breaker

Skills
- Reading: Summarize
- Inquiry: Calculate

Power Ratings You are already familiar with different amounts of electric power. The power rating of a bright light bulb, for example, might be 100 W. The power rating of a dimmer bulb might be 60 W. The brighter bulb transforms (or uses) electrical energy at a faster rate than the dimmer bulb.

Calculating Power The power of a light bulb or appliance depends on two factors: voltage and current.

🔑 **Power is calculated by multiplying voltage by current.**

$$\text{Power} = \text{Voltage} \times \text{Current}$$

The units are watts (W) = volts (V) × amperes (A). The equation can also be rearranged to let you solve for current if you know power and voltage.

$$\text{Current} = \frac{\text{Power}}{\text{Voltage}}$$

✏️ **Summarize** Summarize what you have learned from these two pages.

_____

_____

_____

_____

_____

_____

_____

do the math! ─ TECH & DESIGN ─

Many appliances around your home are labeled with their power ratings. In the United States, standard wall outlets supply 120 volts.

△ **Calculate** Determine the current running through each of these appliances. (The toaster has been done for you.)

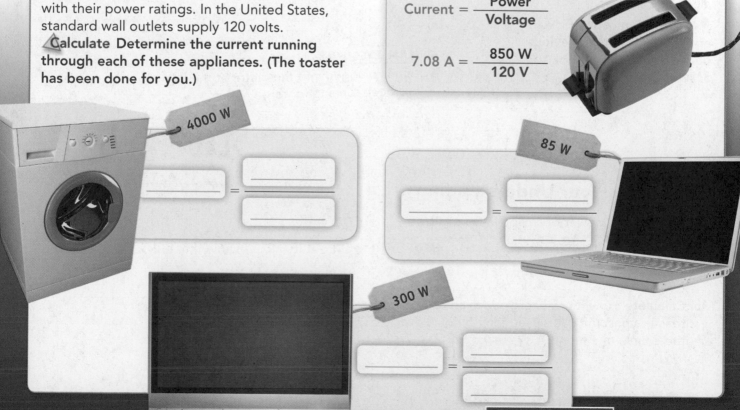

850 W

$$\text{Current} = \frac{\text{Power}}{\text{Voltage}}$$

$$7.08 \text{ A} = \frac{850 \text{ W}}{120 \text{ V}}$$

4000 W

85 W

300 W

Paying for Electrical Energy

The electric bill that comes to your home charges for the month's energy use, not power. Power tells you how much energy an appliance uses in a certain amount of time. 🔑 **The total amount of energy used is equal to the power of the appliance multiplied by the amount of time the appliance is used.**

$$\text{Energy} = \textbf{Power} \times \textbf{Time}$$

Electric power is usually measured in thousands of watts, or kilowatts (kW). To go from watts to kilowatts, you divide by 1,000. Time is measured in hours. A common unit of electrical energy is the kilowatt-hour (kWh).

$$\text{Kilowatt-hours} = \textbf{Kilowatts} \times \textbf{Hours}$$

A refrigerator averages a power of 0.075 kW (75 W). Knowing that, you can calculate how much energy it will use in one month (about 720 hours).

$$\text{Energy} = \textbf{0.075 kW} \times \textbf{720 hours}$$

$$\text{Energy} = \textbf{54 kWh}$$

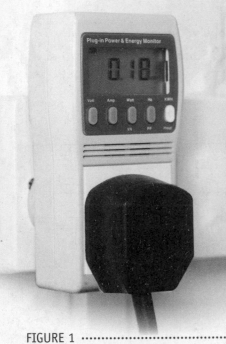

FIGURE 1 ·······························

Electrical Energy
There are devices that let you measure the energy usage of electronic devices.

✎ **Apply Concepts** Pick an appliance from the previous page. Use the notebook to answer the questions.

1. What would the monitor display if the appliance you picked was plugged in for three hours?

2. [CHALLENGE] Calculate the power rating for the appliance that is plugged into the meter at the left. Assume that it has been running for three hours.

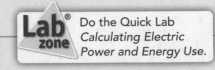

Do the Quick Lab
Calculating Electric Power and Energy Use.

🔑 Assess Your Understanding

1a. Review The power of an appliance can be found by multiplying _____ by _____.

b. Calculate How much energy does an 850 W toaster consume if it is used for 1.5 hours over the course of a month?

_____

_____

got it?

○ I get it! Now I know that electric power and energy depend on _____

_____

○ I need extra help with _____

How Can Electric Shocks Be Prevented?

A **short circuit** is a connection that allows current to take the path of least resistance. Touching a frayed wire causes a short circuit, since current can flow through the person rather than through the wire. Since the new path has less resistance, the current can be very high. Many bodily functions, such as heartbeat, breathing, and muscle movement, are controlled by electrical signals. Because of this, electric shocks can be fatal.

Shocks can be prevented with devices that redirect current or break circuits. Ground wires connect the circuits in a building directly to Earth, giving charges an alternate path in the event of a short circuit. The **third prong** you may have seen on electrical plugs connects the metal parts of appliances to the building's ground wire. Any circuit connected to Earth in this way is **grounded**.

The circuits in your home also contain devices that prevent circuits from overheating, since overheated circuits can result in fires. **Fuses** are devices that melt if they get too hot. This breaks the circuit. **Circuit breakers** are switches that will bend away from circuits as they heat up. Unlike fuses, which break when they are triggered, circuit breakers can be reset.

FIGURE 2 ···

Fuses

Fuses are often found in appliances such as coffee makers. A fuse will melt and break, cutting off the circuit, before the appliance can get so hot that it catches fire.

✎ **Infer** What other electronic devices may contain fuses? Explain your reasoning.

_____

_____

_____

Do the Quick Lab
*Electric Shock and
Short Circuit Safety.*

🔑 **Assess Your Understanding**

got it? ···

○ **I get it!** Now I know that electric safety devices _____

_____

_____

○ **I need extra help with** _____

323

7 Study Guide

REVIEW
THE BIG
?

The basic features of an electric circuit are _____

_____

_____

LESSON 1 Electric Charge and Static Electricity

🔑 Charges that are the same repel each other. Charges that are different attract each other.

🔑 There are four methods by which charges can redistribute themselves to build up static electricity: by friction, by conduction, by induction, and by polarization.

Vocabulary
- electric force • electric field
- static electricity • conservation of charge
- friction • conduction
- induction • polarization • static discharge

LESSON 2 Electric Current

🔑 When electric charges are made to flow through a material, they produce an electric current.

🔑 The atoms in conductors have loosely bound electrons that can move freely. Electrons in insulators cannot move freely among atoms.

🔑 Current flow is affected by the energy of the charges and the properties of the objects that the charges flow through.

Vocabulary
- electric current • electric circuit
- conductor • insulator • voltage • resistance

LESSON 3 Electric Circuits

🔑 Ohm found that the current, voltage, and resistance in a circuit are always related in the same way.

🔑 All electric circuits have the same basic features: devices that are run by electrical energy, sources of electrical energy, and conducting wires.

Vocabulary
- Ohm's law • series circuit • parallel circuit

LESSON 4 Electric Power and Safety

🔑 Power is calculated by multiplying voltage by current.

🔑 The total amount of energy used is equal to the power of the appliance multiplied by the amount of time the appliance is used.

🔑 Shocks can be prevented with devices that redirect current or break circuits.

Vocabulary
- power • short circuit • third prong
- grounded • fuse • circuit breaker

Review and Assessment

LESSON 1 Electric Charge and Static Electricity

1. What type of charge transfer occurs when two objects are rubbed together?

   a. friction   b. induction

   c. conduction   d. polarization

2. The transfer of electrons from a cloud to the ground during a lightning strike is an example of _____

3. **Apply Concepts** Draw the electric field for a single positive charge. Be sure to show which way the field lines point.

4. **Relate Cause and Effect** Explain what happens to the electrons in a metal object when it is held near a negatively charged object. What happens to the overall charge of the metal object?

   _____

   _____

   _____

   _____

   _____

5. **Write About It** A park needs a sign to tell visitors what to do during a thunderstorm. Write a paragraph that explains why standing under a tall tree during a thunderstorm is dangerous.

LESSON 2 Electric Current

6. Which of these objects is an insulator?

   a. gold ring   b. copper coin

   c. glass rod   d. steel fork

7. An electric current is _____

   _____

8. **Classify** The appliances in your home can be made of several different materials. What kinds of materials are the wires made of? What kinds of materials surround the wire for safety?

   _____

   _____

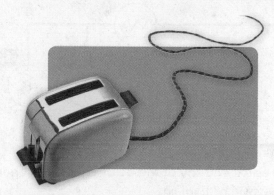

9. **Infer** Copper wires carry electric current from power plants to users. How is the resistance of these power lines likely to vary during the year in an area that has very hot summers? Explain.

   _____

   _____

   _____

   _____

10. **Make Models** Water will not flow down a flat slide because there is no potential energy difference between the two ends. How could this situation be represented in an electric circuit? Explain your reasoning.

   _____

   _____

   _____

Electric Circuits

11. Lisa built an electric circuit. When she added a second light bulb, the first bulb became dimmer. What type of circuit did Lisa build?

   a. series   **b.** parallel

   c. open   **d.** short

12. According to Ohm's law, the resistance in a circuit can be determined by _____

_____

Use the diagram below to answer Questions 13 and 14.

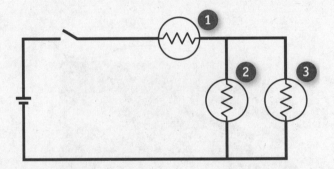

13. Predict Will any of the bulbs light if you open the switch? Explain.

_____

_____

14. Control Variables Which bulbs would continue to shine if Bulb 1 broke? Which would shine if Bulb 2 broke instead? Explain.

_____

_____

_____

_____

15. math! Most homes contain 120-V outlets. Suppose you have lamps with resistances of 120 Ω, 144 Ω, and 240 Ω. Predict which one will draw the most current. Check your prediction by calculating the current that runs through each lamp.

Electric Power and Safety

16. What unit is used to measure electric power?

   a. ampere (A)   **b.** volt (V)

   c. watt (W)   **d.** ohm (Ω)

17. An appliance's total electrical energy consumption is calculated by _____

_____

18. Infer If you touch an electric wire and get a shock, what can you infer about the resistance of your body compared to the resistance of the circuit?

_____

_____

19. Calculate A device draws 40 A of current and has a 12-V battery. What is its power?

_____

 How does an electric circuit work?

20. Identify the parts that make up the circuit in a laptop computer. Describe what happens inside the circuit when the computer is on.

_____

_____

_____

_____

_____

_____

_____

_____

_____

_____

Standardized Test Prep

Read each question and choose the best answer.

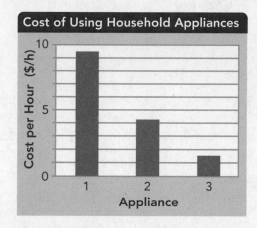

Cost of Using Household Appliances

1. **Which of the following is a valid interpretation of the graph?**

   A The voltage is highest in Appliance 1.

   B Appliance 1 uses the most power.

   C During one month, a family pays more to run Appliance 1 than Appliance 2.

   D Appliance 1 draws the least current.

2. **Your alarm clock has a voltage of 120 V and a resistance of 1200 Ω. What current does the alarm clock draw?**

   A 0.10 A

   B 10.0 A

   C 12.0 A

   D 100 A

3. **You want to build a device that can conduct current but will be safe if touched by a person. Which of the following pairs of materials could you use?**

   A glass to conduct and rubber to insulate

   B copper to conduct and silver to insulate

   C sand to conduct and plastic to insulate

   D silver to conduct and plastic to insulate

4. **How does a fuse prevent electrical fires?**

   A by providing a path for excess charges to get to the ground

   B by melting if the current gets too high

   C by reducing the voltage supplied to electrical devices

   D by storing potential energy for later use

5. **What happens when an object is rubbed against another object to charge by friction?**

   A Electrons are transferred from one object to another.

   B Electrons in one of the objects disappear.

   C Electrons in one object suddenly become negatively charged.

   D Electrons are created by the friction between the objects.

Constructed Response

Use your knowledge of science to help you answer Question 6. Write your answer on a separate sheet of paper.

6. A lightning bolt can have a voltage of over 100 million volts. Explain why lightning cannot power your cell phone but a 6-volt battery can. Then explain what would happen if a 100-million-volt battery was plugged into a cell phone. Use Ohm's law in your answer.

SOMETHING for NOTHING

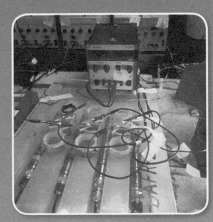

▲ This complicated device can supposedly harness free energy.

The race is on to find a new, cheap energy source. Any online search for "free energy" will find a lot of Web sites. These sites promise clean, free electricity if you buy or invest in their devices.

But can they back up their promises? Many sites suggest that the power companies have conspired against the people who have discovered and invented these free-energy devices. One site even claims that there is a fourth law of motion. This fourth law is an extension of Newton's Third Law of Motion. If every action has an equal and opposite reaction, the site claims, then that reaction can power the original action.

Debate It Some free-energy devices claim to be able to generate electricity using a perpetual motion machine. Some claim to harness latent heat from the air. Some claim to use magnets. Research how energy is generated, and evaluate these claims. Debate as a class whether it is possible to have truly free energy.

Does free electricity really exist? Some people say yes. ▽

∨ In 1913, Nikola Tesla patented a turbine that ran off of steam. Many people have tried to find a way to use Tesla's engine to generate free electricty.

Going GREEN

Every time you turn on a light, you are using energy. We know this, but we don't always think about where the energy comes from. In most cases, that energy has come from fossil fuels, extracted from the ground, refined, and burned for their energy, in a process that causes a lot of pollution. Some scientists and government policymakers are exploring green (environmentally friendly) sources of energy.

According to the U.S. Environmental Protection Agency (EPA), green energy comes from technologies that don't produce waste products that will harm the environment. This includes resources like solar power and wind power, as well as geothermal energy from hot springs under the Earth's crust.

Reduced air pollution is just one of many benefits of green energy. Green energy also lowers greenhouse gas emissions and can cost less for consumers—like your family! Going green also creates jobs. Having many different sources makes the energy grid more stable. If one source stops working, we will still be able to get energy from other sources. What's not to love? Unfortunately, green energy technologies are expensive to develop.

△ The flow of water is a renewable resource. But hydroelectric dams can damage habitats by changing the course of rivers.

Debate It Research the benefits and costs of developing green energy technologies. Organize a classroom debate about the costs and benefits of green energy. Be prepared to argue both sides of the issue.

HOW CAN THIS TRAIN MOVE WITHOUT TOUCHING THE TRACK?

How are electricity and magnetism related?

This type of train is called a maglev, or magnetic levitation train, and operates at speeds of 430 km/h (about twice as fast as a conventional train). It does not have a traditional engine, which means it does not give off any pollutants. Instead, the maglev train uses electricity in the track to power magnets that propel the train forward and levitation magnets to keep the train floating about 10 mm above the track.

△Draw Conclusions How can this train move without touching the track?

_____

_____

_____

_____

Watch the **Untamed Science** video to learn more about magnetism and electromagnetism.

Magnetism and Electromagnetism

8 Getting Started

Check Your Understanding

1. Background Read the paragraph below and then answer the question.

While Chung works, his computer shuts down. Both the street and his house are dark, so he knows there is no **electricity**. A fallen tree has snapped an electric wire. The wire was the **conductor** that brought him power. Chung reaches for the light switch, but then remembers that no **electric current** will flow when he turns it on.

> **Electricity** is a form of energy sometimes created by the movement of charged particles.
>
> A material through which charges can easily flow is a **conductor.**
>
> **Electric current** is the continuous flow of electric charges through a material.

• How can electricity be restored to Chung's house?

_____

_____

Vocabulary Skill

Use Context to Determine Meaning Science books often use unfamiliar words. Look for context clues in surrounding words and phrases to figure out the meaning of a new word. In the paragraph below, look for clues to the meaning of *magnetic force*.

The attraction or repulsion between magnetic poles is **magnetic force.** A force is a push or pull that can cause an object to change its motion. A magnetic force is produced when magnetic poles interact.

Example	Magnetic force
Definition	*n.* attraction or repulsion between magnetic poles
Explanation	Force is a push or pull.
Other Information	Magnetic force is produced when magnetic poles interact.

2. Quick Check In the paragraph above, circle the explanation of the word *force.*

magnetic pole

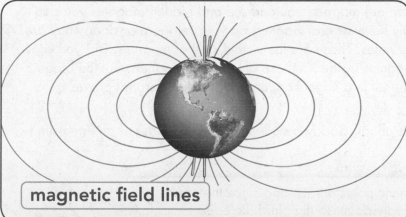

magnetic field lines

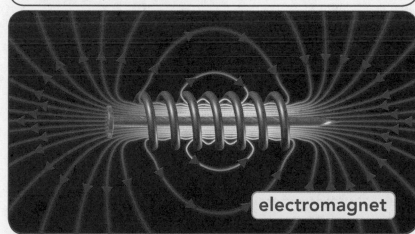

electromagnet

generator

Scenario Investigation

Is the North Pole Really the South Pole?

Purpose To investigate the magnetic poles of Earth

Materials
- compass
- two bar magnets
- paper clip
- refrigerator magnets
- nonmagnetic objects
- map of the community
- index card

Scenario

Magnets are everywhere. In your home there are magnets you can see and hidden magnets you don't see. If you're like most people, you probably have several magnets on your refrigerator door. They are holding up coupons, pictures, and reminder notes. Those are the visible kind of magnets. Did you know that every electric motor has at least two magnets inside it? Those are hidden magnets. But the biggest magnet of all is right under your feet. Earth itself is a huge magnet, and the detector that proves it's a magnet is a compass.

You have read about magnets in your textbook. Today a student in your class asked an interesting question.

> Since opposite magnetic poles attract, and since the north end of a compass needle points to the North Pole, isn't Earth's North Pole really the South Pole?

Some students laughed, and the student who asked the question was embarrassed. But your teacher said this was a very good question and has challenged your class to come up with a logical answer.

Procedure

☐ **1. If the Paper Clip Sticks ...** Humans cannot taste, smell, see, hear, or feel the presence of a magnet. But we can detect magnets using metals such as iron and steel. Metals only work as detectors if the magnetic field is strong enough. Your teacher will give you an assortment of objects. Use a paper clip to check which of the objects are magnets.

☐ **2. It Takes One to Know One** Magnets themselves make good magnet detectors, too. A magnet will attract or repel another magnet. In that way, a magnet can tell you something about the magnet it detects. Test this out with two bar magnets. Which ends attract and which ends repel?

Attract _____

Repel _____

Procedure (continued)

☐ **3. A Compass Is a Magnet Detector** Use a compass to investigate the magnetic field around one of the bar magnets. Which end of the compass points toward the south pole of the bar magnet, and which end points toward the north pole? (Be careful not to let the compass touch the bar magnet. A touch can change the poles of the compass needle.)

End pointing to south pole _____

End pointing to north pole _____

☐ **4. Where on the Map Does the Compass Point?** Examine the map your teacher gave you. The north arrow on the map points in the direction of Earth's North Pole. When you stand facing north, which end of your compass points toward the North Pole of Earth?

_____

Conclusion

Let's see what you learned about magnets and Earth's poles.

☐ **1.** Name two magnet poles that attract one another.

_____

☐ **2.** Which end of a compass needle points toward the south pole of a bar magnet?

_____

☐ **3.** Which end of a compass needle points toward Earth's North Pole?

_____

☐ **4.** Is Earth's North Pole a magnetic north pole or a magnetic south pole?

_____

Your science teacher thinks your discovery will surprise many people. How can you tell the world about it without confusing people? A reporter from your local paper is coming this afternoon to interview you about your discovery. Think about what you want to say and organize the order in which you would say it. Write your ideas on an index card so that you won't forget them when you are being interviewed.

What Is Magnetism?

UNLOCK
THE BIG

🔑 **What Are the Properties of Magnets?**

🔑 **How Do Magnetic Poles Interact?**

my planet diary

Crocodile Sense

Crocodiles are threatened animals. So, if they are not protected, they may become endangered and then disappear altogether. However, in Florida, many crocodiles live where people do, so they threaten people's safety.

To keep both people and crocodiles safe, biologists tried to move crocodiles away from people. But there was a problem. Crocodiles use Earth's magnetic field to help them navigate. Whenever they relocated a crocodile, it eventually returned, if it was not killed on the way back. But then the biologists heard that scientists in Mexico had taped a magnet to each side of a crocodile's head before relocating it. They thought that the magnets would inter- fere with the crocodile's ability to use Earth's magnetic field to find its way back. Biologists here did the same thing. So far, it has been successful.

FUN FACTS

Communicate Discuss the following questions with a partner. Write your answers below.

Why do you think it is important to relocate crocodiles?

_____

_____

_____

_____

_____

_____

Lab ® Do the Inquiry Warm-Up
zone Natural Magnets.

What Are the Properties of Magnets?

Imagine that you're in Shanghai, China, zooming along in a maglev train propelled by magnets. Your 30-kilometer trip from the airport to the city station takes less than eight minutes. The same trip in a taxi would take about an hour.

Vocabulary
- magnet • magnetism
- magnetic pole • magnetic force

Skills
↻ Reading: Summarize
△ Inquiry: Infer

Magnets When you think of magnets, you might think about the objects that hold notes to your refrigerator. But magnets can be large, like the one in Figure 1. They can be small like those on your refrigerator, in your wallet, on your kitchen cabinets, or on security tags at a store. A **magnet** is any material that attracts iron and materials that contain iron.

Discovering Magnets Magnets have many modern uses, but they are not new. The ancient Greeks discovered that a rock called magnetite attracted materials containing iron. The rocks also attracted or repelled other magnetic rocks. The attraction or repulsion of magnetic materials is called **magnetism.**

Magnets have the same properties as magnetite rocks. ⚷ Magnets attract iron and materials that contain iron. Magnets attract or repel other magnets. In addition, one end of a magnet will always point north when allowed to swing freely.

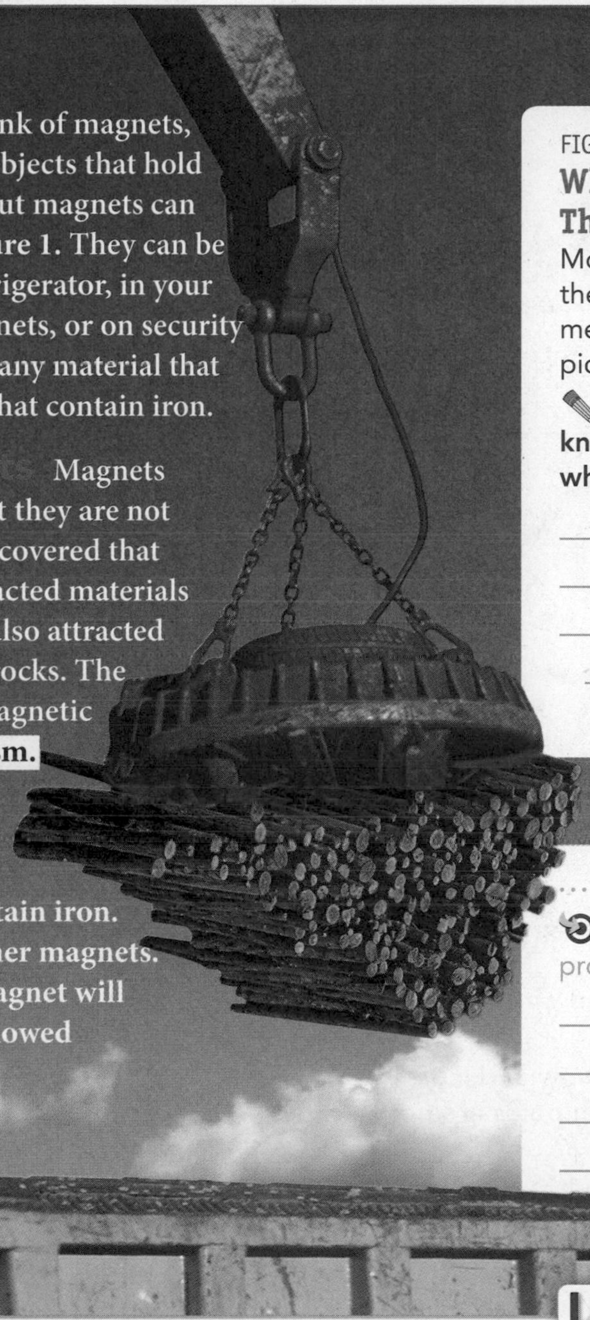

FIGURE 1 ·······
What's Wrong With This Picture?
Most people would not expect the powerful magnet used at a metal scrap yard to be able to pick up wood.

✏ **Explain** Use what you know about magnets to explain why this scene is impossible.

_____

_____

_____

_____

✏

↻ **Summarize** Summarize the properties of magnetite.

_____

_____

_____

_____

Lab zone   Do the Lab Investigation
Detecting Fake Coins.

⚷ Assess Your Understanding

got it? ·······

○ **I get it!** Now I know that three properties of magnets are that magnets _____

_____

_____

○ **I need extra help with** _____

_____

How Do Magnetic Poles Interact?

Any magnet, no matter what its size or shape, has two ends. Each one is called a **magnetic pole.** The magnetic effect of a magnet is strongest at the poles. The pole of a magnet that points north is labeled the *north pole.* The other pole is labeled the *south pole.* A magnet always has both a north pole and a south pole.

Magnetic Interactions What happens if you bring two magnets together? The answer depends on how you hold the poles of the magnets. If you bring the north pole of one magnet near the south pole of another, the two unlike poles attract one another. However, if you bring two north poles together, the like poles move away from each other. **Magnetic poles that are unlike attract each other, and magnetic poles that are alike repel each other.** You can see how bar magnets interact in **Figure 2.**

FIGURE 2 ···

Attraction and Repulsion

These pairs of magnets show how magnetic poles interact.

✎ **Relate Text and Visuals** Draw and label what happens when two south poles are near each other.

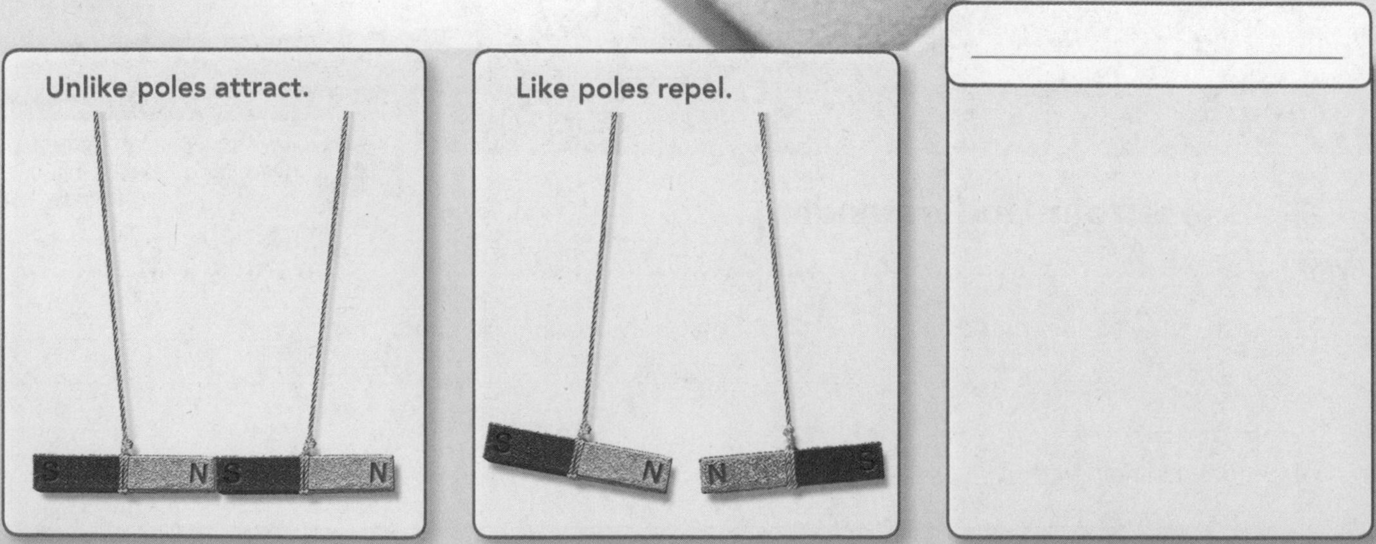

North pole

Unlike poles attract.

S   N   S   N

Like poles repel.

S   N   N   S

Magnetic Force The attraction or repulsion between magnetic poles is **magnetic force.** A force is a push or a pull that can cause an object to move. A magnetic force is produced when magnetic poles come near each other and interact. Any material that exerts a magnetic force is a magnet.

Train car

S
N

Repulsive force

Guideway

apply it!

Train car

The maglev train you read about earlier depends on magnetic force to float above the guideway, or track. The magnetic force is produced by magnets in the bottom of the train and in the guideway.

Magnets

Guideway

1 Infer For the train to float, which pole of the guideway's magnet should face the north pole of the train car's magnet?

_____

2 CHALLENGE List some advantages of the fact that the train does not touch the guideway.

_____

_____

Lab zone® Do the Quick Lab *Magnetic Poles.*

🔑 Assess Your Understanding

1a. Identify What areas of a magnet have the strongest magnetic effect?

_____

_____

_____

b. Relate Cause and Effect How can two magnets demonstrate magnetic force?

_____

_____

_____

got it? ···

○ **I get it!** Now I know that magnetic poles that are unlike _____

and magnetic poles that are alike _____

○ **I need extra help with** _____

_____

Magnetic Fields

🔑 **What Is a Magnetic Field's Shape?**

🔑 **What Is Earth's Magnetic Field Like?**

my planet Diary

Cow Magnets

You probably know that cows eat grass. Did you know that they also eat metal? When cows graze, they may ingest metal objects that contain iron such as nails, wires, and old cans. If the metal is sharp, it could pierce the cow's stomach, causing infection, illness, or even death.

To ensure that their cows are safe, farmers have their cows swallow a magnet. Once inside the cow's stomach, the magnet attracts the iron in the metal that the cow eats. This keeps the metal from moving around and possibly puncturing other organs. One magnet can protect a cow for life.

FUN FACTS

Read the following questions. Write your answers below.

1. Why is it dangerous for a cow to eat metal?

_____

_____

_____

_____

2. As a farmer, what else could you do to keep metal objects from harming the cows?

_____

_____

 Lab zone Do the Inquiry Warm-Up *Predict the Field.*

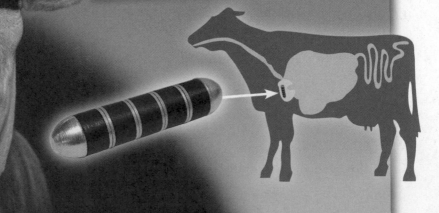

Vocabulary
- magnetic field • magnetic field lines
- compass • magnetic declination

Skills
- 🔁 Reading: Identify the Main Idea
- △ Inquiry: Observe

What Is a Magnetic Field's Shape?

You know that a magnetic force is strongest at the poles of a magnet. But magnetic force is not limited to the poles. It is exerted all around a magnet. The area of magnetic force around a magnet is known as its **magnetic field.** Because of magnetic fields, magnets can interact without even touching.

Representing Magnetic Field Lines Figure 1

shows the magnetic field of a bar magnet. The **magnetic field lines** are shown in purple. Magnetic field lines are lines that map out the invisible magnetic field around a magnet. 🔑 **Magnetic field lines spread out from one pole, curve around the magnet, and return to the other pole.** The lines form complete loops from pole to pole and never cross. Arrowheads indicate the direction of the magnetic field lines. They always leave the north pole and enter the south pole. The closer together the lines are, the stronger the field. Magnetic field lines are closest together at the poles.

FIGURE 1 ···

Magnetic Field Lines

Magnetic fields are invisible, but you can represent a field using magnetic field lines.

✎ **Complete the tasks below.**

1. **Relate Text and Visuals** In the boxes, identify where the magnetic field is strong and where it is weak.

2. **CHALLENGE** Forces that affect objects without touching them are called *field* forces. Is gravity a field force? Explain.

_____

_____

_____

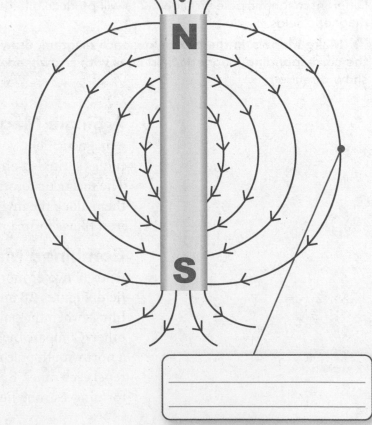

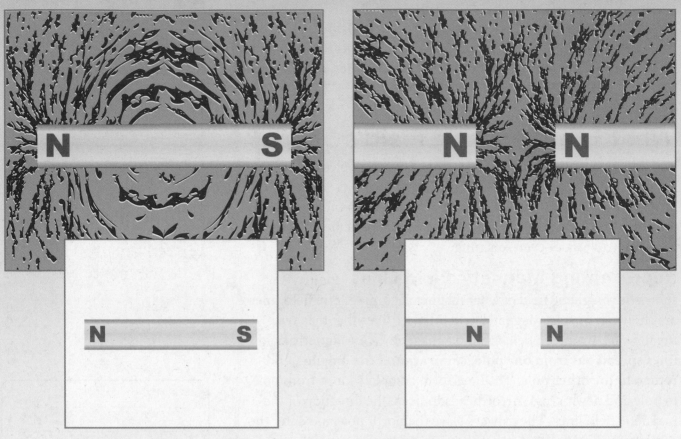

FIGURE 2 ··
Magnetic Fields
Different magnetic pole arrangements will produce different magnetic fields.

✎ **Make Models** In the box below each diagram, draw the corresponding magnetic field lines with arrowheads to show direction.

A Single Magnetic Field Although you cannot see a magnetic field, you can see its effects. **Figure 2A** shows iron filings sprinkled on a sheet of clear plastic that covers one magnet. The magnetic forces of the magnet act on the iron filings and align them along the invisible magnetic field lines. The result is that the iron filings form a pattern similar to magnetic field lines.

Combined Magnetic Fields When the magnetic fields of two or more magnets overlap, the result is a combined field. **Figures 2B** and **2C** show the effects of magnetic force on iron filings when the poles of two bar magnets are brought near each other. Compare the pattern of a north-north pole arrangement and a north-south pole arrangement. The fields from two like poles repel each other. But the fields from unlike poles attract each other, forming a strong field between the magnets.

C Combined Magnetic Field, North-South

S   N

S   N

apply it!

When magnets come together, you can feel magnetic forces.

❶ Observe You hold two refrigerator magnets and push them toward each other. What will you observe that lets you know that the fields of the magnets are interacting?

_____

_____

_____

❷ Develop Hypotheses Why might a magnet that sticks to your refrigerator be unable to pick up a faraway paper clip?

_____

_____

_____

_____

_____

Lab zone® Do the Quick Lab *Spinning in Circles.*

🔑 Assess Your Understanding

1a. Define What is a magnetic field?

_____

_____

_____

_____

_____

b. Describe Describe the magnetic field of a south-south pole arrangement.

_____

_____

_____

_____

got it? ....

○ **I get it!** Now I know that a magnetic field's shape is _____

_____

_____

○ **I need extra help with** _____

_____

What Is Earth's Magnetic Field Like?

People have used compasses as tools for navigation for centuries. A **compass** is a device that has a magnet on a needle that spins freely. It is used for navigation because its needle usually points north. But why does that happen? In the late 1500s an Englishman, Sir William Gilbert, proved that a compass behaves as it does because Earth acts as a giant magnet. **Just like a bar magnet, Earth has a magnetic field around it and two magnetic poles.** So, the poles of a magnetized compass needle align themselves with Earth's magnetic field. See Earth's magnetic field in **Figure 3**.

Earth's Core
Earth's core is a large sphere of metal that occupies Earth's center. The core is divided into two parts—the outer core and the inner core. The outer core is made of hot swirling liquid iron. The motion of this iron creates a magnetic field similar to the magnetic field of a bar magnet.

🎯 **Identify the Main Idea**
What is the main idea in the Earth's Core section?

_____
_____
_____
_____
_____

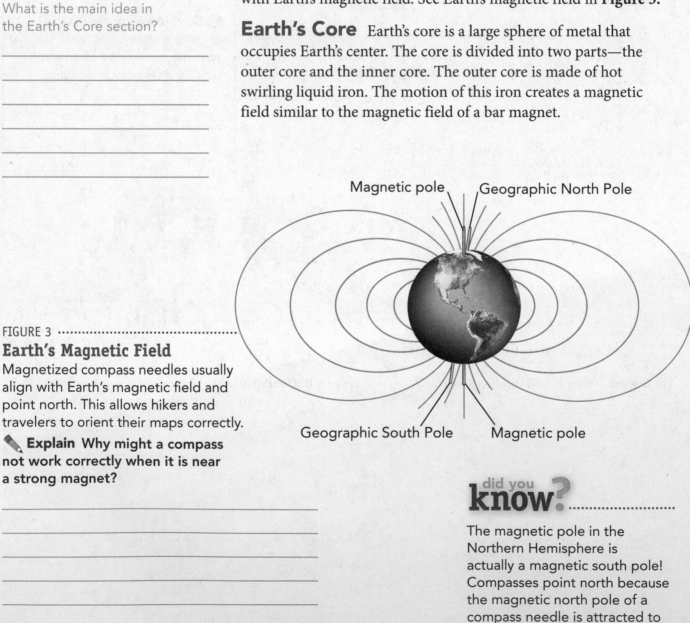

FIGURE 3 ···

Earth's Magnetic Field
Magnetized compass needles usually align with Earth's magnetic field and point north. This allows hikers and travelers to orient their maps correctly.

✏️ **Explain** Why might a compass not work correctly when it is near a strong magnet?

_____
_____
_____
_____
_____
_____

Magnetic pole   Geographic North Pole

Geographic South Pole   Magnetic pole

did you know?·····················

The magnetic pole in the Northern Hemisphere is actually a magnetic south pole! Compasses point north because the magnetic north pole of a compass needle is attracted to the magnetic south pole in the Northern Hemisphere.

Earth's Magnetic Poles You know that Earth has geographic poles. But Earth also has magnetic poles that are located on Earth's surface where the magnetic force is strongest. As you just saw in **Figure 3,** the magnetic poles are not in the same place as the geographic poles. Suppose you could draw a line between you and the geographic North Pole. Then imagine a second line drawn between you and the magnetic pole in the Northern Hemisphere. The angle between these two lines is the angle between geographic north and the north to which a compass needle points. This angle is known as **magnetic declination.**

The magnetic declination of a location changes. Earth's magnetic poles do not stay in one place as the geographic poles do.

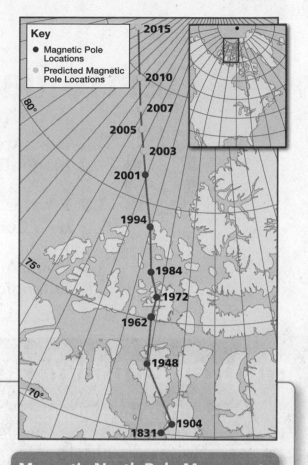

Key
- Magnetic Pole Locations
- Predicted Magnetic Pole Locations

2015
2010
2007
2005
2003
2001
1994
1984
1972
1962
1948
1904
1831

80°
75°
70°

do the math!

The last expedition to directly observe the pole's location was in May 2001. The map shows estimated positions after 2001.

❶ Calculate What is the total distance the pole traveled from 1948 to 2001?

_____

_____

❷ Interpret Data What was the mean speed of the pole's movement from 1948 to 2001? What was the mode?

_____

_____

Magnetic North Pole Movement

Year of Reading	Distance Moved Since Previous Reading (km)
1948	420
1962	150
1972	120
1984	120
1994	180
2001	287

Lab zone   Do the Quick Lab
Earth's Magnetic Field.

🔑 Assess Your Understanding

got it? ·

○ I get it! Now I know that Earth has a magnetic field _____

_____

○ I need extra help with _____

Electromagnetic Force

UNLOCK
THE BIG
?

🔑 How Are Electric Currents and Magnetic Fields Related?

🔑 What Is a Magnetic Field Produced by a Current Like?

🔑 What Are the Characteristics of Solenoids and Electromagnets?

my planet diary

FUN FACTS

More Than Just Plastic

How do plastic cards with stripes, such as your library card, work? The black stripe on the back of the card is made up of tiny magnetic particles. Information can be recorded on the stripe. When a card is swiped through a card-reading machine, the cardholder's information is relayed from the card to a computer or sent to a place for verification.

If the card is placed near magnetic material, the arrangement of the magnetic particles on the stripe can get rearranged. Once this happens, the card becomes useless because it no longer holds the cardholder's information. If you are ever given a credit card to use, make sure you keep it away from magnets or else you may leave the store empty-handed!

Communicate Discuss the question with a partner. Then write your answer below.

List types of cards that have a magnetic stripe.

_____

_____

_____

_____

_____

_____

Lab® Do the Inquiry Warm-Up
zone Electromagnetism.

Vocabulary
- electromagnetism • solenoid
- electromagnet

Skills
⟳ Reading: Relate Cause and Effect
△ Inquiry: Predict

How Are Electric Currents and Magnetic Fields Related?

You know that a magnet has a magnetic field. But did you know that an electric current produces a magnetic field? In 1820, the Danish scientist Hans Christian Oersted (UR STED) accidentally discovered this fact. He was teaching a class at the University of Copenhagen. During his lecture he produced a current in a wire just like the current in a battery-powered flashlight. When he brought a compass near the wire, he observed that the compass needle changed direction.

Oersted's Experiment Oersted could have assumed that something was wrong with his equipment, but instead he decided to investigate further. So he set up several compasses around a wire. With no current in the wire, all of the compass needles pointed north. When he produced a current in the wire, he observed that the compass needles pointed in different directions to form a circle. Oersted concluded that the current had produced a magnetic field around the wire. Oersted's results showed that magnetism and electricity are related.

Cause	Effect
There is no current in the wire.	_____ _____ _____ _____
_____ _____ _____ _____	The compass needles pointed in different directions to form a circle.

✎

⟳ **Relate Cause and Effect**
Use the information about Oersted's experiment to complete the chart.

Electric Current and Magnetism

Oersted's experiment showed that wherever there is electricity, there is magnetism. 🔑 **An electric current produces a magnetic field.** This relationship between electricity and magnetism is called **electromagnetism.** Although you cannot see electromagnetism directly, you can see its effect. That is, a compass needle moves when it is in a magnetic field produced by an electric current, as you can see in **Figure 1.**

FIGURE 1 ·······················

Moving Compass Needles

These photographs show you how an electric current produces a magnetic field.

✎ **Interpret Photos** In the boxes, explain what is happening to the compass needles when the current in the wire is turned on or off.

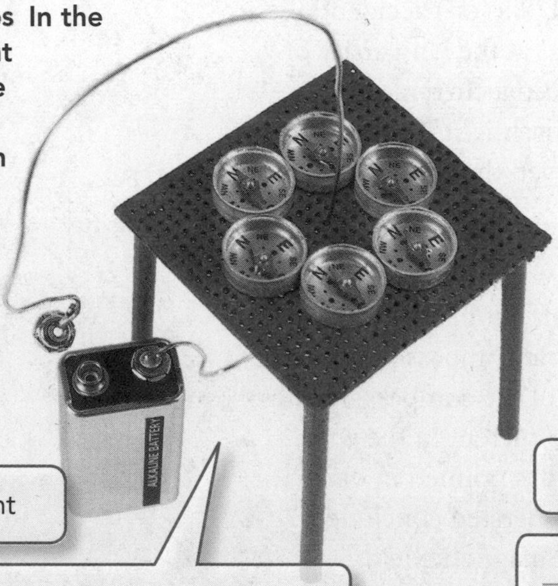

Without current

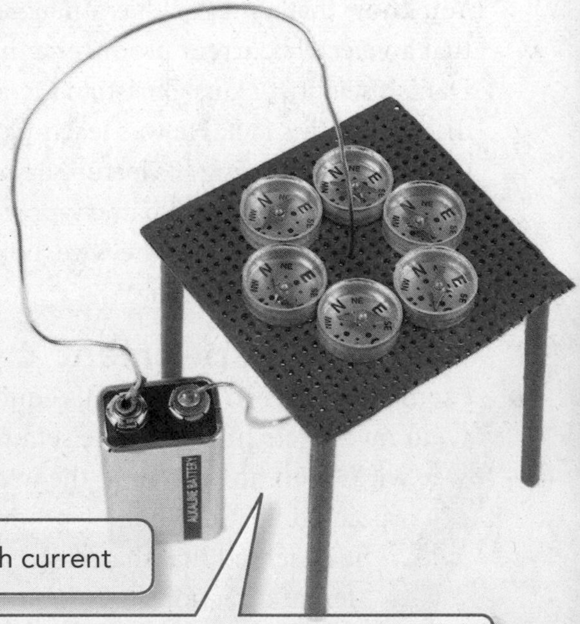

With current

Lab zone Do the Quick Lab *Electric Current and Magnetism.*

🔑 Assess Your Understanding

1a. Explain What did Oersted conclude?

_____

_____

_____

b. 🔄 **Relate Cause and Effect** How does a current affect a compass?

_____

_____

_____

got_{it?} ··

○ **I get it!** Now I know that an electric current produces a _____

○ **I need extra help with** _____

_____

What Is a Magnetic Field Produced by a Current Like?

🔑 **The magnetic field produced by a current has a strength and a direction. The field can be turned on or off, have its direction reversed, or have its strength changed.** To turn a magnetic field produced by a current on or off, you turn the current on or off. To change the direction of the magnetic field, you reverse the direction of the current.

There are two ways to change the strength of a magnetic field. First, you can increase the amount of current in the wire. Second, you can make a loop or coil in the wire. The magnetic field around the wire forms a circle. When you make a loop in a wire, the magnetic field lines bunch close together inside the loop. This strengthens the magnetic field. Every additional loop strengthens the magnetic field even more. **Figure 2** shows three different ways to change the characteristics of a magnetic field.

FIGURE 2 ···

Change Magnetic Field Characteristics

✏️ **Interpret Diagrams** Write the ways used to change the magnetic fields in diagrams A and B. In diagram C, draw a picture to show a third way to change magnetic fields and describe it.

C

A

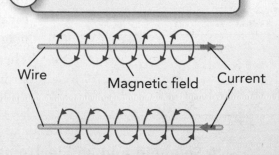

Wire   Magnetic field   Current

B

Bunched magnetic field

Lab® zone   Do the Quick Lab *Magnetic Fields From Electric Current.*

🔑 **Assess Your Understanding**

got_{it}? ···

○ **I get it!** Now I know that the magnetic field produced by a current can be changed by _____

_____

○ **I need extra help with** _____

_____

349

What Are the Characteristics of Solenoids and Electromagnets?

You know that you can strengthen the magnetic field around a wire with a current by coiling the wire. 🔑 **Both solenoids and electromagnets use electric current and coiled wires to produce strong magnetic fields.**

Solenoids By running current through a wire which is wound into many loops, you strengthen the magnetic field in the center of the coil as shown in **Figure 3**. A coil of wire with a current is called a **solenoid.** The two ends of a solenoid act like the poles of a magnet. However, the north and south poles change when the direction of the current changes.

Electromagnets If you place a material with strong magnetic properties inside a solenoid, the strength of the magnetic field increases. This is because the material, called a ferromagnetic material, becomes a magnet. A solenoid with a ferromagnetic core is called an **electromagnet.** Both the current in the wire and the magnetized core produce the magnetic field of an electromagnet. Therefore, the overall magnetic field of an electromagnet is much stronger than that of a solenoid. An electromagnet is turned on and off by turning the current on and off.

FIGURE 3 ···

A Solenoid and an Electromagnet

An electromagnet is a solenoid with a ferromagnetic core.

✏️ Interpret Diagrams **Explain how the diagram shows you that the magnetic field of the electromagnet is stronger than that of the solenoid on its own.**

_____

_____

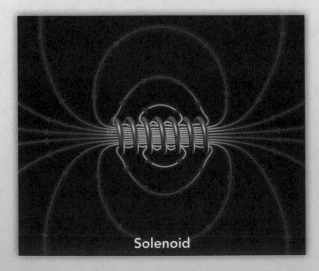

Solenoid

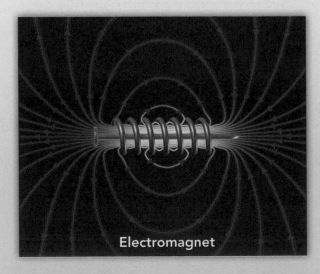

Electromagnet

Regulating Strength You can increase the strength of an electromagnet in four ways. First, you can increase the current in the solenoid. Second, you can add more loops of wire to the solenoid. Third, you can wind the coils of the solenoid closer together. Finally, you can use a material that is more magnetic than iron for the core. Alnico is such a material.

Using Electromagnets Electromagnets are very common. They are used in electric motors, earphones, and many other everyday objects. Electromagnets are even used in junkyards to lift old cars and other heavy steel objects.

Vocabulary Use Context to Determine Meaning Underline clues in the text that help you determine the meaning of *alnico*.

apply it!

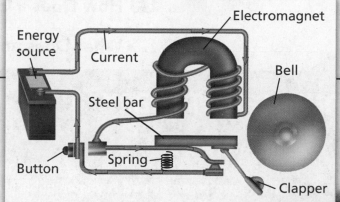

An electromagnet makes a doorbell ring. A pushed button closes the circuit and turns on the electromagnet. Current flows through the electromagnet, producing a strong magnetic field.

1 Predict What effect will the magnetic field have on the steel bar? The clapper?

_____

_____

_____

2 CHALLENGE What turns off the electromagnet?

_____

Do the Quick Lab *Electromagnet.*

🔑 Assess Your Understanding

2a. Define What is a solenoid?

_____

_____

b. Apply Concepts What are four ways to make an electromagnet stronger?

_____

_____

_____

_____

got it?

○ **I get it!** Now I know that both solenoids and

electromagnets _____

_____

_____

_____

○ **I need extra help with** _____

_____

_____

Electricity, Magnetism, and Motion

UNLOCK THE BIG ?

🔑 **How Is Electrical Energy Transformed Into Mechanical Energy?**

🔑 **How Does a Galvanometer Work?**

🔑 **What Does an Electric Motor Do?**

MY PLANET DiARY

DISCOVERY

Miniature Motor

In 1960, scientist and California Institute of Technology (Caltech) professor Richard Feynman publicly offered a prize of $1,000 to the first person to build an electric motor no larger than 0.3969 cubic millimeters. A Caltech graduate named William McLellan accepted the challenge. He used a toothpick, microscope slides, fine hairs from a paintbrush, and wires only 1/80th of a millimeter wide to build the world's smallest motor. McLellan showed his tiny motor to Feynman and collected the $1,000 prize. Scientists today have found many uses for tiny motors in products such as high-definition televisions, cars, and ink-jet printers.

McLellan's prize-winning micro motor is only 0.5 mm wide.

Communicate Work with a partner to answer the question.

What might be some other uses of tiny motors?

_____

_____

_____

_____

_____

_____

 Lab zone Do the Inquiry Warm-Up *How Are Electricity, Magnets, and Motion Related?*

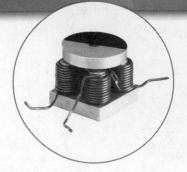

How Is Electrical Energy Transformed Into Mechanical Energy?

What do trains, fans, microwave ovens, and clocks have in common? The answer is that these objects, along with many other everyday objects, use electricity. In addition, all these objects move or have moving parts. How does electricity produce motion?

Energy and Motion

As you know, magnetic force can produce motion. For example, magnets move together or apart when they are close. You also know that an electric current in a wire produces a magnetic field. So, a magnet can move a wire with a current, just as it would move another magnet. The direction of movement depends on the direction of the current. See **Figure 1**.

The ability to move an object over a distance is called energy. The energy associated with electric currents is called electrical energy. The energy an object has due to its movement or position is called mechanical energy.

Energy Transformation

Energy can be transformed from one form into another. ⚷ **When a wire with a current is placed in a magnetic field, electrical energy is transformed into mechanical energy.** This transformation happens when the magnetic field produced by the current causes the wire to move.

FIGURE 1 ·····································
Producing Motion
A wire with a current can be moved by a magnet.

✎ **Complete the tasks.**

1. **Identify** What affects the direction of the wire's movement?

_____

_____

2. **Classify** In each box, write down the type of energy that is being pointed out.

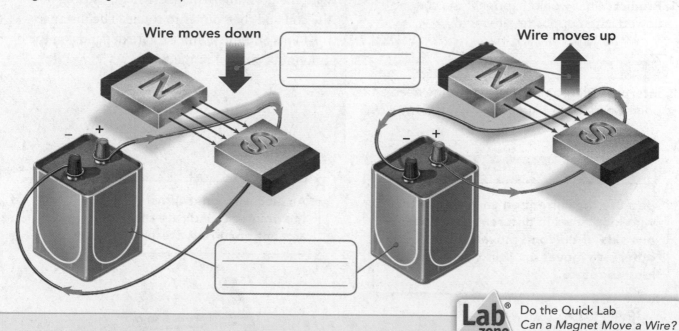

Wire moves down

Wire moves up

Lab® zone Do the Quick Lab
Can a Magnet Move a Wire?

⚷ Assess Your Understanding

got it? ··

○ **I get it!** Now I know that when a wire with a current is placed in a magnetic field, electrical energy

_____

○ **I need extra help with** _____

_____

_____

How Does a Galvanometer Work?

You have learned that a straight wire with a current moves when it is placed in a magnetic field. But what happens if you place a loop of wire with a current in a magnetic field? Look at **Figure 2**. The current in one side of the loop flows in the opposite direction than the current in the other side of the loop. The direction of the current determines the direction in which the wire moves. Therefore, the sides of the loop move in opposite directions. Once each side has moved as far up or down as it can go, it will stop moving. As a result, the loop can rotate only a half turn.

Inside a Galvanometer The rotation of a wire loop in a magnetic field is the basis of a galvanometer. A **galvanometer** is a device that measures small currents. ⬤━ **An electric current turns the pointer of a galvanometer.** In a galvanometer, an electromagnet is suspended between opposite poles of two permanent magnets. The electromagnet's coil is attached to a pointer, as you can see in **Figure 2**. When a current is in the electromagnet's coil, it produces a magnetic field. This field interacts with the permanent magnet's field, causing the coil and the pointer to rotate. The distance the loops and the pointer rotate depends on the amount of current in the wire.

> **⊙ Sequence** In the second paragraph on this page, underline and number the steps that explain how a galvanometer works.

FIGURE 2 ·······················

How a Galvanometer Works

✎ Answer the questions about a galvanometer.

1. **Predict** What would happen if the current flowed in the opposite direction?

_____

_____

2. **Interpret Diagrams** Where does the needle point when there is no current?

_____

_____

A Because the current on each side of the wire loop flows in different directions, one side of the loop moves down as the other side moves up. This causes the loop to rotate.

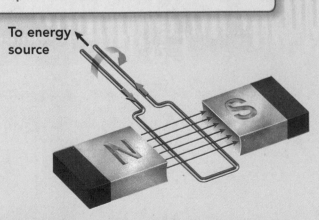

To energy source

B An electromagnet turns the pointer to indicate the amount of current present.

Uses of Galvanometers

A galvanometer has a scale that is marked to show how much the pointer turns for a known current. You can use the galvanometer to measure an unknown current. Galvanometers are useful in everyday life. For example, electricians use them in their work. Some cars use them as fuel gauges. Galvanometers are also used in lie detectors to measure how much current a person's skin conducts. People who are stressed sweat more. Water conducts electricity. Therefore, their moist skin conducts more electric current.

do the math!

This data from a galvanometer show the current conducted by a person's skin. The current is measured in microsiemens, a unit used to measure small amounts of electricity.

Minutes	0	4	8	12	16	20
Microsiemens	5	7	3	1	8	10

1 ▲ **Graph** Use the data in the table to plot points on the graph.

2 **CHALLENGE** What would a point at (24, 12) tell you about the person?

_____

_____

_____

_____

_____

_____

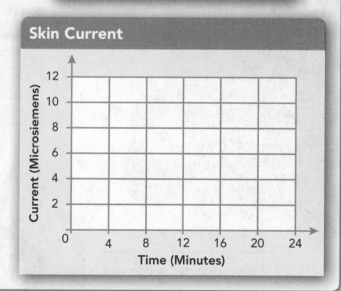

Skin Current

(graph: y-axis "Current (Microsiemens)" from 0 to 12; x-axis "Time (Minutes)" from 0 to 24)

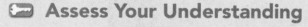

Do the Quick Lab
How Galvanometers Work.

Assess Your Understanding

1a. Review What does a galvanometer measure?

_____

b. Relate Cause and Effect What causes the pointer to move in a galvanometer?

_____

_____

got it?

○ I get it! Now I know that a galvanometer works by using _____

_____

○ I need extra help with _____

_____

What Does an Electric Motor Do?

Have you ever wondered how a remote-controlled car moves? A remote-controlled car's wheels are turned by a rod, or axle, which is connected to an electric motor. An **electric motor** is a device that uses an electric current to turn an axle. 🔑 **An electric motor transforms electrical energy into mechanical energy.**

Look at **Figure 3** to read about the parts of a motor.

If current only flowed in one direction through the armature, the armature could only rotate a half a turn. However, the brushes and commutator enable the current in the armature to change direction. Current always flows from the positive to the negative terminal of a battery. The current in the armature is reversed each time the commutator moves to a different brush. This causes the side of the armature that just moved up to move down. The side that just moved down will move up. The armature rotates continuously. See **Figure 4.**

FIGURE 3 ·······································

Parts of a Motor

A simple electric motor contains four parts.

✎ **Observe Which part of an electric motor must be attached directly to the energy source?**

_____

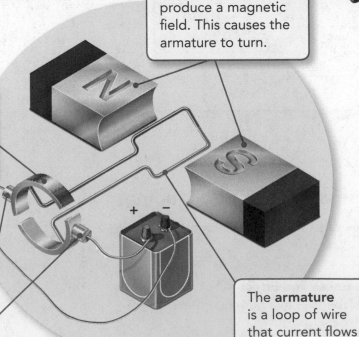

Permanent magnets produce a magnetic field. This causes the armature to turn.

The **commutator** consists of two semicircular pieces of metal. It conducts current from the brushes to the armature.

Brushes conduct current to the rest of the commutator. They do not move.

The **armature** is a loop of wire that current flows through.

FIGURE 4 ···

How a Motor Works

The magnetic field around the armature interacts with the field of the permanent magnet, allowing the armature to turn continuously. The direction of the current determines which way the armature turns.

✎ **Infer** Based on the direction the armature is turning in each diagram, draw arrows showing the direction of the current.

The current is in opposite directions on each side of the armature causing one side to move up while the other side moves down.

The commutator rotates with the armature. The direction of current reverses with each half turn so the armature spins continuously.

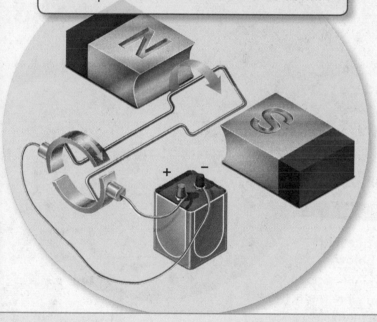

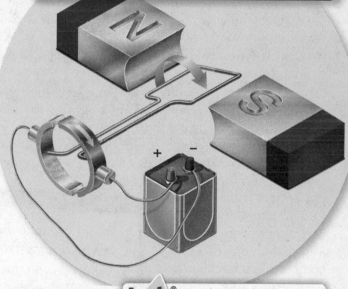

Do the Quick Lab *Parts of an Electric Motor.*

🔑 Assess Your Understanding

2a. Define What is an electric motor?

_____

_____

_____

_____

b. Summarize What makes the armature turn continuously?

_____

_____

got it?

○ **I get it!** Now I know that an electric motor transforms _____

_____

_____

○ **I need extra help with** _____

_____

_____

357

LESSON 5
Electricity From Magnetism

UNLOCK THE BIG ?

🔑 **How Can an Electric Current Be Produced in a Conductor?**

🔑 **How Does a Generator Work?**

🔑 **What Does a Transformer Do?**

my planet Diary

CAREERS

MRI Technologist

Does working in the medical field interest you? Are you good at operating devices? Do you have a knack for soothing anxious people? If you answered yes, you should think about becoming an Magnetic Resonance Imaging (MRI) technologist.

When a patient is put into an MRI machine, radio waves and magnetic fields are used to create images of the patient's internal structures. The doctors use these detailed pictures to determine what is wrong with the patient. The MRI technologist's responsibilities include operating the MRI machine, comforting nervous patients, and maintaining patient confidentiality. You can become an MRI technologist by completing a bachelor's degree program, an associate's degree program, or a certificate program.

Read the following question. Write your answer below.

What do you think might happen to the MRI image if you wore metal jewelry while in the MRI machine? Why?

_____

_____

_____

Lab ® zone

Do the Inquiry Warm-Up
Electric Current Without a Battery.

Vocabulary
- electromagnetic induction • direct current
- alternating current • generator • transformer

Skills
↻ Reading: Ask Questions
△ Inquiry: Make Models

How Can an Electric Current Be Produced in a Conductor?

An electric motor uses electrical energy to produce motion. Can motion produce electrical energy? In 1831, scientists discovered that moving a wire in a magnetic field can cause an electric current. This current allows electrical energy to be supplied to homes, schools, and businesses all over the world.

To understand how electrical energy is supplied by your electric company, you need to know how current is produced. A magnet can make, or induce, current in a conductor, such as a wire, as long as there is motion. 🔑 An electric current is induced in a conductor when the conductor moves through a magnetic field. Generating electric current from the motion of a conductor through a magnetic field is called **electromagnetic induction.** Current that is generated in this way is called induced current.

✎ **Ask Questions** Read the paragraph. Then write two questions that you still have about producing electric current.

_____

_____

_____

_____

_____

_____

_____

_____

_____

_____

_____

Induction of Electric Current

Induction of Electric Current Michael Faraday and Joseph Henry each found that motion in a magnetic field will induce a current. Either the conductor can move through the magnetic field, or the magnet can move. In **Figure 1,** a conductor, the coil of wire, is connected to a galvanometer, forming a closed circuit. If the coil and the magnet do not move, the galvanometer's pointer does not move. However, when either the wire coil or the magnet moves, the galvanometer registers a current. Moving the coil or the magnet induces the current without any voltage source. The direction of an induced current depends on the direction that the coil or magnet moves. When the motion is reversed, the direction of the current also reverses.

FIGURE 1

Motion Produces a Current

Electric current is induced in a wire whenever the magnetic field around it is changing. The field changes when either the magnet or the wire moves.

✎ **Complete the tasks.**

1. **Describe** Under each diagram, label the direction of the current using *clockwise* or *counterclockwise*.

2. **CHALLENGE** Make a general statement that relates the motion of the circuit (up or down) to the direction of the current (clockwise or counterclockwise).

_____
_____
_____
_____
_____
_____
_____
_____
_____
_____

Moving Coil

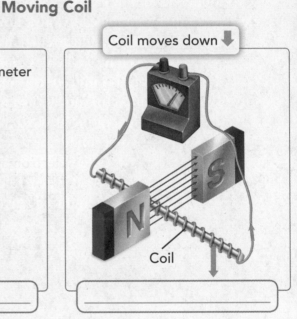

Moving Magnet

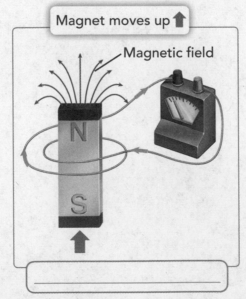

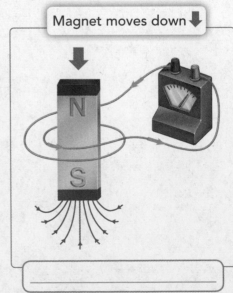

Alternating and Direct Current

A current with charges that flow in one direction is called **direct current,** or DC. A battery produces direct current when a battery is placed in a circuit and charges flow in one direction. They move from one end of the battery, around the circuit, and into the other end of the battery.

If a wire in a magnetic field changes direction repeatedly, the induced current also keeps changing direction. A constantly reversing current is called **alternating current,** or AC. You could induce alternating current by moving either the coil or the magnet up and down repeatedly in the **Figure 1** circuit.

Alternating current has a major advantage over direct current. An AC voltage can be easily raised or lowered. This means that a high voltage can be used to send electrical energy over great distances. Then the voltage can be reduced to a safer level for everyday use. The electric current in the circuits in homes, schools, and other buildings is alternating current. Look at **Figure 2** to learn about how electricity has changed over time.

1860

1882
Direct Current

Thomas Edison opens a generating plant in New York City. It serves an area of about 2.6 square kilometers.

1880

1888
Alternating Current

Nikola Tesla receives patents for a system of distributing alternating current.

Today
Direct and Alternating Current

An electric car runs on direct current from its battery. However, alternating current is needed to charge the battery.

FIGURE 2 ·····························
The History of Electricity
The work of several scientists brought electricity from the laboratory into everyday use.

✏ **Draw Conclusions** Why do you think we use alternating current today?

_____

_____

Lab zone® Do the Quick Lab *Inducing an Electric Current.*

🔑 Assess Your Understanding

1a. Describe How can you use a magnet to induce a current?

_____

_____

b. Classify Give an example of an electronic appliance that runs on AC and one that runs on DC.

_____

_____

got it? ···

○ **I get it!** Now I know that electric current is induced when _____

_____

○ **I need extra help with** _____

_____

361

How Does a Generator Work?

An electric **generator** is a device that transforms mechanical energy into electrical energy. 🔑 **A generator uses motion in a magnetic field to produce current.**

In **Figure 3,** you can see how an AC generator works. Turn the crank, and the armature rotates in the magnetic field. As the armature rotates, one side of it moves up as the other moves down. This motion induces a current in the armature. Slip rings turn with the armature. The turning slip rings allow current to flow into the brushes. When the brushes are connected to a circuit, the generator can be used as an energy source.

The electric company uses giant generators to produce most of the electrical energy you use each day. Huge turbines turn the armatures of the generators. Turbines are circular devices with many blades. They spin when water, steam, or hot gas flows through them. This turns the armatures, which generates electric current.

FIGURE 3 ·······························

How a Generator Works
In a generator, an armature rotates in a magnetic field to induce a current.

✏️ **Describe** Write what each part of the generator does in the boxes.

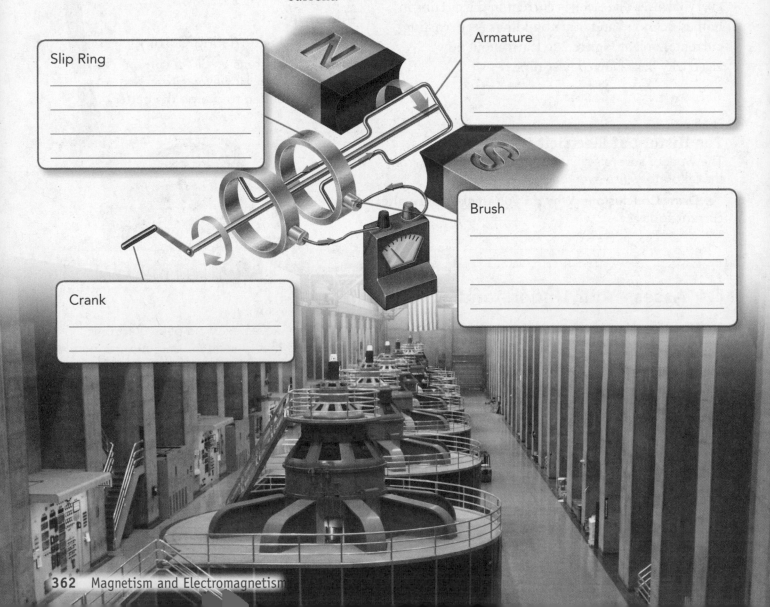

Slip Ring
_____
_____
_____

Armature
_____
_____
_____

Brush
_____
_____
_____

Crank
_____
_____

ZAP!

How are electricity and magnetism related?

FIGURE 4 ··
Wind-up cell phone chargers are small generators that let you charge your cell phone anywhere.

✎ **Analyze Models and Systems** Complete the tasks below.

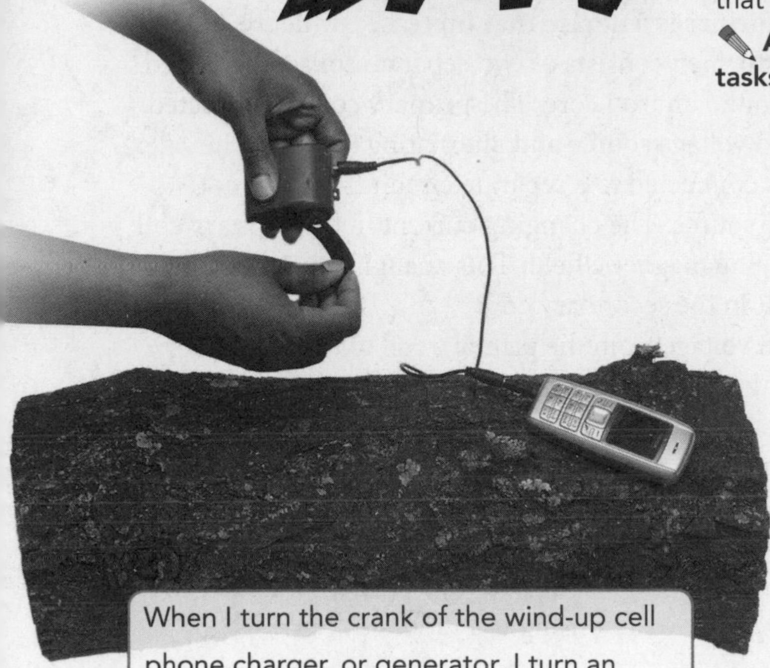

When I turn the crank of the wind-up cell phone charger, or generator, I turn an armature in a(n) _____. This generates a(n) _____ in the wire, which powers the phone.

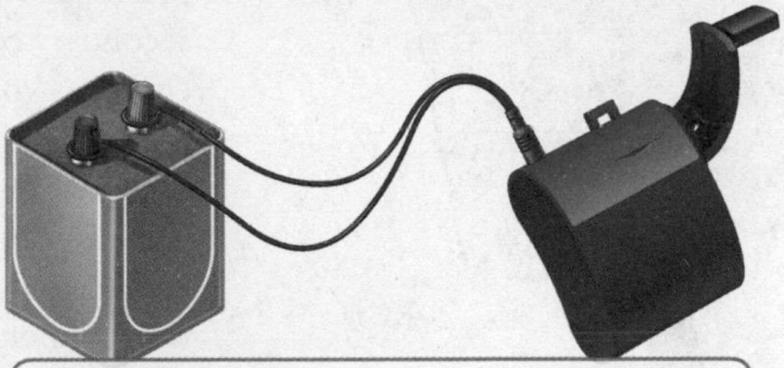

If you connect the output wires of the charger to a battery, _____ will flow through the armature, producing a _____. The permanent magnet in the charger will then cause the armature to _____. Draw what you will observe that lets you know this is happening.

Lab zone Do the Quick Lab *How Generators Work.*

🔑 Assess Your Understanding

2a. Review What is one way to induce an electric current?

_____
_____
_____

b. ANSWER THE BIG ? How are electricity and magnetism related?

_____
_____
_____
_____

got**it?** ··

○ **I get it!** Now I know a generator produces current by _____
_____

○ **I need extra help with** _____
_____

What Does a Transformer Do?

The electrical energy generated by electric companies is transmitted over long distances at very high voltages. However, in your home, electrical energy is used at much lower voltages. Transformers change the voltage so you can use electricity.

🔑 **A transformer is a device that increases or decreases voltage.** A **transformer** consists of two separate coils of insulated wire wrapped around an iron core. The primary coil is connected to a circuit with a voltage source and alternating current. The secondary coil is connected to a separate circuit that does not contain a voltage source. The changing current in the primary coil produces a changing magnetic field. This changing magnetic field induces a current in the secondary coil.

The change in voltage from the primary coil to the secondary coil depends on the number of loops in each coil. In step-up transformers, as shown in **Figure 5,** the primary coil has fewer loops than the secondary coil. Step-up transformers increase voltage. In step-down transformers, the primary coil has more loops. Voltage is reduced. The greater the difference between the number of loops in the primary and secondary coils in a transformer, the more the voltage will change. The relationship is a ratio.

$$\frac{\text{voltage }_{primary}}{\text{voltage }_{secondary}} = \frac{\text{coils }_{primary}}{\text{coils }_{secondary}}$$

$$\frac{120\text{ v}}{6\text{ v}} = 20$$

In this transformer, the voltage in the primary coil is twenty times higher than the voltage in the secondary coil. This means there are twenty times as many loops in the primary coil as there are in the secondary coil. If the primary coil has forty loops, then the secondary coil has two.

FIGURE 5 ·····························

Transformers

A step-up transformer, like the one shown below, is used to help transmit electricity from generating plants. Step-down transformers are used in power cords for some small electronics.

✏️ **Make Models Draw wire loops to show both the primary and secondary coils of this step-down transformer.**

This kind of plug contains a step-down transformer.

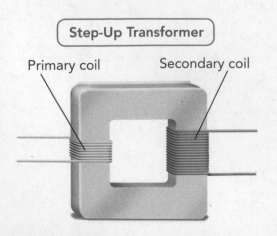

Step-Up Transformer

Primary coil   Secondary coil

Step-Down Transformer

do the math!

Transforming Electricity

The illustration shows how transformers change voltage between the generating plant and your home. For each transformer in the illustration below, state whether it is a step-up or step-down transformer.

In the boxes, calculate the ratio of loops in the primary coil to loops in the secondary coil.

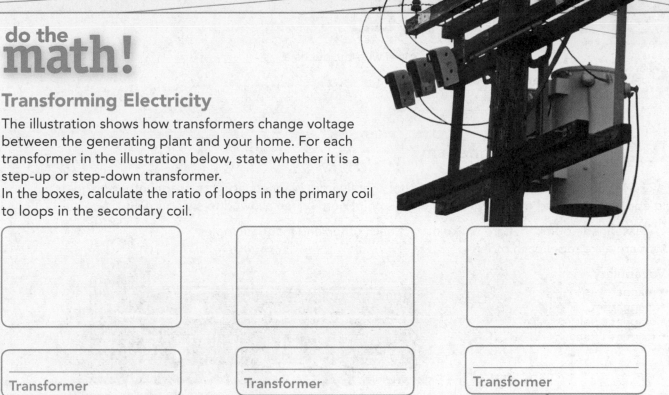

_____
Transformer

_____
Transformer

_____
Transformer

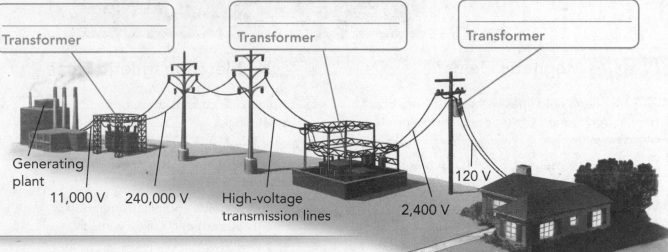

Generating plant

11,000 V   240,000 V   High-voltage transmission lines   2,400 V   120 V

Lab® zone
Do the Quick Lab
How Transformers Work.

🔑 Assess Your Understanding

3a. Identify Which coil has more loops in a step-down transformer?

_____
_____
_____

b. Infer Why do some appliances have step-down transformers built in?

_____
_____
_____

got it? •••

○ **I get it!** Now I know a transformer is a device used to _____
_____

○ **I need extra help with** _____
_____

8 Study Guide

REVIEW
THE BIG
?

_____ in a wire produces a _____
and movement of a wire through a _____
produces _____.

LESSON 1 What Is Magnetism?

🔑 Magnets attract iron and materials that contain iron. Magnets attract or repel other magnets. In addition, one end of a magnet will always point north when allowed to swing freely.

🔑 Magnetic poles that are unlike attract each other, and magnetic poles that are alike repel each other.

Vocabulary
- magnet
- magnetism
- magnetic pole
- magnetic force

LESSON 2 Magnetic Fields

🔑 Magnetic field lines spread out from one pole, curve around the magnet, and return to the other pole.

🔑 Like a bar magnet, Earth has a magnetic field around it and two magnetic poles.

Vocabulary
- magnetic field
- magnetic field lines
- compass
- magnetic declination

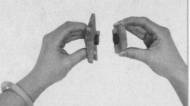

LESSON 3 Electromagnetic Force

🔑 An electric current produces a magnetic field.

🔑 The magnetic field produced by a current can be turned on or off, reverse direction, or change its strength.

🔑 Both solenoids and electromagnets use electric current and coiled wires to produce strong magnetic fields.

Vocabulary
- electromagnetism • solenoid • electromagnet

LESSON 4 Electricity, Magnetism, and Motion

🔑 By placing a wire with a current in a magnetic field, electrical energy can be transformed into mechanical energy.

🔑 An electric current turns the pointer of a galvanometer.

🔑 An electric motor transforms electrical energy into mechanical energy.

Vocabulary
- galvanometer • electric motor

LESSON 5 Electricity From Magnetism

🔑 An electric current is induced in a conductor when the conductor moves through a magnetic field.

🔑 A generator uses motion in a magnetic field to produce current.

🔑 A transformer is a device that increases or decreases voltage.

Vocabulary
- electromagnetic induction • direct current
- alternating current • generator • transformer

Review and Assessment

LESSON 1 What Is Magnetism?

1. A magnet is attracted to a soup can because the can has

   a. a south pole.   **b.** a north pole.

   c. a magnetic field.   **d.** iron in it.

2. Any magnet, no matter its shape, has two ends, and each one is called

   a _____

3. **Predict** What will happen to a bar magnet suspended from a string when it swings freely?

   _____

   _____

   _____

4. **Interpret Diagrams** In the diagram, what do the arrows represent? Explain your answer.

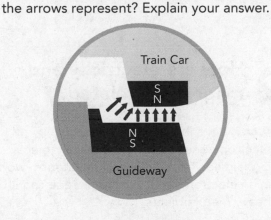

   _____

   _____

   _____

   _____

5. **Design Experiments** If two magnets' poles are not labeled, how can you tell which poles are the same and which are different?

   _____

   _____

   _____

   _____

LESSON 2 Magnetic Fields

6. A compass works because its magnetic needle

   a. points east.   **b.** spins freely.

   c. points west.   **d.** repels magnets.

7. _____ map out the magnetic field around a magnet.

8. **Make Models** How is Earth like a magnet?

   _____

   _____

   _____

9. **Draw Conclusions** Look at the diagram below. Is the left magnetic pole a north or south pole? Explain your answer.

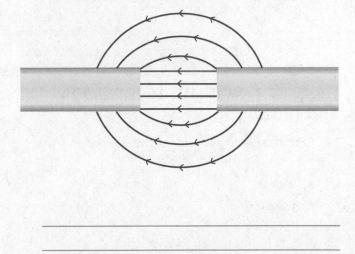

   _____

   _____

   _____

   _____

10. **Write About It** Imagine that you are the early inventor of the compass. Write an advertisement for your product that tells explorers how a compass works.

367

LESSON 3 Electromagnetic Force

11. The relationship between electricity and magnetism is called

   a. electrical energy.   **b.** induced current.

   c. electromagnetism. **d.** ferromagnetism.

12. A coil of wire with a current is called

   a _____

13. Relate Cause and Effect You have a magnetic field produced by a current. What would you do to change the direction and increase the strength of the field?

_____

_____

_____

_____

_____

LESSON 4 Electricity, Magnetism, and Motion

14. Electrical energy is transformed into mechanical energy in a

   a. motor.   **b.** solenoid.

   c. transformer. **d.** electromagnet.

15. A galvanometer is a device that

   measures _____

16. Compare and Contrast How is a motor similar to a galvanometer? How is it different?

_____

_____

_____

_____

_____

_____

LESSON 5 Electricity From Magnetism

17. A device that changes the voltage of alternating current is a

   a. transformer.   **b.** motor.

   c. generator.   **d.** galvanometer.

18. Generating a current by moving a conductor in a magnetic field is _____

_____

19. **Write About It** You are a television news reporter covering the opening of a new dam that will help to generate electrical energy. Write a short news story describing how the dam transforms mechanical energy from the motion of the water into electrical energy.

APPLY THE BIG ? How are electricity and magnetism related?

20. A crane in a junkyard may have an electromagnet to lift heavy metal objects. Explain how electricity and magnetism work in an electromagnet so that a crane can lift heavy metal objects.

_____

_____

_____

_____

_____

_____

_____

_____

Standardized Test Prep

Read each question and choose the best answer.

The graph below shows how a solenoid's loops affect its magnetic field strength. Use the graph to answer Question 1.

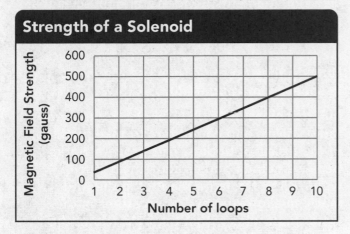

Strength of a Solenoid

1. **Predict the strength of a 12-loop solenoid.**

   A   300 gauss   B   600 gauss
   C   700 gauss   D   1200 gauss

2. **You can increase a step-up transformer's voltage with**

   A   a power source connected to the primary coil.
   B   a source connected to the secondary coil.
   C   increasing the number of loops in the primary coil.
   D   increasing the number of loops in the secondary coil.

3. **To measure the current induced by moving a wire through a magnetic field, which piece of equipment would a scientist need?**

   A   a galvanometer
   B   a transformer
   C   an insulated wire
   D   an LED

4. **What happens when a magnet moves through a coil of wire?**

   A   The magnet loses magnetism.
   B   current is induced in the wire.
   C   A current is induced in the magnet.
   D   Electrical energy is transformed into mechanical energy.

5. **How does Earth's magnetic field compare with that of a bar magnet?**

   A   Their magnetic fields increase with size.
   B   The attractive force of their magnetic fields is greatest at the poles.
   C   The attractive force of their magnetic fields is greatest at the center.
   D   Electric current causes them to lose magnetism.

Constructed Response

Use the diagram below and your knowledge of cells to help you answer Question 6 Write your answer on a separate sheet of paper.

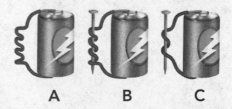

A   B   C

6. **Three electromagnets are illustrated in the diagram above. Will the electromagnet labeled A or B produce a stronger magnetic field? Will the electromagnet B or C produce a stronger field? Explain your answers.**

Technology and Society

MAGNETIC PICTURES

Doctors can look inside your body to detect infection, bleeding, or tumors in the brain—without surgery or high-energy radiation that can damage tissues. They can get very detailed views of ligaments, tendons, and muscles that reveal injuries. They can find breast cancers that mammograms miss, and they can map areas of low blood flow after a heart attack. How do they do this? They use Magnetic Resonance Imaging (MRI).

MRI machines use powerful electromagnets, radio waves, and computers to take pictures of the inside of bodies. This process works because human bodies contain so much water. First, the large magnet in the MRI machine aligns the hydrogen atoms in the water molecules within the field. Then, the machine emits a radio frequency pulse that spins all of the hydrogen atoms the same way. The hydrogen atoms release energy in the form of a radio signal as they return to their normal positions, and computers can turn that signal into pictures. Healthy tissues respond differently to the magnet than unhealthy or damaged tissues.

Research It MRI scanning rooms have strict rules about what is allowed inside because metal objects can become deadly. Research the safety concerns for MRI use on humans. Then write a safety brochure to share your findings.

Now, instead of using X-rays, doctors use magnets to look in detail at systems inside the body. ▼

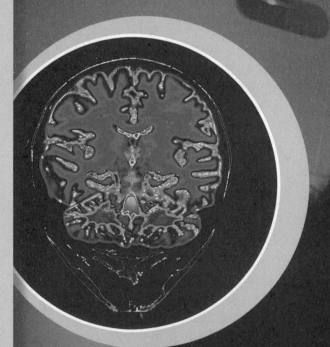

▲ This MRI of a healthy brain shows both hemispheres in bright pink and the cerebellum in green.

A SHOCKING MESSAGE!

In the 1830s, before the telephone had been invented, people were experimenting with ways to communicate across long distances. Samuel Morse and Alfred Vail discovered that it was possible to use an electromagnet to send a signal through cheap wire.

The electromagnet is part of an electric circuit. On one end of the wire is a telegraph switch. Closing the switch completes the circuit, sending an electric current through the wire. Opening the switch stops the current. On the other end of the wire is a telegraph with an electromagnet, a metal key, and a metal plate. As the electric current flows through the electromagnet, a magnetic field forms.

Signal It Work with a partner to find resources that will help you construct your own electromagnetic telegraph machine! Predict which materials will best conduct a signal, and then verify your predictions by building a model.

The metal key is then attracted to the metal plate. The sender can close and open the switch quickly, making a short clicking sound called a "dot" on the other end. Or, the sender can hold the switch closed and create a longer sound, called a "dash." Leaving the switch open for a moment comes across as a "space," or a break in the sounds.

This pattern of dots, dashes, and spaces became a new tool for communicating without using voices—Morse code. Telegraph operators could spell out words and phrases. Three dots, followed by three dashes, followed by three dots, for example, is the Morse code signal for SOS, or help!

WHAT KEEPS THIS HANG GLIDER FLYING?

How does the sun's energy affect Earth's atmosphere?

Imagine yourself lazily soaring like a bird above Earth. The quiet, gentle winds and warm sun are so relaxing. No noisy engine, no flapping wings, but wait, what's keeping you aloft? Everyone knows that humans can't fly. **Develop Hypotheses** How does this hang glider fly?

_____

_____

_____

_____

_____

_____

_____

Watch the **Untamed Science** video to learn more about Earth's atmosphere.

The Atmosphere

9 Getting Started

Check Your Understanding

1. **Background** Read the paragraph below and then answer the question.

Helen blows up a balloon. She adds it to a large garbage bag already full of balloons. Its low **weight** makes the bag easy to carry, but its large **volume** might be a problem fitting it in the car. Capturing air in a balloon makes it easier to understand that air has **mass.**

> **Weight** is a measure of the force of gravity on an object.
>
> **Volume** is the amount of space that matter occupies.
>
> **Mass** is the amount of matter in an object.

• How could the bag's volume make it difficult to fit in the car?

_____

_____

Vocabulary Skill

Word Origins Many words come to English from other languages. Learning a few common Greek word parts can help you understand new science words.

Greek Word Part	Meaning	Example
-meter	measure	barometer, *n.* an instrument that measures air pressure
thermo-	heat	thermosphere, *n.* the outer layer of Earth's atmosphere

2. **Quick Check** Use the Greek word parts above to write a definition of a thermometer.

_____

_____

atmosphere

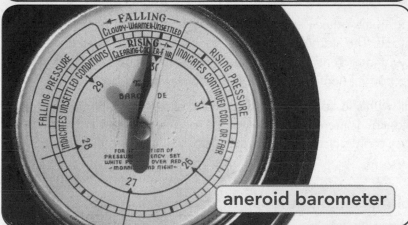

aneroid barometer

troposphere

wind

Chapter Preview

LESSON 1
- weather • atmosphere
- water vapor
- 🎯 Summarize
- △ Infer

LESSON 2
- density • air pressure
- barometer • mercury barometer
- aneroid barometer • altitude
- 🎯 Relate Cause and Effect
- △ Develop Hypotheses

LESSON 3
- troposphere • stratosphere
- mesosphere • thermosphere
- ionosphere • exosphere
- 🎯 Identify Supporting Evidence
- △ Interpret Data

LESSON 4
- electromagnetic waves
- radiation • infrared radiation
- ultraviolet radiation • scattering
- greenhouse effect
- 🎯 Ask Questions
- △ Graph

LESSON 5
- temperature • thermal energy
- thermometer • heat
- convection • conduction
- convection currents
- 🎯 Identify the Main Idea
- △ Infer

LESSON 6
- wind • anemometer
- windchill factor • local winds
- sea breeze • land breeze
- global winds • Coriolis effect
- latitude
- 🎯 Identify Supporting Evidence
- △ Draw Conclusions

Scenario Investigation

Mile-High Baseball

Purpose To investigate the effect of air density on the flight of an object

Materials
- two 6 inch × 6 inch aluminum foil squares
- stopwatch
- two sheets of plain copier paper

Scenario

Denver, Colorado, is called "The Mile-High City" because it sits about one mile above sea level. Denver is the highest city in the United States with a Major League Baseball team, the Colorado Rockies.

The Rockies hit many more home runs during home games than during away games. You might say the Rockies have the ultimate home-field advantage. The stadium where the Rockies play has been called "the greatest hitter's park in baseball history." Home runs hit there travel farther than home runs hit in other ballparks. There are even players who can hit home runs in Denver but nowhere else.

The commissioner of Major League Baseball wants to know why it is so much easier to hit home runs in Denver. Is it the result of gravity or air resistance? Is there anything that the league can do to take away what some consider an unfair advantage? As a physicist and a baseball fan, you have volunteered to answer the commissioner's questions.

The Effect of Altitude on Baseball Flight

Initial speed of ball (m/s)	Distance traveled at sea level (m) (elevation 0 m)	Distance traveled in Denver (m) (elevation 1,609 m)	Distance traveled in Mount Everest (m) (elevation 8,848 m)	Distance traveled in a vacuum (m)
35	72.9	77.2	94.5	123.1
40	85.3	91.0	115.2	160.8
45	96.9	104.2	135.7	203.5
50	107.7	116.5	155.8	251.2

Procedure

☑ **1. Gravity or Friction** Discuss with your partners how both gravity and air density change as you go higher in the atmosphere. Which do you think changes more? Explain.

☑ **2. Share Your Ideas** After discussing this with your group, share your answer with another team and compare your reasons. When your teacher asks, share your ideas with the class.

☑ **3. Lessening the Impact** _____ As a baseball moves through the air, it pushes air molecules out of the way, but the air also pushes back. The faster the ball moves, the greater the air pushes back. This is called air resistance. Since Denver is a mile above sea level, its air is less dense, meaning there is less air resistance. How can you decrease air resistance? Work with your team to think of some possibilities.

Procedure *(continued)*

4. **Test Your Ideas** Time how long it takes for a sheet of paper to fall to the floor. Record the time in the table provided. Next, change the shape of the paper in a way that you think will make it fall faster. You cannot change the mass of the paper. Drop the paper from the same height as before, and record the new fall time.

Object	Fall Time
paper	
altered paper	
foil	
altered foil	

5. **Does the Material Make a Difference?** Repeat Step 5 using a sheet of aluminum foil and record your results.

Conclusion

Let's see what you learned about how air density affects an object's flight.

1. Which is more likely to affect a baseball hit in Denver: decreased gravity or decreased air density? Explain.

_____

_____

2. Why is the air less dense in Denver?

_____

_____

3. Why do you think less air density causes the baseballs to travel further?

_____

_____

4. How do you think home runs would be affected at a baseball stadium that was located below sea level? (Hint: Below sea level means the altitude is lower than the altitude of the surface of the ocean.)

_____

_____

Write a letter to the baseball commissioner explaining why there are more home runs in Denver than in other cities. Include one suggestion for counteracting the effect of air density at Denver's altitude. Explain why you think your idea will work. Make sure to discuss the science behind your idea.

The Air Around You

UNLOCK THE BIG ?

🔑 **What Is the Composition of Earth's Atmosphere?**

🔑 **How Is the Atmosphere a System?**

MY PLANET DIARY — VOICES FROM HISTORY

Antoine Lavoisier

French chemist Antoine Lavoisier was determined to solve a puzzle: How could a metal burned to a powder weigh more than the original metal? In his 1772 lab notes he observed, "Sulphur, in burning . . . gains weight." So did mercury. Lavoisier thought a gas in the air was combining with the mercury as it burned, making it heavier. Then he heated the mercury powder to a higher temperature. It turned back to liquid mercury and a gas. Lavoisier observed that a mouse exposed to the gas could breathe it. He named the gas *principe oxygine*. Today we call it oxygen.

Discuss Lavoisier's experiment with a partner and answer the question below.

Why do you think Lavoisier exposed a mouse to the gas he collected from the mercury?

_____

_____

_____

Lab *zone* Do the Inquiry Warm-Up *How Long Will the Candle Burn?*

What Is the Composition of Earth's Atmosphere?

The sun disappears behind thick, dark clouds. In the distance you see a bright flash. Then you hear a crack of thunder. You make it home just as the downpour begins. The weather changed quickly— that was close!

Weather is the condition of Earth's atmosphere at a particular time and place. But what is the atmosphere? Earth's **atmosphere** (AT muh sfeer) is the envelope of gases that surrounds the planet. **Earth's atmosphere consists of nitrogen, oxygen, carbon dioxide, water vapor, and other gases, as well as particles of liquids and solids.**

Vocabulary
- weather
- water vapor
- atmosphere

Skills
↻ Reading: Summarize
△ Inquiry: Infer

Nitrogen The most abundant gas in the atmosphere is nitrogen. It makes up a little more than three fourths of the air we breathe. Nitrogen occurs in all living things and makes up about 3 percent of the weight of the human body.

Oxygen Although oxygen is the second most abundant gas in the atmosphere, it makes up only about 21 percent of the volume. Plants and animals take oxygen directly from the air and use it to release energy from their food.

Oxygen is also involved in many other processes. A fire uses oxygen rapidly as it burns. Without oxygen, a fire will go out. Some processes use oxygen more slowly. Steel in cars and other objects reacts slowly with oxygen to form iron oxide, or rust.

Carbon Dioxide Carbon dioxide makes up much less than 1 percent of the atmosphere, but it is essential to life. Plants must have carbon dioxide to produce food. The cells of animals break down food and give off carbon dioxide as a waste product.

When fuels like coal and gasoline are burned, they also release carbon dioxide. Burning these fuels increases the amount of carbon dioxide in the atmosphere.

Other Gases Oxygen and nitrogen together make up 99 percent of dry air. Argon makes up most of the other 1 percent. The remaining gases are called trace gases because only small amounts of them are present.

FIGURE 1 ·····································
Gases in the Air
The atmosphere is a thin layer of gases.

✎ Graph **Identify which circle graph shows the correct percentage of gases in the atmosphere. Shade in the key and the graph. Give your graph a title.**

Key
☐ Nitrogen
☐ Oxygen
☐ Other gases

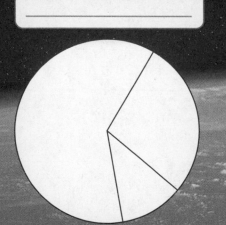

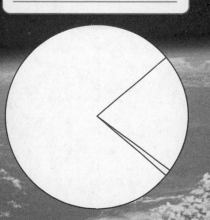

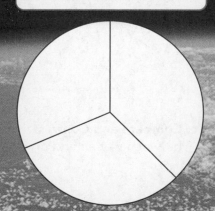

apply it!

The amount of water vapor in the air can differ from place to place.

1 There is more water vapor in the (desert/ rain forest) than in the (desert/rain forest).

2 ◢**Infer** What evidence do you see for your answer to Question 1?

_____

_____

_____

3 CHALLENGE What factors might affect the amount of water vapor in the air?

_____

_____

_____

Water Vapor So far, we've discussed the composition of dry air. But in reality, air is not dry. Air contains **water vapor**—water in the form of a gas. Water vapor is invisible. It is not the same thing as steam, which is made up of tiny droplets of liquid water.

The amount of water vapor in the air varies greatly from place to place and from time to time. Water vapor plays an important role in Earth's weather. Clouds form when water vapor condenses out of the air to form tiny droplets of liquid water or crystals of ice. If these droplets or crystals become heavy enough, they fall as rain or snow.

Particles Pure air contains only gases. But pure air exists only in laboratories. In the real world, air contains tiny solid and liquid particles of dust, smoke, salt, and chemicals. You can see some of these particles in the air around you, but most of them are too small to see.

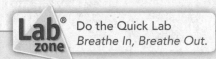 Do the Quick Lab
Breathe In, Breathe Out.

🔑 Assess Your Understanding

1a. Define The _____ is the

envelope of _____ that

surrounds Earth.

b. List What are the four most common gases in dry air?

_____

_____

c. Compare and Contrast What is the difference between wet air and dry air?

_____

_____

got it?

○ **I get it!** Now I know that the atmosphere

is made up of _____

_____

_____

_____

○ **I need extra help with** _____

_____

_____

_____

How Is the Atmosphere a System?

The atmosphere is a system that interacts with other Earth systems, such as the ocean. The atmosphere has many different parts. Some of these parts you can actually see, such as clouds. But most parts of the atmosphere—like air, wind, and energy—you can't see. Instead, you might feel a wind when it blows on you. Or you might feel energy from the sun warming your face on a cool winter day.

At first, the wind that blows and the heat you feel may seem unrelated. But as you'll learn, the different parts of the atmosphere interact with one another. **Events in one part of the atmosphere affect other parts of the atmosphere.**

Energy from the sun drives the motions in the atmosphere. A storm such as the hurricane in **Figure 2** involves a tremendous amount of energy. The spiraling shape of a hurricane is due in part to forces resulting from Earth's rotation. A hurricane also gains energy from warm ocean water. Since the ocean water is warmed by the sun, a hurricane's energy comes mostly from the sun.

Summarize Write a short summary of the third paragraph.

_____

_____

_____

_____

_____

FIGURE 2

Parts of the Atmosphere

List What parts of the atmosphere interact?

_____

_____

_____

_____

Lab zone
Do the Quick Lab *What Is the Source of Earth's Energy?*

Assess Your Understanding

got it? ....

O **I get it!** Now I know that events in one part of the atmosphere _____

_____

O **I need extra help with** _____

_____

UNLOCK THE BIG **?**

🔑 **What Are Some Properties of Air?**

🔑 **What Instruments Measure Air Pressure?**

🔑 **How Does Altitude Affect Air Pressure and Density?**

MY PLANET DIARY

DISCOVERY

Flying High

Astronauts aren't the only people who go into space. High-altitude pilots who fly above 15,250 meters are in a zone with conditions similar to deep space. At these heights, air pressure is so low that blood can boil. A pilot can also pass out in less than a minute from lack of oxygen. To survive, pilots wear pressure suits. These suits weigh about 16 kilograms and are custom-built for each pilot. They inflate in an emergency, keeping air pressure stable for the pilot. The suits are "very, very restrictive," says pilot David Wright. "But it saves your life, so you're able to put up with that."

Discuss your answer with a classmate.

Pilots wear pressure suits in addition to flying in a pressurized plane. Why do you think this is so?

_____

_____

_____

Lab zone® Do the Inquiry Warm-Up *Does Air Have Mass?*

What Are Some Properties of Air?

How do you know air exists? You can't see it. Instead, you have to understand what air does. It may seem to you that air has no mass. But the air in the atmosphere consists of atoms and molecules, which have mass. 🔑 **Because air has mass, it also has other properties, including density and pressure.**

Vocabulary

- density
- air pressure
- barometer
- mercury barometer
- aneroid barometer
- altitude

Skills

🔁 Reading: Relate Cause and Effect

△ Inquiry: Develop Hypotheses

Density The amount of mass in a given volume of air is its **density.** You calculate the density of a substance by dividing its mass by its volume. If there are more molecules in a given volume, the density is greater. If there are fewer molecules, the density is less.

Pressure The atmosphere is heavy. Its weight exerts a force on surfaces like you. The force pushing on an area or surface is called pressure. **Air pressure** is the result of the weight of a column of air pushing on an area.

As **Figure 1** shows, there is a column of air above you that extends all the way up through the entire atmosphere. In fact, the weight of the column of air above your desk is about the same as the weight of a large school bus. So why doesn't air pressure crush your desk? The reason is that the molecules in air push in all directions—down, up, and sideways. The air pushing down on top of your desk is balanced by the air pushing up on the bottom of your desk.

FIGURE 1 ···
Air Column
The weight of the column of air above you puts pressure on you.

✎ **Answer the questions below.**

1. **Describe** What's an air column?

_____

_____

2. **Apply Concepts** Add arrows to the diagram below to indicate how the pressure from air molecules keeps you from being crushed.

Do the Quick Lab
Properties of Air.

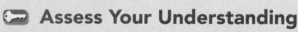 Assess Your Understanding

got it? ··

○ I get it! Now I know that air has properties such as _____

_____

○ I need extra help with _____

_____

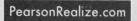

What Instruments Measure Air Pressure?

Air pressure can change daily. A denser substance has more mass per unit volume than a less dense one. So denser air exerts more pressure than less dense air. A **barometer** (buh RAHM uh tur) is an instrument that is used to measure air pressure. 🗝 **The two common kinds of barometers are mercury barometers and aneroid barometers.**

Mercury Barometers Look at **Figure 2** to see a mercury barometer model. A **mercury barometer** consists of a long glass tube that is closed at one end and open at the other. The open end of the tube rests in a dish of mercury. The closed end of the tube is almost a vacuum—the space above the mercury contains very little air. The air pressing down on the surface of the mercury in the dish is equal to the pressure exerted by the weight of the column of mercury in the tube. When the air pressure increases, it presses down more on the surface of the mercury. Greater air pressure forces the column of mercury higher. So, the level of the mercury in the tube shows you the pressure of the air that day.

Vocabulary Greek Word Origins
The Greek word part *baro-* means "weight." How would it relate to the word part *-meter*?

_____

_____

_____

FIGURE 2 ·······································

Reading a Mercury Barometer

✎ **Apply Concepts** Use the drawing of the barometer on the right to show what a low air pressure reading looks like.

1. Shade in the level of the mercury in the tube and in the dish.

2. Describe what is happening.

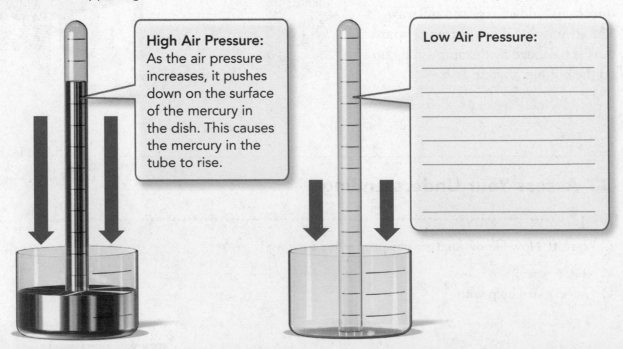

High Air Pressure:
As the air pressure increases, it pushes down on the surface of the mercury in the dish. This causes the mercury in the tube to rise.

Low Air Pressure:

Aneroid Barometers

If you have a barometer at home, it's probably an aneroid barometer. The word *aneroid* means "without liquid." An **aneroid barometer** (AN uh royd) has an airtight metal chamber, as shown in **Figure 3**. The metal chamber is sensitive to changes in air pressure. When air pressure increases, the thin walls of the chamber are pushed in. When the pressure drops, the walls bulge out. The chamber is connected to a dial by a series of springs and levers. As the shape of the chamber changes, the needle on the dial moves.

Units of Air Pressure

Weather reports use several different units for air pressure. Most weather reports for the general public use inches of mercury. For example, if the column of mercury in a mercury barometer is 30 inches high, the air pressure is "30 inches of mercury" or "30 inches."

National Weather Service maps indicate air pressure in millibars. The pressure of the atmosphere is equal to one bar. One inch of mercury is about 33.86 millibars, so 30 inches of mercury is equal to about 1,016 millibars.

FIGURE 3 ·······························

Inside an Aneroid Barometer

An aneroid barometer has an airtight metal chamber, shown in red, below.

✎ **Identify** Label the diagram that shows the aneroid barometer under high pressure and the diagram that shows it under low pressure.

Lab zone ® Do the Quick Lab *Soda Bottle Barometer.*

🔑 Assess Your Understanding

1a. Name What two instruments are commonly used to measure air pressure?

_____

_____

b. Identify What units are used to measure air pressure?

_____

_____

c. CHALLENGE How many millibars are equal to 27.23 inches of mercury?

_____

got it? ·······························

○ **I get it!** Now I know that air pressure can be measured _____

_____

○ **I need extra help with** _____

_____

_____

How Does Altitude Affect Air Pressure and Density?

The higher you hike on a mountain, the more changes you'll notice. The temperature will drop, and the plants will get smaller. But you might not notice another change that is happening. At the top of the mountain, the air pressure is less than the air pressure at sea level—the average level of the oceans. **Altitude,** or elevation, is the distance above sea level. 🔑 **Air pressure decreases as altitude increases. As air pressure decreases, so does density.**

Altitude Affects Air Pressure Suppose you have a stack of books. Which book has more weight on it, the second book from the top or the book at the bottom? The second book from the top has the weight of only one book on top of it. The book at the bottom of the stack has the weight of all the books pressing on it.

Air at sea level is like the bottom book. Sea-level air has the weight of the whole atmosphere pressing on it. Air near the top of the atmosphere is like the second book from the top. There, the air has less weight pressing on it and thus has lower air pressure.

6 km

5 km

4 km

3 km

2 km

Which hiker has the least pressure on him/her?

_____

1 km

Sea level

Altitude Also Affects Density

As you go up through the atmosphere, the density of the air decreases. This means the gas molecules that make up the atmosphere are farther apart at high altitudes than they are at sea level. If you were near the top of a tall mountain and tried to run, you would quickly get out of breath. Why? The air contains 21 percent oxygen, whether you are at sea level or on top of a mountain. However, since the air is less dense at a high altitude, each cubic meter of air you breathe has fewer oxygen molecules than at sea level. So you would become short of breath more quickly at a high altitude.

↺ Relate Cause and Effect
Underline the sentence that explains how altitude can make you short of breath.

FIGURE 4 ....

Effect of Altitude on Pressure and Density

✎ **Complete the activities below.**

1. **Relate Evidence and Explanation** Draw the air column above each hiker on the mountain. Then answer the question below the hikers.

2. **Make Models** In the empty circles below, draw how densely packed you think the molecules would be at the altitudes shown.

Lab® zone Do the Quick Lab *Effects of Altitude on the Atmosphere.*

🔑 Assess Your Understanding

2a. Define What is altitude?

_____

b. Summarize How does air pressure change as altitude increases?

_____

_____

c. Predict What changes in air pressure would you expect if you carried a barometer down a mine shaft?

_____

_____

_____

_____

got it? ....

○ I get it! Now I know the properties of air

_____

_____

○ I need extra help with _____

_____

_____

_____

387

Layers of the Atmosphere

UNLOCK THE BIG

🔑 **What Are the Four Main Layers of the Atmosphere?**

🔑 **What Are the Characteristics of the Atmosphere's Layers?**

my PLANET DiARY

MISCONCEPTION

Earth's Atmosphere

Misconception: The blanket of gases that makes up Earth's atmosphere is thick.

Fact: Earth's atmosphere extends far out into space, at least as far again as the radius of Earth. However, most of the atmosphere is so thin that it would be hard to tell it apart from the vacuum of space. Most of the gas in the atmosphere is found close to Earth's surface. In fact, half of the gas in the atmosphere is found in the bottom 5.5 kilometers—the height of a tall mountain! The rest of the gas extends thinly out into space for thousands of kilometers.

Evidence: The mass of the atmosphere is surprisingly small. In fact, a thin column of air 1 cm² extending out into space for thousands of kilometers has about the same mass as a 1-liter bottle of water.

Talk about these questions with a classmate and then record your answers.

1. Where is most of the gas in the atmosphere found?

_____

_____

_____

2. Why do you think that people think of the atmosphere as a thick layer around Earth?

_____

_____

 Do the Inquiry Warm-Up *Is Air There?*

What Are the Four Main Layers of the Atmosphere?

Imagine taking a trip upward into the atmosphere in a hot-air balloon. You begin on a warm beach near the ocean, at an altitude of 0 kilometers above sea level.

You hear a roar as the balloon's pilot turns up the burner to heat the air in the balloon. The balloon begins to rise, and Earth's surface gets farther away. As the balloon reaches an altitude of 3 kilometers, you realize the air is getting colder. At 6 kilometers you begin to have trouble breathing. The air is becoming less dense. It's time to go back down.

Six kilometers is pretty high. In fact, it's higher than all but the very tallest mountains. But there are still hundreds of kilometers of atmosphere above you. It may seem as though air is the same from the ground to the edge of space. But air pressure and temperature change with altitude. 🔑 **Scientists divide Earth's atmosphere into four main layers classified according to changes in temperature. These layers are the troposphere, the stratosphere, the mesosphere, and the thermosphere.**

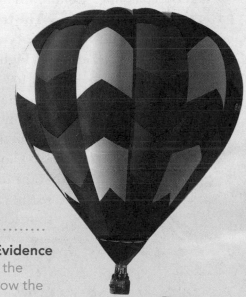

✏️

🎯 **Identify Supporting Evidence**
Underline the evidence in the text above that explains how the atmosphere changes as you go up in a hot-air balloon.

Lab zone® Do the Quick Lab *Layers of the Atmosphere.*

🔑 **Assess Your Understanding**

got it? ....

○ I get it! Now I know that the atmosphere has four main layers: _____

_____

○ I need extra help with _____

_____

What Are the Characteristics of the Atmosphere's Layers?

Unless you become an astronaut, you won't make a trip to the upper atmosphere. But if you could make that journey, what would you see? Read on to learn more about the conditions you would experience in each layer of the atmosphere.

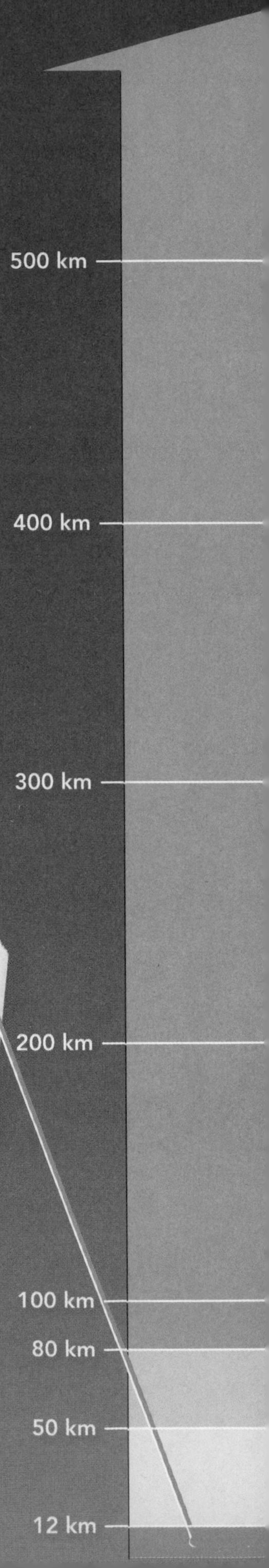

The Troposphere You live in the inner, or lowest, layer of Earth's atmosphere, the **troposphere** (TROH puh sfeer). *Tropo-* means "turning" or "changing." Conditions in the troposphere are more variable than in the other layers. **The troposphere is the layer of the atmosphere in which Earth's weather occurs.** The troposphere is about 12 kilometers thick, as you can see in **Figure 1**. However, it varies from 16 kilometers thick above the equator to less than 9 kilometers thick above the North and South poles. Although it's the shallowest layer, the troposphere is the most dense. It contains almost all the mass of the atmosphere.

As altitude increases in the troposphere, the temperature decreases. On average, for every 1-kilometer increase in altitude, the air gets about 6.5°C cooler. At the top of the troposphere, the temperature stops decreasing and stays at about –60°C. Water here forms thin, feathery clouds of ice.

FIGURE 1 ·······························
The Atmosphere Layers
✎ **Observe** Use the journal pages in this lesson to record your observations of the layers of the atmosphere.

Altitude _____

Temperature _____
_____

Observations
_____
_____
_____
_____

500 km ——

400 km ——

300 km ——

200 km ——

100 km ——
80 km ——

50 km ——

12 km ——

The Stratosphere

The Stratosphere The **stratosphere** extends from the top of the troposphere to about 50 kilometers above Earth's surface. *Strato-* means "layer" or "spread out." 🔑 **The stratosphere is the second layer of the atmosphere and contains the ozone layer.**

The lower stratosphere is cold, about −60°C. Surprisingly, the upper stratosphere is warmer than the lower stratosphere. Why is this? The middle portion of the stratosphere has a layer of air where there is much more ozone than in the rest of the atmosphere. Ozone is a form of oxygen that has three atoms in each molecule instead of the usual two. When ozone absorbs energy from the sun, the energy is converted into heat, warming the air. The ozone layer protects living things from ultraviolet radiation from the sun.

Altitude _____

Temperature _____

Observations _____

_____

do the math!

Changing Temperatures

The graph shows how temperatures in the atmosphere change with altitude. Use it to answer the questions below.

1 **Read Graphs** What is the temperature at the bottom of the stratosphere?

_____

2 **Interpret Data** What layer of the atmosphere has the lowest temperature?

_____

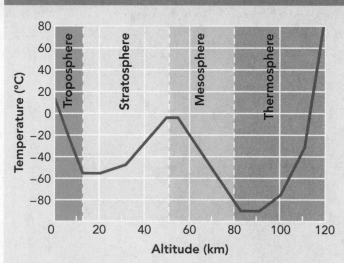

Temperature in the Atmosphere

3 [CHALLENGE] How does temperature change with altitude in the troposphere?

_____

_____

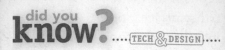

The Mesosphere Above the stratosphere, a drop in temperature marks the beginning of the next layer, the **mesosphere.** *Meso-* means "middle," so the mesosphere is the middle layer of the atmosphere. The mesosphere begins 50 kilometers above Earth's surface and ends at an altitude of 80 kilometers. In the upper mesosphere, temperatures approach –90°C.

The mesosphere is the layer of the atmosphere that protects Earth's surface from being hit by most meteoroids. Meteoroids are chunks of stone and metal from space. What you see as a shooting star, or meteor, is the trail of hot, glowing gases the meteoroid leaves behind in the mesosphere as it burns up.

Altitude _____

Temperature _____

_____

Observations _____

500 km

400 km

300 km

200 km

100 km

80 km

50 km

12 km

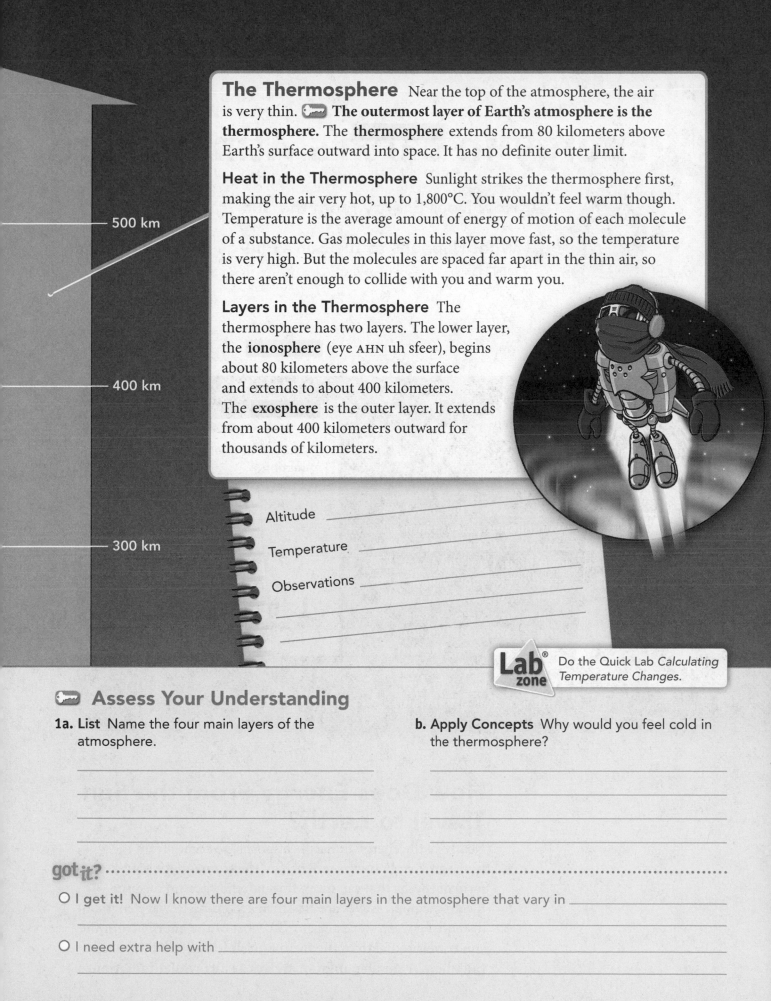

The Thermosphere

Near the top of the atmosphere, the air is very thin. 🔑 **The outermost layer of Earth's atmosphere is the thermosphere.** The **thermosphere** extends from 80 kilometers above Earth's surface outward into space. It has no definite outer limit.

Heat in the Thermosphere Sunlight strikes the thermosphere first, making the air very hot, up to 1,800°C. You wouldn't feel warm though. Temperature is the average amount of energy of motion of each molecule of a substance. Gas molecules in this layer move fast, so the temperature is very high. But the molecules are spaced far apart in the thin air, so there aren't enough to collide with you and warm you.

Layers in the Thermosphere The thermosphere has two layers. The lower layer, the **ionosphere** (eye AHN uh sfeer), begins about 80 kilometers above the surface and extends to about 400 kilometers. The **exosphere** is the outer layer. It extends from about 400 kilometers outward for thousands of kilometers.

500 km

400 km

300 km

Altitude _____

Temperature _____

Observations _____

_____

_____

Lab zone® Do the Quick Lab *Calculating Temperature Changes.*

🔑 **Assess Your Understanding**

1a. List Name the four main layers of the atmosphere.

_____
_____
_____
_____

b. Apply Concepts Why would you feel cold in the thermosphere?

_____
_____
_____
_____

got it? ....

○ **I get it!** Now I know there are four main layers in the atmosphere that vary in _____
_____

○ **I need extra help with** _____
_____

393

Energy in Earth's Atmosphere

UNLOCK THE BIG **?**

🔑 **How Does Energy From the Sun Travel to Earth?**

🔑 **What Happens to the Sun's Energy When It Reaches Earth?**

my pLaneT DiaRY

BLOG

Posted by: Amanda

Location: Hastings, New York

I love to swim. One time I was swimming at a beach in the summer. I was swimming for a long time. I got out to eat and dried off in about half an hour. Then I went swimming again, and it clouded over. I got out, and it took about an hour to dry off this time. The sun was behind clouds, so it took longer for me to dry off. I found it very interesting.

Read the blog and answer the question.

Why did it take Amanda longer to dry off the second time?

_____

_____

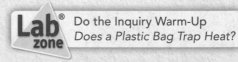

Lab zone ® Do the Inquiry Warm-Up *Does a Plastic Bag Trap Heat?*

How Does Energy From the Sun Travel to Earth?

Nearly all the energy in Earth's atmosphere comes from the sun. This energy travels to Earth as **electromagnetic waves,** a form of energy that can move through the vacuum of space. Electromagnetic waves are classified according to wavelength, or distance between wave peaks. 🔑 **Most of the energy from the sun travels to Earth in the form of visible light and infrared radiation. A smaller amount arrives as ultraviolet radiation.**

Vocabulary
- electromagnetic waves • radiation
- infrared radiation • ultraviolet radiation
- scattering • greenhouse effect

Skills
↪ Reading: Ask Questions
△ Inquiry: Graph

Visible Light Visible light includes all of the colors that you see in a rainbow: red, orange, yellow, green, blue, and violet. The different colors are the result of different wavelengths. Red and orange light have the longest wavelengths, while blue and violet light have the shortest wavelengths, as shown in **Figure 1.**

Nonvisible Radiation The direct transfer of energy by electromagnetic waves is called **radiation.** One form of electromagnetic energy, **infrared radiation,** has wavelengths that are longer than wavelengths for red light. Infrared radiation is not visible by humans, but can be felt as heat. The sun also gives off **ultraviolet radiation,** which is an invisible form of energy with wavelengths that are shorter than wavelengths for violet light. Ultraviolet radiation can cause sunburns.

FIGURE 1 ·······························
Radiation From the Sun
Energy travels to Earth as electromagnetic waves.
✏ **Identify** Label the types of electromagnetic radiation in the diagram.

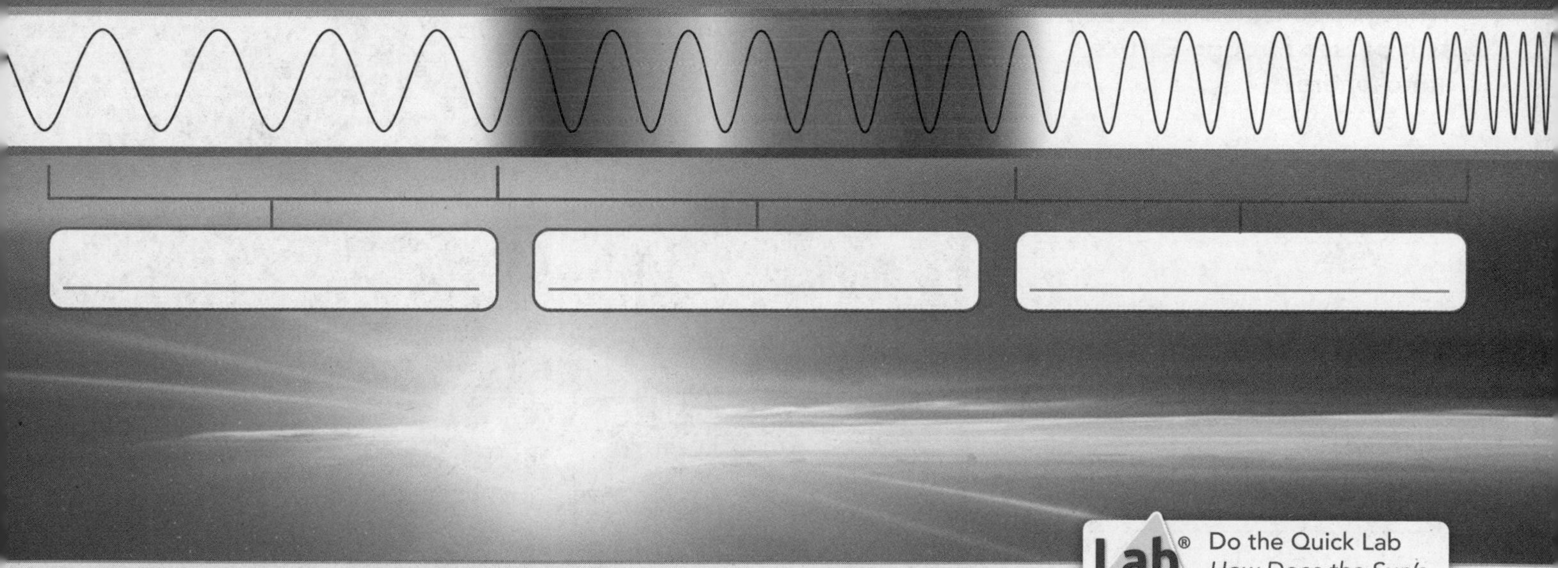

Assess Your Understanding

got it? ···

O **I get it!** Now I know energy from the sun reaches Earth as _____

_____

O **I need extra help with** _____

_____

Lab® Do the Quick Lab
zone *How Does the Sun's Energy Reach Earth?*

What Happens to the Sun's Energy When It Reaches Earth?

Sunlight must pass through the atmosphere before it reaches Earth's surface. The path of the sun's rays is shown in **Figure 2**. 🔑 **Some sunlight is absorbed or reflected by the atmosphere before it can reach the surface. The rest passes through the atmosphere to the surface.**

Upper Atmosphere Different wavelengths of radiation are absorbed by different layers in the atmosphere. For example, some ultraviolet radiation is absorbed by the ozone layer in the stratosphere. Infrared radiation penetrates farther into the atmosphere before some of it is absorbed by water vapor and carbon dioxide.

FIGURE 2 ·······························

Energy in the Atmosphere

Some wavelengths reach Earth's surface. Other wavelengths are completely or partially absorbed in the atmosphere.

✎ **Compare and Contrast** What happens to the radiation as it passes through Earth's atmosphere?

_____

_____

_____

_____

_____

_____

_____

_____

_____

_____

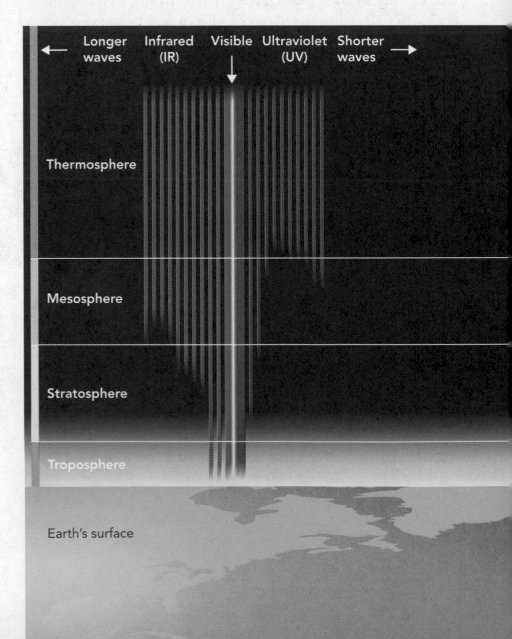

Troposphere Clouds act as mirrors, reflecting sunlight back into space. Dust-size particles and gases in the atmosphere disperse light in all directions, a process called **scattering.** When you look at the sky, the light you see has been scattered by gas molecules in the atmosphere. Gas molecules scatter short wavelengths of visible light (blue and violet) more than long wavelengths (red and orange). Scattered light looks bluer than ordinary sunlight. That's why the clear daytime sky looks blue.

Earth's Surface It may seem like a lot of the sun's energy is absorbed by gases in the atmosphere or reflected by clouds and particles. However, about 50 percent of the energy that reaches Earth's surface is absorbed by land and water and changed into heat. Look at **Figure 3** to see what happens to incoming sunlight at Earth's surface.

⊙ **Ask Questions** Before you read, preview the headings on these two pages. Ask a question you'd like to have answered. After you read, answer your question.

_____

_____

_____

_____

_____

_____

apply _it!_

The materials at Earth's surface shown below reflect different amounts of energy.

① ◢**Graph** Use the higher percentages below to draw a bar graph. Give it a title.

② Based on your graph, which material reflects the most sunlight? Which absorbs the most?

_____

③ CHALLENGE Predict what might happen if a forested area was replaced with an asphalt parking lot.

_____

_____

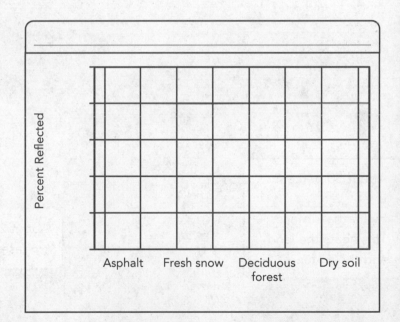

Percent Reflected

| Asphalt | Fresh snow | Deciduous forest | Dry soil |

Asphalt

5–10% reflected

Fresh snow

80–90% reflected

Deciduous forest

15–20% reflected

Dry soil

20–25% reflected

FIGURE 3 ••

Energy at Earth's Surface

✎ **Identify** What's happening to energy in the lower atmosphere and at Earth's surface? Find out by using the words in the word bank below to complete each sentence.

Word Bank

reflected   absorbed   radiated

Words may be used more than once.

✎ **Draw Conclusions** Using the diagram below, draw a conclusion about energy at Earth's surface.

_____

_____

_____

About 25 percent of incoming sunlight is _____ by clouds, dust, and gases in the atmosphere.

About 50 percent is _____ by Earth's surface. This heats the land and the water.

About 20 percent is _____ by gases and particles in the atmosphere.

Some absorbed energy is _____ back into the atmosphere.

About 5 percent is _____ by the surface back into the atmosphere.

Earth's Energy Budget What happens to the energy that heats the land and water? 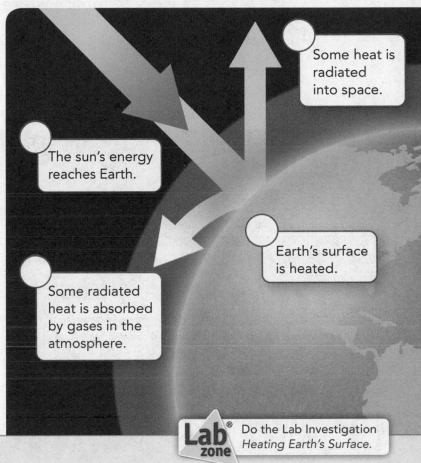 **Earth's surface radiates some energy back into the atmosphere as infrared radiation.** Much of this infrared radiation doesn't immediately travel all the way back into space. Instead, it's absorbed by water vapor, carbon dioxide, methane, and other gases in the air. The energy from the absorbed radiation heats the gases in the air. These gases in turn hold heat in Earth's atmosphere in a process called the **greenhouse effect.**

The greenhouse effect, shown in **Figure 4,** is a natural process. It keeps Earth's atmosphere at a temperature that is comfortable for most living things. Over time, the amount of energy absorbed by the atmosphere and Earth's surface is in balance with the amount of energy radiated into space. In this way, Earth's average temperatures remain fairly constant. But scientists have evidence that human activities may be altering this process.

FIGURE 4 ··································

Greenhouse Effect

The greenhouse effect is a natural heat-trapping process.

✎ **Sequence** Number each step in the diagram to show how the greenhouse effect takes place. Discuss the diagram with a partner.

Some heat is radiated into space.

The sun's energy reaches Earth.

Earth's surface is heated.

Some radiated heat is absorbed by gases in the atmosphere.

Lab ® Do the Lab Investigation
zone *Heating Earth's Surface.*

🔑 Assess Your Understanding

1a. Summarize What happens to most of the sunlight that reaches Earth?

_____

_____

b. Interpret Diagrams In **Figure 3,** what percentage of incoming sunlight is reflected by clouds, dust, and gases in the atmosphere?

_____

c. Predict How might conditions on Earth be different without the greenhouse effect?

_____

_____

_____

_____

got it? ···

O **I get it!** Now I know some energy _____

_____

O **I need extra help with** _____

_____

399

Heat Transfer

🔑 **How Is Temperature Measured?**

🔑 **How Is Heat Transferred?**

MY PLANET DIARY

SCIENCE IN THE KITCHEN

From the Freezer to the Table

French fries are on many restaurant menus. But have you ever wondered how they get from the freezer to the table? It takes a little science in the kitchen to make it happen.

First, you heat oil in a fryer until it's around 340°F. Then, the frozen potato slices are dropped in. Hot oil moves from the bottom of the fryer and begins to heat the potatoes. Exposure to so much heat causes the water in the potatoes to boil. This is indicated by bubbles rising to the surface of the oil. As the outside of the potato heats up, it transfers heat to the inside of the potato slice. In a matter of minutes it's crunchy on the outside and soft on the inside.

Answer the following question and discuss it with a partner.

Explain in your own words what happens when the potatoes are exposed to heat.

_____

_____

_____

Lab zone® Do the Inquiry Warm-Up *What Happens When Air Is Heated?*

How Is Temperature Measured?

All substances are made up of tiny particles (atoms and molecules) that are constantly moving. The faster the particles are moving, the more energy they have. **Temperature** is the *average* amount of energy of motion of each particle of a substance. In **Figure 1,** the hot tea in the teapot is the same temperature as the hot tea in the teacup. But do they have the same thermal energy?

Vocabulary

- temperature • thermal energy
- thermometer • heat • convection
- conduction • convection currents

Skills

🔄 Reading: Identify the Main Idea
△ Inquiry: Infer

Thermal energy measures the *total* energy of motion in the particles of a substance. This means that the tea in the pot has more thermal energy than the tea in the cup because it has more mass.

Measuring Temperature

Temperature is an important factor affecting weather. 🔑 **Air temperature is usually measured with a thermometer.** A **thermometer** is a device that measures temperature. Some thermometers have a thin glass tube with a bulb on one end that holds liquid mercury or colored alcohol. When the air temperature increases, the temperature of the liquid in the bulb increases. This causes the liquid to expand and rise up the column.

Temperature Scales

Temperature is measured in units called degrees. Two temperature scales are the Celsius scale and the Fahrenheit scale. On the Celsius scale at sea level, the freezing point of water is 0°C, while the boiling point is 100°C. On the Fahrenheit scale at sea level, the freezing point of water is 32°F and the boiling point is 212°F. To convert from Farenheit to Celsius, you would use the following formula:

$$\frac{\text{Fahrenheit} - 32}{1.8} = \text{Celsius}$$

FIGURE 1 ·····················

Measuring Temperature

✏️ **Read and then answer the questions.**

1. **Review** Circle the correct word in this sentence: The tea in the cup has (the same/less/more) thermal energy than the tea in the pot.

2. **Calculate** If the tea in the cup cooled to 70°F, what would a Celsius thermometer read?

_____

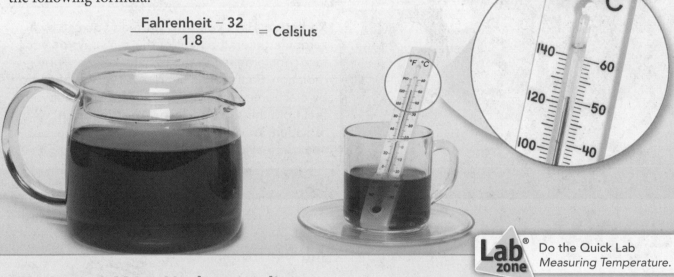

Lab zone® Do the Quick Lab
Measuring Temperature.

🔑 Assess Your Understanding

got it? ··

○ I get it! Now I know that temperature and thermal energy are different because _____

_____

○ I need extra help with _____

_____

How Is Heat Transferred?

Heat is thermal energy that is transferred from a hotter object to a cooler one. ☞ Heat is transferred in three ways: convection, conduction, and radiation.

1 **Convection** In fluids (liquids and gases), atoms and molecules can move easily from one place to another. As they move, their energy moves along with them. The transfer of heat by the movement of a fluid is called **convection.**

2 **Conduction** The transfer of heat between two substances that are in direct contact is called **conduction.** In **Figure 2,** heat is being conducted between the pot and the grate and between the pot and the liquid. When a fast-moving molecule bumps into a slower-moving molecule, the faster molecule transfers some of its energy to the slower one. The closer together the molecules are in a substance, the better they conduct heat. Conduction works well in some solids, such as metals, but not as well in liquids and gases. Air and water do not conduct heat well.

3 **Radiation** Have you ever warmed yourself by a campfire or felt the heat of the sun's rays on your face? You are feeling the transfer of energy by radiation. Radiation is the direct transfer of energy by electromagnetic waves. Most of the heat you feel from the sun travels to you as infrared radiation. You cannot see infrared radiation, but you can feel it as heat.

FIGURE 2 ·······································
Heat Transfer
✎   Use the numbers provided in the text to identify each type of heat transfer in the photo.

apply it!

Heat transfer occurs when a warm radiator heats a room.

🔺**Infer** What type of heat transfer could keep the paper in the air? Draw arrows on the image to indicate your answer and explain below.

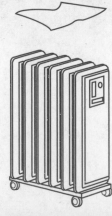

_____

_____

_____

Heating the Troposphere Radiation, conduction, and convection work together to heat the troposphere. Notice in **Figure 3** how the sun's radiation heats Earth's surface during the day. The land gets warmer than the air. Air doesn't conduct heat well. So only the first few meters of the troposphere are heated by conduction. When ground-level air warms up, its molecules move more rapidly. As they bump into each other they move farther apart, making the air less dense. Cooler, denser air sinks toward the surface, forcing the warmer air to rise. The upward movement of warm air and the downward movement of cool air form convection currents. 🔑 Heat is transferred mostly by convection within the troposphere.

✏️ **Identify the Main Idea**
Underline the main idea in the paragraph at the left.

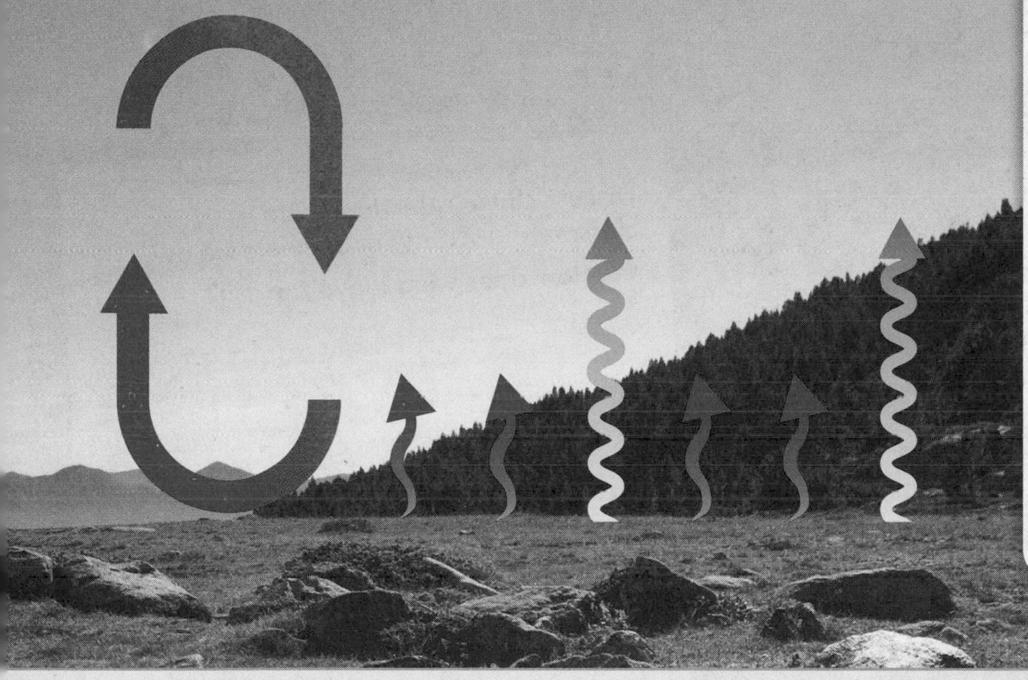

FIGURE 3 ·····························
Heating the Troposphere
✏️ **Summarize** Describe the process of heat transfer taking place in the diagram at the left.

_____
_____
_____
_____
_____
_____
_____
_____
_____
_____

Lab zone® Do the Quick Lab
Temperature and Height.

🔑 **Assess Your Understanding**

1a. Explain Why is convection more important than conduction in the troposphere?

_____
_____
_____

b. Apply Concepts Explain how a convection current can enable a hawk or eagle to soar upward without flapping its wings.

_____
_____
_____

got it? ··

○ **I get it!** Now I know that heat transfer happens in three ways in the atmosphere: _____
_____

○ **I need extra help with** _____
_____

403

Winds

UNLOCK THE BIG ?

🔑 **What Causes Winds?**

🔑 **How Do Local Winds and Global Winds Differ?**

MY PLANET DIARY

EXTREME SPORTS

Windsurfing

Imagine being able to ride a wave at almost 81 km/h—not in a boat powered by a motor but on a board powered only by the wind. That's what windsurfing is all about.

Windsurfers stand on a sailboard, which is similar to a surfboard. But the sailboard has a mast and a sail that the surfer can control with his or her hands. It uses a sail to capture wind and move the surfer along the surface of the water. Jim Drake, one of the first inventors of windsurfing, points out:

"It's the simplicity of standing up so you can adjust your weight and move quickly, as well as actively participate in transmitting the sail's forces to the board."

Discuss these questions with a classmate. Write your answers below.

1. How does wind move the sail?

_____

_____

_____

2. How have you experienced the effects of wind?

_____

_____

_____

Lab zone® Do the Inquiry Warm-Up *Does the Wind Turn?*

Vocabulary
- wind • anemometer • windchill factor
- local winds • sea breeze • land breeze
- global winds • Coriolis effect • latitude

Skills
- Reading: Identify Supporting Evidence
- Inquiry: Draw Conclusions

What Causes Winds?

Air is a fluid, so it can move easily from place to place. But how does it do that? **Differences in air pressure cause the air to move.** **Wind** is the movement of air parallel to Earth's surface. Winds move from areas of high pressure to areas of lower pressure.

Most differences in air pressure are caused by the unequal heating of the atmosphere. Recall that convection currents form when an area of Earth's surface is heated by the sun's rays. Air over the heated surface expands and becomes less dense. As the air becomes less dense, its air pressure decreases. If a nearby area is not heated as much, the air above the less-heated area will be cooler and denser. The cool, dense air with a higher pressure flows underneath the warm, less dense air. This forces the warm air to rise.

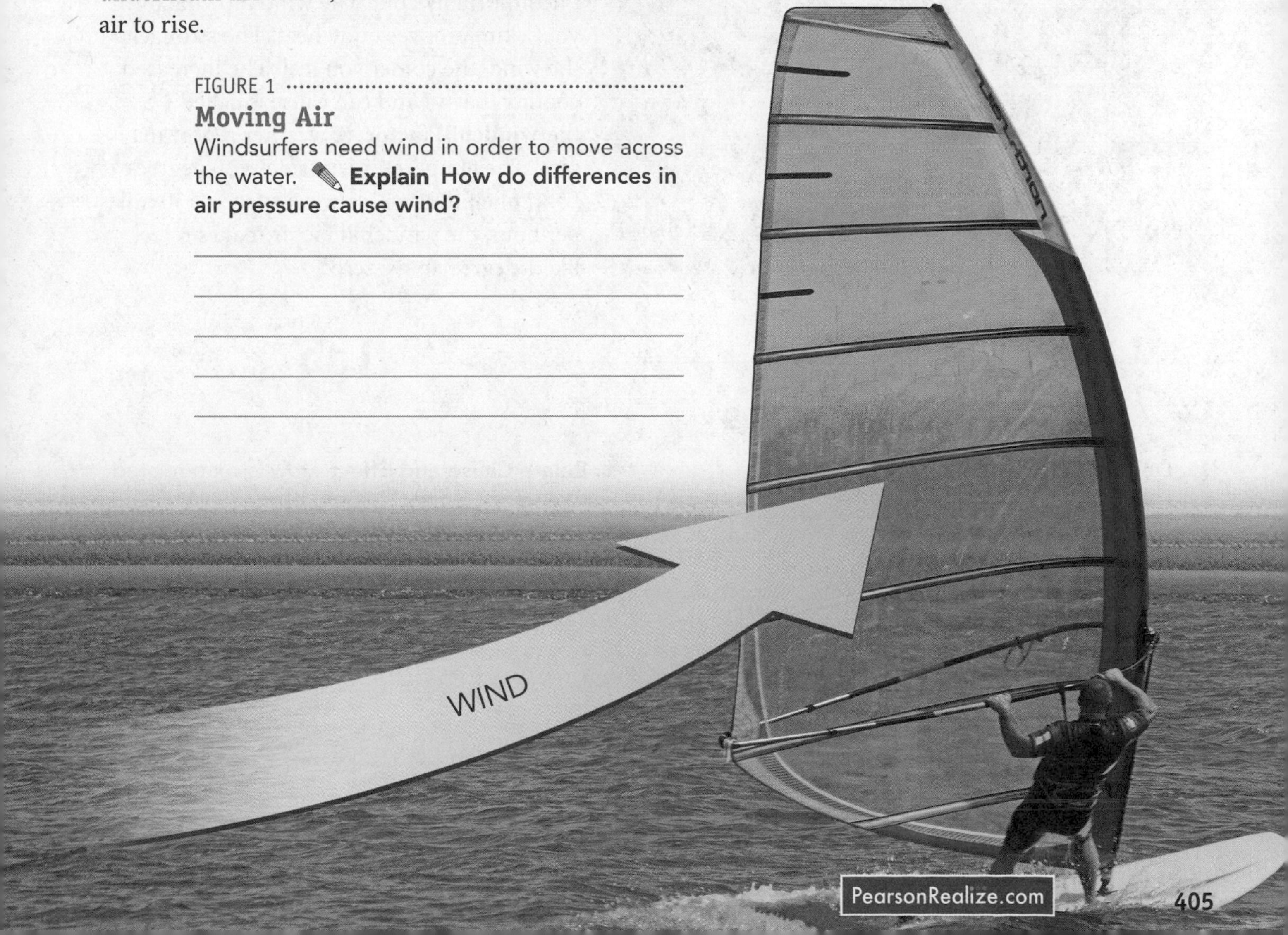

FIGURE 1 ·····························

Moving Air
Windsurfers need wind in order to move across the water. **Explain** How do differences in air pressure cause wind?

_____

_____

_____

_____

WIND

Measuring Wind

Winds are described by their direction and speed. Winds can blow from all directions: north, south, east, and west. Wind direction is determined with a wind vane. The wind swings the wind vane so that one end points into the wind. The name of a wind tells you where the wind is coming from. For example, a south wind blows from the south toward the north. A north wind blows to the south.

Wind speed can be measured with an **anemometer** (an uh MAHM uh tur). An anemometer has three or four cups mounted at the ends of spokes that spin on an axle. The force of the wind against the cups turns the axle. A meter connected to the axle shows the wind speed. **Figure 2** shows a wind vane and an anemometer.

Windchill Factor

On a warm day, a cool breeze can be refreshing. But during the winter, the same breeze can make you feel uncomfortably cold. The wind blowing over your skin removes body heat. The stronger the wind, the colder you feel. The increased cooling that a wind can cause is called the **windchill factor.** A weather report may say, "The temperature outside is 20 degrees Fahrenheit. But with a wind speed of 30 miles per hour, the windchill factor makes it feel like 1 degree above zero."

FIGURE 2 ·······················

Wind Direction and Speed

✎ **Identify** Based on the direction of the wind vane, which direction would your kite be flying? Indicate your answer by shading in your kite.

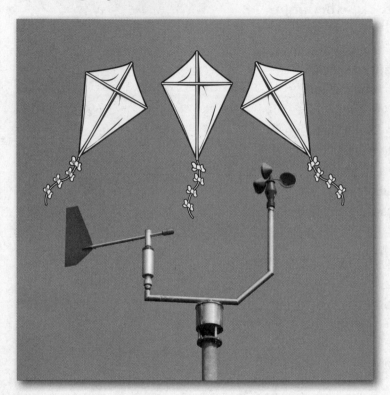

Lab zone® Do the Quick Lab
Build a Wind Vane.

🔑 Assess Your Understanding

1a. Define What is wind?

_____

_____

_____

b. Relate Cause and Effect How is wind related to air pressure and temperature?

_____

_____

_____

got**it?** ···

○ **I get it!** Now I know that wind is _____

_____

○ **I need extra help with** _____

_____

How Do Local Winds and Global Winds Differ?

Have you ever noticed a breeze at the beach on a hot summer day? Even if there is no wind inland, there may be a cool breeze blowing in from the water. This breeze is an example of a local wind.

Local Winds Winds that blow over short distances are called local winds. 🔑 **The unequal heating of Earth's surface within a small area causes local winds.** These winds form only when large-scale winds are weak. Two types of local winds are sea breezes and land breezes, as shown in **Figure 3.**

FIGURE 3 ·······································

Local Winds

✏️ **Relate Text and Visuals** Read about sea breezes. Add arrows to the bottom diagram to indicate how a land breeze develops. Then summarize the process.

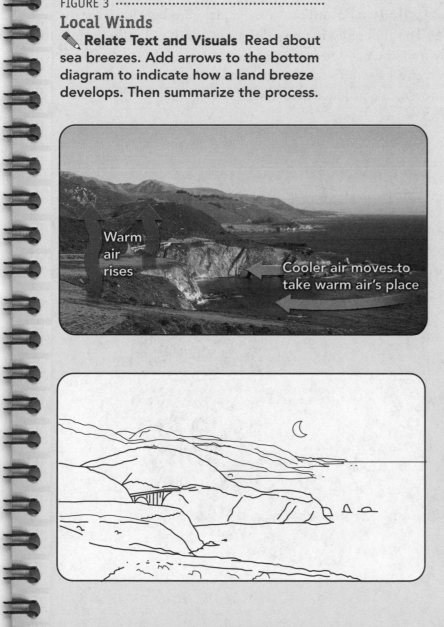

Warm air rises

Cooler air moves to take warm air's place

Sea Breeze During the day, the land warms up faster than the water. The air over the land gets warmer than the air over the water. This warm air is less dense. It expands and rises, creating a low-pressure area. Cool air blows inland from over the water and moves underneath the warm air, causing a sea breeze. A **sea breeze** or a lake breeze is a local wind that blows from an ocean or lake.

Land Breeze At night, the process is reversed. The flow of air from land to a body of water forms a **land breeze.**

_____

_____

_____

_____

_____

_____

Global Winds

Global winds are winds that blow steadily from specific directions over long distances. 🔌 **Like local winds, global winds are created by the unequal heating of Earth's surface. But unlike local winds, global winds occur over a large area.** In **Figure 4,** you can see how the sun's radiation strikes Earth. In the middle of the day near the equator, the sun is almost directly overhead. The direct rays from the sun heat Earth's surface intensely. Near the poles, the sun's rays strike Earth's surface at a lower angle. The sun's energy is spread out over a larger area, so it heats the surface less. As a result, temperatures near the poles are much lower than they are near the equator.

Global Convection Currents

How do global winds develop? Temperature differences between the equator and the poles produce giant convection currents in the atmosphere. Warm air rises at the equator, and cold air sinks at the poles. Therefore air pressure tends to be lower near the equator and greater near the poles. This difference in pressure causes winds at Earth's surface to blow from the poles toward the equator. Higher in the atmosphere, however, air flows away from the equator toward the poles. Those air movements produce global winds.

FIGURE 4 ·······························

Heating of Earth's Surface

✏️ **Interpret Diagrams** The angle of the sun's rays causes temperature differences at Earth's surface.

1. Label the areas where the sun hits Earth most directly (M) and least directly (L).

2. CHALLENGE Draw a convection current in the atmosphere north of the equator.

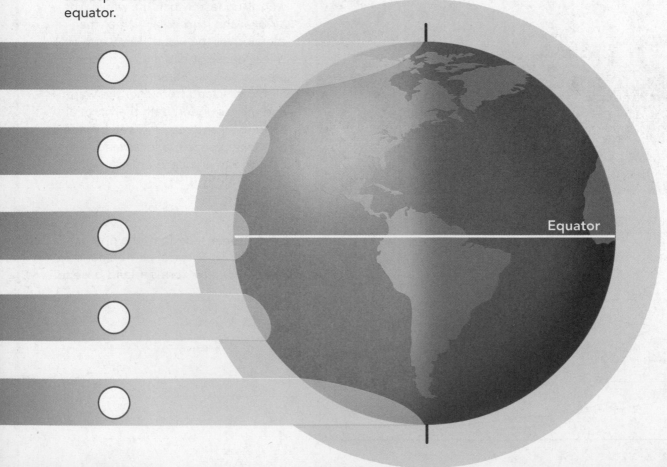

Equator

The Coriolis Effect If Earth did not rotate, global winds would blow in a straight line from the poles toward the equator. Because Earth is rotating, however, global winds do not follow a straight path. As the winds blow, Earth rotates from west to east underneath them, making it seem as if the winds have curved. The way Earth's rotation makes winds curve is called the **Coriolis effect** (kawr ee OH lis). Because of the Coriolis effect, global winds in the Northern Hemisphere gradually turn toward the right. A wind blowing toward the south gradually turns toward the southwest. In the Southern Hemisphere, winds curve toward the left.

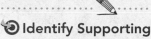

Identify Supporting Evidence Underline the text that describes how winds blow due to the Coriolis effect.

apply it!

The Coriolis effect determines the direction of global winds.

1 Look at the globe on the left. Shade in the arrows that show the direction the global winds would blow without the Coriolis effect.

2 Look at the globe on the right. Shade in the arrows that show the direction the global winds blow as a result of the Coriolis effect.

3 Draw Conclusions Based on your last answer, what direction do global winds blow in the Northern Hemisphere? In the Southern Hemisphere?

_____

_____

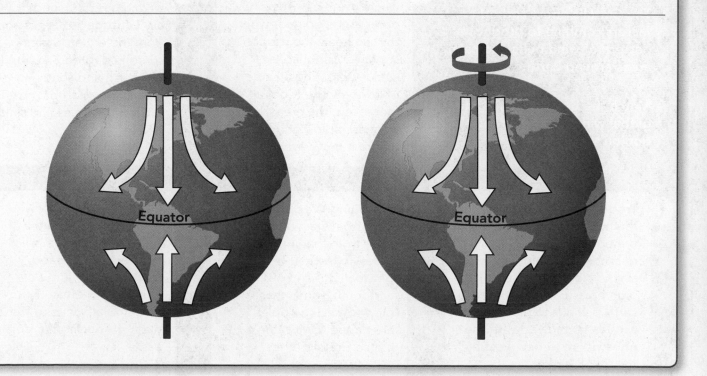

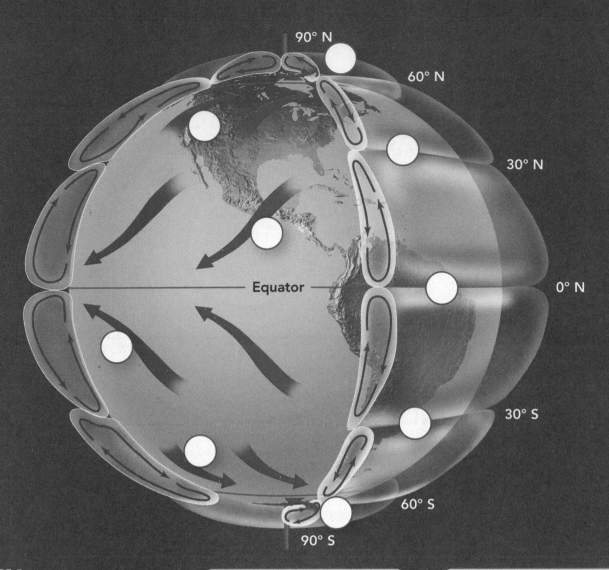

90° N

60° N

30° N

0° N

30° S

60° S

90° S

Equator

FIGURE 5 ·······················

Global Wind Belts

The Coriolis effect and other factors combine to produce a pattern of wind belts and calm areas around Earth.

✎ Relate Text and Visuals
Match the descriptions of the global winds with their location on the globe.

A **Doldrums** are a calm area where warm air rises. They occur at the equator where the sun heats the surface strongly. Warm air rises steadily, creating an area of low pressure. Cool air moves into the area, but is warmed rapidly and rises before it moves very far.

B **Horse Latitudes** are two calm areas of sinking air. **Latitude** is the distance from the equator, measured in degrees. At about 30° north and south latitudes, the air stops moving toward the poles and sinks.

C **Trade Winds** blow from the horse latitudes toward the equator. As cold air over the horse latitudes sinks, it forms a region of high pressure. This causes surface winds to blow. The winds that blow toward the equator are turned west by the Coriolis effect.

D **Prevailing Westerlies** blow from west to east, away from the horse latitudes. In the mid-latitudes, between 30° and 60° north and south, winds that blow toward the poles are turned toward the east by the Coriolis effect.

E **Polar Easterlies** blow cold air away from the poles. Air near the poles sinks and flows back toward lower latitudes. The Coriolis effect shifts these polar winds to the west, producing the polar easterlies.

Parts of the Atmosphere

EXPLORE THE BIG ?

How does the sun's energy affect Earth's atmosphere?

FIGURE 6 ··

Earth's atmosphere is a system made up of many different parts.

✏ **Communicate** In the space below, draw a picture or a diagram that helps you understand the relationship between the concepts in the word bank. Explain your diagram to a classmate.

Word Bank	
atmosphere	air pressure
convection	radiation
global winds	

Lab zone® Do the Quick Lab
Modeling Global Wind Belts.

🔑 Assess Your Understanding

2a. Summarize What causes local winds?

_____

_____

b. Identify What is a global wind?

_____

_____

c. ANSWER THE BIG ? How does the sun's energy affect Earth's atmosphere?

_____

_____

_____

_____

got it? ··

○ **I get it!** Now I know that winds blow locally and globally due to _____

_____

○ **I need extra help with** _____

_____

411

The sun's energy affects Earth's atmosphere by _____ Earth's surface, causing differences in _____ that result in _____.

LESSON 1 The Air Around You

🔑 Earth's atmosphere consists of nitrogen, oxygen, carbon dioxide, water vapor, and other gases, as well as particles of liquids and solids.

🔑 Events in one part of the atmosphere affect other parts of the atmosphere.

Vocabulary
• weather
• atmosphere
• water vapor

LESSON 2 Air Pressure

🔑 Because air has mass, it also has other properties, including density and pressure.

🔑 Two common kinds of barometers are mercury barometers and aneroid barometers.

🔑 Air pressure decreases as altitude increases. As air pressure decreases, so does density.

Vocabulary
• density • air pressure • barometer
• mercury barometer • aneroid barometer
• altitude

LESSON 3 Layers of the Atmosphere

🔑 Scientists divide Earth's atmosphere into four main layers according to changes in temperature.

🔑 Earth's weather occurs in the troposphere. The stratosphere contains the ozone layer.

🔑 The mesosphere protects Earth from meteoroids. The thermosphere is the outermost layer of Earth's atmosphere.

Vocabulary
• troposphere • stratosphere • mesosphere
• thermosphere • ionosphere • exosphere

LESSON 4 Energy in Earth's Atmosphere

🔑 The sun's energy travels to Earth as visible light, infrared radiation, and ultraviolet radiation.

🔑 Some sunlight is absorbed or reflected by the atmosphere. Some of the energy Earth absorbs is radiated back out as infrared radiation.

Vocabulary
• electromagnetic waves • radiation
• infrared radiation • ultraviolet radiation
• scattering • greenhouse effect

LESSON 5 Heat Transfer

🔑 Air temperature is usually measured with a thermometer.

🔑 Heat is transferred in three ways: convection, conduction, and radiation.

🔑 Heat is transferred mostly by convection within the troposphere.

Vocabulary
• temperature • thermal energy • thermometer
• heat • convection • conduction
• convection currents

LESSON 6 Winds

🔑 Winds are caused by differences in air pressure.

🔑 The unequal heating of Earth's surface within a small area causes local winds.

🔑 Global winds are caused by the unequal heating of Earth's surface over a large area.

Vocabulary
• wind • anemometer • windchill factor
• local winds • sea breeze • land breeze
• global winds • Coriolis effect • latitude

Review and Assessment

LESSON 1 The Air Around You

1. Which gas forms less than one percent of the atmosphere, but is essential to life?

   a. carbon dioxide   **b.** oxygen

   c. hydrogen   **d.** nitrogen

2. Weather occurs in Earth's troposphere, which is _____

_____

3. Draw Conclusions Why is it difficult to include water vapor in a graph of the percentages of various gases in the atmosphere? How could you solve the problem?

_____

_____

_____

_____

LESSON 2 Air Pressure

4. When density increases, the number of molecules in a volume

   a. increases.   **b.** decreases.

   c. stays the same.   **d.** varies.

5. One force affecting an object is air pressure, which is _____

_____

6. Apply Concepts Why can an aneroid barometer measure elevation as well as air pressure?

_____

_____

7. **Write About It** Suppose you're on a hot-air balloon flight. Describe how air pressure and the amount of oxygen would change during your trip. What would the changes feel like?

LESSON 3 Layers of the Atmosphere

8. The layers of the atmosphere are classified according to changes in

   a. altitude.   **b.** air pressure.

   c. distance.   **d.** temperature.

9. Sequence List the layers of the atmosphere in order, moving up from Earth's surface.

_____

_____

10. The ozone layer is important because

_____

_____

_____

11. Infer Why are clouds at the top of the troposphere made of ice crystals rather than drops of water?

_____

_____

12. Compare and Contrast How are the upper and lower parts of the stratosphere different?

_____

_____

_____

_____

13. Calculate The table shows the temperature at various altitudes above Omaha, Nebraska, on a January day. Suppose an airplane was 6.8 kilometers above Omaha. What is the approximate temperature at this height?

_____

Altitude (kilometers)	0	1.6	3.2	4.8	6.4	7.2
Temperature (°C)	0	−4	−9	−21	−32	−40

LESSON 4 Energy in Earth's Atmosphere

14. How does **most** of the energy from the sun travel to Earth's surface?

   a. convection   **b.** conduction

   c. radiation   **d.** scattering

15. What are three forms of radiation that come from the sun?

_____

16. Relate Cause and Effect Why do people need to wear sunscreen at the beach?

_____

_____

_____

_____

_____

LESSON 5 Heat Transfer

17. What is the main way heat is transferred in the troposphere?

   a. radiation currents   **b.** reflection currents

   c. conduction currents **d.** convection currents

18. Compare and Contrast A pail of lake water is the same temperature as a lake. Compare the thermal energy of the pail of water with the thermal energy of the lake.

_____

_____

_____

_____

_____

19. **Write About It** Describe an example of heat transfer in your daily life.

LESSON 6 Winds

20. The calm areas near the equator where warm air rises are

   a. horse latitudes.   **b.** trade winds.

   c. doldrums.   **d.** polar easterlies.

21. Nights often feature land breezes, which blow

_____

22. Relate Cause and Effect How does the movement of hot air at the equator and cold air at the poles produce global wind patterns?

_____

_____

_____

_____

_____

_____

APPLY THE BIG ❓ How does the sun's energy affect Earth's atmosphere?

23. Imagine you are sailing around the world. What winds would you expect to find on different parts of your route? Explain the role of the sun's energy in creating those winds.

_____

_____

_____

_____

_____

_____

_____

_____

_____

_____

Standardized Test Prep

Read each question and choose the best answer.

1. Which of the following determines the movement of global winds?

   A humidity and temperature
   B infrared and ultraviolet radiation
   C prevailing winds and upper air currents
   D convection currents in the atmosphere and the Coriolis effect

2. What is the most abundant gas in the atmosphere?

   A ozone
   B water vapor
   C oxygen
   D nitrogen

3. What happens to air with increased altitude?

   A temperature increases
   B pressure decreases
   C pressure increases
   D wind speed decreases

4. Which layer of the atmosphere protects Earth from meteoroids?

   A mesosphere
   B troposphere
   C ionosphere
   D stratosphere

5. Uneven heating of Earth's atmosphere causes which of the following?

   A global temperature increase
   B infrared radiation
   C the greenhouse effect
   D local and global winds

Constructed Response

Use the diagram and your knowledge of science to answer Question 6. Write your answer on another sheet of paper.

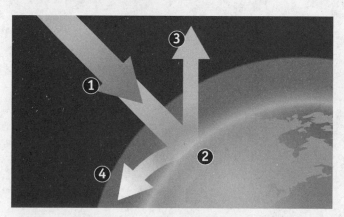

6. Describe the process that results in the greenhouse effect. How does it affect Earth's atmosphere?

When someone mentions the National Aeronautics and Space Administration (NASA), you might think of missions to Mars or Pluto. However, many of NASA's missions help us understand our own planet. In 2004, NASA launched *Aura*, the third satellite in its Earth Observing System (EOS) program. *Aura* helps scientists study the chemistry of the atmosphere.

The *Aura* mission seeks to answer three questions about our atmosphere.

1. Is the ozone layer recovering? *Aura* helps scientists monitor atmospheric gases, such as chlorofluorocarbons (CFCs), that affect the ozone layer. If the ozone layer does not recover, scientists predict that we will need to learn to better protect ourselves from the sun. In the next 10 years, will we need SPF 100 sunscreen?

2. How do pollutants affect air quality? *Aura* monitors levels of ozone, particulate matter, carbon monoxide, nitrogen dioxide, and sulfur dioxide. The data help scientists understand—and predict—the movement of air pollutants. Are attempts to reduce air pollution working?

3. How is Earth's climate changing? *Aura* checks levels of greenhouse gases in the atmosphere to help scientists build more accurate models of climate change. This way, we will have a better idea of how to plan for long-term climate change. Will you need to invest in a really good raincoat?

Research It Research NASA's EOS program. What are the major satellites in this program? Which Earth systems are they designed to monitor? What discoveries has the EOS program made? Make a display with information and pictures to show what you find out.

Up, Up, and Away!

Bobbing along in the sky, hot air balloons look like a fun way to spend a day. Before the invention of satellites or airplanes, though, scientists used hot air balloons to study the atmosphere. Riding in their balloons, scientists recorded air temperatures and humidity, and even gathered information about cosmic rays. For more than 150 years, balloons were cutting-edge atmospheric observatories.

Research It Find out more about the history of ballooning. How did scientific research using balloons contribute to early space missions? Make a timeline showing balloonists' discoveries.

PLUGGING INTO THE JET STREAM

It's windy up there! About 10 kilometers above Earth's surface, the jet stream winds blow constantly. The winds average 80 to 160 km/h, and they can reach 400 km/h. If we could harness just a small fraction of the wind's energy, we could meet the electricity needs of everyone on Earth!

Scientists are testing designs for high-altitude wind farms. They propose that kite-like wind generators flying above Earth could generate electricity. Cables could then transfer the electricity to Earth.

Design It Research the proposed designs for wind farms in the sky. Make a graphic organizer to show the proposed designs, the risks, and the ways scientists are addressing these risks.

WHAT CLUES CAN PREDICT A STORM?

THE BIG ?

How do meteorologists predict the weather?

This tornado bearing down on this home in Kansas in June of 2004 reached wind speeds of 254–331 km/h. The state of Kansas had 124 tornadoes that year. Although tornadoes can occur anywhere, the United States leads the world with more than 1,000 tornadoes per year. **Observe** **How could you predict a tornado was coming?**

Watch the **Untamed Science** video to learn more about weather.

CHAPTER

Weather 10

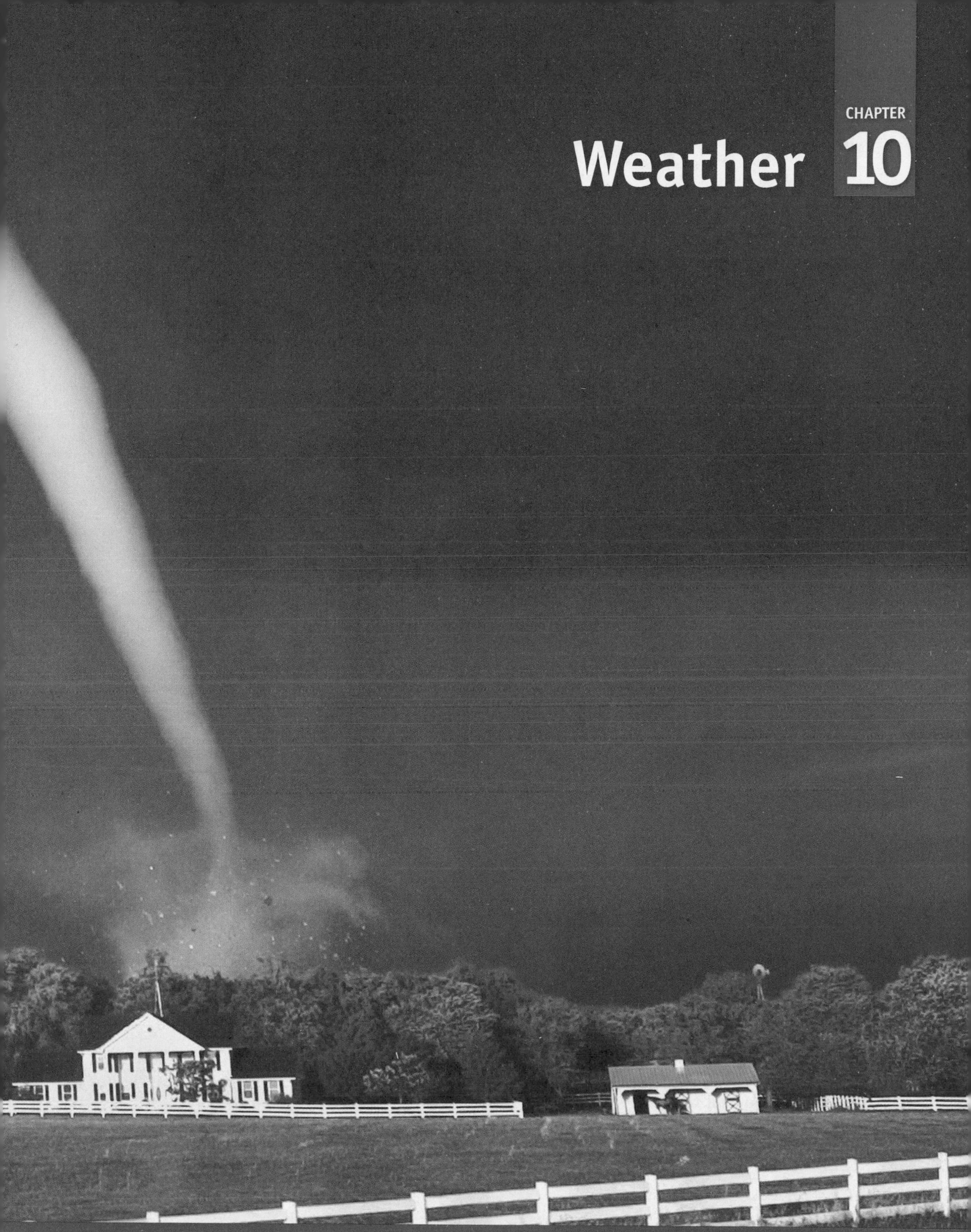

10 Getting Started

Check Your Understanding

1. **Background** Read the paragraph below and then answer the question.

"Is that smoke over the baseball field?" Eddie asked Cara in the park. "No," she replied. "It's **fog**." "Ah, water **vapor**," Eddie said. "No," Cara said. "If you can see it, it's water droplets suspended in the **atmosphere**. Water vapor is an invisible gas and can't be seen."

> **Fog** is made up of clouds that form near the ground.
>
> **Vapor** is water in the form of a gas.
>
> The **atmosphere** is the envelope of gases surrounding Earth.

• What does water vapor in the atmosphere look like?

_____

_____

Vocabulary Skill

Prefixes A prefix is a word part that is added at the beginning of a word to change its meaning. For example, the prefix *anti-* means "against" or "opposed to" and is used frequently in science. In the word *antivenom*, the prefix *anti-* is added to the word *venom* to form *antivenom*, meaning "against poison."

Prefix	Meaning	Example
psychro-	cold	psychrometer, *n.*
alto-	high	altocumulus, *n.*; altostratus, *n.*
anti-	against or opposed to	anticyclone, *n.*

2. **Quick Check** Review the prefixes above. Then predict what the word *altocumulus* means using what you know about the prefix *alto-*. After reading the chapter, revise your definition as needed.

_____

_____

_____

cirrus

precipitation

front

tornado

Chapter Preview

LESSON 1
- water cycle • evaporation
- condensation • humidity
- relative humidity • psychrometer
- ⟳ Sequence
- △ Interpret Data

LESSON 2
- dew point • cirrus • cumulus
- stratus
- ⟳ Summarize
- △ Predict

LESSON 3
- precipitation • rain gauge
- flood • drought
- ⟳ Relate Cause and Effect
- △ Calculate

LESSON 4
- air mass • tropical • polar
- maritime • continental
- jet stream • front • occluded
- cyclone • anticyclone
- ⟳ Relate Text and Visuals
- △ Classify

LESSON 5
- storm • thunderstorm • lightning
- hurricane • storm surge
- tornado • evacuate
- ⟳ Outline
- △ Infer

LESSON 6
- meteorologist • isobar
- isotherm
- ⟳ Compare and Contrast
- △ Predict

Predicting the Weather Is No Sport

Purpose   To predict weekend weather by following the movement of weather systems across the United States

Materials
- daily weather maps for one week (Monday–Friday)
- tracing paper
- two blank maps of the United States

Scenario

You are the sports reporter for the newspaper in your town. The paper's weather forecaster is going on vacation this Friday, and it's your turn to forecast the weekend weather. This is a real problem because you're not a meteorologist! You can't even forecast the winner of your town's high school football games.

The forecaster tries to calm you: "Don't worry. A few days of weather maps will show you what's coming. Watch the low- and high-pressure systems and fronts as they move across the United States." The forecaster also recommends that you ask yourself the following questions:

- What direction do the fronts move?
- How fast do they move?
- Is colder or warmer weather coming?
- Is rain moving your way?

The forecaster's last piece of advice is "Just pay attention, and forecasting is easy."

Procedure

☑ **1. Five Days of Maps** Each day for the next five days your teacher will give you a copy of the day's weather map from the local newspaper.

☑ **2. Panic on Monday** Don't panic yet. All you can do today is examine the map and make a copy of it. Notice the position of high- and low-pressure systems and fronts, the daily high temperatures, and the type and amount of precipitation. Pay attention to anything you think might be helpful in predicting your weekend weather. Trace the map onto tracing paper.

☑ **3. Tuesday** Trace Tuesday's map and compare it to Monday's map. Notice that the weather moves. Pay close attention to the direction and speed of that movement. Based on movement alone, try to predict tomorrow's high temperature and precipitation for your town.

Procedure *(continued)*

☑ **4. Wednesday** Trace Wednesday's map. Was your prediction right? Is it raining? How hot will it be today? Is the weather still moving the same direction? Is it still moving at the same speed? Take what you learn and use Wednesday's map to predict Thursday's weather.

_____

_____

☑ **5. Thursday** Trace Thursday's map. Ask yourself the same questions from Step 4 and use Thursday's map to predict Friday's weather.

_____

_____

Conclusion

Let's see what you learned about the movement of weather across the country.

☑ **1.** According to the weather maps, does precipitation seem to come with high pressure or low pressure?

_____

☑ **2.** In what direction does weather usually move across the United States? What causes weather to move in this direction?

_____

_____

_____

☑ **3.** If a front passed through your town during the week, name the type of front, the day it came through, and tell how the weather changed. If a front didn't pass through your town, choose another city and answer the questions.

_____

_____

_____

Friday is the big day. Time has run out, and you have learned everything you could. Your paper's regular weather forecaster left for vacation. It's time for you to write the weather forecast for the weekend edition of the paper. What will the weather be on Saturday and Sunday? Use two blank maps of the United States to show where you think the pressure systems and fronts will be this weekend. Where will it be raining or snowing? Provide a key for any symbols you use.

Prepare a more detailed forecast for the weather in your town for each day. Predict the high and low temperatures. Will it rain or snow where you live? Will it be cloudy or sunny? You can present your forecast in a chart or in complete sentences. Over the weekend, pay attention to the weather to see how you did.

Water in the Atmosphere

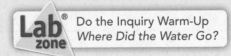

UNLOCK THE BIG ?

🔑 How Does Water Move Through the Atmosphere?

🔑 What Is Relative Humidity and How Is It Measured?

my planeT DiaRY

The Driest Place on Earth

The Atacama Desert in Chile is so dry that there are places where humans have never measured a single drop of rain. But even the Atacama has some moisture in the air. A dense fog along the coastline, known as *camanchaca*, often flows inland from the Pacific Ocean. At one point, the people of the fishing village Chungungo set up nets above the mountains to catch the fog. Water condensed on the nets and then was collected and sent through pipes that brought the water to the village.

Chile
Uruguay
Argentina
Pacific Ocean
Atlantic Ocean

FUN FACT

Write your answers to each question below. Then discuss your answers with a partner.

1. Why did the people of Chungungo need to use nets to catch moisture in the air?

_____

_____

2. What would be one way of collecting water where you live?

_____

Lab® zone Do the Inquiry Warm-Up *Where Did the Water Go?*

How Does Water Move Through the Atmosphere?

During a rainstorm, the air feels moist. On a clear, cloudless day, the air may feel dry. As the sun heats the land and oceans, the sun provides energy to change the amount of water in the atmosphere. Water is always moving between Earth's atmosphere and surface.

The movement of water through Earth's systems, powered by the sun's energy, is the **water cycle**. 🔑 **In the water cycle, water vapor enters the atmosphere by evaporation from the oceans and other bodies of water and leaves by condensation**. **Evaporation** is the process by which molecules of liquid water escape into the air after becoming water vapor. **Condensation** is the process by which water vapor becomes liquid water.

Vocabulary
• water cycle • evaporation • condensation
• humidity • relative humidity • psychrometer

Skills
⟳ Reading: Sequence
△ Inquiry: Interpret Data

Water vapor is also added to the air by living things. Water enters the roots of plants, rises to the leaves, and is released into the air as water vapor. Animals also release water vapor into the air every time they exhale.

As part of the water cycle, shown in **Figure 1,** some of the water vapor in the atmosphere condenses to form clouds. Rain and snow fall from the clouds toward the surface as precipitation. The water then runs off the surface or moves through the ground, back into lakes, streams, and eventually the oceans. Then the water cycle starts all over again with evaporation.

⟳ **Sequence** Starting with precipitation, list the order of the steps of the water cycle.

_____

_____

_____

_____

FIGURE 1 ·····················

The Water Cycle
In the water cycle, water moves from plants, lakes, rivers, and oceans into the atmosphere and then falls back to Earth.

✎ **Summarize** Use the word bank to label the parts of the water cycle.

Word Bank

Condensation

Evaporation

Precipitation

Surface runoff

Lab zone® Do the Quick Lab *Water in the Air.*

🔑 Assess Your Understanding

got it? ·······························

○ I get it! Now I know that in the water cycle _____

_____

○ I need extra help with _____

_____

What Is Relative Humidity and How Is It Measured?

How is the quantity of water vapor in the atmosphere measured? **Humidity** is a measure of the amount of water vapor in the air. The ability of air to hold water vapor depends on its temperature. Warm air can hold more water vapor than cool air.

Relative Humidity Weather reports usually refer to the water vapor in the air as relative humidity. **Relative humidity** is the percentage of water vapor that is actually in the air compared to the maximum amount of water vapor the air can hold at a particular temperature. For example, at 10°C, 1 cubic meter of air can hold at most 8 grams of water vapor. If there were 8 grams of water vapor in the air, then the relative humidity of the air would be 100 percent. Air with a relative humidity of 100 percent is said to be saturated. If the air had 4 grams of vapor, the relative humidity would be 50 percent.

Measuring Relative Humidity **Relative humidity can be measured with an instrument called a psychrometer.** A **psychrometer** (sy KRAHM uh tur) has two thermometers, a wet-bulb thermometer and a dry-bulb thermometer. As shown in **Figure 2,** the wet bulb is covered by a moist cloth. When the psychrometer is "slung," or spun, air blows over both thermometers. Because the wet-bulb thermometer is cooled by evaporation, its reading drops.

If the relative humidity is high, the water on the wet bulb evaporates slowly, and the wet-bulb temperature does not change much. If the relative humidity is low, the water on the wet bulb evaporates rapidly, and the wet-bulb temperature drops by a large amount. The relative humidity can be found by comparing the temperatures of the wet-bulb and dry-bulb thermometers.

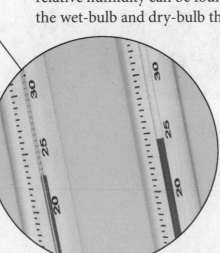

Wet bulb

Dry bulb

FIGURE 2 ....

Sling Psychrometer

🖉 **Relate Text and Visuals** Read the psychrometer and compare the two Celsius temperatures. Is the relative humidity low or high? How do you know?

_____

_____

_____

_____

do the math!

Relative Humidity

Relative humidity is affected by temperature. Use the data table to answer the questions below. First, find the dry-bulb temperature in the left column of the table. Then find the difference between the wet- and dry-bulb temperatures across the top of the table. The number in the table where these two readings intersect indicates the percentage of relative humidity.

1 ⚠ **Interpret Data** At noon the readings on a sling psychrometer are 18°C for the dry bulb and 14°C for the wet bulb. What is the relative humidity?

_____

2 ⚠ **Interpret Data** At 5 P.M. the reading on the dry bulb is 12°C and the reading on the wet bulb is 11°C. Determine the new relative humidity.

_____

3 [CHALLENGE] What was the difference in relative humidity between noon and 5 P.M.? How was the relative humidity affected by air temperature?

_____

_____

Relative Humidity

Dry-Bulb Reading (°C)	Difference Between Wet- and Dry-Bulb Readings (°C)				
	1	2	3	4	5
10	88	76	65	54	43
12	88	78	67	57	48
14	89	79	69	60	50
16	90	80	71	62	54
18	91	81	72	64	56
20	91	82	74	66	58
22	92	83	75	68	60

Do the Quick Lab *Measuring to Find the Dew Point.*

🔑 Assess Your Understanding

1a. Review What is humidity?

_____

_____

b. Calculate Suppose a sample of air can hold at most 10 grams of water vapor. If the sample actually has 2 grams of water vapor, what is its relative humidity?

_____

c. Compare and Contrast How are humidity and relative humidity different?

_____

_____

_____

_____

_____

_____

got it?

○ **I get it!** Now I know that relative humidity is _____

_____ and it can be measured with _____

○ **I need extra help with** _____

_____

Clouds

UNLOCK THE BIG

?

🔑 **How Do Clouds Form?**

🔑 **What Are the Three Main Types of Clouds?**

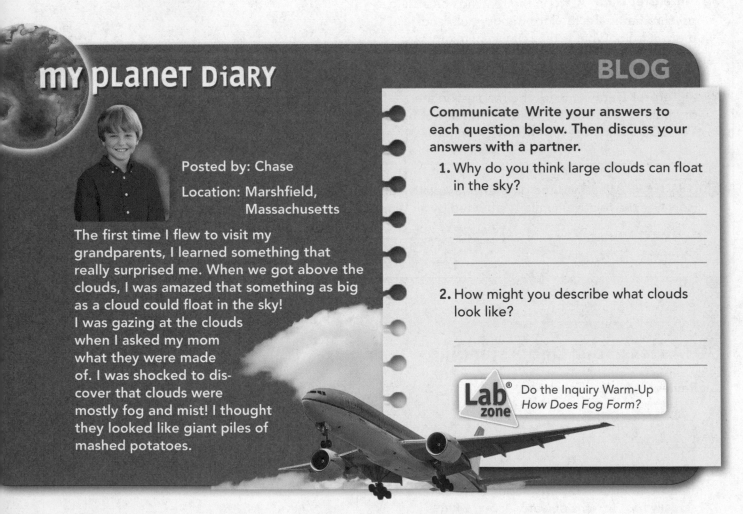

MY PLANET DIARY

BLOG

Posted by: Chase

Location: Marshfield, Massachusetts

The first time I flew to visit my grandparents, I learned something that really surprised me. When we got above the clouds, I was amazed that something as big as a cloud could float in the sky! I was gazing at the clouds when I asked my mom what they were made of. I was shocked to discover that clouds were mostly fog and mist! I thought they looked like giant piles of mashed potatoes.

Communicate Write your answers to each question below. Then discuss your answers with a partner.

1. Why do you think large clouds can float in the sky?

_____

_____

_____

2. How might you describe what clouds look like?

_____

_____

Lab® zone Do the Inquiry Warm-Up *How Does Fog Form?*

How Do Clouds Form?

When you look at a cloud, you are seeing millions of tiny water droplets or ice crystals. 🔑 **Clouds form when water vapor in the air condenses to form liquid water or ice crystals.** Molecules of water vapor in the air become liquid water in a process called condensation. How does water in the atmosphere condense? Two conditions are required for condensation: cooling of the air and the presence of particles in the air.

Vocabulary
- dew point • cirrus
- cumulus • stratus

Skills
↻ Reading: Summarize
△ Inquiry: Predict

The Role of Cooling As you have learned, cold air holds less water vapor than warm air. As air cools, the amount of water vapor it can hold decreases. The water vapor condenses into tiny droplets of water or ice crystals. The temperature at which condensation begins is called the **dew point.** If the dew point is above freezing, the water vapor forms droplets. If the dew point is below freezing, the water vapor may change directly into ice crystals.

The Role of Particles For water vapor to condense and form clouds, tiny particles must be present in the atmosphere so that the water has a surface on which to condense. Most of these particles are salt crystals, dust from soil, or smoke. Water vapor also condenses on solid surfaces, such as blades of grass or window panes. Liquid water that condenses from the air onto a cooler surface is called dew. Ice deposited on a surface that is below freezing is called frost.

↻ **Summarize** What is the difference between dew and frost?

_____

_____

_____

_____

_____

FIGURE 1 ....
How Clouds Form
Clouds form when warm, moist air rises and cools.
✎ **Interpret Diagrams**
Fill in the blanks to complete the sentences about cloud formation.

❸ Water vapor condenses on tiny _____ in the air.

❶ Warm, moist air rises from the surface. As air rises, it _____

❷ At a certain height, air cools to the dew point and _____ begins.

Lab zone® Do the Quick Lab *How Clouds Form.*

🔑 **Assess Your Understanding**
got it? ....

○ **I get it!** Now I know that clouds form when _____

_____

○ **I need extra help with** _____

_____

What Are the Three Main Types of Clouds?

🔑 **Scientists classify clouds into three main types based on their shape: cirrus, cumulus, and stratus. Clouds are further classified by their altitude.** Each type of cloud is associated with a different type of weather.

(km)

13

12

11

10

9

8

7

6

5

4

3

2

1

Cirrus

Cumulonimbus

Altocumulus

Altostratus

Cumulus

Fog

Cirrus Clouds

Wispy, feathery clouds are called **cirrus** (SEER us) clouds. *Cirrus* comes from a word meaning "a curl." Cirrus clouds form at high altitudes, usually above 6 km, and at low temperatures. They are made of ice crystals and indicate fair weather.

Altocumulus and Altostratus

Clouds that form between 2 and 6 km above Earth's surface have the prefix *alto-*, which means "high." The two main types of these clouds are altocumulus and altostratus. These are "medium-level" clouds that are higher than regular cumulus and stratus clouds, but lower than cirrus clouds. These clouds indicate precipitation.

Cumulus Clouds

Clouds that look like cotton are called **cumulus** (KYOO myuh lus) clouds. The word *cumulus* means "heap" in Latin. Cumulus clouds form less than 2 km above the ground, but they may extend upward as much as 18 km. Short cumulus clouds usually indicate fair weather. Towering clouds with flat tops, or cumulonimbus clouds, often produce thunderstorms. The suffix *-nimbus* means "rain."

Fog

Clouds that form near the ground are called fog. Fog can form when the ground cools at night after a humid day.

CHALLENGE What happens to fog after sunrise?

FIGURE 2 ···

Cloud Types

There are many different types of clouds.
△ Predict Read about clouds in the text. Then fill in the table to predict the weather that you would expect with each type of cloud.

Cloud	Weather
Cirrus	
Cirrocumulus	
Cumulus	
Cumulonimbus	
Stratus	
Nimbostratus	

Cirrocumulus

Cirrocumulus Clouds

Cirrocumulus clouds, which look like cotton balls, often indicate that a storm is on its way.

Stratus Clouds

Clouds that form in flat layers are known as **stratus** (STRAT us) clouds, from the Latin word *strato*, meaning "spread out." Stratus clouds usually cover all or most of the sky and are a dull, gray color. As stratus clouds thicken, they may produce drizzle, rain, or snow. They are then called *nimbostratus* clouds.

Nimbostratus   **Stratus**

---

apply it!

1 Observe Look out your window and identify the clouds you see. What kind of clouds are they? Circle a cloud on the page that looks most like one of the clouds you see.

_____

_____

2 △ Predict From what you know about this type of cloud, what sort of weather would you expect over the next 24 hours? Why?

_____

_____

Do the Quick Lab *Identifying Clouds.*

🔑 Assess Your Understanding

1a. Describe Briefly describe the shapes of the three main types of clouds.

_____

_____

_____

b. Classify Classify each of the following cloud types as low-level, medium-level, or high-level.

Altocumulus _____

Altostratus _____

Cirrocumulus _____

Cirrus _____

Cumulus _____

Nimbostratus _____

Stratus _____

got it? ··

○ **I get it!** Now I know that the three main types of clouds are _____

_____

○ **I need extra help with** _____

_____

_____

431

Precipitation

UNLOCK
THE BIG

🗝 **What Are the Common Types of Precipitation?**

🗝 **What Are the Causes and Effects of Floods and Droughts?**

my planeт DiaRY

Cloud Seeding

Is that a space weapon you see in this photo? Not at all. This scientist in China is launching tiny crystals of silver iodide into the air to make rain. Clouds often contain water droplets that have cooled below 0°C. But the droplets do not freeze unless they can condense onto solid particles. When the silver iodide crystals reach the clouds, the droplets can condense onto them. Once that happens, the droplets can fall as rain.

Some scientists think that cloud seeding can increase rainfall by 10 percent. Others think that this is unlikely. In the United States, several western states are trying cloud seeding. Dry states, such as Wyoming and Utah, need as much rainfall as they can get.

TECHNOLOGY

Write your answer to each question below. Then discuss your answers with a partner.

1. Why would scientists want to find a way to make it rain?

_____

_____

_____

_____

2. Name a situation when you would want it to rain.

_____

_____

Lab ® Do the Inquiry Warm-Up
zone   *How Can You Make Hail?*

Vocabulary
- precipitation • rain gauge
- flood • drought

Skills
🔊 Reading: Relate Cause and Effect
△ Inquiry: Calculate

What Are the Common Types of Precipitation?

Suppose you could control the weather. If you wanted it to rain, you would have to get the water from somewhere.

Water evaporates from every water surface on Earth and eventually falls back to the surface. **Precipitation** is any form of water that falls from clouds and reaches Earth's surface. It is a vital part of the water cycle. In warm climates, precipitation is almost always rain. In colder regions, it may fall as snow or ice. 🔑 **Common types of precipitation include rain, sleet, freezing rain, snow, and hail.**

Rain The most common kind of precipitation is rain. As shown in **Figure 1,** drops of water are called rain if they are at least 0.5 millimeters in diameter. Precipitation made up of smaller drops of water is called drizzle. Precipitation of even smaller drops is called mist.

Measuring Rain What if scientists need to measure how much rain has fallen? An open-ended tube that collects rain is called a **rain gauge.** The amount of rain is measured by dipping a ruler into the water or by reading a scale. For rainfall to be measured more accurately, a rain gauge may have a funnel at the top that collects ten times as much rain as the tube alone would without it. The depth is easier to measure. To get the actual depth of rain, it is necessary to divide by ten.

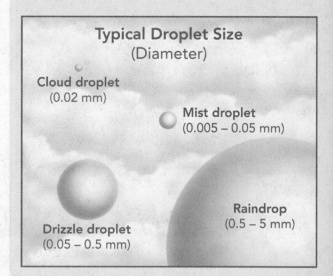

FIGURE 1 ·······························
Water Droplets
Cloud droplets condense to become larger droplets.
✏️ △Calculate Determine how many times larger the diameter of a large (5 mm) raindrop is than the diameter of a cloud droplet.

_____

_____

Typical Droplet Size
(Diameter)

Cloud droplet (0.02 mm)

Mist droplet (0.005 – 0.05 mm)

Drizzle droplet (0.05 – 0.5 mm)

Raindrop (0.5 – 5 mm)

FIGURE 2 ·······························
Rain Gauge
The rain gauge, measuring in centimeters, collects ten times the actual depth of rain that falls.
✏️ △Calculate How much rain has fallen so far?

_____

Freezing Rain

On a cold day, raindrops can sometimes fall as liquid water but freeze when they touch a cold surface. This kind of precipitation is called freezing rain.

Snow

You probably know that snow-flakes have an endless number of different shapes and patterns, many with six sides or branches. A snowflake forms when water vapor in a cloud is converted directly into ice crystals. Snow-flakes often join together into large clumps of snow in which the crystals are hard to see.

FIGURE 3 ·······················

Freezing Precipitation

There are four types of freezing precipitation: freezing rain, snow, sleet, and hail.

✎ Review Circle the temperature range in the air and on the ground for which you would expect each kind of precipitation. In some cases, more than one choice may be correct.

Precipitation	Air Temperature	Ground Temperature
Rain	Above 0 °C / At or below 0 °C	Above 0 °C / At or below 0 °C
Freezing rain	Above 0 °C / At or below 0 °C	Above 0 °C / At or below 0 °C
Sleet	Above 0 °C / At or below 0 °C	Above 0 °C / At or below 0 °C
Snow	Above 0 °C / At or below 0 °C	Above 0 °C / At or below 0 °C
Hail	Above 0 °C / At or below 0 °C	Above 0 °C / At or below 0 °C

Hail

A hailstone is a round pellet of ice larger than 5 millimeters in diameter. If you cut a hailstone in half, you would see layers of ice, like the layers of an onion. Hail forms only inside cumulonimbus clouds during thunderstorms. A hailstone starts as an ice pellet inside a cold region of a cloud. Strong updrafts carry the hailstone up through the cold region many times. Each time the hailstone goes through the cold region, a new layer of ice forms around it. Eventually the hailstone becomes heavy enough to fall to the ground. Because hailstones can grow large, hail can cause damage to crops, buildings, and vehicles.

Sleet

Sometimes raindrops fall through a layer of air that is below 0°C, the freezing point of water. As they fall, the raindrops freeze into solid particles of ice. Ice particles smaller than 5 millimeters in diameter are called sleet.

Measuring Snow Rain is not the only kind of precipitation meteorologists measure. Have you ever walked through a large snowstorm and wanted to know exactly how much snow had fallen?

Snowfall is usually measured in two ways: by using a simple measuring stick or by melting collected snow and measuring the depth of water it produces. On average, 10 centimeters of snow contains about the same amount of water as 1 centimeter of rain. However, light, fluffy snow contains far less water than heavy, wet snow does.

apply it!

A rain gauge with a wide funnel collects ten times the actual depth of rain that falls. After the rain ends, the water level is at 15 centimeters.

1 How much rain actually fell?

_____

2 **Calculate** If snow had fallen instead, how deep would that snow have been?

_____

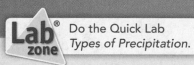 Do the Quick Lab *Types of Precipitation.*

⚷ Assess Your Understanding

1a. Define What is precipitation?

_____

_____

_____

b. Draw Conclusions What factors determine if precipitation falls as freezing rain or as sleet?

_____

_____

_____

got it? ....

○ **I get it!** Now I know that the common types of precipitation are _____

_____

○ **I need extra help with** _____

_____

What Are the Causes and Effects of Floods and Droughts?

In September 2008, just three years after Hurricane Katrina, Hurricane Gustav blasted the coasts of Louisiana and Mississippi. Lakes and rivers overflowed. The result was severe flooding.

Floods A **flood** is an overflowing of water in a normally dry area. The floods caused by Gustav fortunately were not as devastating as those caused by Katrina. Because of the flooding caused by Katrina, more than 100,000 homes and businesses were destroyed, along with many bridges and highways.

Causes and Effects of Floods Not all floods are as severe as those caused by a hurricane. **Small or large, many floods occur when the volume of water in a river increases so much that the river overflows its channel.** As rain and melting snow add more water, a river gains speed and strength. A flooding river can uproot trees and pluck boulders from the ground. It can even wash away bridges and buildings.

People who live near rivers try to control floods with dams and levees. A dam is a barrier across a river that may redirect the flow of the river to other channels or store floodwaters so they can be released slowly. A levee is an embankment built along a river to prevent flooding of the surrounding land. People sometimes strengthen levees with sandbags or stones and concrete. But powerful floodwaters can sometimes break through dams and levees.

FIGURE 4 ···

Flooding Caused by Hurricane Gustav
Hurricane Gustav hit the Gulf Coast in September 2008, causing severe flooding. ✎ **Answer the questions below.**

1. **Infer** What sort of damage would you expect to your home if this flood took place in the area where you live?

   _____

   _____

2. [CHALLENGE] A "100-year flood" is the flooding elevation that has a 1% chance of happening each year. Why is the name misleading?

   _____

   _____

Relate Cause and Effect
What causes a flood? A drought?

_____

_____

_____

_____

_____

_____

FIGURE 5 ···
Drought in Texas
In July 1998, a drought hit Wharton County, Texas. This farmer lost about 50 percent of his normal cereal crop to the drought.

Droughts

If you went away for a month and no one was around to water your plants, what would happen to them? They would probably die from lack of water. A long period of scarce rainfall or dry weather is known as a **drought** (drowt). A drought reduces the supplies of groundwater and surface water. A drought can result in a shortage of water for homes and businesses.

Causes and Effects of Droughts

Droughts are usually caused by dry weather systems that remain in one place for weeks or months at a time. Long-term droughts can devastate a region. Droughts can cause crop failure. A drought can even cause famine in places where people must grow their own food. Streams and ponds dry up, and people and animals suffer.

People can prepare for droughts in several ways. When dry conditions first occur, people can begin conserving water. Farmers can grow drought-resistant plants that have been bred to withstand dry conditions. By practicing water and soil conservation, people can ensure that when droughts do occur, people will be prepared for their effects.

Lab zone Do the Quick Lab *Floods and Droughts.*

Assess Your Understanding

2a. Explain What are two ways to help reduce the dangers of floods?

_____

b. Make Judgments Your community is considering building a dam on a nearby river to reduce flooding. Would you support this proposal? Explain.

_____

_____

_____

_____

_____

_____

_____

_____

got**it?** ···

○ **I get it!** Now I know that floods are caused

by _____

and droughts are caused by _____

_____

○ **I need extra help with** _____

_____

_____

437

Air Masses

🔑 **What Are the Major Air Masses?**

🔑 **What Are the Main Types of Fronts?**

🔑 **What Weather Do Cyclones and Anticyclones Bring?**

my pLaneT DiaRY

MISCONCEPTION

Cyclones and Tornadoes

Misconception: A cyclone is another name for tornado.

Fact: Both cyclones and tornadoes are spinning storm systems. Both rotate around an area of low pressure. However, tornadoes cover a much smaller area than cyclones do. And tornado winds reach much higher speeds.

Evidence: Outside the tropics, cyclones can be 1,000 to 4,000 kilometers across. Tropical cyclones, which are powerful hurricanes, are smaller, ranging from 100 to 1,000 kilometers across. But tornadoes are smaller still. Tornadoes range in size from a few meters to 1,600 meters across. Tornado winds are the fastest known winds on Earth. They can reach speeds of 480 km/h, but are usually much slower. Cyclone winds are strong, but do not move as fast as the fastest tornado winds. Tropical cyclone winds rarely reach more than 320 km/h.

Think about the cyclones and tornadoes you have heard about as you answer the following questions.

1. Which kind of storm do you think would cause damage over a larger area, a cyclone or a tornado? Why?

_____

_____

_____

2. Have you ever seen water swirl down a drain? How is it related to a tornado?

_____

_____

 Lab **zone** ® Do the Inquiry Warm-Up *How Do Fluids of Different Densities Move?*

Vocabulary
- air mass • tropical • polar • maritime
- continental • jet stream • front
- occluded • cyclone • anticyclone

Skills
↻ **Reading:** Relate Text and Visuals
△ **Inquiry:** Classify

What Are the Major Air Masses?

When you have a certain type of weather taking place outside, that's because a certain type of air mass is influencing the weather. An **air mass** is a huge body of air in the lower atmosphere that has similar temperature, humidity, and air pressure at any given height. Scientists classify air masses according to temperature and humidity. ▭ **Four major types of air masses influence the weather in North America: maritime tropical, continental tropical, maritime polar, and continental polar.**

As shown in **Figure 1**, the characteristics of an air mass depend on the temperatures and moisture content of the region over which the air mass forms. Remember that temperature affects air pressure. Cold, dense air has a higher pressure, while warm, less-dense air has a lower pressure. **Tropical,** or warm, air masses form in the tropics and have low air pressure. **Polar,** or cold, air masses form north of 50° north latitude and south of 50° south latitude. Polar air masses have high air pressure.

Whether an air mass is humid or dry depends on whether it forms over water or land. **Maritime** air masses form over oceans. Water evaporates from the oceans, so the air can become very humid. **Continental** air masses form over land. Continental air masses have less exposure to large amounts of moisture from bodies of water. Therefore, continental air masses are drier than maritime air masses.

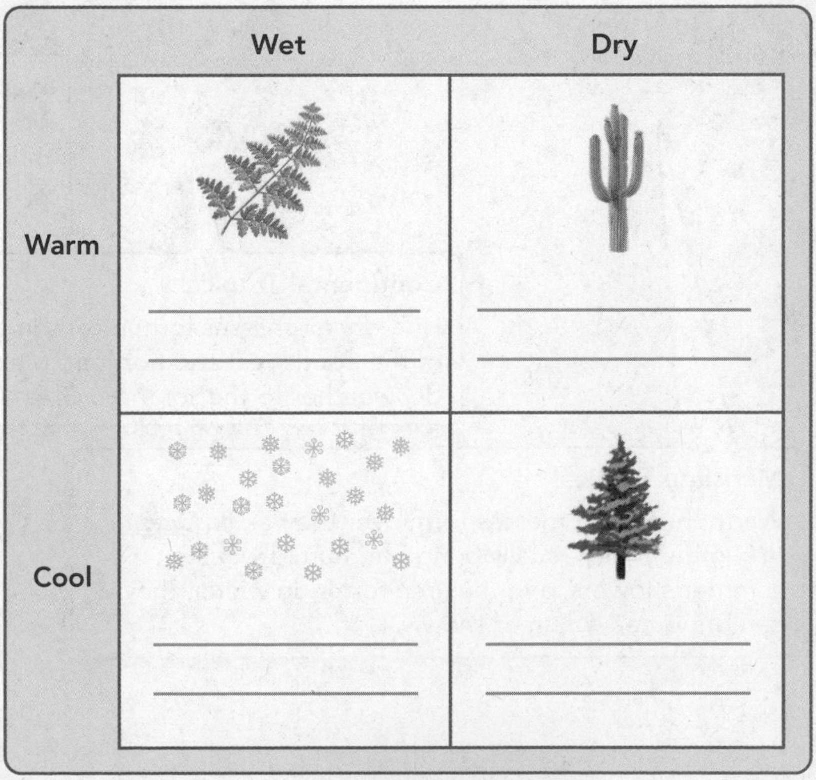

FIGURE 1 ·······························

Types of Air Masses
Air masses can be classified according to temperature and humidity.
✏ △ **Classify** Fill in the table. Classify each type of air mass as *maritime* or *continental* and as *tropical* or *polar*.

FIGURE 2 ··

North American Air Masses

Air masses can be warm or cold, and humid or dry. ⚠️ **Classify Identify the two unlabeled air masses on the page by their descriptions.**

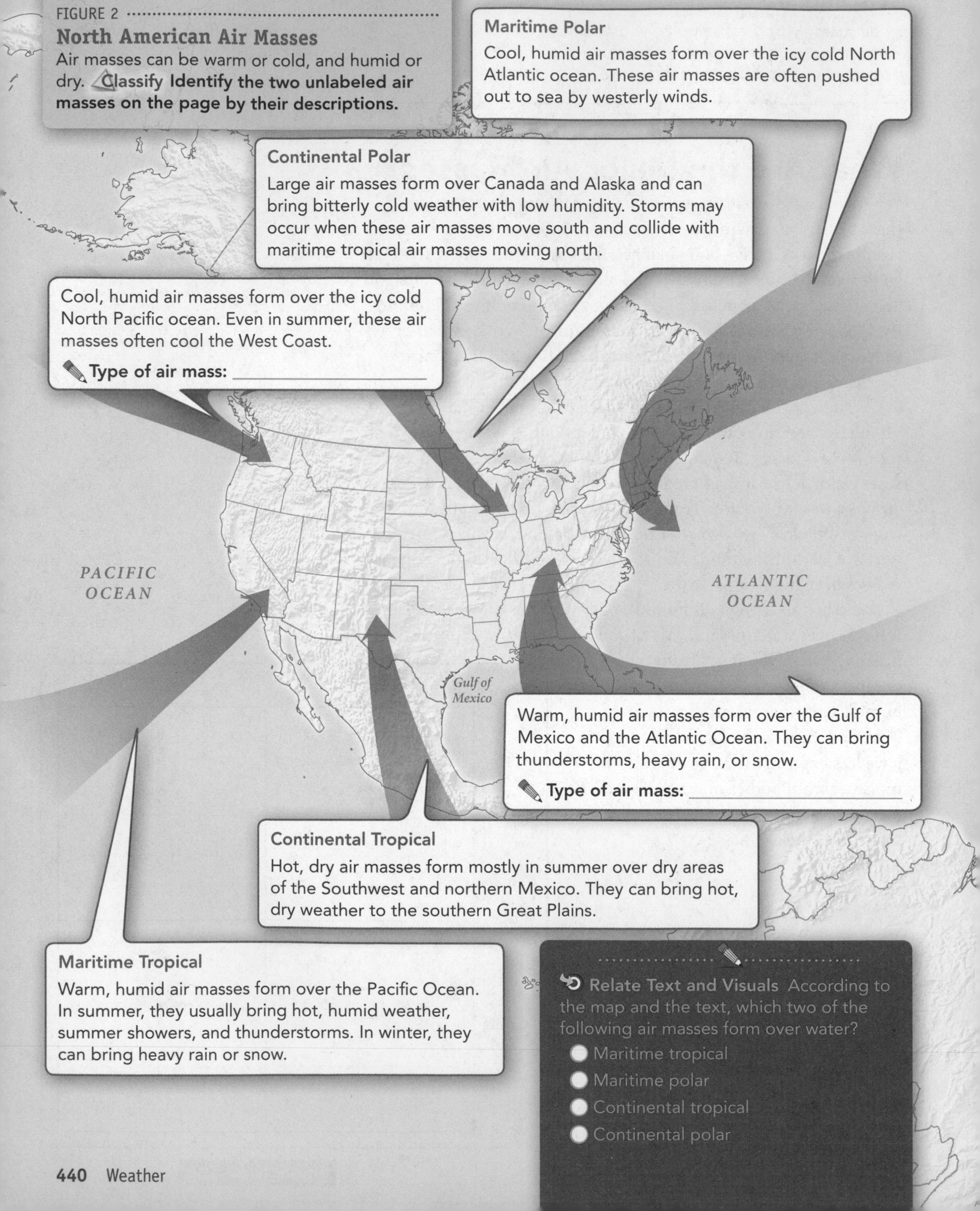

Maritime Polar

Cool, humid air masses form over the icy cold North Atlantic ocean. These air masses are often pushed out to sea by westerly winds.

Continental Polar

Large air masses form over Canada and Alaska and can bring bitterly cold weather with low humidity. Storms may occur when these air masses move south and collide with maritime tropical air masses moving north.

Cool, humid air masses form over the icy cold North Pacific ocean. Even in summer, these air masses often cool the West Coast.

✏️ **Type of air mass:** _____

PACIFIC OCEAN

ATLANTIC OCEAN

Gulf of Mexico

Warm, humid air masses form over the Gulf of Mexico and the Atlantic Ocean. They can bring thunderstorms, heavy rain, or snow.

✏️ **Type of air mass:** _____

Continental Tropical

Hot, dry air masses form mostly in summer over dry areas of the Southwest and northern Mexico. They can bring hot, dry weather to the southern Great Plains.

Maritime Tropical

Warm, humid air masses form over the Pacific Ocean. In summer, they usually bring hot, humid weather, summer showers, and thunderstorms. In winter, they can bring heavy rain or snow.

🔄 **Relate Text and Visuals** According to the map and the text, which two of the following air masses form over water?

- ⚪ Maritime tropical
- ⚪ Maritime polar
- ⚪ Continental tropical
- ⚪ Continental polar

How Air Masses Move When an air mass moves into an area and interacts with other air masses, it causes the weather to change, sometimes drastically. In the continental United States, air masses are commonly moved by the prevailing westerlies and jet streams.

Prevailing Westerlies The prevailing westerlies, the major wind belts over the continental United States, generally push air masses from west to east. For example, maritime polar air masses from the Pacific Ocean are blown onto the West Coast, bringing low clouds and showers.

Jet Streams Embedded within the prevailing westerlies are jet streams. **Jet streams** are bands of high-speed winds about 10 kilometers above Earth's surface. As jet streams generally blow from west to east, air masses are carried along their tracks.

Fronts As huge masses of air move across the land and the oceans, they collide with each other, but do not easily mix. Think about a bottle of oil and water. The less-dense oil floats on top. Something similar happens when two air masses of different temperature and humidity collide. They do not easily mix. The boundary where the air masses meet becomes a **front.** Storms and changeable weather often develop along fronts like the one in **Figure 3.**

FIGURE 3

How a Front Forms
The boundary where unlike air masses meet is called a front. A front may be 15 to 600 km wide and extend high into the troposphere.

⊙ **Relate Text and Visuals** What kind of weather would develop along the front shown in the photo?

_____

_____

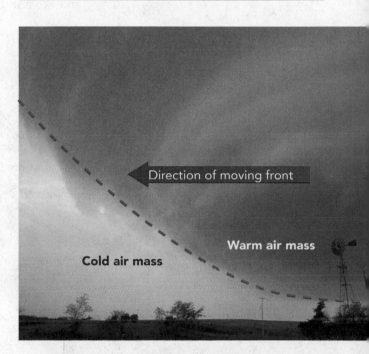

Direction of moving front

Warm air mass

Cold air mass

Lab zone   Do the Quick Lab
Tracking Air Masses.

🔑 **Assess Your Understanding**

1a. Review What two characteristics are used to classify air masses?

_____

b. Apply Concepts What type of air mass would form over the northern Atlantic Ocean?

_____

c. Classify Classify the four major types of air masses according to moisture content.

_____

_____

_____

_____

got it?

○ **I get it!** Now I know that the four major types of air masses are _____

_____

○ I need extra help with _____

_____

441

What Are the Main Types of Fronts?

When you leave school in the afternoon, you may find that the weather is different from when you arrived in the morning. That might be because a front has just recently passed through the area. 🗝 **Colliding air masses can form four types of fronts: cold fronts, warm fronts, stationary fronts, and occluded fronts.** The kind of front that develops depends on the characteristics of the air masses and the direction in which they move.

FIGURE 4 ···

Types of Fronts

✎ **Infer** Identify the type of weather brought by each front as it passes through an area.

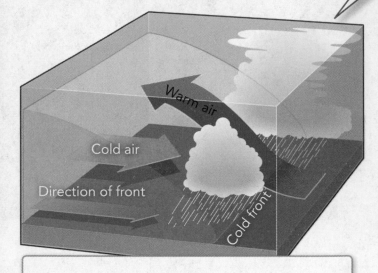

Cold Fronts

Cold air is dense and tends to sink. Warm air is less dense and tends to rise. When a faster cold air mass runs into a slower warm air mass, the denser cold air slides under the lighter warm air. The warm air is pushed upward along the leading edge of the colder air. A cold front forms.

As the warm air rises, it expands and cools. The rising air soon reaches the dew point, the temperature at which water vapor in the air condenses. Clouds form. Heavy rain or snow may fall.

Cold fronts tend to arrive quickly, because their leading edges move along the ground. They can cause abrupt weather changes, including thunderstorms. After a cold front passes, colder, drier air moves in, often bringing clear skies, a shift in wind direction, and lower temperatures.

Warm Fronts

Clouds and precipitation also accompany warm fronts. At a warm front, a fast-moving warm air mass overtakes a slower cold air mass. Because cold air is denser than warm air, the warm air moves over the cold air. If the warm air is humid, light rain or snow falls along the front. If the air is dry, scattered clouds form. Because warm fronts arrive slowly, the weather may be rainy or cloudy for several days. After a warm front passes, the weather tends to be warmer and humid.

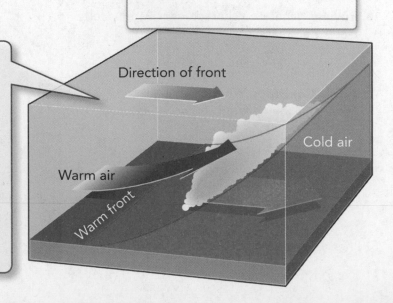

Occluded Fronts

The most complex weather situation occurs at an occluded front, where a warm air mass is caught between two cooler air masses. The denser cool air masses move underneath the less dense warm air mass and push the warm air upward. The two cooler air masses meet in the middle and may mix. The temperature near the ground becomes cooler. The warm air mass is cut off, or **occluded,** from the ground. As the warm air cools and its water vapor condenses, the weather may turn cloudy and rain or snow may fall.

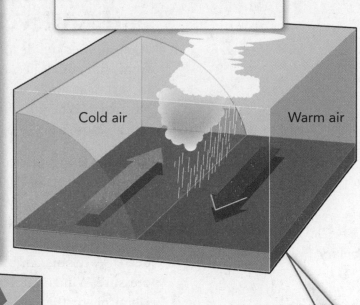

Cold air   Warm air

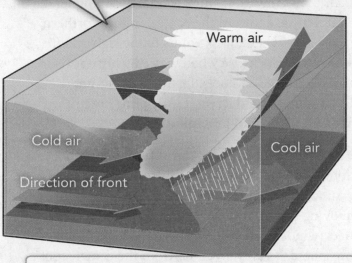

Warm air

Cold air   Cool air

Direction of front

Stationary Fronts

Sometimes cold and warm air masses meet, but neither one can move the other. In this case, the front is called a stationary front. Where the warm and cool air meet, water vapor in the warm air condenses into rain, snow, fog, or clouds. But if a stationary front stalls, it may bring many days of clouds and precipitation.

Do the Quick Lab
Weather Fronts.

🔑 Assess Your Understanding

2a. Define What is a front?

_____

_____

b. Describe What type of weather occurs as a warm front moves through an area?

_____

_____

c. Classify What types of fronts would cause several days of rain and clouds?

_____

_____

got it?

○ **I get it!** Now I know that the four main types of fronts are _____

_____

_____

_____

○ I need extra help with _____

_____

_____

_____

_____

443

What Weather Do Cyclones and Anticyclones Bring?

As air masses collide to form fronts, the boundary between the fronts sometimes becomes distorted. This distortion can be caused by surface features, such as mountains, or strong winds, such as the jet stream. When this happens, the air begins to swirl. The swirling air can cause a low-pressure center to form.

Cyclones   A circled *L* on a weather map stands for "low," and indicates an area of relatively low air pressure. A swirling center of low air pressure is a **cyclone,** from a Greek word meaning "wheel." You can see a cyclone in **Figure 5.**

As warm air at the center of a cyclone rises, the air pressure decreases. Cooler air blows inward from nearby areas of higher air pressure. Winds spiral inward toward the center. In the Northern Hemisphere, the Coriolis effect deflects winds to the right. So the cyclone winds spin counterclockwise when viewed from above.

As air rises in a cyclone, the air cools, forming clouds and precipitation. 🔑 **Cyclones and decreasing air pressure are associated with clouds, wind, and precipitation.**

Anticyclones   As its name suggests, an anticyclone is the opposite of a cyclone. **Anticyclones** are high-pressure centers of dry air, shown by an *H* on a weather map. Winds spiral outward from the center, moving toward areas of lower pressure. Because of the Coriolis effect, winds in an anticyclone spin clockwise in the Northern Hemisphere. As air moves out from the center, cool air moves downward from higher in the troposphere. The cool air warms up, so its relative humidity drops. 🔑 **The descending air in an anticyclone generally causes dry, clear weather.**

Vocabulary Prefixes How does knowing the meaning of the prefix *anti-* help you remember how an anticyclone spins?

_____

_____

_____

_____

FIGURE 5 ·······································

Cyclones and Anticyclones

✎ **Interpret Diagrams** Label each diagram as either a cyclone or an anticyclone. In each circle, draw an arrow to show the direction of air motion for the system as it would be seen from above.

apply it!

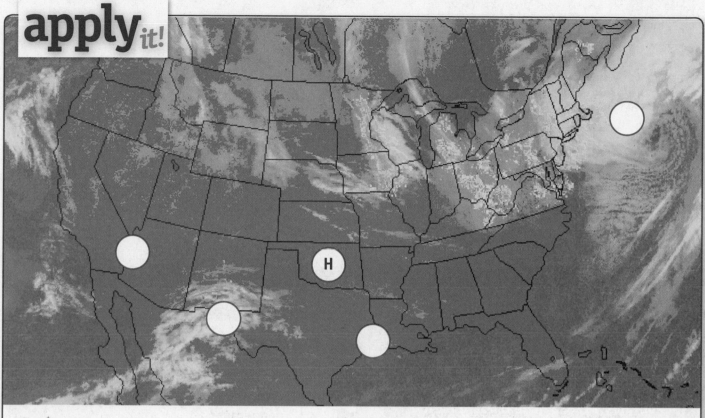

1 ⚠ **Classify** Fill in the empty circles with either *L* for a low-pressure center or *H* for a high-pressure center.

2 CHALLENGE What information on the map helped you decide if an area's air pressure was low or high?

_____

_____

 Do the Quick Lab
Cyclones and Anticyclones.

⚷ Assess Your Understanding

3a. Identify What is a cyclone?

_____

b. 👁 **Relate Text and Visuals** How does air move in a cyclone?

_____

_____

c. Compare and Contrast What kind of weather is associated with a cyclone? What kind of weather is associated with an anticyclone?

_____

_____

_____

_____

got it? ....

○ **I get it!** Now I know that cyclones cause _____

and anticyclones cause _____

○ I need extra help with _____

_____

Storms

UNLOCK THE BIG Q?

🔑 **How Do the Different Types of Storms Form?**

🔑 **How Can You Stay Safe in a Storm?**

my planet diary

DISASTERS

The Blizzard of 1978

In February 1978, a huge blizzard hit the northeastern United States. Weather stations recorded hurricane-force winds, and many cities received record-breaking amounts of snow. The storm hovered over New England, and heavy snow fell for almost 33 hours without letting up.

In Massachusetts, people driving on highways abandoned their cars when the snow became too deep to drive through. Rescuers used cross-country skis and snowmobiles to help evacuate the roads. Stranded drivers returned home any way they could. The governor of Massachusetts declared a state of emergency. He called in the National Guard to clear the roads of snow. It took almost a week until the roads opened again.

Communicate Write your answers to each question below. Then discuss your answers with a partner.

1. What do you think made the blizzard so dangerous?

_____

_____

_____

2. Besides the hurricane-force winds and the roads filling with snow, what other hazards do you think the blizzard caused?

_____

_____

 Do the Inquiry Warm-Up *Can You Make a Tornado?*

Vocabulary
- storm • thunderstorm • lightning
- hurricane • storm surge • tornado • evacuate

Skills
⟳ Reading: Outline
△ Inquiry: Infer

How Do the Different Types of Storms Form?

The Blizzard of 1978 was one of the most intense storms ever to hit the northeastern United States. A **storm** is a violent disturbance in the atmosphere. Storms involve sudden changes in air pressure, which cause rapid air movements. There are several types of severe storms: winter storms, thunderstorms, hurricanes, and tornadoes.

Winter Storms In the winter in the northern United States, a large amount of precipitation falls as snow. ⟳ **All year round, most precipitation begins in clouds as snow. If the air is colder than 0°C all the way to the ground, the precipitation falls as snow.** Heavy snow can block roads, trapping people in their homes and delaying emergency vehicles. Extreme cold can damage crops and cause water pipes to burst.

Some places, including Buffalo and Rochester in upstate New York, get a lot more snow than others. In an average winter, nearly three meters of snow fall on these cities due to lake-effect snow, as shown in **Figure 1.** Buffalo is located east of Lake Erie. Rochester is located south of Lake Ontario. In the fall and winter, the land near these lakes cools much more rapidly than the water in the lakes. When a cold, dry air mass moves southeast across one of the lakes, it picks up water vapor and heat. As soon as the air mass reaches the other side of the lake, the air rises and cools again. The water vapor condenses and falls as snow.

FIGURE 1 ·······························

Lake-Effect Snow
As cold, dry air moves across the warmer water, it becomes more humid as water vapor evaporates from the lake surface. When the air reaches land and cools, lake-effect snow falls.

✏ **Interpret Maps** Circle the cities that receive lake-effect snow. In the box on the map, name a city that does not get it and explain why.

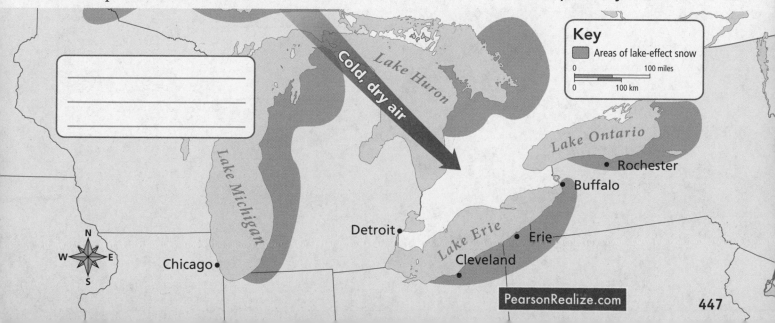

Key
Areas of lake-effect snow
0   100 miles
0   100 km

Cold, dry air

Lake Huron
Lake Ontario
Lake Michigan
Rochester
Buffalo
Detroit
Lake Erie
Erie
Chicago
Cleveland

know?

A fulgurite forms when lightning strikes sand or sandy soil. The temperature of the lightning is so high that it melts the sand and forms a tube made of glass.

Thunderstorms Do you find thunderstorms frightening? Exciting? As you watch the brilliant flashes of lightning and listen to long rolls of thunder, you may wonder what causes them.

How Thunderstorms Form A **thunderstorm** is a small storm often accompanied by heavy precipitation and frequent thunder and lightning. 🔑 **Thunderstorms form in large cumulonimbus clouds, also known as thunderheads.** Most cumulonimbus clouds form on hot, humid afternoons or evenings. They also form when warm air is forced upward along a cold front. In both cases, the warm, humid air rises rapidly, as shown in **Figure 2.** The air cools, forming dense thunderheads with water condensing into rain droplets. Heavy rain falls, sometimes along with hail. Within the thunderhead are strong upward and downward winds known as updrafts and downdrafts. Many thunderstorms form in the spring and summer in southern states or on the western plains.

FIGURE 2 ·······································

How Thunderstorms Form

A thunderstorm forms when warm, humid air rises rapidly within a cumulonimbus cloud.
✏️ **Interpret Diagrams** Fill in the captions noting the direction of the warm, humid air and the cold air.

Storm movement

Heavy rain

Lightning and Thunder During a thunderstorm, areas of positive and negative electrical charges build up in the storm clouds. **Lightning** is a sudden spark, or electrical discharge, as these charges jump between parts of a cloud, between nearby clouds, or between a cloud and the ground. Lightning is similar to the shocks you sometimes feel when you touch a metal object on a very dry day. Because lightning is electricity, it is easily conducted by metal.

What causes thunder? A lightning bolt can heat the air near it to as much as 30,000°C, much hotter than the sun's surface. The rapidly heated air expands explosively. Thunder is the sound of the explosion. Because light travels faster than sound, you see lightning before you hear thunder.

Thunderstorm Damage Thunderstorms can cause severe damage. The heavy rains associated with thunderstorms can flood low-lying areas. Lightning can also cause damage. When lightning strikes the ground, the hot, expanding air can shatter tree trunks or start forest fires. When lightning strikes people or animals, it acts like a powerful electric shock. Lightning can cause unconsciousness, serious burns, and heart failure.

Floods A major danger during severe thunderstorms is flooding. Some floods occur when so much water pours into a stream or river that its banks overflow, covering the surrounding land with water. In urban areas, floods can occur when the ground is already saturated by heavy rains. The water can't soak into the water-logged ground or the many areas covered with buildings, roads, and parking lots. A flash flood is a sudden, violent flood that occurs shortly after a storm.

FIGURE 3 ·······················

Lightning Damage
Lightning can cause fires, serious damage, and injuries. ✏️ **Infer Which is more likely to be hit by lightning, a metal or a wooden boat? Why?**

Outline After reading the text on this page, complete the outline by adding details about how a hurricane forms.

I. Hurricanes
  A. How a Hurricane Forms

1._____
  _____
  _____
  _____
2._____
  _____
  _____
3._____
  _____
  _____

Hurricanes

A **hurricane** is a tropical cyclone with winds of 119 km/h or higher. A typical hurricane is about 600 kilometers across. Hurricanes form in the Atlantic, Pacific, and Indian oceans. In the western Pacific, they are called typhoons. In the Indian ocean, they are simply called cyclones.

How Hurricanes Form A typical hurricane that strikes the United States forms in the Atlantic Ocean north of the equator in August, September, or October. **A hurricane begins over warm ocean water as a low-pressure area, or tropical disturbance.** If the tropical disturbance grows in size and strength, it becomes a tropical storm, which may then become a hurricane.

Look at **Figure 4** to see how a hurricane forms. A hurricane draws its energy from the warm, humid air at the ocean's surface. As this air rises and forms clouds, more air is drawn into the system. Inside the storm are bands of very high winds and heavy rains. Winds spiral inward toward the area of lowest pressure at the center. The lower the air pressure at the center of a storm, the faster the winds blow toward the center. Hurricane winds may be as strong as 320 km/h.

Hurricane winds are strongest in a narrow band around the storm's center. At the center is a ring of clouds, called the eyewall, that encloses a quiet "eye." The wind gets stronger as the eye approaches. When the eye arrives, the weather changes suddenly. The air grows calm and the sky may clear. After the eye passes, the storm resumes, but the wind blows from the opposite direction.

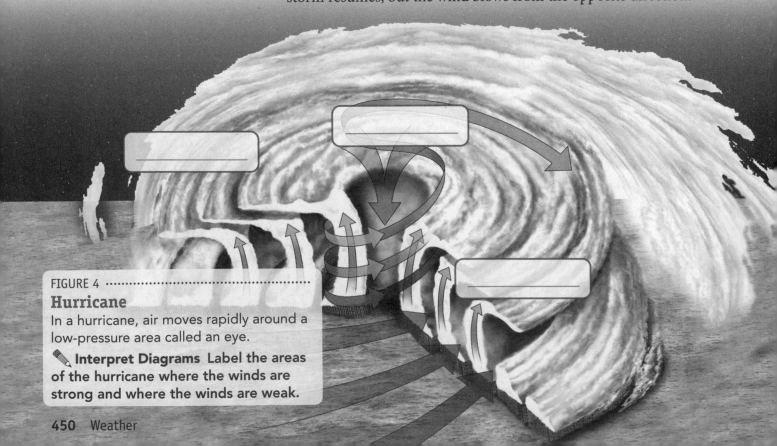

FIGURE 4
Hurricane
In a hurricane, air moves rapidly around a low-pressure area called an eye.

✎ **Interpret Diagrams** Label the areas of the hurricane where the winds are strong and where the winds are weak.

August 24, 2005: Katrina approaches Florida.

August 26, 2005: Hurricane Katrina picks up strength over the Gulf of Mexico.

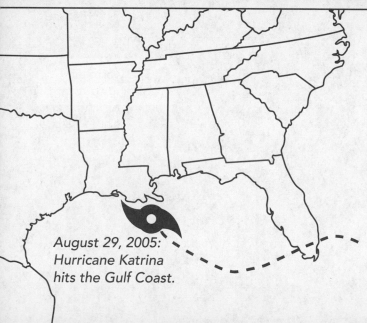

August 29, 2005: Hurricane Katrina hits the Gulf Coast.

How Hurricanes Move Hurricanes can last longer than other storms—a week or more. During that period, they can travel thousands of kilometers. Hurricanes that form in the Atlantic Ocean are steered by easterly trade winds toward the Caribbean islands and the southeastern United States. After a hurricane passes over land, it no longer has warm, moist air to draw energy from. The hurricane gradually weakens, although heavy rainfall may continue for several days.

Hurricane Damage When a hurricane comes ashore, it brings high waves and severe flooding, as well as wind damage. The low pressure and high winds of the hurricane over the ocean raise the level of the water as much as 6 meters above normal sea level. The result is a **storm surge,** a "dome" of water that sweeps across the coast where the hurricane lands. Storm surges can cause great damage, washing away beaches, destroying coastal buildings, and eroding the coastline.

FIGURE 5 ···
Hurricane Katrina
The picture shows the path of Hurricane Katrina.

✏ **Predict** On the picture, draw lines showing the possible paths the hurricane could have taken after reaching land. What happens to a hurricane after it reaches land?

451

Tornadoes

A tornado is one of the most frightening and intense types of storms. A **tornado** is a rapidly whirling, funnel-shaped cloud that reaches down from a thunderstorm to touch Earth's surface. If a tornado occurs over a lake or ocean, the storm is called a waterspout. Tornadoes are usually brief, but can be deadly. They may touch the ground for 15 minutes or less and be only a few hundred meters across. But an intense tornado's wind speed may approach 500 km/h.

How Tornadoes Form Tornadoes can form in any situation involving severe weather. 🔑 **Tornadoes most commonly develop in thick cumulonimbus clouds—the same clouds that bring thunderstorms.** Tornadoes often occur when thunderstorms are likely—in spring and early summer, late in the afternoon when the ground is warm.

Tornado Alley Tornadoes occur in nearly every part of the United States. However, the Great Plains often have the kind of weather pattern that is likely to create tornadoes: A warm, humid air mass moves north from the Gulf of Mexico into the lower Great Plains, and a cold, dry air mass moves south from Canada. When the air masses meet, the cold air moves under the warm air, forcing it to rise. A line of thunderstorms called a squall line is likely to form, with storms traveling northeast. A single squall line can produce ten or more tornadoes.

FIGURE 6 ···

Tornado Formation

About 1,200 tornadoes occur in the United States every year. Weather patterns on the Great Plains result in a "tornado alley."

✏️ **Interpret Maps Pick a state on the map (or your home state) and indicate whether its risk of tornadoes is low or high.**

_____

_____

_____

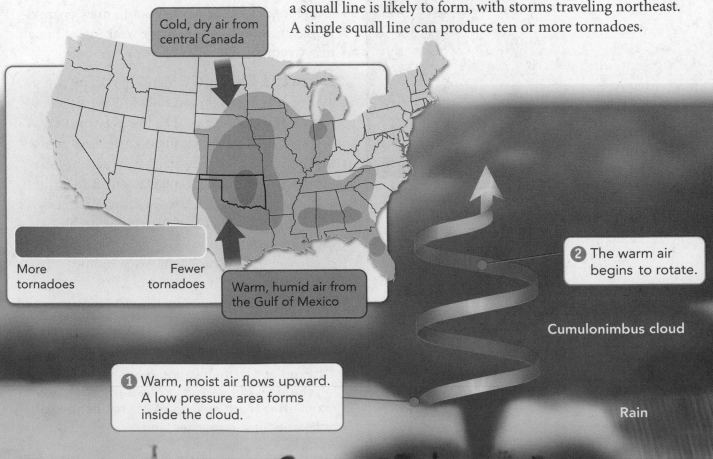

Cold, dry air from central Canada

More tornadoes — Fewer tornadoes

Warm, humid air from the Gulf of Mexico

① Warm, moist air flows upward. A low pressure area forms inside the cloud.

② The warm air begins to rotate.

Cumulonimbus cloud

Rain

Tornado Damage Tornado damage comes from both strong winds and flying debris. The low pressure inside the tornado sucks objects into the funnel. Tornadoes can move large objects and scatter debris many miles away. One tornado tore a sign off in Oklahoma and dropped it 50 km away in Arkansas! A tornado can level houses on one street but leave neighboring houses standing.

Tornadoes are ranked on the Enhanced Fujita scale by the amount of damage they cause. The scale was named for the scientist who devised the original scale, Dr. T. Theodore Fujita. As shown in **Figure 7,** the scale goes from light damage (EF0) to extreme damage (EF5). Only about one percent of tornadoes are ranked as EF4 or EF5.

FIGURE 7 ·····································

Tornado Damage

✎ CHALLENGE **How would you rank this tornado damage on the Enhanced Fujita scale? Why?**

_____

_____

_____

Enhanced Fujita Scale	Types of Damage
F0	Branches break off trees
F1	Mobile homes overturned
F2	Trees uprooted
F3	Roofs and walls torn down
F4	Houses levelled
F5	Houses carried away

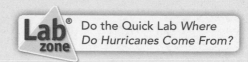

Do the Quick Lab *Where Do Hurricanes Come From?*

🔑 **Assess Your Understanding**

1a. Identify What is a hurricane?

_____

_____

_____

_____

b. Explain How do hurricanes form?

_____

_____

_____

_____

_____

c. Compare and Contrast How do hurricanes differ from tornadoes?

_____

_____

_____

_____

_____

_____

_____

_____

_____

got **it?** ·······································

○ **I get it!** Now I know that the main kinds of storms are _____

_____

_____

○ **I need extra help with** _____

_____

_____

_____

_____

453

How Can You Stay Safe in a Storm?

A winter storm or a thunderstorm can be fun to watch if you're in a safe place. But you don't want to be near a hurricane or tornado if you can avoid it.

Winter Storm Safety Imagine being caught in a snowstorm when the wind suddenly picks up. High winds can blow falling snow sideways or pick up snow from the ground and suspend it in the air. This situation can be dangerous because the blowing snow limits your vision and makes it easy to get lost. Also, strong winds cool a person's body rapidly. 🔑 **If you are caught in a snowstorm, try to find shelter from the wind.** Cover exposed parts of your body and try to stay dry. If you are in a car, keep the engine running only if the exhaust pipe is clear of snow.

Thunderstorm Safety The safest place to be during a thunderstorm is indoors. Avoid touching telephones, electrical appliances, or plumbing fixtures. It is usually safe to stay in a car. The electricity will move along the metal skin of the car and jump to the ground. However, do not touch any metal inside the car. 🔑 **During thunderstorms, avoid places where lightning may strike. Also, avoid objects that can conduct electricity, such as metal objects and bodies of water.**

How can you remain safe if you are caught outside during a thunderstorm? Do not seek shelter under a tree, because lightning may strike the tree. Instead, find a low area away from trees, fences, and poles. Crouch with your head down. If you are swimming or in a boat, get to shore and find shelter away from the water.

Hurricane Safety Today, weather satellites can track the paths of hurricanes. So people now receive a warning well in advance of an approaching hurricane. A "hurricane watch" indicates that hurricane conditions are possible in an area within the next 36 hours. You should be prepared to **evacuate** (ee VAK yoo ayt), or move away temporarily. A "hurricane warning" means that hurricane conditions are expected within the next 24 hours. 🔑 **If you hear a hurricane warning and are told to evacuate, leave the area immediately.**

FIGURE 8

Evacuation Site
In September 2005, the city of Dallas opened up shelters such as the Reunion Arena for people who fled Hurricane Katrina.

✎ **Explain** What is the difference between a hurricane watch and a hurricane warning?

_____

_____

_____

_____

_____

_____

apply it!

_____

_____

The two signs in the pictures show warnings about possible storms.

1 **Infer** Match each safety sign to the appropriate storm.

2 In the space to the right, draw a sign to show how one could stay safe in a thunderstorm or winter storm.

Tornado Safety

A "tornado watch" is an announcement that tornadoes are possible in your area. A "tornado warning" is an announcement that a tornado has been seen in the sky or on weather radar. If you hear a tornado warning, move to a safe area as soon as you can. Do not wait until you actually see the tornado.

🔑 **The safest place to be during a tornado is in a storm shelter or a basement.** If there is no basement, move to the middle of the ground floor. Stay away from windows and doors. Lie under a sturdy piece of furniture. If you are outdoors, lie flat in a ditch.

Lab ® Do the Quick Lab
zone _Storm Safety._

🔑 Assess Your Understanding

2a. List Based on the safety steps, list the four storms from least to most dangerous.

_____

_____

_____

b. Solve Problems How can a community make sure people stay safe in a storm?

_____

_____

_____

got it? ....

○ **I get it!** Now I know that to stay safe in a storm I should either _____

or, in the case of a hurricane, I should _____

○ **I need extra help with** _____

_____

Predicting the Weather

UNLOCK THE BIG

🔑 **How Do You Predict the Weather?**

🔑 **What Can You Learn From Weather Maps?**

my planet diary

Meteorologist Mish Michaels

Mish Michaels uses computers in her work every day to sort data from weather satellites, radar, and weather stations from all over the world. Then she shares her weather forecasts with television viewers in Boston, Massachusetts.

Michaels became interested in weather while in kindergarten in Maryland. She watched a tornado damage her family's apartment complex. Since then, she has been fascinated by storms. Michaels went on to major in meteorology at Cornell University.

Michaels is devoted to educating others about weather. She supports the WINS program (Women in the Natural Sciences) of Blue Hill Weather Observatory in Milton, Massachusetts. The program inspires girls to pursue careers in math, science, and technology.

Communicate After you read about Mish Michaels, answer these questions with a partner.

1. Why do you think that meteorologists depend so heavily on computers?

_____

_____

_____

2. What subjects do you think future meteorologists need to study in school?

_____

_____

 Lab zone   Do the Inquiry Warm-Up *Predicting Weather.*

Vocabulary
- meteorologist
- isobar
- isotherm

Skills
- ⟳ Reading: Compare and Contrast
- △ Inquiry: Predict

How Do You Predict the Weather?

The first step in weather forecasting is to collect data, either from direct observations or through the use of instruments. For example, if a barometer shows that the air pressure is falling, you can expect an approaching low-pressure area, possibly bringing rain or snow.

Making Simple Observations You can read weather signs in the clouds, too. Cumulus clouds often form on warm days. If they grow larger and taller, they can become cumulonimbus clouds, which may produce a thunderstorm. If you can see thin cirrus clouds high in the sky, a warm front may be approaching.

Even careful weather observers often turn to meteorologists for weather information. **Meteorologists** (mee tee uh RAHL uh jists) are scientists who study and try to predict weather.

Interpreting Complex Data Meteorologists interpret information from a variety of sources. ⟳ **Meteorologists use maps, charts, computers, and other technology to analyze weather data and to prepare weather forecasts.**

Weather reporters get their information from the National Weather Service, which uses balloons, satellites, radar, and surface instruments to gather data.

Red sky at night,
Sailors delight;
Red sky at morning,
Sailors take warning.

Evening red and morning gray
Will send the travelers on their way;
Evening gray and morning red
Will bring down rain upon their head.

FIGURE 1 ·········
Red Sky

Many people have their own weather sayings. Many of these sayings are based on long-term observations.

✎ Write your own weather poem in the space below.

Using Technology Techniques for predicting weather have changed dramatically in recent years. Short-range forecasts—forecasts for up to five days—are now fairly reliable. Meteorologists can also make somewhat accurate long-range predictions. Technological improvements in gathering weather data and using computers have improved the accuracy of weather forecasts.

FIGURE 2 ···
Weather Technology

✎ **Explain** why better technology leads to improved weather forecasting.

_____

_____

_____

Automated Weather Stations
Weather stations gather data from surface locations for temperature, air pressure, relative humidity, rainfall, and wind speed and direction. The National Weather Service has established a network of more than 1,700 surface weather observation sites.

Weather Balloons
Weather balloons carry instruments into the troposphere and lower stratosphere. The instruments measure temperature, air pressure, and humidity.

Weather Satellites
Satellites orbit Earth in the exosphere, the uppermost layer of the atmosphere. Cameras on weather satellites can make images of Earth's surface, clouds, storms, and snow cover. Satellites also collect data on temperature, humidity, solar radiation, and wind speed and direction.

Computer Forecasts
Computers process weather data quickly to help forecasters make predictions. The computer works through thousands of calculations using equations from weather models to make forecasts.

 Lab zone Do the Quick Lab *Modeling Weather Satellites.*

🔑 Assess Your Understanding
got it? ··

○ **I get it!** Now I know that meteorologists prepare weather forecasts using _____

_____

○ **I need extra help with** _____

_____

What Can You Learn From Weather Maps?

A weather map is a "snapshot" of conditions at a particular time over a large area. There are many types of weather maps.

Weather Service Maps Data from many local weather stations all over the country are assembled into weather maps at the National Weather Service. The way maps display data is shown in the Apply It feature below. The simplified weather map at the end of this lesson includes a key that shows weather station symbols.

On some weather maps you see curved lines. These lines connect places with similar conditions of temperature or air pressure. **Isobars** are lines joining places on the map that have the same air pressure. (*Iso* means "equal" and *bar* means "weight.") The numbers on the isobars are the pressure readings. These readings may be given in inches of mercury or in millibars.

Isotherms are lines joining places that have the same temperature. The isotherm may be labeled with the temperature in degrees Fahrenheit, degrees Celsius, or both.

⟳ Compare and Contrast
How are isobars and isotherms alike? How do they differ?

_____

_____

_____

_____

_____

_____

_____

apply it!

The tables below show what various weather symbols represent.

❶ Apply Concepts According to the weather map symbol below, what are the amount of cloud cover and the wind speed?

_____

❷ Predict Would you expect precipitation in an area marked by this weather symbol? Why?

_____

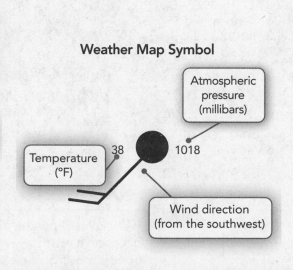

Cloud Cover (%)	Symbol
0	○
10	◐
20–30	◔
40	◑
50	◑
60	◕
70–80	◕
90	◑
100	●

Weather Map Symbol

Atmospheric pressure (millibars)

Temperature (°F)

38   ●   1018

Wind direction (from the southwest)

Wind Speed (mi/h)	Symbol
1–2	
3–8	
9–14	
15–20	
21–25	
26–31	
32–37	
38–43	
44–49	
50–54	
55–60	
61–66	
67–71	
72–77	

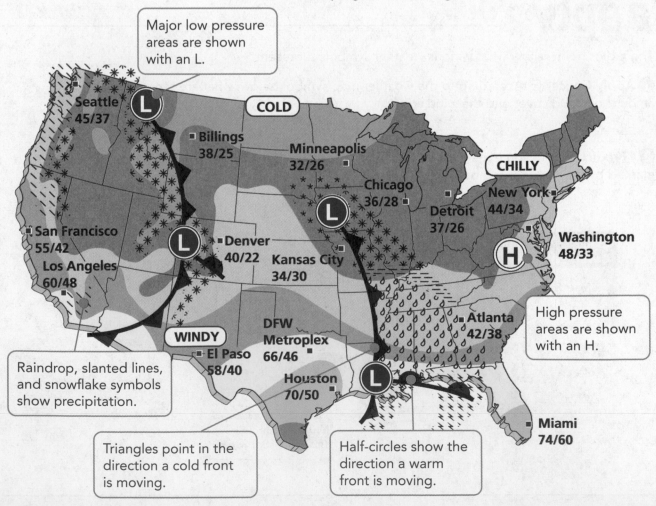

FIGURE 3 ......

Newspaper Weather Map

The symbols on this map show fronts, high- and low-pressure areas, the high and low temperature readings for different cities, and precipitation. The color bands indicate different temperature ranges.

✎ **Answer the questions below.**

1. **Interpret Maps** Identify the weather that will occur in Denver according to this map.

_____

2. **CHALLENGE** Can you predict the weather in Denver a week later? Explain.

_____

Newspaper Weather Maps
Maps in newspapers are simplified versions of maps produced by the National Weather Service. **Figure 3** shows a typical newspaper weather map. From what you have learned in this lesson, you can probably interpret most symbols on this map. 🔑 **Standard symbols on weather maps show fronts, areas of high and low pressure, types of precipitation, and temperatures.** Note that the high and low temperatures are given in degrees Fahrenheit instead of Celsius.

Limits of Weather Forecasts
As computers have grown more powerful, and new satellites and radar technologies have been developed, scientists have been able to make better forecasts. But even with extremely powerful computers, it is unlikely that forecasters will ever be able to predict the weather accurately a month in advance. This has to do with the so-called "butterfly effect." The atmosphere works in such a way that a small change in the weather today can mean a larger change in the weather a week later! The name refers to a scientist's suggestion that even the flapping of a butterfly's wings causes a tiny disturbance in the atmosphere. A tiny event might cause a larger disturbance that could—eventually—grow into a large storm.

Major low pressure areas are shown with an L.

Raindrop, slanted lines, and snowflake symbols show precipitation.

High pressure areas are shown with an H.

Triangles point in the direction a cold front is moving.

Half-circles show the direction a warm front is moving.

Seattle 45/37
Billings 38/25
Minneapolis 32/26
Chicago 36/28
Detroit 37/26
New York 44/34
CHILLY
COLD
Washington 48/33
San Francisco 55/42
Denver 40/22
Kansas City 34/30
Los Angeles 60/48
WINDY
DFW Metroplex 66/46
El Paso 58/40
Houston 70/50
Atlanta 42/38
Miami 74/60

460 Weather

Predicting the Weather
How do meteorologists predict the weather?

FIGURE 4 ·····································

Using a Weather Map

✏️ What would you tell the people of Miami, Kansas City, and Seattle about tomorrow's weather? Explain why.

_____

_____

_____

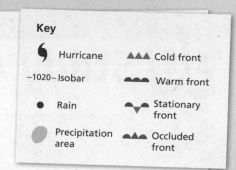

Key

🌀 Hurricane		▲▲▲	Cold front
−1020− Isobar		〰️〰️	Warm front
● Rain		∨∨∨	Stationary front
🔵 Precipitation area		▲▲▲	Occluded front

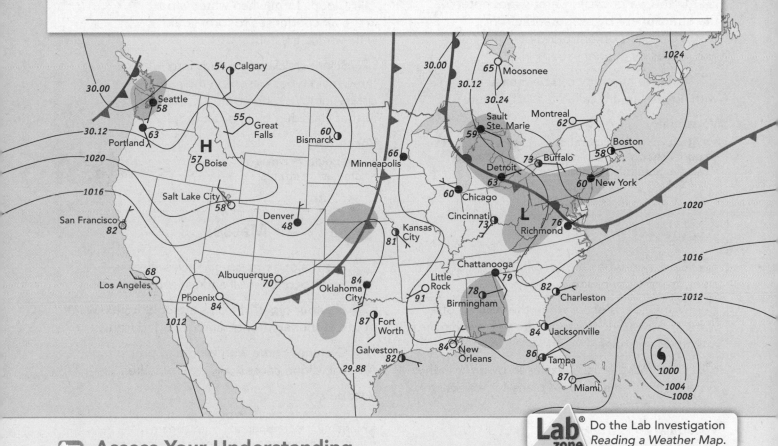

🔑 Assess Your Understanding

1a. Explain What is a weather map?

_____

_____

_____

b. ❓ How do meteorologists predict the weather?

_____

_____

_____

_____

Lab zone Do the Lab Investigation
Reading a Weather Map.

got it?

○ **I get it!** Now I know that standard symbols on weather maps show _____

_____

○ **I need extra help with** _____

_____

461

10 Study Guide

Meteorologists predict the weather by collecting data about _____,
_____ , _____ , and _____ .

LESSON 1 Water in the Atmosphere

🔑 In the water cycle, water vapor enters the atmosphere by evaporation from the oceans and other bodies of water and leaves by condensation.

🔑 Relative humidity can be measured with an instrument called a psychrometer.

Vocabulary
• water cycle • evaporation
• condensation • humidity
• relative humidity • psychrometer

LESSON 2 Clouds

🔑 Clouds form when water vapor in the air condenses to form liquid water or ice crystals.

🔑 Scientists classify clouds into three main types based on their shape: cirrus, cumulus, and stratus. Clouds are further classified by their altitude.

Vocabulary
• dew point • cirrus
• cumulus • stratus

LESSON 3 Precipitation

🔑 Common types of precipitation include rain, sleet, freezing rain, snow, and hail.

🔑 Many floods occur when the volume of water in a river increases so much that the river overflows its channel.

🔑 Droughts are usually caused by dry weather systems that remain in one place for weeks or months at a time.

Vocabulary
• precipitation • rain gauge • flood • drought

LESSON 4 Air Masses

🔑 The major air masses are classified as maritime or continental and as tropical or polar.

🔑 The four types of fronts are cold fronts, warm fronts, stationary fronts, and occluded fronts.

🔑 Cyclones come with wind and precipitation. An anticyclone causes dry, clear weather.

Vocabulary
• air mass • tropical • polar
• maritime • continental • jet stream
• front • occluded • cyclone • anticyclone

LESSON 5 Storms

🔑 Most precipitation begins in clouds as snow.

🔑 Thunderstorms and tornadoes form in cumulonimbus clouds.

🔑 A hurricane begins over warm ocean water as a low-pressure area, or tropical disturbance.

🔑 Always find proper shelter from storms.

Vocabulary
• storm • thunderstorm • lightning
• hurricane • storm surge • tornado • evacuate

LESSON 6 Predicting the Weather

🔑 Meteorologists use maps, charts, computers, and other technology to prepare weather forecasts.

🔑 Standard symbols on weather maps show fronts, air pressure, precipitation, and temperature.

Vocabulary
• meteorologist • isobar
• isotherm

Review and Assessment

LESSON 1 Water in the Atmosphere

1. Infer What is the energy source for the water cycle?

_____

2. math! At 3 P.M., a dry-bulb thermometer reading is 66°F. The wet-bulb reading is 66°F. What is the relative humidity? Explain.

_____
_____
_____
_____
_____
_____
_____

LESSON 2 Clouds

3. What type of cloud forms at high altitudes and appears wispy and feathery?

  a. stratus   **b.** altocumulus

  c. cumulus   **d.** cirrus

4. One type of cloud is a nimbostratus, which is

_____
_____
_____

5. Infer Why do clouds usually form high in the air instead of near Earth's surface?

_____
_____
_____
_____

LESSON 3 Precipitation

6. What is the name for raindrops that freeze as they fall through the air?

  a. dew   **b.** sleet

  c. hail   **d.** frost

7. Rain and hail are both precipitation, which is

_____
_____
_____
_____

8. Write About It It is winter where Jenna lives. It's been snowing all day, but now the snow has changed to sleet and then to freezing rain. What is happening to cause these changes? In your answer, explain how snow, sleet, and freezing rain form.

LESSON 4 Air Masses

9. What do you call a hot air mass that forms over land?

_____

10. Predict What type of weather is most likely to form at the front shown below?

_____
_____
_____

463

LESSON 5 Storms

11. What are very large tropical cyclones with high winds called?

    a. storm surges   **b.** tornadoes

    c. hurricanes   **d.** thunderstorms

12. Thunderstorms usually contain lightning,

which is _____

_____

_____

13. Make Judgments What do you think is the most important thing people should do to reduce the dangers of storms?

_____

_____

_____

_____

LESSON 6 Predicting the Weather

14. On a weather map, lines joining places with the same temperature are called

    a. low-pressure systems.   **b.** isotherms.

    c. high-pressure systems.   **d.** isobars.

15. To predict weather, meteorologists use

_____

_____

_____

16. Apply Concepts How does the butterfly effect keep meteorologists from accurately forecasting the weather a month in advance?

_____

_____

_____

_____

How do meteorologists predict the weather?

17. Meteorologists use information from many sources to make predictions about the weather. The weather map shows that right now it is sunny in Cincinnati, but the weather report for tomorrow shows a major snowstorm. Using the map, explain how a meteorologist is able to make this prediction. Include details on weather technology used and the atmospheric conditions that lead to a snowstorm. Make sure to discuss clouds, air masses, fronts, temperature, and pressure.

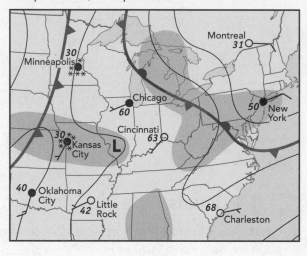

_____

_____

_____

_____

_____

_____

_____

_____

_____

_____

_____

Standardized Test Prep

Read each question and choose the best answer.

1. The table below shows the amount of rainfall in different months.

Average Monthly Rainfall			
Month	**Rainfall**	**Month**	**Rainfall**
January	1 cm	July	49 cm
February	1 cm	August	57 cm
March	1 cm	September	40 cm
April	2 cm	October	20 cm
May	25 cm	November	4 cm
June	52 cm	December	1 cm

Which two months had the <u>most</u> rainfall?

A June and August **B** January and March

C June and July **D** August and May

2. When the temperature equals the dew point, what is the relative humidity?

A zero **B** 10%

C 50% **D** 100%

3. How does the jet stream influence weather?

A by elevating temperature and pressure

B by lowering pressure and humidity

C by reducing temperature and density

D by moving air masses to produce fronts

4. Low pressure over warm ocean water may produce which of the following conditions?

A fair weather

B a thunderstorm

C a hurricane

D a tornado

5. Which of the following map symbols identifies a place likely to experience fair weather?

A isobars

B H for *high pressure*

C isotherms

D H for *high temperature*

Constructed Response

Use the diagram below and your knowledge of science to help you answer Question 6. Write your answer on a separate piece of paper.

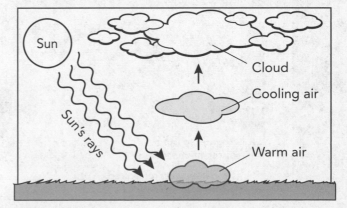

6. Describe the process by which a cloud forms. What two conditions are necessary for this process to occur? How does this process compare to the process by which dew or frost form?

Kids Doing Science

The S'COOL project

Schools around the world are teaming up to help scientists at the National Aeronautics and Space Administration (NASA). Since 1998, students have been helping NASA check satellite observations through a project called Students' Cloud Observations On-Line (S'COOL).

NASA tells schools in the program the date and time when the project satellites will be passing over different regions of the world. When a satellite passes over their school, students observe the clouds in the sky. Students can also measure weather data such as temperature and relative humidity. These observations are uploaded to the project Web site. Then NASA scientists compare the satellite data with the students' observations. This process, called ground truthing, helps scientists determine how accurate the satellite data are.

◀ Students' observations are compared to data collected by satellites like this one.

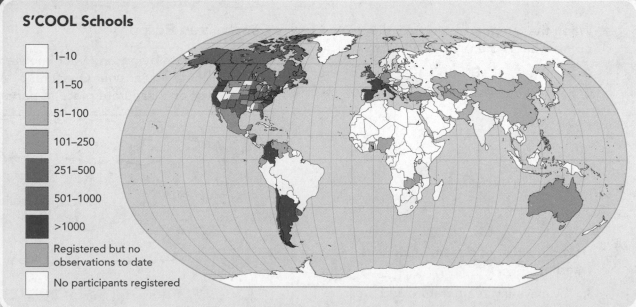

S'COOL Schools

- 1–10
- 11–50
- 51–100
- 101–250
- 251–500
- 501–1000
- >1000
- Registered but no observations to date
- No participants registered

▲ Schools around the world participate in the S'COOL program. The map above shows where they are. If you had to recruit schools to help NASA get complete data, where would you look for schools?

Research It Make a record book. Use it to keep a weeklong log of cloud formations and weather conditions, including photos or sketches, at a specific time each day.

Tracking Hurricanes

with Latitude and Longitude

Do you understand the important bulletin on the computer screen? Lines of latitude and longitude are imaginary lines that crisscross Earth's surface. Because the lines cross, they can help you describe any location on Earth, including the location of hurricanes. A location's latitude is always written before its longitude.

Hurricane Hilda is located in the Atlantic Ocean off the southeastern coast of the United States.

Write About It Assume that Hurricane Hilda is following a straight path. Using the information in the bulletin and the map, try to predict the path the hurricane will take to reach land, and how long it will take to get there. Compare your predicted path with the path of a real hurricane. Evaluate your prediction. Does the bulletin provide enough information for you to make a precise prediction? Write a paragraph explaining why or why not.

ATTENTION

HURRICANE HILDA IS CURRENTLY
LOCATED AT 30°N, 74°W.
IT IS MOVING 21 KM/H NW.
ALL RESIDENTS OF NEARBY
COASTAL AREAS ARE ADVISED
TO EVACUATE IMMEDIATELY.

Hurricane Hilda is currently located at 30° N, 74° W. You can plot the hurricane's location on a map. What information do you need to predict where it will reach land? ▶

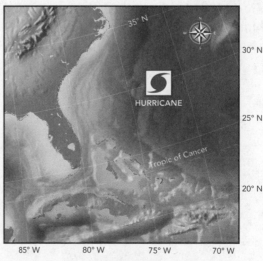

487

WHAT'S HAPPENING TO THE MOON?

THE BIG ?

How do Earth, the moon, and the sun interact?

This photograph shows a series of images of the moon taken over the course of an evening. Why do you think the moon looks different in each image? Develop Hypotheses Explain what you think happened during the period of time shown in the photograph.

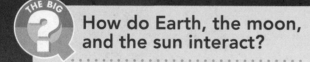

Watch the **Untamed Science** video to learn more about the moon.

CHAPTER 1

Earth, Moon, and Sun

11 Getting Started

Check Your Understanding

1. **Background** Read the paragraph below and then answer the question.

Santiago is studying a globe. He sees that Earth has North and South poles. The globe **rotates** around a line through its center between the two poles. Another line called the **equator** divides Earth into two halves, the **Northern Hemisphere** and the **Southern Hemisphere**.

> To **rotate** is to spin in place around a central line, or axis.
>
> The **equator** is the imaginary line that divides Earth into two halves, the **Northern Hemisphere** and the **Southern Hemisphere**.

• Where is the equator found?

_____

_____

Vocabulary Skill

Identify Multiple Meanings Words you use every day may have different meanings in science. Look at the different meanings of the words below.

Word	Everyday Meaning	Scientific Meaning
weight	*n.* a heavy object used for exercise **Example:** The athlete lifted *weights* to build strength.	*n.* a measure of the force of gravity on an object **Example:** The object's *weight* was 10 newtons.
force	*v.* to use power to make someone do something **Example:** She had to *force* herself to get up early.	*n.* a push or pull exerted on an object **Example:** You exert *force* when you open and close a door.

2. **Quick Check** Circle the sentence below that uses the scientific meaning of *force*.

• The *force* of gravity holds objects in their orbits.

• Her parents are trying to *force* her to get a job.

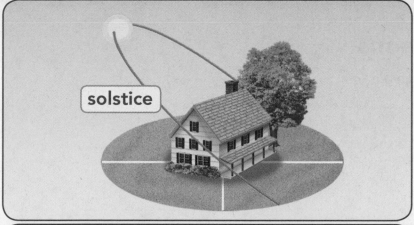

solstice

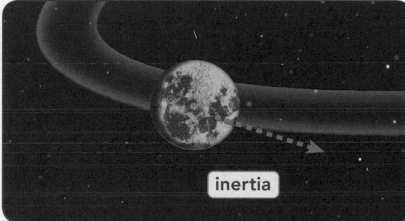

inertia

phase

solar eclipse

Chapter Preview

Smearing Causes Seasons

Purpose To investigate the cause of seasons

Materials
- overhead projector
- screen
- 3 index cards
- sheet of paper with a 2 cm × 2 cm square cut into the center

Scenario

> Put a huge spoonful of peanut butter in the center of a slice of bread, and you have a big glob of peanut butter to eat! If you dare to bite into it, the peanut butter sticks to the roof of your mouth and your teeth. Talking and swallowing become almost impossible.
>
> Suppose you have a whole loaf of bread and the same spoonful of peanut butter. If you smear the spoonful of peanut butter evenly across ten slices of bread, will you still have to eat a big glob? Will talking and swallowing still be difficult?

As a scientist with a good understanding of how the universe works, you have been asked to explain the cause of the seasons to a class of third-graders. You know that roughly the same amount of solar energy leaves the sun every day. You also know that Earth is always about the same distance away from the sun. If those things are true, how can you explain to third-graders why we are colder in winter and hotter in summer? The first thing that came to your mind was peanut butter. What does smearing peanut butter on slices of bread have to do with the seasons?

Procedure

☑ **1. Concentrated Energy** Light and heat are two forms of energy. Just like peanut butter, light and heat can be packed into a small area. They can also be spread thinly over a larger area. Your teacher will demonstrate this using an overhead projector to shine a square of light onto a screen. A volunteer will measure the height and width of the square in centimeters. Record the measurements here:

height _____   width _____

☑ **2. How Much Area Is It?** Let's pretend that the amount of light passing through the square on the overhead is 1,000 energy units. Calculate the area over which these 1,000 units of energy are concentrated on the screen.

area = height × width = _____

☑ **3. How Strong Is It?** Divide the 1,000 units of energy by the area of the light on the screen to determine the energy concentration on the screen.

$$\text{energy concentration} = \frac{1000 \text{ energy units}}{\text{area}} = \underline{\hspace{3cm}}$$

☑ **4. Smearing the Peanut Butter** Your teacher will now tilt the screen at a 23.5° angle, which is the same angle as Earth's tilt. A volunteer will measure the height and the length of both bases of the trapezoid the light forms on the screen. Record the measurements here in centimeters:

height _____

short base _____ long base _____

☑ **5. The Angled Area** Notice that the light now spreads over a larger area and is in the shape of a trapezoid instead of a square. To calculate the area of a trapezoid, find the average of its two bases, and multiply that average by the height.

$$\text{area} = \left(\frac{\text{short side} + \text{long side}}{2} \right) \times \text{height} = \underline{\hspace{4cm}}$$

☑ **6. Equal Energy, Greater Area** Now determine the slanted energy concentration on the screen using the same method as Step 3. _____

☑ **7. Stronger or Weaker?** Is the light energy more concentrated when the screen is straight or when it is at an angle? Explain. _____

_____

☑ **8. Heat vs. Light** If an equal amount of energy falls on a small area and a large area, which area would experience a greater increase in temperature? _____

Conclusion

Let's see what you learned about how energy from the sun differs in summer and winter.

☑ **1.** How can the same amount of solar energy warm your town less in the winter than in the summer?

_____

_____

☑ **2.** In winter, is the United States more like the straight or slanted screen? In summer? Explain.

_____

_____

With a partner, prepare notes on index cards for your presentation of how the tilt of Earth causes the seasons. You can describe the demonstration you will use or explain the concept with words and pictures. In both cases, make sure your explanation will make sense to a class of third-graders.

The Sky From Earth

UNLOCK
THE BIG
?

🗝 **What Can You See in the Night Sky?**

🗝 **How Do Objects in the Sky Appear to Move?**

MY PLANET DIARY

BIOGRAPHY

Watching the Stars

When you look up at the night sky, what questions do you ask yourself? Do you wonder why the stars seem to move, or why the moon shines? Aryabhata (ar yah BAH tah) was an early Indian astronomer who thought about these questions. He was born in India in A.D. 476.

Many historians think that Aryabhata realized that the stars appear to move from east to west because Earth rotates from west to east. He also wrote that the moon and the planets shine because they reflect light from the sun. And he made all these inferences using just his eyes and his mind. The first telescopes wouldn't come along for more than a thousand years!

Communicate Discuss Aryabhata's discoveries with a partner. Then answer the questions below.

1. What did Aryabhata infer about the motion of Earth?

_____
_____
_____

2. What questions do you think about when you look at stars, the moon, or the planets?

_____
_____
_____

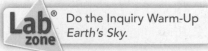

Lab zone® Do the Inquiry Warm-Up *Earth's Sky.*

Vocabulary
- satellite - planet - meteor
- comet - star - constellation

Skills
- Reading: Identify the Main Idea
- Inquiry: Predict

What Can You See in the Night Sky?

Depending on how dark the sky is where you are, you might see 2,000 or 3,000 stars using just your eyes. 🔑 On a clear night, you may see stars, the moon, planets, meteors, and comets.

Moon About half of every month, Earth's moon outshines everything else in the night sky. The moon is Earth's only natural satellite. A **satellite** is a body that orbits a planet.

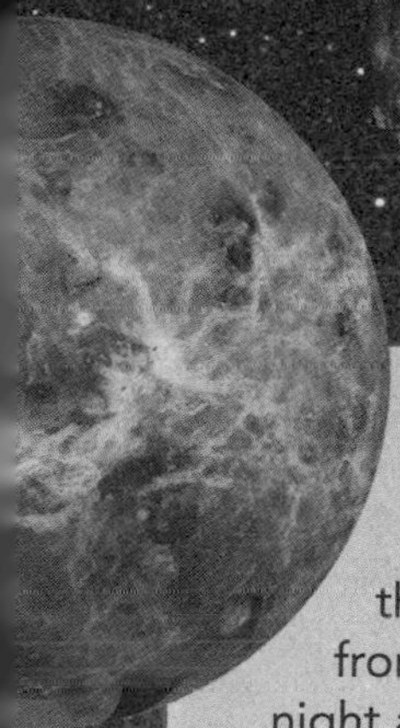

Planets You may see objects that move from night to night against the background stars. These are planets. A **planet** is an object that orbits the sun, is large enough to have become rounded by its own gravity, and has cleared the area of its orbit. There are eight planets in the solar system. Five are visible from Earth without a telescope: Mercury, Venus, Mars, Jupiter, and Saturn.

Meteors and Comets Have you ever seen a "shooting star"? These sudden bright streaks are called **meteors**. A meteor is the streak of light produced when a small object burns up entering Earth's atmosphere. You can see a meteor on almost any night. Comets are rarer. A **comet** is a cold mixture of dust and ice that gives off a long trail of light as it approaches the sun.

Stars Stars appear as tiny points of light. However, scientists infer that a **star** is a giant ball of hot gas, mainly composed of hydrogen and helium. As seen from Earth, the positions of stars relative to each other do not seem to change.

FIGURE 1 ·······················
These photos show examples of stars, planets, and other objects.

✏ **Observe** What can you observe about the objects shown on this page? Include at least two different objects.

_____
_____
_____
_____
_____

Constellations

For thousands of years humans have seen patterns in groups of stars and given names to them. 🔑 **A constellation is a pattern or group of stars that people imagined to represent a figure, animal, or object.** Astronomers also use the word *constellation* for an area of the sky and all the objects in that area.

Different cultures have identified different constellations. In Western culture, there are 88 constellations. Most constellation names used today come from the ancient Greeks, who probably took them from the Egyptians and Mesopotamians.

Some constellations' names come from Latin. The constellation Leo, for example, is named from the Latin word meaning "lion." Some constellations are named for people or animals in Greek myths. You may have read some of these myths in school. Do the names *Pegasus* or *Perseus* sound familiar? They are mythological characters and also constellations.

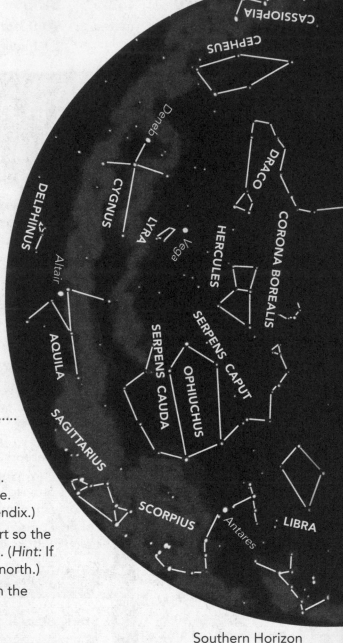

Eastern Horizon

Southern Horizon

FIGURE 2 ·······································

How to Use a Star Chart

To use a star chart at night, follow these steps.

1. Choose the chart that fits your location and season. This is a summer chart for the Northern Hemisphere. (There are charts for the other seasons in the Appendix.)

2. Hold the chart upright in front of you. Turn the chart so the label at the bottom matches the direction you face. (*Hint:* If you are looking at the Big Dipper, you are looking north.)

3. Hold the chart at eye level. Compare the figures on the bottom half of the chart to the sky in front of you.

apply it!

❶ **Interpret Diagrams** Find these constellations in **Figure 2**. Then write each constellation's name by its picture.

❷ [CHALLENGE] Choose another constellation from **Figure 2**. What does it represent? Do research to find out.

_____

_____

_____

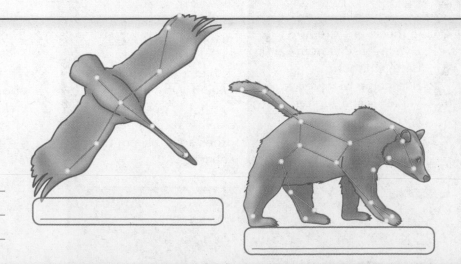

476 Earth, Moon, and Sun

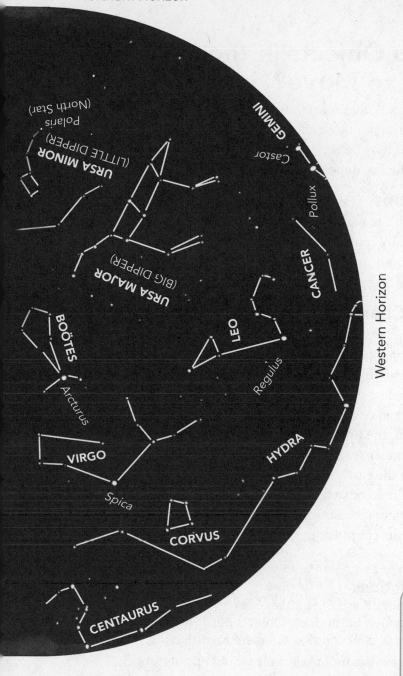

Northern Horizon

GEMINI

Castor

Pollux

Polaris (North Star)

URSA MINOR (LITTLE DIPPER)

URSA MAJOR (BIG DIPPER)

BOÖTES

CANCER

LEO

Regulus

Arcturus

VIRGO

Spica

HYDRA

CORVUS

CENTAURUS

Western Horizon

Finding Constellations A star chart, like the one shown in **Figure 2,** can help you find constellations in the night sky. Read the instructions for how to use the chart. It may seem a little strange at first, but with some practice, these charts are easy to use. Here is one tip to help you get started.

You can probably recognize the Big Dipper. This group of stars is actually not a constellation itself. It is part of the constellation Ursa Major, or the Great Bear. The two stars at the end of the dipper's "bowl" are called the Pointers.

Picture an imaginary line between those two stars. If you continue it away from the "bowl," the first fairly bright star you'll reach is called Polaris (po LA ris). Polaris is commonly called the North Star. It is located close to the sky's North Pole.

In the Appendix, you can find star charts for all four seasons. Take one outside on a clear night and see what you can find!

Lab zone® Do the Quick Lab *Observing the Night Sky.*

🔑 Assess Your Understanding

got it? ·····································

○ I get it! Now I know that objects visible in the night sky include _____

_____

_____

_____

○ I need extra help with _____

_____

_____

_____

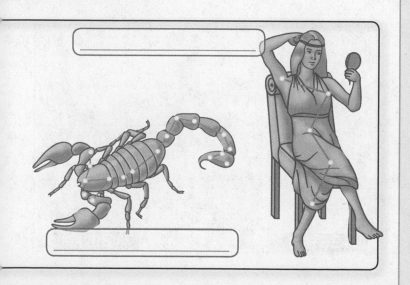

How Do Objects in the Sky Appear to Move?

Stars, planets, and other objects appear to move over time. They do move in space, but those actual motions and their apparent, or visible, motions may be very different. **The apparent motion of objects in the sky depends on the motions of Earth.**

Star Motions

Stars generally appear to move from east to west through the night. As Aryabhata thought, this apparent motion is actually caused by Earth turning from west to east. The sun's apparent motion during the day is also caused by Earth's motion. **Figure 3** shows how this kind of apparent motion occurs.

Seasonal Changes

Constellations and star patterns remain the same year after year, but which ones you can see varies from season to season. For example, you can find Orion in the eastern sky on winter evenings. But by spring, you'll see Orion in the west, disappearing below the horizon shortly after sunset.

These seasonal changes are caused by Earth's orbit around the sun. Each night, the position of most stars shifts slightly to the west. Soon you no longer see stars once visible in the west, and other stars appear in the east.

There are a few constellations that you can see all year long. These are the ones closest to the North Star. As Earth rotates, these constellations never appear to rise or set.

🔴 **Identify the Main Idea**
Underline the main idea in the paragraph called Star Motions.

FIGURE 3 ··

Opposite Motions

The restaurant on top of Seattle's Space Needle in Washington rotates much as Earth does. Objects outside appear to move in the opposite direction that the restaurant turns.

◢ **Predict** Draw the mountain as it would appear at each time shown.

6:00 P.M.   6:35 P.M.   7:20 P.M.

Motion of restaurant

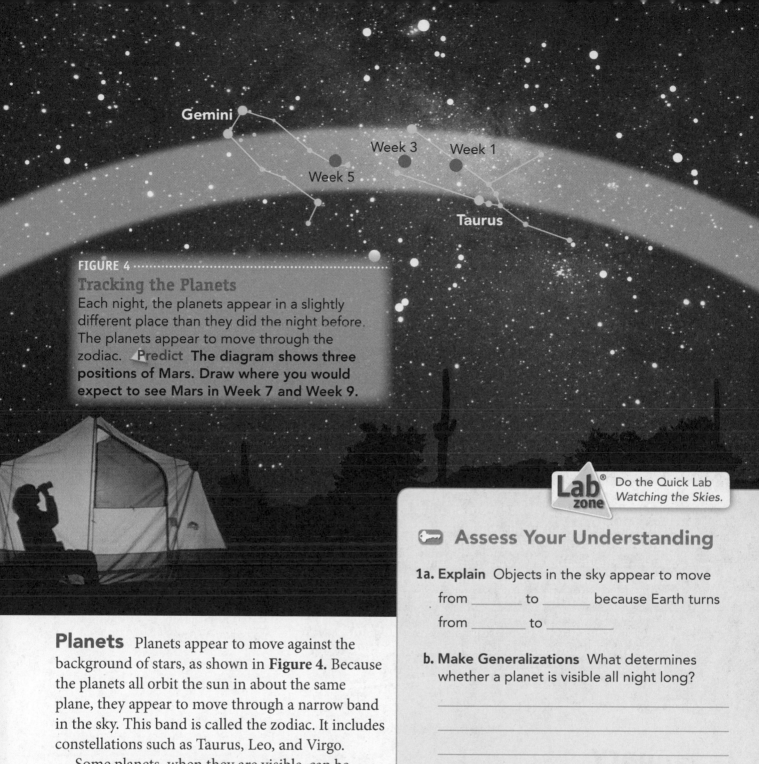

Gemini

Week 3

Week 1

Week 5

Taurus

FIGURE 4

Tracking the Planets
Each night, the planets appear in a slightly different place than they did the night before. The planets appear to move through the zodiac. **Predict** **The diagram shows three positions of Mars. Draw where you would expect to see Mars in Week 7 and Week 9.**

Planets Planets appear to move against the background of stars, as shown in **Figure 4.** Because the planets all orbit the sun in about the same plane, they appear to move through a narrow band in the sky. This band is called the zodiac. It includes constellations such as Taurus, Leo, and Virgo.

Some planets, when they are visible, can be seen all night long. Mars, Jupiter, and Saturn are all farther from the sun than Earth is. Sometimes, Earth passes between them and the sun. When this occurs, the planets are visible after sunset, once the sun's bright light no longer blocks the view.

You can see Venus and Mercury only in the evening or morning. They are closer to the sun than Earth, and so they always appear close to the sun. Venus is the brightest object in the night sky, other than the moon. Mercury appears low in the sky and is visible for a limited time around sunrise or sunset.

Lab zone ® Do the Quick Lab *Watching the Skies.*

Assess Your Understanding

1a. Explain Objects in the sky appear to move from _____ to _____ because Earth turns from _____ to _____

b. Make Generalizations What determines whether a planet is visible all night long?

_____
_____
_____
_____

got it? ···

○ **I get it!** Now I know that objects in the sky appear to move _____
_____
_____

○ **I need extra help with** _____
_____
_____

479

Earth in Space

UNLOCK THE BIG ?

🔑 **How Does Earth Move?**

🔑 **What Causes Seasons?**

my plaNeT DiaRy

The Seasons

Misconception: The seasons change because Earth's distance from the sun changes.

Fact: Seasons are the result of Earth's tilted axis.

Evidence: Earth's distance from the sun does change, but that's not why Earth has seasons. If that were the cause, people in the Northern and Southern hemispheres would have the same seasons at the same time. Instead, seasons in the Northern and Southern hemispheres are reversed. As Earth moves around the sun, sometimes the Northern Hemisphere is tilted toward the sun. At other times the Southern Hemisphere is tilted toward the sun.

MISCONCEPTION

Before you read the rest of this lesson, answer the questions below.

1. Why are summers generally warmer than winters?

_____
_____
_____
_____

2. Where on Earth is the tilt of Earth least likely to affect seasons? Why?

_____
_____
_____
_____

Lab zone® Do the Inquiry Warm-Up *What Causes Day and Night?*

January 21

Where are you and what are you doing today?

Vocabulary
- axis • rotation • revolution • orbit
- calendar • solstice • equinox

Skills
↺ Reading: Sequence
△ Inquiry: Infer

How Does Earth Move?

Until a few hundred years ago, most people thought that Earth stood still and the sun, moon, and stars moved around it. But today, scientists know that Earth itself moves and that objects seem to move across the sky because of Earth's motion. 🔑 **Earth moves in space in two major ways: rotation and revolution.**

Rotation The imaginary line that passes through Earth's center and the North and South poles is Earth's **axis.** The spinning of Earth on its axis is called **rotation.**

Earth's rotation causes day and night, as you can see in **Figure 1.** As Earth rotates eastward, the sun appears to move west across the sky. As Earth continues to turn to the east, the sun appears to set in the west. Sunlight can't reach the side of Earth facing away from the sun, so it is night there. It takes Earth about 24 hours to rotate once. As you know, each 24-hour cycle of day and night is called a day.

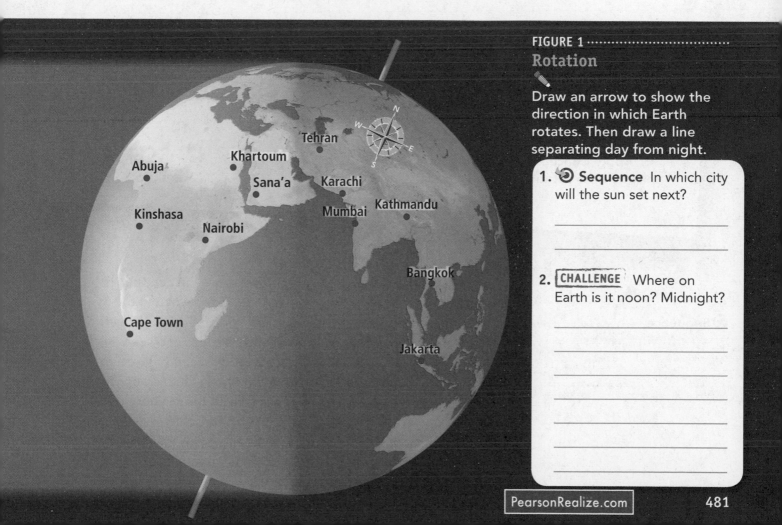

FIGURE 1
Rotation

✎

Draw an arrow to show the direction in which Earth rotates. Then draw a line separating day from night.

1. ↺ **Sequence** In which city will the sun set next?

_____

_____

2. [CHALLENGE] Where on Earth is it noon? Midnight?

_____

_____

_____

_____

_____

_____

Revolution In addition to rotating, Earth travels around the sun. **Revolution** is the movement of one object around another. One revolution of Earth around the sun is called a year. Earth's path, or **orbit,** is a slightly elongated circle, or ellipse. Earth's orbit brings the planet closest to the sun in January.

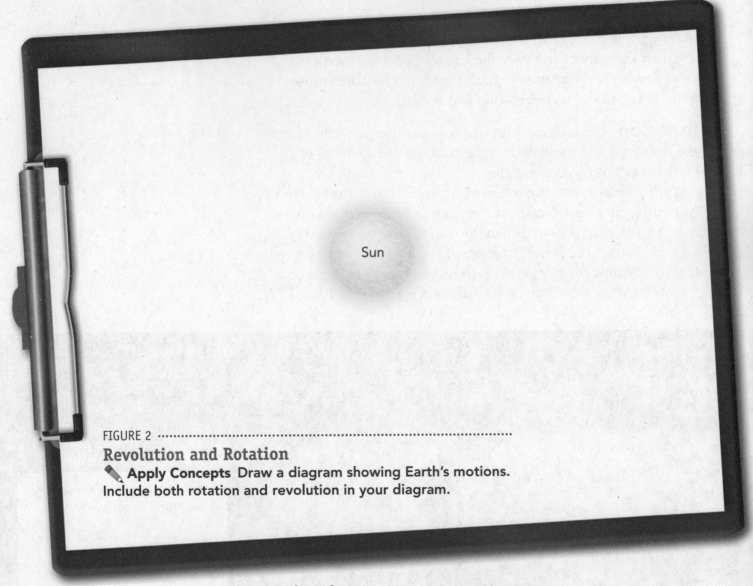

Sun

FIGURE 2 ··
Revolution and Rotation
✏️ **Apply Concepts** Draw a diagram showing Earth's motions. Include both rotation and revolution in your diagram.

····················· ✏️ ·····················
Sequence Which calendar discussed in this section was developed most recently?

_____

Calendars People of many cultures have divided time based on the motions of Earth and the moon. They have used the motions to establish calendars. A **calendar** is a system of organizing time that defines the beginning, length, and divisions of a year.

The most common calendar today is divided into years, months, and days. One year equals the time it takes Earth to complete one orbit. One day equals the time it takes Earth to turn once on its axis. People also divide the year into months based on the moon's cycle. The time from one full moon to another is about 29 days, though modern months do not match the moon's cycle exactly.

The History of the Calendar

Egyptian

The ancient Egyptians created one of the first calendars. Based on star motions, they calculated that the year was about 365 days long. They divided the year into 12 months of 30 days each, with an extra 5 days at the end.

Roman

The Romans borrowed the Egyptian calendar. But Earth's orbit actually takes about 365¼ days. The Romans adjusted the Egyptian calendar by adding one day every four years. You know this fourth year as "leap year," when February is given 29 days instead of its usual 28. Using leap years helps to ensure that annual events, such as the beginning of summer, occur on the same date each year.

Gregorian

The Roman calendar was off by a little more than 11 minutes a year. Over the centuries, these minutes added up. By the 1500s, the beginning of spring was about ten days too early. To straighten things out, Pope Gregory XIII dropped ten days from the year 1582. He also made some other minor changes to the Roman system to form the calendar that we use today.

Lab zone® Do the Quick Lab *Sun Shadows*.

Assess Your Understanding

1a. Identify What are the two major motions of Earth as it travels through space?

_____

b. Explain Which motion causes day and night?

_____

c. Infer Why do people use Earth's motions to determine units of time?

_____

_____

_____

got it? ....

○ **I get it!** Now I know that Earth moves by _____

_____

○ **I need extra help with** _____

_____

What Causes Seasons?

Many places that are far from Earth's equator and its poles have four distinct seasons: winter, spring, summer, and autumn. But there are differences in temperature from place to place. For instance, it is generally warmer near the equator than near the poles. Why?

How Sunlight Hits Earth

Figure 3 shows how sunlight strikes Earth's surface. Notice that, near the equator, sunlight hits Earth's surface from almost overhead. Near the poles, sunlight arrives at a steep angle. As a result, it is spread out over a greater area. That's why it is warmer near the equator than near the poles.

Earth's Tilted Axis

If Earth's axis were straight up and down relative to its orbit, temperatures in an area would remain fairly constant year-round. There would be no seasons. 🔑 **Earth has seasons because its axis is tilted as it revolves around the sun.**

Notice in **Figure 4** that Earth's axis is always tilted at an angle of 23.5° from the vertical. The North Pole always points in the same direction. As Earth revolves around the sun, the north end of its axis is tilted away from the sun for part of the year and toward the sun for part of the year. Summer and winter are caused by Earth's tilt as it revolves around the sun.

FIGURE 3 ·······················

Sunlight on Earth

The diagram shows how Earth's tilted axis affects the strength of sunlight in different places.

⚠️ **Infer** Draw a circle around the area where sunlight is most direct. Mark an X on the places that sunlight reaches, but where it is less direct.

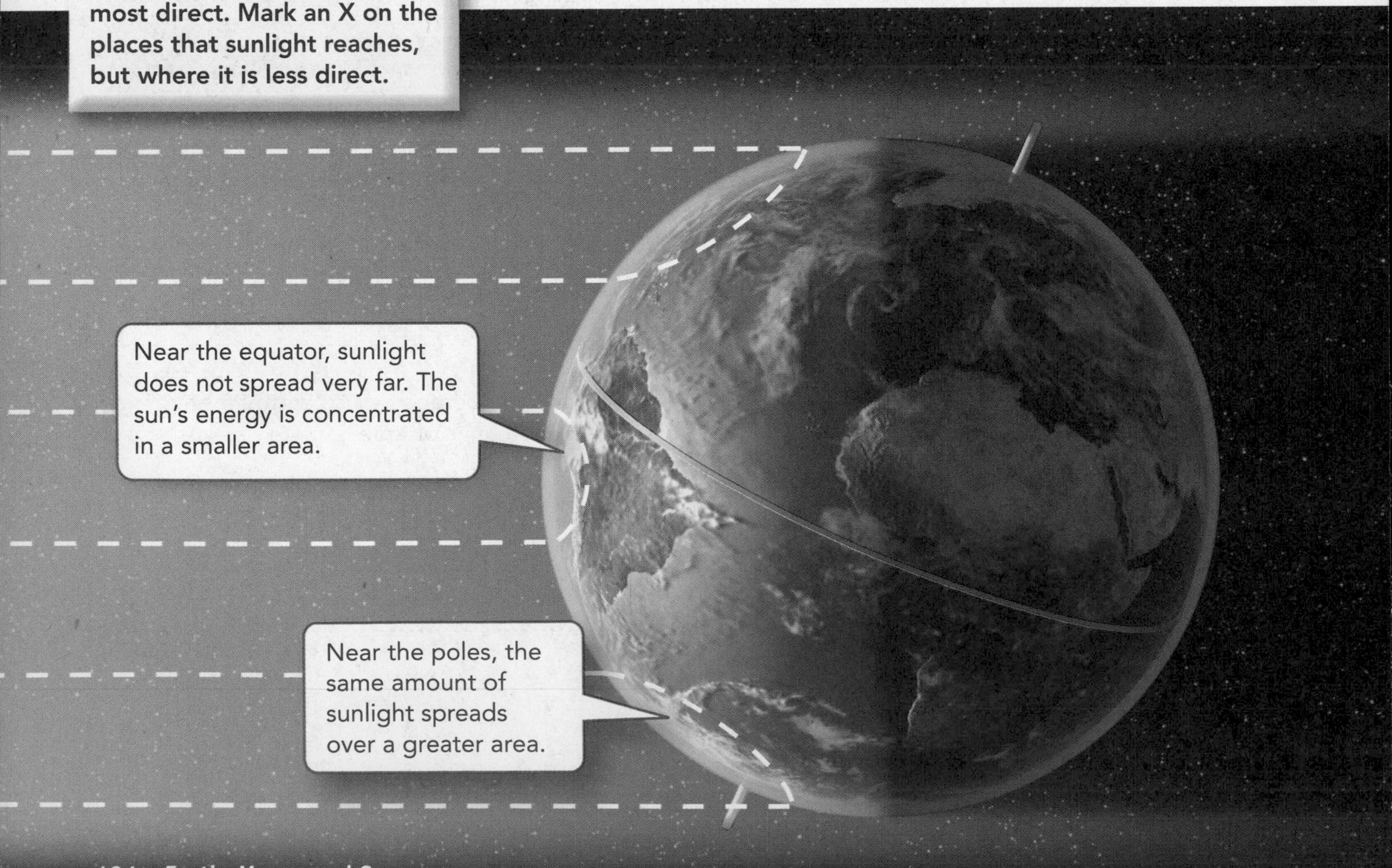

Near the equator, sunlight does not spread very far. The sun's energy is concentrated in a smaller area.

Near the poles, the same amount of sunlight spreads over a greater area.

June In June, the north end of Earth's axis is tilted toward the sun. In the Northern Hemisphere, the noon sun is high in the sky and there are more hours of daylight than darkness. The sun's rays are concentrated. It is summer in the Northern Hemisphere.

At the same time south of the equator, the sun's energy is spread over a larger area. The sun is low in the sky and days are shorter than nights. It is winter in the Southern Hemisphere.

December In December, people in the Southern Hemisphere receive the most direct sunlight, so it is summer. At the same time, the sun's rays in the Northern Hemisphere are more slanted and there are fewer hours of daylight. So it is winter in the Northern Hemisphere.

March

June

December

September

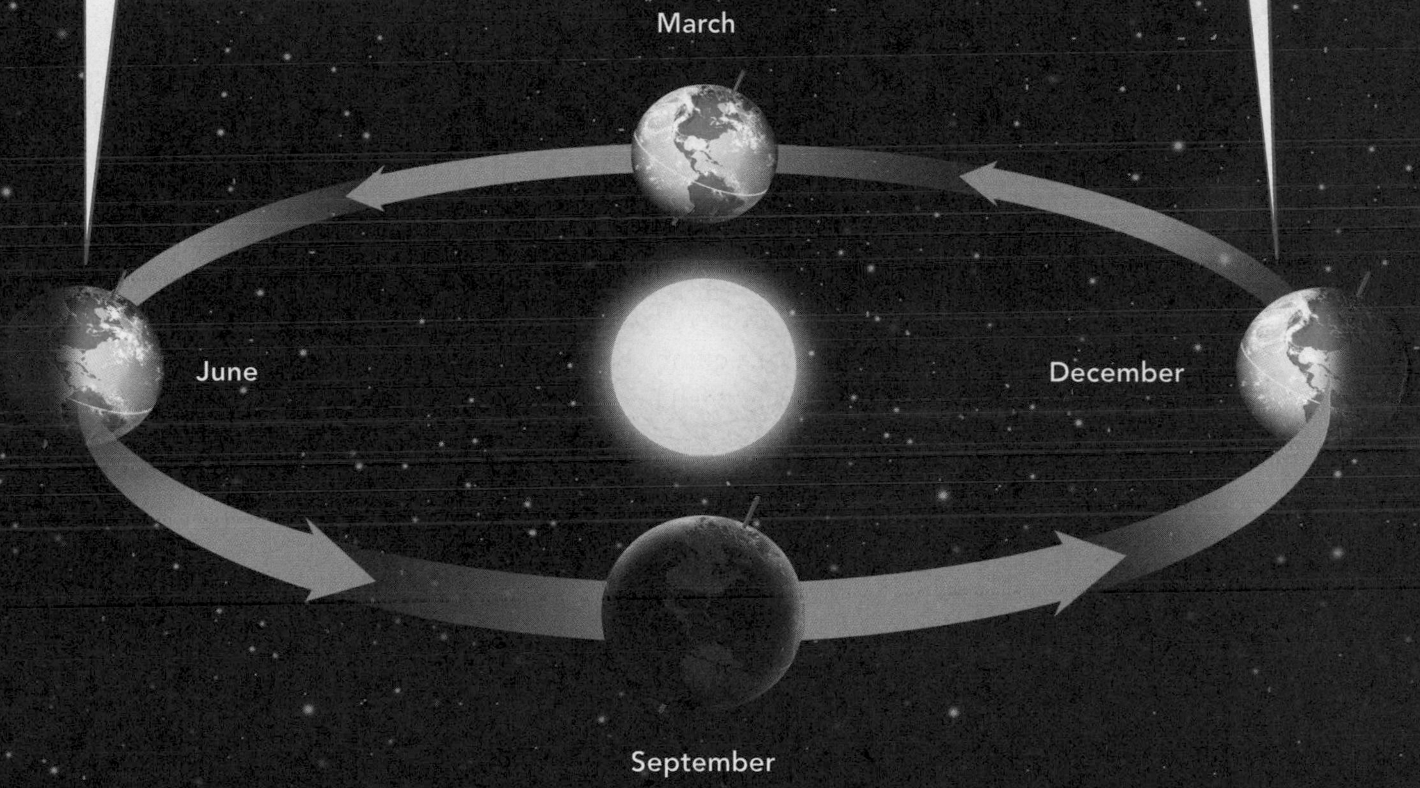

FIGURE 4 ·······················
Seasons
The diagram shows how Earth moves during the year. It is not drawn to scale.

✎ **Make Generalizations** Describe the weather and sunlight in the Northern and Southern hemispheres in March and September.

_____
_____
_____
_____
_____
_____
_____
_____

Solstices

The sun appears farthest north of the equator once each year and farthest south once each year. Each of these days is known as a **solstice** (SOHL stis). The day when the sun appears farthest north is the summer solstice in the Northern Hemisphere and the winter solstice in the Southern Hemisphere. This solstice occurs around June 21 each year. It is the longest day of the year in the Northern Hemisphere and the shortest day in the Southern Hemisphere. As you can see in **Figure 5,** the sun rises to the northeast and sets to the northwest.

Similarly, around December 21, the sun appears farthest south. This is the winter solstice in the Northern Hemisphere and the summer solstice in the Southern Hemisphere. The sun rises to the southeast and sets to the southwest.

Equinoxes

Halfway between the solstices, neither hemisphere is tilted toward the sun. The noon sun is directly overhead at the equator, rises due east, and sets due west. Each of these days is known as an **equinox,** which means "equal night." During an equinox, day and night are each about 12 hours long everywhere. The vernal (spring) equinox occurs around March 21 and marks the beginning of spring in the Northern Hemisphere. The fall, or autumnal, equinox occurs around September 22. It marks the beginning of fall in the Northern Hemisphere.

FIGURE 5 ·····································

Solstices and Equinoxes

The diagrams show the apparent path of the sun at the solstices and equinoxes in the Northern Hemisphere. The sun rises and sets farthest north at the June solstice and farthest south at the December solstice.

✎ **Apply Concepts** Draw the sun's path at the equinoxes and the December solstice for the Southern Hemisphere.

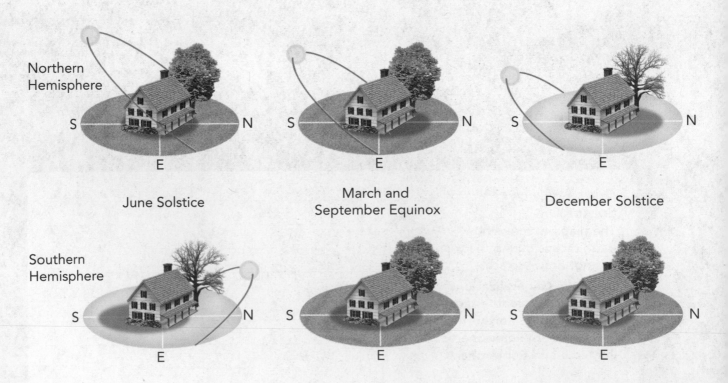

Northern Hemisphere

S   N   S   N   S   N

E   E   E

June Solstice   March and September Equinox   December Solstice

Southern Hemisphere

S   N   S   N   S   N

E   E   E

do the math! Sample Problem

Calculating Percents

The table shows the number of hours of sunlight in three cities at different times of year. What percentage of a 24-hour day has sunlight in Guadalajara on January 1?

STEP 1 Divide the number of hours of sunlight by the total number of hours.

$$\frac{\text{Hours of sunlight}}{\text{Total hours}} = \frac{10.90 \text{ hours}}{24 \text{ hours}} = 0.45$$

STEP 2 Multiply by 100 to find the percent.

$$0.45 \times 100 = 45\%$$

In Guadalajara, 45% of a 24-hour day has sunlight on January 1.

City	Approximate Latitude	Hours of Daylight			
		January 1	April 1	July 1	October 1
Helsinki, Finland	60°N	5.98	13.33	18.80	11.45
Philadelphia, United States	40°N	9.38	12.68	14.95	11.77
Guadalajara, Mexico	20°N	10.90	12.37	13.37	11.95

1 Calculate What percentage of a day has sunlight in Helsinki on July 1?

_____

2 Calculate What is the difference in the percentage of the day that has sunlight in Helsinki and in Philadelphia on January 1?

_____

3 Infer What percentage of the day would you expect to have sunlight at the equator in January? In June?

_____
_____

 Do the Lab Investigation
Reasons for the Seasons.

Assess Your Understanding

2a. Define The noon sun is directly overhead at the equator during (a solstice/an equinox).

b. Relate Cause and Effect What causes the seasons? _____
_____
_____
_____

c. Predict How would the seasons be different if Earth were not tilted on its axis? Explain.

_____
_____
_____
_____
_____

got it? ···

○ **I get it!** Now I know that Earth's seasons are caused by _____
_____

○ **I need extra help with** _____
_____

Gravity and Motion

🔑 **What Determines Gravity?**

🔑 **What Keeps Objects in Orbit?**

my planet diary

Gravity Assists

You might think that gravity only brings objects down. But gravity can also speed things up and send them flying! If a space probe comes close to a planet, the planet's gravity changes the probe's path. Engineers plan space missions to take advantage of these "gravity assists." A gravity assist can shorten the probe's interplanetary trip by many years. The diagram shows how the probe *Voyager 2* used gravity assists to visit all four outer planets!

Path of spacecraft

TECHNOLOGY

Use what you know about gravity to answer this question.

How does a planet's gravity change the path of a space probe?

_____

_____

_____

 Do the Inquiry Warm-Up *What Factors Affect Gravity?*

What Determines Gravity?

Earth revolves around the sun in a nearly circular orbit. The

Vocabulary
- force • gravity • law of universal gravitation
- mass • weight • inertia • Newton's first law of motion

Skills
↻ Reading: Ask Questions
△ Inquiry: Draw Conclusions

Gravity Newton hypothesized that the force that pulls an apple to the ground also pulls the moon toward Earth, keeping it in orbit. This force, called **gravity,** attracts all objects toward each other. Newton's **law of universal gravitation** states that every object in the universe attracts every other object. ⊶ **The strength of the force of gravity between two objects depends on two factors: the masses of the objects and the distance between them.**

Gravity, Mass, and Weight The strength of gravity depends in part on the masses of each of the objects. **Mass** is the amount of matter in an object. Because Earth is so massive, it exerts a much greater force on you than this book does.

The measure of the force of gravity on an object is called **weight**. Mass doesn't change, but an object's weight can change depending on its location. On the moon, you would weigh about one sixth as much as on Earth. This is because the moon has less mass than Earth, so the pull of the moon's gravity on you would also be less.

Gravity and Distance Gravity is also affected by the distance between two objects. The force of gravity decreases rapidly as distance increases. If the distance between two objects doubles, the force of gravity decreases to one fourth of its original value.

did you know?

You could say we owe our understanding of gravity to disease! In 1665, Isaac Newton was a student. Then a disease called plague shut down the university for 18 months. Newton had to go home. While he was there, he thought of the ideas that led to his theory. (But it may not be true that he got the idea when an apple fell from a tree.)

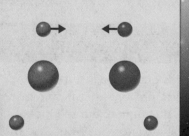

FIGURE 1 ·················
Gravity, Mass, and Distance
✎ **Compare and Contrast** Draw arrows showing the force of gravity in the second and third pictures.

The longer the arrow, the greater the force.

Lab® Do the Quick Lab
zone *What's Doing the Pulling?*

⊶ Assess Your Understanding

got it? ··

○ **I get it!** Now I know that the force of gravity depends on _____

_____

○ **I need extra help with** _____

_____

What Keeps Objects in Orbit?

If the sun and Earth are constantly pulling on one another because of gravity, why doesn't Earth fall into the sun? Similarly, why doesn't the moon crash into Earth? The fact that such collisions have not occurred shows that there must be another factor at work. That factor is called inertia.

Inertia The tendency of an object to resist a change in motion is **inertia.** You feel the effects of inertia every day. When you are riding in a car and it stops suddenly, you keep moving forward. If you didn't have a seat belt on, your inertia could cause you to bump into the car's windshield or the seat in front of you. The more mass an object has, the greater its inertia. An object with greater inertia is more difficult to start or stop.

Isaac Newton stated his ideas about inertia as a scientific law. **Newton's first law of motion** says that an object at rest will stay at rest and an object in motion will stay in motion with a constant speed and direction unless acted on by a force.

Orbital Motion Why do Earth and the moon remain in orbit? 🔑 **Newton concluded that inertia and gravity combine to keep Earth in orbit around the sun and the moon in orbit around Earth.** You can see how this occurs in **Figure 2.**

Ask Questions Before you read the paragraphs under Inertia, write a question you would like to have answered. Look for the answer as you read.

_____

_____

_____

_____

FIGURE 2
Orbital Motion

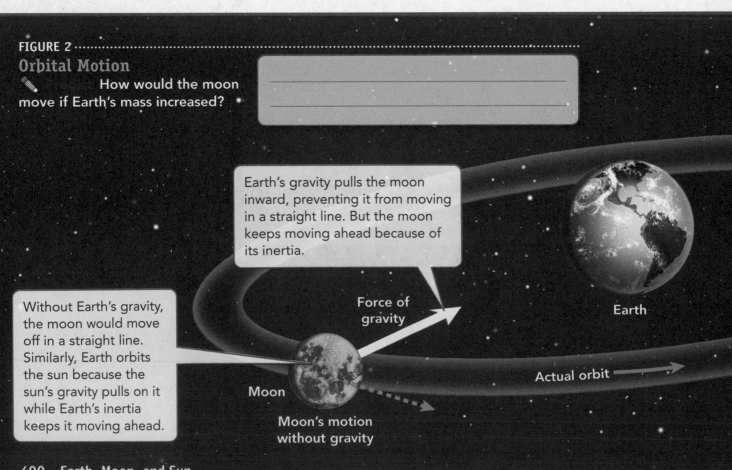

How would the moon move if Earth's mass increased?

_____

_____

Earth's gravity pulls the moon inward, preventing it from moving in a straight line. But the moon keeps moving ahead because of its inertia.

Without Earth's gravity, the moon would move off in a straight line. Similarly, Earth orbits the sun because the sun's gravity pulls on it while Earth's inertia keeps it moving ahead.

Force of gravity

Earth

Moon

Actual orbit

Moon's motion without gravity

do the math! Analyzing Data

Gravity Versus Distance

As a rocket leaves a planet's surface, the force of gravity between the rocket and the planet changes. Use the graph to answer the questions below.

1 Read Graphs The variables being graphed

are _____

and _____

2 Read Graphs What is the force of gravity on the rocket at the planet's surface?

_____

3 Read Graphs What is the force of gravity on the rocket at two units (twice the planet's radius from its center)?

_____

4 Make Generalizations In general, how does the force of gravity on the rocket change as its distance from the planet increases?

_____

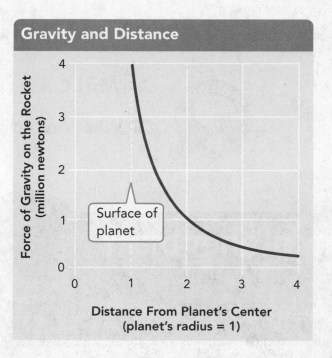

Gravity and Distance

Force of Gravity on the Rocket (million newtons)

Surface of planet

Distance From Planet's Center (planet's radius = 1)

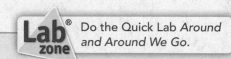

Do the Quick Lab *Around and Around We Go.*

🔑 Assess Your Understanding

1a. Identify What two factors keep a planet in orbit around the sun?

_____

b. Draw Conclusions What keeps Earth from falling into the sun?

_____

c. CHALLENGE How would a planet move if the sun suddenly disappeared? Explain.

_____
_____
_____
_____

got it? ....

○ **I get it!** Now I know that objects are kept in orbit by _____
_____

○ **I need extra help with** _____
_____

Phases and Eclipses

 **UNLOCK THE BIG Q?**

🔑 **What Causes the Moon's Phases?**

🔑 **What Are Eclipses?**

my pLaneT DiaRY

BLOG

Posted by: Nicole

Location: Bernhard's Bay, New York

One night, my mom, dad, and I were coming home from eating dinner. When we got out of the car, we saw that the moon was turning red. We looked at the moon for a while. Then our neighbor called and said that it was a lunar eclipse. It was an amazing sight.

Think about your own experiences as you answer the question below.

What is the most interesting or unusual event you have ever seen in the sky?

_____
_____
_____
_____

 Lab zone® Do the Inquiry Warm-Up *How Does the Moon Move?*

What Causes the Moon's Phases?

Have you ever been kept awake by bright moonlight? The light streaming through your window actually comes from the sun! The moon does not shine with its own light. Instead, it reflects light from the sun. When the moon is full, this light may be bright enough to read by! But at other times, the moon is just a thin crescent in the sky. The different shapes of the moon you see from Earth are called **phases.** Phases are caused by the motions of the moon around Earth.

Vocabulary

- phase
- eclipse
- solar eclipse
- umbra
- penumbra
- lunar eclipse

Skills

⟳ Reading: Relate Text and Visuals

△ Inquiry: Make Models

Motions of the Moon When you look up at the moon, you may see what looks like a face. What you are really seeing is a pattern of light-colored and dark-colored areas on the moon's surface that just happens to look like a face. Oddly, this pattern never seems to move. The same side of the moon, the "near side," always faces Earth. The "far side" of the moon always faces away from Earth. Why? The answer has to do with the moon's motions.

Like Earth, the moon moves through space in two ways. The moon revolves around Earth and also rotates on its own axis. The moon rotates once on its axis in the same time that it takes to revolve once around Earth. Thus, a "day" on the moon is the same length as a month on Earth. For this reason, the same side of the moon always faces Earth, as you can see in **Figure 1.**

As the moon orbits Earth, the relative positions of the moon, Earth, and sun change. ⟳ **The changing relative positions of the moon, Earth, and sun cause the phases of the moon.**

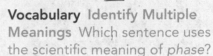

Vocabulary Identify Multiple Meanings Which sentence uses the scientific meaning of *phase*?

- ◯ The doctor told the parent that the child was just going through a phase.
- ◯ The moon goes through a cycle of phases every month.

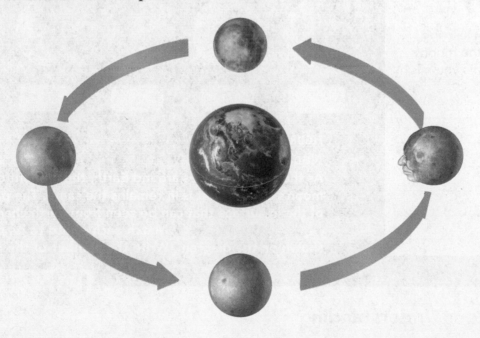

FIGURE 1

The Moon's Motion

The diagram shows the moon's rotation and revolution. ✎ **Infer** Find the face on the rightmost view of the moon. Draw the face as it would appear on each view.

[CHALLENGE] How would the moon appear from Earth if the moon did not rotate?

_____

_____

Phases of the Moon

Half the moon is almost always in sunlight. But since the moon orbits Earth, you see the moon from different angles. The phase of the moon you see depends on how much of the sunlit side of the moon faces Earth.

During the new moon phase, the side of the moon facing Earth is not lit. As the moon revolves around Earth, you see more of the lit side of the moon, until you see all of the lit side. As the month continues, you see less of the lit side. You can see these changes in **Figure 2**. About 29.5 days after the last new moon, a new moon occurs again.

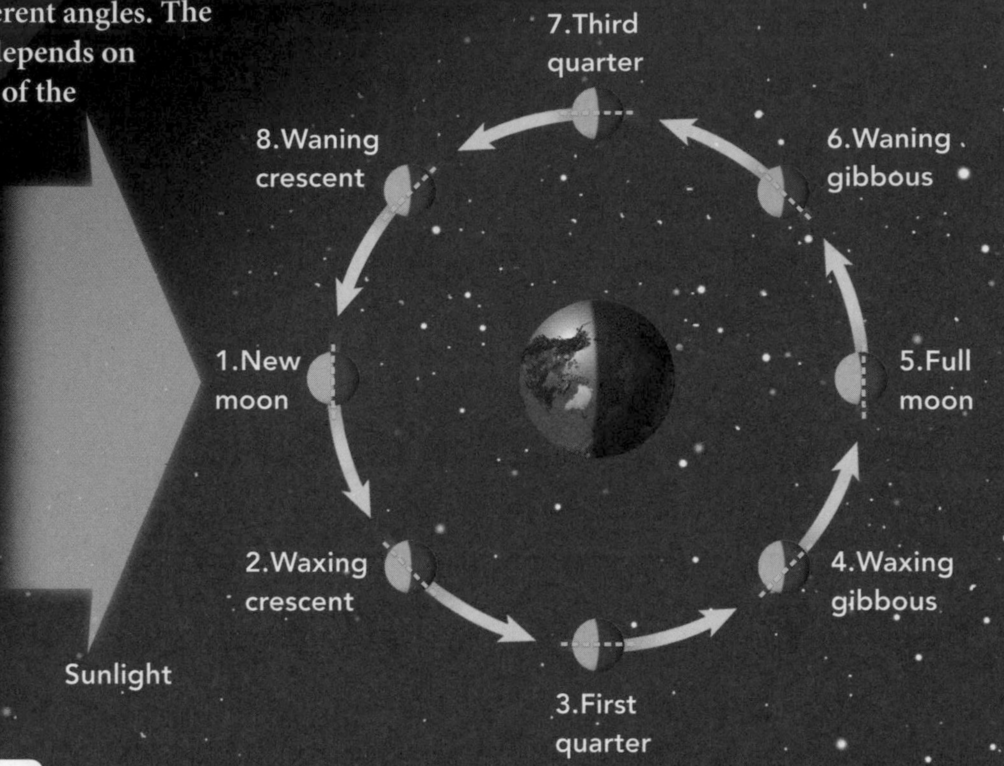

Sunlight

7. Third quarter

8. Waning crescent

6. Waning gibbous

1. New moon

5. Full moon

2. Waxing crescent

4. Waxing gibbous

3. First quarter

apply it!

⚠️ **Make Models** Describe a way to model the moon's phases using items you might have at home.

_____

_____

_____

_____

_____

_____

FIGURE 2 ·······················
Moon Phases
As the moon revolves around Earth, the amount of the moon's surface that is lit remains the same. The part of the lit surface that can be seen from Earth changes.

✎ Interpret Diagrams **Match each photo to its phase shown on the diagram. Write the number of the phase.**

Lab zone® Do the Quick Lab Moon Phases.

🔑 Assess Your Understanding

got it? ··

○ I get it! Now I know that moon phases are caused by _____

_____

○ I need extra help with _____

_____

What Are Eclipses?

The moon's orbit around Earth is slightly tilted with respect to Earth's orbit around the sun. As a result, the moon travels above and below Earth's orbit. But on rare occasions, Earth, the moon, and the sun line up.

When an object in space comes between the sun and a third object, it casts a shadow on that object, causing an **eclipse** (ih KLIPS) to take place. There are two types of eclipses: solar eclipses and lunar eclipses. (The words *solar* and *lunar* come from the Latin words for "sun" and "moon.")

Solar Eclipses During a new moon, the moon lies between Earth and the sun. 🔑 A solar eclipse occurs when the moon passes directly between Earth and the sun, blocking sunlight from Earth. The moon's shadow then hits Earth.

Total Solar Eclipses The very darkest part of the moon's shadow is the umbra (UM bruh). You can see how the umbra strikes Earth in **Figure 3**. Within the umbra, the sun's light is completely blocked. Only people within the umbra experience a total solar eclipse. During a total solar eclipse, the sky grows as dark as night. The air gets cool and the sky becomes an eerie color. You can see the stars and the solar corona, which is the faint outer atmosphere of the sun.

Partial Solar Eclipses The moon casts another part of its shadow that is less dark than the umbra. This larger part of the shadow is called the penumbra (peh NUM bruh). In the penumbra, part of the sun is visible from Earth. During a solar eclipse, people in the penumbra see only a partial eclipse.

FIGURE 3 ······························
Solar Eclipse
The diagram shows the moon's penumbra and umbra during an eclipse. It is not drawn to scale.

↺ Relate Text and Visuals

Mark an X to show where a total solar eclipse would be visible. Circle the area in which a partial solar eclipse would be visible.

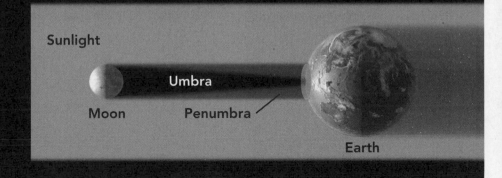

Sunlight

Umbra

Moon

Penumbra

Earth

Lunar Eclipses During most months, the moon moves near Earth's shadow but not quite into it. A **lunar eclipse** occurs at a full moon when Earth is directly between the moon and the sun. You can see a lunar eclipse in Figure 4. 🔑 During a lunar eclipse, Earth blocks sunlight from reaching the moon. Lunar eclipses occur only when there is a full moon because the moon is closest to Earth's shadow at that time.

↺ Relate Text and Visuals
Mark an X on the photograph above that shows a total eclipse.

Total Lunar Eclipses Like the moon's shadow in a solar eclipse, Earth's shadow has an umbra and a penumbra. When the moon is in Earth's umbra, you see a total lunar eclipse. Unlike a total solar eclipse, a total lunar eclipse can be seen anywhere on Earth that the moon is visible. So you are more likely to see a total lunar eclipse than a total solar eclipse.

Partial Lunar Eclipses For most lunar eclipses, Earth, the moon, and the sun are not quite in line, and only a partial lunar eclipse results. A partial lunar eclipse occurs when the moon passes partly into the umbra of Earth's shadow. The edge of the umbra appears blurry, and you can watch it pass across the moon for two or three hours.

FIGURE 4 ·····················
Lunar Eclipse
As the moon moves through Earth's shadow, total and partial eclipses occur. This diagram is not to scale.

✎ *Infer* Draw a circle labeled *T* to show where the moon would be during a total eclipse. Draw two circles labeled *P* to show two places the moon could be during a partial eclipse.

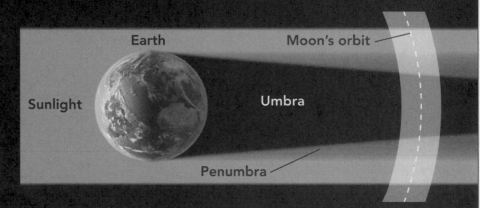

Earth

Moon's orbit

Sunlight

Umbra

Penumbra

EXPLORE THE BIG ?

Seasons and Shadows

How do Earth, the moon, and the sun interact?

FIGURE 5 ···

Look at the diagram below. (The diagram is not
to scale.) Identify what season it is in the Northern Hemisphere,
what the phase of the moon is, and what kind of eclipse, if any,
could occur.

Season

_____

Moon Phase

_____

Eclipse

_____

Use the above
diagram as a
model. Draw the
arrangement of
Earth, the moon,
and the sun
during a total
lunar eclipse in
December.

Lab zone® Do the Quick Lab *Eclipses.*

🔑 Assess Your Understanding

1a. Explain A (solar/lunar) eclipse occurs when
the moon passes into Earth's shadow. A
(solar/lunar) eclipse occurs when Earth passes
into the moon's shadow.

b. ANSWER THE BIG ? How do Earth, the moon, and the sun
interact? _____

_____

_____

_____

got it? ···

○ **I get it!** Now I know that eclipses occur when _____

_____

○ **I need extra help with** _____

_____

497

UNLOCK THE BIG 🔑 **What Are Tides?**

MY PLANET DIARY

A River in Reverse

If you were visiting New Brunswick in Canada, you might see the Saint John River flowing into the ocean. But six hours later, you might find that the river changed direction while you were gone! How could this happen? The Saint John River really does reverse course twice a day. At low tide, it empties into the Bay of Fundy, shown below. At high tide, the Bay of Fundy's tide pushes into the river, forcing the river to run in the opposite direction. The Bay of Fundy's tides are among the highest in the world.

FUN FACT

Use your experience to answer the questions.

1. Why does the Saint John River change direction?

_____

_____

_____

2. Have you ever seen a natural event that surprised you? Why was it surprising?

_____

_____

_____

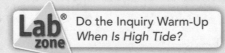

Lab zone® Do the Inquiry Warm-Up *When Is High Tide?*

High tide

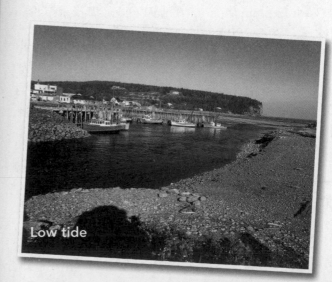

Low tide

Vocabulary
- tide
- spring tide
- neap tide

Skills
- Reading: Relate Cause and Effect
- Inquiry: Observe

What Are Tides?

The reversing Saint John River is caused by ocean **tides,** the rise and fall of ocean water that occurs every 12.5 hours or so. The water rises for about six hours, then falls for about six hours.

The Tide Cycle The force of gravity pulls the moon and Earth (including the water on Earth's surface) toward each other. **Tides are caused mainly by differences in how much gravity from the moon and the sun pulls on different parts of Earth.**

At any one time on Earth, there are two places with high tides and two places with low tides. As Earth rotates, one high tide occurs on the side of Earth that faces the moon. The second high tide occurs on the opposite side of Earth. **Figure 1** explains why.

Relate Cause and Effect As you read **Figure 1**, underline the causes of high and low tides.

FIGURE 1

Tides

You can think of Earth as a ball surrounded by a layer of water, as shown here. The layer is really much thinner than this, but is drawn thicker so it is easier to see.

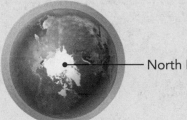
— North Pole

The Near Side The moon's gravity pulls a little more strongly on the water on the side closest to the moon than on Earth as a whole. This difference causes a bulge of water on the side of Earth closest to the moon. This bulge causes high tide.

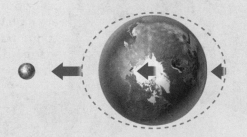

The Far Side The moon's gravity pulls more weakly on the water on the far side of Earth than on Earth as a whole. Since Earth is pulled more strongly, the water is "left behind." Water flows toward the far side, causing high tide. Halfway between the high tides, water flows toward the high tides, causing low tide.

Interpret Diagrams Write an *H* where high tides occur and an *L* where low tides occur.

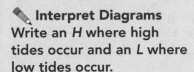

The Sun's Role Even though the sun is about 150 million kilometers from Earth, it is so massive that its gravity affects the tides. The sun pulls the water on Earth's surface toward it. 🔑 Changes in the positions of Earth, the moon, and the sun affect the heights of the tides during a month.

New Moon

The sun, the moon, and Earth are nearly in a line during a new moon. The gravity of the sun and the moon pull in the same direction. Their combined forces produce a tide with the greatest difference between consecutive low and high tides, called a **spring tide.** The term "spring tide" comes from an Old English word, *springen*, meaning "to jump."

First Quarter

During the moon's first-quarter phase, the line between Earth and the sun is at right angles to the line between Earth and the moon. The sun's pull is at right angles to the moon's pull. This arrangement produces a **neap tide**, a tide with the least difference between consecutive low and high tides. Neap tides occur twice a month.

Full Moon

At full moon, the moon and the sun are on opposite sides of Earth. Since there are high tides on both sides of Earth, a spring tide is also produced. It doesn't matter in which order the sun, Earth, and the moon line up.

Third Quarter

✏️ **Infer** Draw the position of the moon and the tide bulges at third quarter. What kind of tide occurs?

_____

_____

apply it!

The table shows high and low tides at four times in May 2008, in St. John, New Brunswick. St. John is on the Bay of Fundy.

1 Interpret Data Spring tides occurred at two of the times shown. Which two? How do you know?

_____

_____

_____

2 CHALLENGE Would the tide be higher when the moon is on the same side of Earth as New Brunswick or on the opposite side? Why?

_____

_____

_____

_____

_____

High and Low Tides at St. John, New Brunswick

Date	High Tide (meters)	Low Tide (meters)
May 6–7	8.7	0.0
May 13–14	7.1	1.7
May 21	7.5	1.2
May 26	6.9	2.0

Vocabulary Identify Multiple Meanings Does a spring tide always happen in the season of spring? Explain your answer.

_____

_____

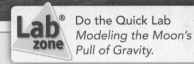

Do the Quick Lab
Modeling the Moon's Pull of Gravity.

🔑 Assess Your Understanding

1a. Review Most coastal areas have _____ high tides and _____ low tides each day.

b. 🔁 Relate Cause and Effect What causes tides?

_____

_____

_____

c. Observe Look at the diagrams on the previous page. What is the angle formed by the sun, Earth, and the moon during a neap tide? A spring tide?

_____

_____

_____

_____

got it? ....

O **I get it!** Now I know that tides are _____

_____

O **I need extra help with** _____

_____

LESSON

6 Earth's Moon

 UNLOCK THE BIG ?

🔑 **What Is the Moon Like?**

my planet Diary

VOICES FROM HISTORY

Galileo Galilei

In 1609, the Italian astronomer Galileo Galilei turned a new tool—the telescope—toward the moon. What he saw amazed him: wide dark areas and strange spots and ridges.

I have been led to that opinion ... that I feel sure that the surface of the Moon is not perfectly smooth ...but that, on the contrary, it is ... just like the surface of the Earth itself, which is varied everywhere by high mountains and deep valleys.

Today, scientists know that Galileo was right. Powerful telescopes have shown the mountains and craters on the moon, and astronauts have walked and driven over the moon's surface.

✏️ **Communicate** Discuss Galileo's observations with a partner. Then answer the questions below.

1. What conclusions did Galileo draw about the moon?

_____

_____

2. How do you think it would feel to make an observation that no one had made before?

_____

_____

_____

Lab zone® Do the Inquiry Warm-Up *Why Do Craters Look Different From Each Other?*

Vocabulary
- maria • crater
- meteoroid

Skills
⟳ Reading: Compare and Contrast
△ Inquiry: Develop Hypotheses

What Is the Moon Like?

For thousands of years, people could see the moon, but didn't know much about it. Galileo's observations were some of the first to show details on the moon's surface. Scientists have since learned more about the moon's features. ⚷ **The moon is dry and airless and has an irregular surface. Compared to Earth, the moon is small and has large variations in its surface temperature.**

Surface Features As **Figure 1** shows, the moon has many unusual structures, including maria, craters, and highlands.

Maria Dark, flat areas, called **maria** (MAH ree uh), are hardened rock formed from huge lava flows that occurred 3–4 billion years ago. The singular form of *maria* is *mare* (MAH ray).

Craters Large round pits called **craters** can be hundreds of kilometers across. These craters were caused by the impacts of **meteoroids,** chunks of rock or dust from space. Maria have relatively few craters. This means that most of the moon's craters formed from impacts early in its history, before maria formed.

Highlands Some of the light-colored features you can see on the moon's surface are highlands, or mountains. The peaks of the lunar highlands and the rims of the craters cast dark shadows. The highlands cover most of the moon's surface.

FIGURE 1 ·····························
Moon Features
This photograph shows the features of the northern part of the side of the moon that you can see from Earth.

✎ **Relate Diagrams and Photos** How is the photograph different from Galileo's drawing on the previous page?

_____
_____
_____
_____
_____

FIGURE 2
Different Worlds
This photo of Earth, taken from orbit around the moon, clearly shows the contrast between the barren moon and water-covered Earth.

Compare and Contrast
Complete the table below to compare and contrast Earth and the moon.

Size and Density
The moon is 3,476 kilometers across, a little less than the distance across the United States. This is about one fourth of Earth's diameter. However, the moon has only one eightieth as much mass as Earth. Though Earth has a very dense core, its outer layers are less dense. The moon's average density is similar to the density of Earth's outer layers. Its gravity is about one sixth of Earth's.

Temperature
At the moon's equator, temperatures range from a torrid 130°C in direct sunlight to a frigid −170°C at night. Temperatures at the poles are even colder. Temperatures vary so much because the moon does not have an atmosphere. The moon's surface gravity is so weak that gases can easily escape into space.

Water
For many years, people thought the moon had no water, except for small amounts of ice. In 2009, scientists using data from several space probes determined that a thin layer of water exists in the moon's soil. The total amount of water is very small, but it is found in many places on the moon's surface.

Origins of the Moon
Scientists have suggested many possible theories for how the moon formed. The theory that seems to best fit the evidence is called the collision-ring theory. About 4.5 billion years ago, when Earth was very young, the solar system was full of rocky debris. Scientists theorize that a planet-sized object collided with Earth. Material from the object and Earth's outer layers was ejected into orbit around Earth, where it formed a ring. Gravity caused this material to clump together to form the moon.

	Density	Temperatures	Atmosphere	Water
Earth				
Moon				

apply it!

Within your lifetime, tourists may be able to travel to the moon. If you were taking a trip to the moon, what would you pack? Remember that the moon is dry, has almost no liquid water, and has no atmosphere.

1 Solve Problems On the packing list to the right, list five items you would need on the moon.

2 CHALLENGE List two items that you could not use on the moon. Why would they not work?

_____
_____
_____
_____
_____
_____
_____

Things to Pack

1. _____
2. _____
3. _____
4. _____
5. _____

Lab zone® Do the Quick Lab *Moonwatching.*

Assess Your Understanding

1a. List What are the three main surface features on the moon?

_____

b. Compare and Contrast How does the moon's gravity compare with Earth's?

_____

c. Develop Hypotheses Write a hypothesis explaining why the moon has very little liquid water.

_____
_____
_____

got it? ....

O **I get it!** Now I know that the characteristics of Earth's moon are _____
_____

O **I need extra help with** _____
_____

11 Study Guide

Interactions between Earth, the moon, and the sun cause _____, _____, _____, and _____.

LESSON 1 The Sky From Earth

🔑 On a clear night, you may see stars, the moon, planets, meteors, and comets.

🔑 A constellation is a pattern or grouping of stars imagined by people to represent figures.

🔑 The apparent motion of objects in the sky depends on the motions of Earth.

Vocabulary
• satellite • planet • meteor • comet
• star • constellation

LESSON 2 Earth in Space

🔑 Earth moves in space in two major ways: rotation and revolution.

🔑 Earth has seasons because its axis is tilted as it revolves around the sun.

Vocabulary
• axis • rotation
• revolution
• orbit • calendar
• solstice • equinox

LESSON 3 Gravity and Motion

🔑 The strength of the force of gravity between two objects depends on two factors: the masses of the objects and the distance between them.

🔑 Newton concluded that inertia and gravity combine to keep Earth in orbit around the sun and the moon in orbit around Earth.

Vocabulary
• force • gravity • law of universal gravitation
• mass • weight • inertia
• Newton's first law of motion

LESSON 4 Phases and Eclipses

🔑 The changing relative positions of the moon, Earth, and sun cause the phases of the moon.

🔑 A solar eclipse occurs when the moon passes directly between Earth and the sun, blocking sunlight from Earth. During a lunar eclipse, Earth blocks sunlight from reaching the moon.

Vocabulary
• phase • eclipse • solar eclipse • umbra
• penumbra • lunar eclipse

LESSON 5 Tides

🔑 Tides are caused by differences in how much gravity from the moon and the sun pulls on different parts of Earth.

🔑 Changes in the positions of Earth, the moon, and the sun affect the heights of the tides during a month.

Vocabulary
• tide • spring tide • neap tide

LESSON 6 Earth's Moon

🔑 The moon is dry and airless and has an irregular surface. Compared to Earth, the moon is small and has large variations in its surface temperature.

Vocabulary
• maria • crater
• meteoroid

Review and Assessment

The Sky From Earth

1. Which of the following objects is found in Earth's atmosphere?

   a. comet   **b.** meteor

   c. moon   **d.** planet

2. Over time, people have given names to groups of stars, called _____

3. **Predict** The constellation Orion appears in the eastern sky in December. Where would you expect it to appear in March? Why?

   _____

   _____

   _____

4. **Write About It** Suppose you were camping on a summer night. Describe what objects you might see in the sky and how the sky would change throughout the night.

Earth in Space

5. What is Earth's annual motion around the sun called?

   a. month   **b.** revolution

   c. rotation   **d.** seasons

6. The _____ occurs when the sun is farthest north of the equator.

7. **Infer** Mars's axis is tilted at about the same angle as Earth's axis. Do you think Mars has seasons? Explain your answer.

   _____

   _____

   _____

8. **Write About It** Write a guide for younger children explaining how Earth's motions are related to the lengths of days and years.

Gravity and Motion

9. The tendency of an object to resist a change in motion is called

   a. force.   **b.** gravity.

   c. inertia.   **d.** weight.

10. An object is kept in orbit by _____

    and _____

11. **Relate Cause and Effect** If you move two objects farther apart, how does the force of gravity between the two objects change?

    _____

12. **Compare and Contrast** How are weight and mass different? _____

    _____

    _____

13. **Explain** Explain Newton's first law of motion in your own words. _____

    _____

    _____

    _____

    _____

    _____

Use this illustration to answer Question 14.

450 N

14. **math!** How much would the person above weigh on the moon? _____

LESSON 4 Phases and Eclipses

15. The moon's shadow falling on Earth causes a

    a. full moon.   b. lunar eclipse.

    c. phase.   d. solar eclipse.

16. The darkest part of the moon's shadow is the

    _____

17. **Relate Cause and Effect** Why does the moon
    have phases? _____

    _____

    _____

18. **Make Generalizations** Which occurs more
    often, a partial or a total lunar eclipse? Why?

    _____

    _____

    _____

LESSON 5 Tides

19. About how long passes between high tides?

    a. 6 hours   b. 12 hours

    c. 24 hours   d. 48 hours

20. The least difference between high and low

    tides occurs during a _____

Use the diagram to answer Question 21.

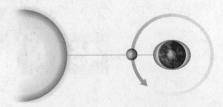

21. **Interpret Diagrams** Does the diagram show a
    spring or a neap tide? How do you know?

    _____

    _____

LESSON 6 Earth's Moon

22. What caused the moon's craters?

    a. maria   b. meteoroids

    c. tides   d. volcanoes

23. The moon's light-colored highlands are

    _____

24. **Explain** Why do temperatures vary so much

    on the moon? _____

    _____

    _____

    _____

25. **Write About It** Suppose you were hired to
    design a spacesuit for use on the moon.
    What characteristics of the moon would be
    important for you to consider? Explain.

APPLY THE BIG ? **How do Earth, the moon, and the sun interact?**

26. Can more people see a total solar eclipse or a
    total lunar eclipse? Explain your answer.

    _____

    _____

    _____

    _____

    _____

    _____

    _____

    _____

    _____

    _____

    _____

Standardized Test Prep

Read each question and choose the best answer.

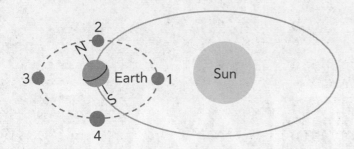

1. Which of the following can occur when the moon is at location 1?

  A   only a lunar eclipse

  B   only a solar eclipse

  C   both a solar and a lunar eclipse

  D   neither a solar nor a lunar eclipse

2. On what does the force of gravity between two objects depend?

  A   mass and weight

  B   speed and distance

  C   weight and speed

  D   mass and distance

3. What happens at a spring tide?

  A   There is only one high tide each day.

  B   There is only one low tide each day.

  C   There is the most difference between consecutive high and low tides.

  D   There is the least difference between consecutive high and low tides.

4. Which motion does Earth complete every 365 days?

  A   eclipse

  B   equinox

  C   revolution

  D   rotation

5. The calendar we use is based on

  A   the time it takes the moon to rotate once on its axis.

  B   the time it takes Earth to complete one orbit.

  C   the occurrence of a solar eclipse.

  D   the length of each season.

Constructed Response

Use the diagram below to answer the question.

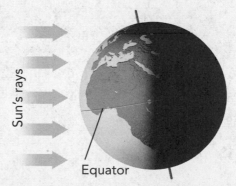

6. In the Northern Hemisphere, is it the summer solstice, winter solstice, or one of the equinoxes? Explain how you know.

KEEPING TRACK
OF
TIME

▲ This sun stone is sometimes called the Aztec calendar. It shows the 20 days in the Aztec month. The Aztec calendar was a solar calendar, with a total of 365 days in a year.

What day of the week is your birthday this year? Better check the calendar.

Calendars were invented to keep track of important events, such as planting schedules and festivals.

Early people noticed certain patterns in nature. The seasons change. The sun rises and sets. The moon changes phases. These patterns became the basis for calendars even before people understood that Earth rotates on an axis and revolves around the sun or that the moon revolves around Earth.

Calendars were lunar (based on the moon), solar (based on the sun), or lunisolar (based on a combination). But none was completely accurate—important events shifted around from one year to the next.

The Gregorian calendar, introduced in 1582, is the standard calendar in use today. It is more accurate than most calendars, but even it requires some tinkering. We add an extra day almost every four years, giving us a leap year. Century years (like 2000) are not leap years unless they are divisible by 400.

Research It There are about 40 different kinds of calendars in use today. Pick one and research it. Write an essay describing the calendar and how it is different from the Gregorian calendar. What does the calendar tell you about the society that uses it?

SPACE SPINOFFS

Do you have any space gadgets in your home? You almost certainly do. The scientists and engineers who have worked on the space program have developed thousands of new materials and devices for use in space. Many of those items are useful on Earth as well. An item that has uses on Earth but was originally developed for use in space is called a space spinoff.

Space spinoffs include many new materials, as well as devices used in consumer products and medical technology. Here are some examples:

Space Technology	Spinoff Use
Joystick controllers	Wheelchairs and video games
Scratch-resistant lenses	Eyeglasses
Freeze-dried foods	Camping provisions
Shock-absorbing helmets	Bicycle helmets
Composite materials	Tennis rackets and golf clubs
Memory metals	Flexible eyeglass frames
Clear ceramics	Dental braces
Shielding material	Houses, cars, and trucks
Computer-aided imaging	Hospital diagnosis techniques
Lasers	Surgical techniques
Longer-life batteries	Pacemakers for hearts

Research It Research space spinoffs developed throughout the history of the space program. Design an illustrated timeline that displays the five spinoffs that you think are the most useful. Display your timeline and defend your choices in class.

▲ Game controllers are an example of space spinoffs.

WHAT MIGHT SATURN'S RINGS BE MADE OF?

THE BIG ?

Why are objects in the solar system different from each other?

This photograph from the *Cassini* space probe shows Saturn and part of its magnificent system of rings. Space probes such as *Cassini* have helped scientists learn more about the objects in the solar system.

△ **Infer** What do you think Saturn's rings are made of? How might they have formed?

Watch the **Untamed Science** video to learn more about the solar system.

_____

_____

_____

_____

_____

_____

The Solar System

Check Your Understanding

1. Background Read the paragraph below and then answer the question.

Tyrone is watching a movie. He sees astronauts explore a planet that **revolves** around a star. As the astronauts travel, they notice that the planet **rotates.** Tyrone knows that **gravity** holds the planet in orbit around the star.

• What causes day and night on a planet?

_____

_____

> **Revolution** is the motion of one object around another.
>
> An object **rotates** when it spins around a central axis.
>
> **Gravity** is the force that attracts all objects toward each other.

Vocabulary Skill

Greek Word Origins Many science words come to English from Greek. In this chapter, you will learn the term *geocentric. Geocentric* comes from the Greek word parts *ge,* meaning "Earth," and *kentron,* meaning "center."

$$\underset{\textbf{Earth}}{ge} + \underset{\textbf{center}}{kentron} = \underset{\textbf{having Earth at the center}}{geocentric}$$

Learn these Greek word parts to help you remember the vocabulary terms.

Greek Word	Meaning	Example
helios	sun	heliocentric, *adj.*
chromas	color	chromosphere, *n.*
sphaira	sphere	photosphere, *n.*

2. Quick Check Predict the meaning of *heliocentric.*

_____

_____

planet

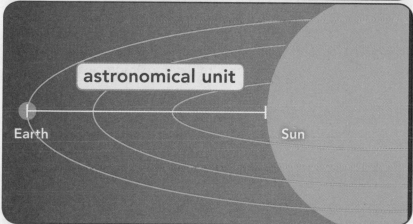

astronomical unit

Earth

Sun

solar system

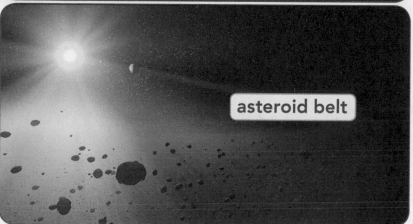

asteroid belt

Chapter Preview

LESSON 1
- geocentric • heliocentric
- ellipse
↻ **Sequence**
△ **Make Models**

LESSON 2
- solar system • astronomical unit
- planet • dwarf planet
- planetesimal
↻ **Identify Supporting Evidence**
△ **Calculate**

LESSON 3
- core • nuclear fusion
- radiation zone • convection zone
- photosphere • chromosphere
- corona • solar wind • sunspot
- prominence • solar flare
↻ **Relate Cause and Effect**
△ **Interpret Data**

LESSON 4
- terrestrial planet
- greenhouse effect
↻ **Compare and Contrast**
△ **Communicate**

LESSON 5
- gas giant • ring
↻ **Outline**
△ **Pose Questions**

LESSON 6
- asteroid belt • Kuiper belt
- Oort cloud • comet
- coma • nucleus • asteroid
- meteoroid • meteor • meteorite
↻ **Summarize**
△ **Classify**

Life on Mars

Human space travelers have ventured into low Earth orbit and to the moon. Mars will probably be the first planet (other than Earth) that people visit. The conditions on Mars are very different from those on Earth. Scientists and engineers continue to work on new technology to help people live and work in such a harsh environment.

In this activity, you will build a model of a base that would allow humans to live on Mars. You will also build a model of a tool that would be used for experiments on Mars.

Identify the Problem

1. You are a space engineer. You want to model a base in which people could live and work on Mars. You also want to model a tool that could help Mars explorers retrieve rock samples. What problem(s) will your designs help solve?

_____

_____

_____

_____

Do Research

Examine photos of the surface of Mars. Study the data sheet that compares conditions on Mars and on Earth. Your teacher will provide these materials.

2. What are the features of Earth that support human life? _____

_____

_____

3. How well suited is the Mars surface for humans? Explain. _____

_____

_____

Go to the materials station(s). Examine the materials. Think about how each one may or may not be useful for your Mars base and tool models. Leave the materials where they are.

4. What are your design constraints? _____

_____

_____

Develop Possible Solutions

5. Describe ways in which you could use the materials to build a model Mars base. Identify at least two problems that your base will address. Also identify materials that you could use to make a tool with which Mars scientists could collect small rock samples. Remember that when scientists are using the tool, they will be wearing heavy gloves that prohibit small motions.

_____

_____

_____

_____

Choose One Solution

6. List the material(s) you will use for your models.

Base: _____

_____

Tool: _____

_____

7. Draw your designs on a separate sheet of paper. Label all the parts.

8. On a separate sheet of paper, describe how you will build your models. For the base, include the scale. A sample scale might be: one centimeter on your model would be equal to 1 meter on an actual Mars base (1 cm: 1 m).

Design and Construct a Prototype

Have your teacher review and approve your designs. Then, gather the materials you need to build your Mars base model and working tool. Build a prototype of each, the first version of your designs. If you can, document your construction process by taking photos or recording video as you go. Be sure to wear goggles as you build and test the tool.

☑ **9.** Measure the dimensions of your finished prototypes. Include the scale of your base, and note the placement of your base features. Record the design details of your base and tool prototypes on a separate sheet of paper.

☑ **10.** Draw a detailed diagram of your base on graph paper. Explain the scale of your prototype. Number and label the features of your base.

☑ **11.** Prepare a numbered index card for each feature of your base that you labeled. Name and describe the features of your base on the cards. Be prepared to demonstrate the use of your tool.

Test the Prototype

☑ **12.** In the table, identify the problems and solutions addressed by your base prototype.

Base Problem	Does your prototype solve this problem?	For your *yes* answers, describe your solution.
Air		
Water		
Food		
Temperature		
Shelter		
Gravity		
Solar Radiation		
Other:		

☑ **13.** Test your tool. Does it pick up a small rock? Can you release the rock into a container? Record the results of your tests below.

_____

Communicate Results

☑ **14.** Collect the materials that document the design, construction, and testing of your prototype. Assemble a portfolio that includes your diagrams, your photographs or video of the process, your scale drawing, and a record of your tool test results.

☑ **15.** Display your portfolios, prototypes, and cards for classmates.

Evaluate and Redesign

16. Summarize how your prototypes of the base and tool worked. Explain what they do well and how they could be improved. Also explain how they met the design constraints.

_____

_____

_____

_____

_____

17. Compare your results with those of your classmates. Did your prototypes address similar problems and solutions? Explain.

_____

_____

_____

_____

Models of the Solar System

UNLOCK THE BIG Q?

🔑 **What Was the Geocentric Model?**

🔑 **How Did the Heliocentric Model Develop?**

my planet diary

CAREER

Picturing the Solar System

When Walter Myers was seven years old, he found a book with drawings of astronauts walking on the moons of Saturn. Ever since, he's been making space pictures himself. At first, he used pencil. Today, he works on computers. He likes using computers because he can create images that are more like photographs, such as the ones below.

As an artist, Mr. Myers can show scenes that haven't been photographed, such as ideas for future spacecraft and the views from another planet's moons. Mr. Myers especially likes creating views of what human visitors to other planets might see. His work has appeared in books, magazines, Web sites, and even on television!

Use what you have read to answer these questions.

1. What tool does Walter Myers use?

_____

2. Why do people use art or other models to show objects in the solar system?

_____
_____
_____
_____

Labzone® Do the Inquiry Warm-Up *What Is at the Center?*

Vocabulary
- geocentric
- heliocentric
- ellipse

Skills
⟳ Reading: Sequence
△ Inquiry: Make Models

What Was the Geocentric Model?

From here on Earth, it seems as if our planet is stationary and that the sun, moon, and stars are moving around Earth. But is the sky really moving above you? Centuries ago, before there were space shuttles or even telescopes, people had no easy way to find out.

Ancient Observations Ancient observers, including the Greeks, Chinese, and Mayans, noticed that the patterns of the stars didn't change over time. Although the stars seemed to move, they stayed in the same position relative to one another. These people also observed planets, which moved among the stars.

Many early observers thought Earth was at the center of the universe. Some Chinese observers thought Earth was under a dome of stars. Many Greek astronomers thought that Earth was inside rotating spheres nested inside each other. These spheres contained the stars and planets. Since *ge* is the Greek word for "Earth," an Earth-centered model is known as a **geocentric** (jee oh SEN trik) model. ⟸ **In a geocentric model, Earth is at the center of the revolving planets and stars.**

Ptolemy's Model About A.D. 140, the Greek astronomer Ptolemy (TAHL uh mee) further developed the geocentric model. Like the earlier Greeks, Ptolemy thought that Earth was at the center of the universe. In Ptolemy's model, however, the planets moved in small circles carried along in bigger circles.

Ptolemy's geocentric model explained the motions observed in the sky fairly accurately. As a result, the geocentric model of the universe was widely accepted for nearly 1,500 years after Ptolemy.

apply it!

Critique Scientific Explanations and Models Describe an experience from everyday life that appears to support the geocentric model.

_____

_____

_____

_____

_____

_____

_____

Lab zone ® Do the Quick Lab *Going Around in Circles.*

⟸ **Assess Your Understanding**

got it? ....

○ I get it! Now I know that the geocentric model is _____

_____

○ I need extra help with _____

_____

How Did the Heliocentric Model Develop?

Not everybody believed in the geocentric system. An ancient Greek scientist named Aristarchus developed a sun-centered model called a heliocentric (hee lee oh SEN trik) system. *Helios* is Greek for "sun." In a **heliocentric** system, Earth and the other planets revolve around the sun. This model was not well received in ancient times, however, because people could not accept that Earth was not at the center of the universe.

FIGURE 1 ······

Changing Models

△ **Make Models** Draw each model of the solar system. Include the sun, Earth, the moon, and Jupiter. Include Jupiter's moons in Galileo's model.

CHALLENGE Why might people not have believed Galileo's discoveries?

_____

_____

1500   ⬤ **1550**

The Copernican Revolution

The Polish astronomer Nicolaus Copernicus further developed the heliocentric model. 🔑 **Copernicus was able to work out the arrangement of the known planets and how they move around the sun.** He published his work in 1543. Copernicus's theory would eventually revolutionize the science of astronomy. But at first many people were unwilling to accept his theory. They needed more evidence to be convinced.

🖉 **Draw Copernicus's model.**

↻ **Sequence** Which astronomer did his work first?

⬤ Tycho Brahe

⬤ Nicolaus Copernicus

⬤ Galileo Galilei

⬤ Johannes Kepler

Brahe and Kepler

Ptolemy and Copernicus both assumed that planets moved in perfect circles. Their models fit existing observations fairly well. But in the late 1500s, the Dutch astronomer Tycho Brahe (TEE koh BRAH uh) made much more accurate observations. Brahe's assistant, Johannes Kepler, used the observations to figure out the shape of the planets' orbits. When he used circular orbits, his calculations did not fit the observations. **After years of detailed calculations, Kepler found that the orbit of each planet is an ellipse.** An **ellipse** is an oval shape.

Tycho Brahe's Observatory

1600

1650

✏ **Draw Kepler's model.**

Galileo's Evidence

In the 1500s and early 1600s, most people still believed in the geocentric model. **However, evidence collected by the Italian scientist Galileo Galilei gradually convinced others that the heliocentric model was correct.** In 1610, Galileo used a telescope to discover four moons around Jupiter. These moons proved that not everything in the sky revolves around Earth. Galileo also discovered that Venus goes through a series of phases similar to the moon's. But Venus would not have a full set of phases if both it and the sun circled around Earth. Therefore, Galileo reasoned, the geocentric model must be incorrect.

✏ **Draw Galileo's model.**

Lab
zone® Do the Quick Lab
A Loopy Ellipse.

🔑 Assess Your Understanding

1a. Review (Kepler/Copernicus) discovered that planets move in ellipses.

b. Relate Evidence and Explanation What discoveries by Galileo support the heliocentric model?

_____

_____

_____

got it?

⭕ **I get it!** Now I know that the heliocentric

model was developed _____

_____

_____

⭕ **I need extra help with** _____

_____

_____

523

UNLOCK THE BIG ?

🔑 **What Makes Up the Solar System?**

🔑 **How Did the Solar System Form?**

my planet diary

Extreme Conditions

Imagine a place where the sun shines 11 times brighter than it does on Earth. How could you keep anything cool there? Engineers had to solve just that problem when designing the Mercury *MESSENGER* spacecraft. In 2008, this spacecraft began to visit Mercury, where temperatures can reach up to 370°C. Engineers designed a sunshade to protect *MESSENGER*'s instruments. It's made from ceramic fabric! The fabric, made of elements such as silicon, aluminum, and boron, is resistant to heat. It reflects most of the sun's heat away from the *MESSENGER* spacecraft, keeping all the instruments at a comfortable room temperature (about 20°C).

TECHNOLOGY

Use what you have read to answer the questions below.

1. Why did engineers need to design a sunshade for Mercury *MESSENGER*?

_____

_____

_____

2. What other challenges do you think there would be for engineers designing a spacecraft to travel to Mercury?

_____

_____

_____

 Lab zone® Do the Inquiry Warm-Up *How Big Is Earth?*

Vocabulary

- solar system • astronomical unit
- planet • dwarf planet
- planetesimal

Skills

↻ Reading: Identify Supporting Evidence

△ Inquiry: Calculate

What Makes Up the Solar System?

Mercury is just one of many objects that make up the solar system. 🔑 **Our solar system consists of the sun, the planets, their moons, and a variety of smaller objects.** The sun is at the center of the solar system, with other objects orbiting around it. The force of gravity holds the solar system together. Earth's solar system is part of the Milky Way galaxy. There are many other galaxies in the universe.

Distances in the Solar System Distances within the solar system are so large that they cannot be easily measured in meters or kilometers. Instead, scientists often use a unit called the astronomical unit. One **astronomical unit** (AU) equals the average distance between Earth and the sun, about 150,000,000 kilometers. The solar system extends more than 100,000 AU from the sun.

do the math!

Converting Units

To convert from astronomical units (AU) to kilometers (km), you can multiply the number of AU by 150,000,000.

1 △ **Calculate** Mars is 1.52 AU from the sun. About how many kilometers is Mars from the sun? _____

2 **Apply Concepts** If you know an object's distance from the sun in kilometers, how can you find its distance in AU? _____

_____

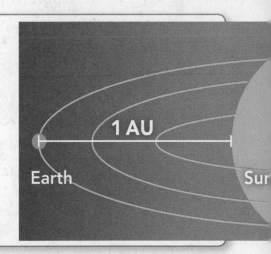

The Sun At the center of our solar system is the sun. The sun is much larger than anything else in the solar system. About 99.85 percent of the mass of the solar system is contained within the sun. Despite being more than a million times the volume of Earth, our sun is actually a very ordinary mid-sized star. Using telescopes, we see stars that have volumes a thousand times greater than the sun's! This turns out to be a very good thing for us. Large stars burn out and die quickly, but our sun will last for five billion more years.

↻ **Identify Supporting Evidence** Underline a sentence that supports the statement, "The sun is much larger than anything else in the solar system."

FIGURE 1 ···

The Solar System

The planets' sizes are shown to scale, but their distances from the sun are not.

✎ **Mark the position of each planet on the distance scale above.**

1. **Interpret Data** Where is the largest gap between planets?

_____

2. **CHALLENGE** Could you show the planets' relative sizes and distances from the sun in the same diagram on one page? Why or why not?

_____

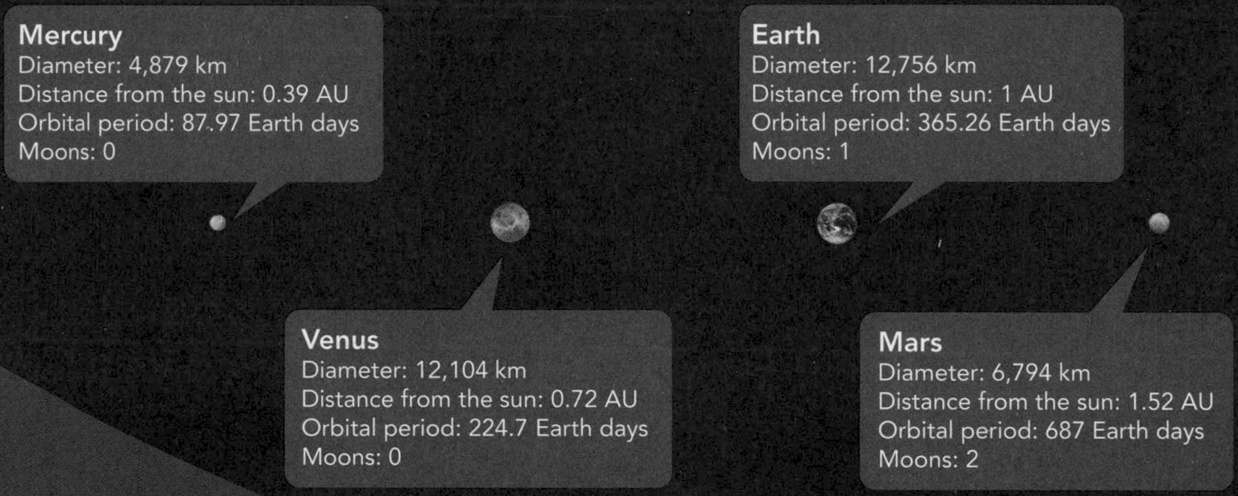

Mercury
Diameter: 4,879 km
Distance from the sun: 0.39 AU
Orbital period: 87.97 Earth days
Moons: 0

Earth
Diameter: 12,756 km
Distance from the sun: 1 AU
Orbital period: 365.26 Earth days
Moons: 1

Venus
Diameter: 12,104 km
Distance from the sun: 0.72 AU
Orbital period: 224.7 Earth days
Moons: 0

Mars
Diameter: 6,794 km
Distance from the sun: 1.52 AU
Orbital period: 687 Earth days
Moons: 2

Planets

There are many different objects in the solar system. How do you decide what is a planet and what isn't? In 2006, astronomers decided that a planet must be round, orbit the sun, and have cleared out the region of the solar system along its orbit. The first four planets are small and are mostly made of rock and metal. The last four planets are very large and are mostly made of gas and liquid. Like Earth, each planet has a "day" and a "year." Its day is the time it takes to rotate on its axis. Its year is the time it takes to orbit the sun. **Figure 1** shows some basic facts about the planets.

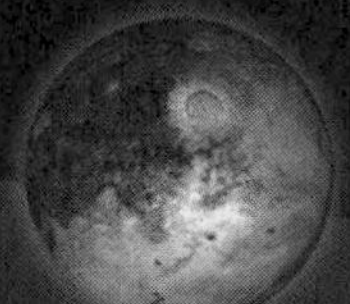

Dwarf Planets

For many years, Pluto was considered the ninth planet in the solar system. But Pluto shares the area of its orbit with other objects. Pluto is now considered a dwarf planet. A dwarf planet is an object that orbits the sun and has enough gravity to be spherical, but has not cleared the area of its orbit. There are five known dwarf planets in our solar system: Pluto, Eris, Ceres, Makemake (MAH keh MAH keh), and Haumea (how MAY uh). As scientists observe more distant objects, the number of dwarf planets might grow.

Satellites

Except for Mercury and Venus, every planet in the solar system has at least one natural satellite, or moon. Earth has the fewest moons, with just one. Jupiter and Saturn each have more than 60! Some dwarf planets also have satellites.

Smaller Objects

The solar system also includes many smaller objects that orbit the sun. Some, called asteroids, are small, mostly rocky bodies. Many asteroids are found in an area between the orbits of Mars and Jupiter. Comets are another large group of solar system objects. Comets are loose balls of ice and rock that usually have very long, narrow orbits.

Saturn
Diameter: 120,536 km
Distance from the sun: 9.54 AU
Orbital period: 29.47 Earth years
Moons: 60+

Neptune
Diameter: 49,258 km
Distance from the sun: 30.07 AU
Orbital period: 163.72 Earth years
Moons: 14+

Uranus
Diameter: 51,118 km
Distance from the sun: 19.19 AU
Orbital period: 83.75 Earth years
Moons: 20+

Jupiter
Diameter: 142,984 km
Distance from the sun: 5.20 AU
Orbital period: 11.86 Earth years
Moons: 60+

Lab ® Do the Lab Investigation
zone *Speeding Around the Sun.*

⌨ Assess Your Understanding

1a. Sequence List the planets in order of increasing distance from the sun.

_____

_____

_____

b. Make Generalizations What is the relationship between a planet's distance from the sun and the length of its year?

_____

_____

got it?

O **I get it!** Now I know that the solar system includes _____

_____

_____

O **I need extra help with** _____

_____

_____

527

How Did the Solar System Form?

Where did the objects in the solar system come from? 🔲 **Scientists think the solar system formed about 4.6 billion years ago from a cloud of hydrogen, helium, rock, ice, and other materials pulled together by gravity.**

A Spinning Disk The process began as gravity pulled the cloud's material together. The cloud collapsed and started to rotate, forming a disk. Most of the material was pulled to the center. As this material became tightly packed, it got hotter and the pressure on it increased.

Eventually, the temperature and pressure became so high that hydrogen atoms were pressed together to form helium. This process, called nuclear fusion, releases large amounts of energy. Once nuclear fusion began, the sun gave off light and became a stable star. Sunlight is one form of the energy produced by fusion.

The Planets Form Away from the sun, planets began to form as gravity pulled rock, ice, and gas together. The rock and ice formed small bodies called **planetesimals** (pla nuh TE suh muhlz). Over time, planetesimals collided and stuck together, eventually combining to form all the other objects in the solar system.

Inner Planets Close to the sun, the solar system was very hot. Most water evaporated, preventing ice from forming. The bodies that formed in this region were comparatively low in mass. Their gravity was too weak to hold on to light gases such as hydrogen and helium. This is why the inner planets are small and rocky.

Outer Planets At greater distances from the sun, temperatures were cooler. Ice formed, adding mass to the planets that formed at these distances. As the planets grew, their gravity was strong enough to hold hydrogen and helium, forming the gas giant planets. Beyond the gas giants, temperatures were even lower. Ice and other materials produced comets and dwarf planets.

FIGURE 2 ···

Formation of the Solar System

✏️ **Sequence** Write the numbers 1 through 4 in the circles to put the images in order.

EXPLORE THE BIG ?

Solve THE SOLAR SYSTEM

Why are objects in the solar system different from each other?

FIGURE 3 ....
Use the clues to complete the puzzle.
Then answer the question.

ACROSS

3 The planet farthest from the sun
4 A loose, icy body with a long, narrow orbit
6 A gas giant planet that is smaller than Jupiter but larger than Neptune
7 The smallest planet in the solar system
8 An object that orbits a planet

DOWN

1 The largest planet in the solar system
2 A planet that formed closer to the sun than Earth but not closest to the sun
5 A small rocky body that orbits the sun

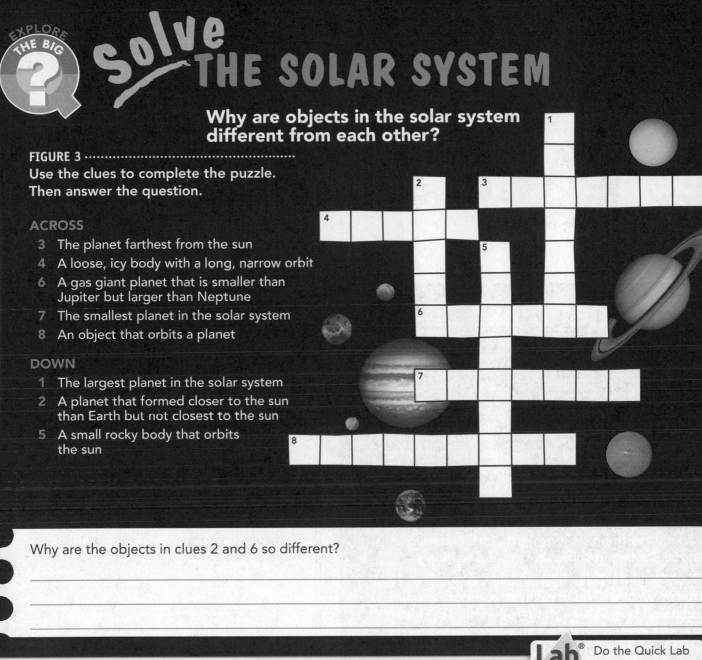

Why are the objects in clues 2 and 6 so different?

_____

_____

_____

 **Lab zone®** Do the Quick Lab *Clumping Planets.*

🔑 Assess Your Understanding

2a. Explain What force formed the solar system?

_____

b. ANSWER THE BIG ? Why are objects in the solar system different from each other?

_____

_____

_____

_____

got it?

○ I get it! Now I know that the solar system formed when _____

_____

_____

○ I need extra help with _____

_____

_____

_____

529

The Sun

UNLOCK THE BIG

🔑 **What Is the Structure of the Sun?**

🔑 **What Features Can You See on the Sun?**

MY PLANET DiARY

DISASTER

Left in the Dark

On March 13, 1989, a flood of electric particles from the sun reached Earth, causing a magnetic storm. Bright streamers of color filled the sky as far south as Jamaica. But in Quebec, Canada, the storm brought problems. At 2:45 A.M., the entire electric power system collapsed. People woke up with no heat or light. Traffic snarled as traffic lights and subways stopped working.

How could particles from the sun take out a power system? The magnetic storm caused an electrical surge through the power lines. Electric stations couldn't handle the extra electricity, and they blew out, taking the power system with them.

✏️ **Communicate** Discuss the Quebec blackout with a partner. Then answer the questions below.

1. What caused the Quebec blackout of 1989?

_____

_____

2. How would your life be affected if a magnetic storm shut down electricity in your area?

_____

_____

_____

Lab zone® Do the Inquiry Warm-Up *How Can You Safely Observe the Sun?*

Vocabulary
- core • nuclear fusion • radiation zone
- convection zone • photosphere • chromosphere
- corona • solar wind • sunspot • prominence
- solar flare

Skills
↻ Reading: Relate Cause and Effect
△ Inquiry: Interpret Data

What Is the Structure of the Sun?

Unlike Earth, the sun has no solid surface. About three fourths of the sun's mass is hydrogen, and about one fourth is helium. There are tiny amounts of other elements. ⌐ **The sun has an interior and an atmosphere. The interior includes the core, the radiation zone, and the convection zone. Figure 1** shows the sun's interior.

FIGURE 1 ···
Layers of the Sun
The diagram shows the layers of the sun's interior.

✎ **Apply Concepts** Draw arrows to show energy as it passes from the sun's core through the radiation and convection zones. Underline clues in the text that help you determine the path.

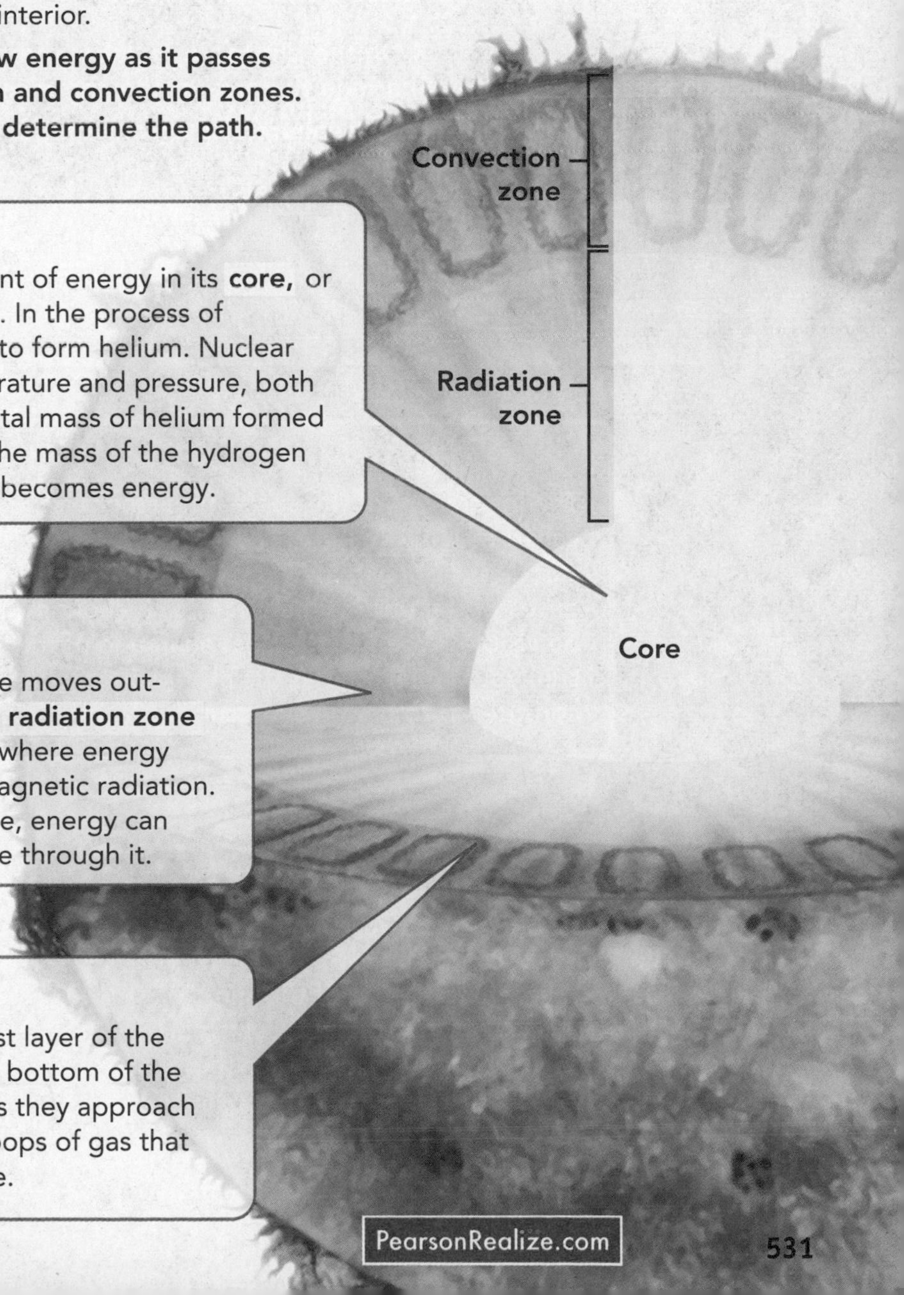

The Core

The sun produces an enormous amount of energy in its **core,** or central region, through nuclear fusion. In the process of **nuclear fusion,** hydrogen atoms join to form helium. Nuclear fusion requires extremely high temperature and pressure, both of which are found in the core. The total mass of helium formed by nuclear fusion is slightly less than the mass of the hydrogen that goes into it. The remaining mass becomes energy.

Convection zone

Radiation zone

Core

The Radiation Zone

The energy produced in the sun's core moves outward through the radiation zone. The **radiation zone** is a region of very tightly packed gas where energy moves mainly in the form of electromagnetic radiation. Because the radiation zone is so dense, energy can take more than 100,000 years to move through it.

The Convection Zone

The **convection zone** is the outermost layer of the sun's interior. Hot gases rise from the bottom of the convection zone and gradually cool as they approach the top. Cooler gases sink, forming loops of gas that move energy toward the sun's surface.

Vocabulary Greek Word Origins
The Greek word *photos* means
"light." What does *photosphere*
mean?

_____

_____

The Sun's Atmosphere The sun has an atmosphere
that stretches far into space, as you can see in Figure 2. The
layers of the atmosphere become less dense the farther they are
from the radiation zone. Like the sun's interior, the atmosphere
is primarily composed of hydrogen and helium. ⊙ The sun's
atmosphere includes the photosphere, the chromosphere, and
the corona. Each layer has unique properties.

FIGURE 2

The Sun's Atmosphere

This image is a combination of two photographs of the
sun. One shows the sun's surface and was taken through a
special filter that shows the sun's features. The other
shows the corona and was taken during an eclipse.

✎ **Relate Text and Visuals** On the photograph, label the
photosphere and corona. Shade in the area of the chromosphere.
CHALLENGE Why can the chromosphere and corona only be seen
from Earth during an eclipse?

_____

_____

_____

The Photosphere

The inner layer of the sun's atmosphere is
called the **photosphere** (FOH tuh sfeer). The
sun does not have a solid surface, but the
gases of the photosphere are thick enough to
be visible. When you look at an image of the
sun, you are looking at the photosphere. It is
considered to be the sun's surface layer.

The Chromosphere

At the start and end of a total eclipse, a reddish
glow is visible just around the photosphere. This
glow comes from the middle layer of the sun's
atmosphere, the **chromosphere** (KROH muh sfeer).
The Greek word *chroma* means "color," so the
chromosphere is the "color sphere."

do the math! Analyzing Data

Solar Temperature
Use the table to answer the questions.

Layer	Temperature (°C)
Core	About 15,000,000
Radiation and Convection Zones	About 4,000,000
Photosphere	About 6,000
Inner Chromosphere	About 4,300
Outer Chromosphere	About 8,300
Corona	About 1,000,000

1 ⚠ **Interpret Data** Which layer is hottest?

_____

2 Compare and Contrast How does the temperature change in the sun's atmosphere differ from the temperature change in the sun's interior?

_____

_____

The Corona
During a total solar eclipse, an even fainter layer of the sun becomes visible, as you can see in **Figure 2**. This outer layer, which looks like a white halo around the sun, is called the **corona**, which means "crown" in Latin. The corona extends into space for millions of kilometers. It gradually thins into streams of electrically charged particles called the **solar wind.**

[_____]

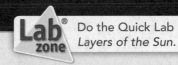
Do the Quick Lab
Layers of the Sun.

🔑 Assess Your Understanding

1a. List List the layers of the sun's interior and atmosphere, starting from the center.

_____

_____

_____

b. Compare and Contrast What is one key difference between the radiation and convection zones?

_____

_____

_____

_____

got it? ....

○ **I get it!** Now I know that the sun's structure includes _____

_____

○ **I need extra help with** _____

_____

_____

_____

What Features Can You See on the Sun?

For hundreds of years, scientists have used special telescopes to study the sun. They have spotted a variety of features on the sun's surface. 🔑 **Features on or just above the sun's surface include sunspots, prominences, and solar flares.**

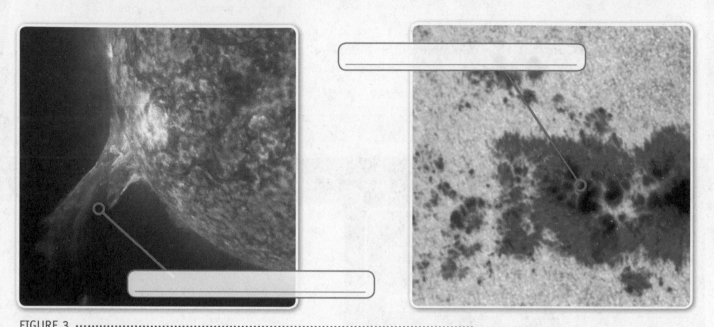

FIGURE 3

Sunspots and Prominences

Sunspots look dark in regular photographs. Some photos of the sun are taken with special filters that show the sun's structure. Sunspots may appear white in these photos. Sunspots are visible in both of the photos above. ✏️ **Classify Label a prominence and a sunspot in the photos.**

🔁 **Relate Cause and Effect**
When prominences join, they cause (sunspots/solar flares).

Sunspots Photographs show dark areas on the sun's surface. These **sunspots** are areas of gas on the sun's surface that are cooler than the gases around them. Cooler gases don't give off as much light as hotter gases, which is why sunspots look dark. Sunspots look small, but in fact they can be larger than Earth. The number of sunspots varies in a regular cycle, with the most sunspots appearing about once every 11 years.

Prominences Sunspots usually occur in groups. Huge loops of gas called **prominences** often link different parts of sunspot regions. You can compare sunspots and prominences in **Figure 3**.

Solar Flares Sometimes the loops in sunspot regions suddenly connect, releasing large amounts of magnetic energy. The energy heats gas on the sun to millions of degrees Celsius, causing the gas to erupt into space. These eruptions are called **solar flares.**

Solar Wind The solar wind is made up of electrical particles from the sun. Solar flares can greatly increase the solar wind, which means that more particles reach Earth's upper atmosphere. Earth's atmosphere and magnetic field normally block these particles. But near the North and South poles, the particles can enter Earth's atmosphere. There, they create powerful electric currents that cause gas molecules in the atmosphere to glow. These particles cause auroras near the poles. They can also cause magnetic storms like the one that caused the blackout in Quebec in 1989. **Figure 4** shows how the solar wind interacts with Earth's magnetic field.

FIGURE 4 ·······························

Solar Wind

Particles from the solar wind spread through the solar system. When they reach Earth, they interact with Earth's magnetic field. (Note: The diagram is not to scale.)

✎ **Make Generalizations** The corona is the least dense layer of the sun's atmosphere. How do you think the density of the solar wind compares to the density of the corona?

_____

_____

_____

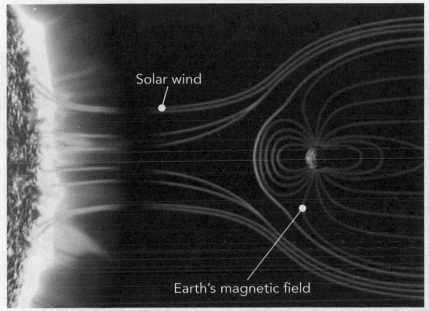

Solar wind

Earth's magnetic field

Do the Quick Lab
Viewing Sunspots.

🔑 **Assess Your Understanding**

2a. Define (Prominences/sunspots) are loops of gas that extend from the sun's surface.

b. Explain Why do sunspots look darker than the rest of the sun's photosphere?

_____

_____

_____

c. 🔄 **Relate Cause and Effect** How is the solar wind related to magnetic storms on Earth?

_____

_____

_____

_____

got it? ···

○ **I get it!** Now I know that features on the sun include _____

_____

○ **I need extra help with** _____

_____

The Inner Planets

UNLOCK THE BIG ?

🔑 **What Do the Inner Planets Have in Common?**

🔑 **What Are the Characteristics of the Inner Planets?**

my planet diary

What's in a Name?

Where in the solar system could you find Lewis and Clark's guide Sacagawea, artist Frida Kahlo, writer Helen Keller, and abolitionist Sojourner Truth all in the same place? On Venus! In fact, almost every feature on Venus is named for a real, fictional, or mythological woman.

In general, the person or people who discover an object or feature in the solar system get to choose its name. But scientists have agreed on some guidelines. Features on Mercury are named for authors, artists, and musicians. Many craters on Mars are named for towns on Earth. And most of the craters on Earth's moon are named for astronomers, physicists, and mathematicians.

FUN FACT

After you read the information to the left, answer the questions below.

1. Who decides what to name a newly discovered feature in the solar system?

_____

_____

2. If you discovered a new planet, how would you decide what to name its features?

_____

_____

_____

Lab zone® Do the Inquiry Warm-Up *Ring Around the Sun.*

Vocabulary
- terrestrial planet
- greenhouse effect

Skills
- Reading: Compare and Contrast
- Inquiry: Communicate

What Do the Inner Planets Have in Common?

Earth, Mercury, Venus, and Mars are more like each other than they are like the outer planets. **The inner planets are small and dense and have rocky surfaces.** The inner planets are often called the **terrestrial planets,** from the Latin word *terra,* which means "Earth." **Figure 1** summarizes data about the inner planets.

The terrestrial planets all have relatively high densities. They are rich in rocky and metallic materials, including iron and silicon. Each has a solid surface. All except Mercury have atmospheres.

FIGURE 1 ·····················

The Inner Planets

Interpret Data Use the table to answer the questions below.

1. Which planet is largest?

_____

2. Which planet has the most moons?

_____

3. Which planet is most similar to Earth in size?

_____

Planet	 Mercury	 Venus	 Earth	 Mars
Diameter (km)	4,879	12,104	12,756	6,794
Period of rotation (Earth days)	58.9	244	1.0	1.03
Average distance from sun (AU)	0.39	0.72	1.0	1.52
Period of revolution (Earth days)	88	224.7	365.2	687
Number of moons	0	0	1	2

Note: Planets are not shown to scale.

Lab zone® Do the Quick Lab *Characteristics of the Inner Planets.*

Assess Your Understanding

got it? ·····················

○ I get it! Now I know that the inner planets are _____

_____

○ I need extra help with _____

_____

What Are the Characteristics of the Inner Planets?

Though the four inner planets have many features in common, they differ in size and composition as well as distance from the sun.

Mercury Would you like to visit a place where the temperature can range from 430°C to below −170°C? ⚷ **Mercury is the smallest terrestrial planet and the planet closest to the sun.** Mercury is not much larger than Earth's moon. The interior of Mercury is probably made up mainly of the dense metal iron.

Mercury's Surface As you can see in **Figure 2,** Mercury has flat plains and craters on its surface. Most of these craters formed early in the history of the solar system. Since Mercury has no water and not much atmosphere, the craters have not worn away over time.

Mercury's Atmosphere Mercury has virtually no atmosphere. Because Mercury's mass is small, its gravity is weak. Gas particles can easily escape into space. However, astronomers have detected small amounts of sodium and other gases around Mercury.

During the day, the side of Mercury facing the sun can reach temperatures of 430°C. Because there is so little atmosphere, the planet's heat escapes at night. Then the temperature drops below −170°C.

Exploring Mercury Much of what astronomers know about Mercury has come from space probes. *Mariner 10* flew by Mercury three times in 1974 and 1975. *Mercury MESSENGER* has passed Mercury several times, and will begin orbiting Mercury in 2011.

Size of Mercury compared to Earth

I'm visiting the planets! As you read this lesson and the next one, keep track of how far I've traveled.

TOTAL AU:

SOL & TOURS

INTERPLANETARY FREQUENT TRAVELER REWARDS PROGRAM

SPF 1000000

FIGURE 2 ···

Mercury

The photo shows Mercury's cratered surface.

✎ **Answer the questions below.**

1. **Solve Problems** List three things a visitor to Mercury would need to bring.

   _____

   _____

   _____

2. **CHALLENGE** Refer to **Figure 1.** How many Mercury days are there in a Mercury year?

   _____

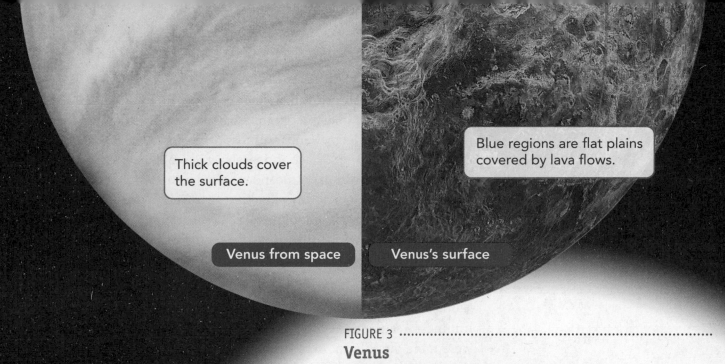

Thick clouds cover the surface.

Blue regions are flat plains covered by lava flows.

Venus from space

Venus's surface

FIGURE 3 ··
Venus
This figure combines images of Venus taken from space with a camera (left) and radar (right). Radar is able to penetrate Venus's thick clouds to reveal the surface. The colors in both images are altered to show more details.

✎ **Infer** Why do scientists need to use radar to study Venus's surface?

_____

_____

Size of Venus compared to Earth

Venus Venus is so similar in size and mass to Earth that it is sometimes called "Earth's twin." Venus's density and internal structure are similar to Earth's. But in other ways Venus and Earth are very different. 🔑 **Venus has a thick atmosphere, an unusual pattern of rotation, and the hottest surface of any planet.**

Venus's Atmosphere Venus's atmosphere is so thick that it is always cloudy. As you can see in **Figure 3,** astronomers can see only a smooth cloud cover over Venus. The thick clouds are made mostly of droplets of sulfuric acid.

At Venus's surface, you would quickly be crushed by the weight of its atmosphere. The pressure of Venus's atmosphere is 90 times greater than the pressure of Earth's atmosphere. You couldn't breathe on Venus because its atmosphere is mostly carbon dioxide.

Venus's Rotation Venus takes about 7.5 Earth months to revolve around the sun. It takes about 8 months for Venus to rotate once on its axis. Thus, Venus rotates so slowly that its day is longer than its year! Oddly, Venus rotates from east to west, the opposite direction from most other planets and moons. Astronomers hypothesize that this unusual rotation was caused by a very large object that struck Venus billions of years ago. Such a collision could have caused the planet to change its direction of rotation. Another hypothesis is that Venus's thick atmosphere could have somehow altered its rotation.

A Hot Planet Because Venus is closer to the sun than Earth is, it receives more solar energy than Earth does. Much of this radiation is reflected by Venus's atmosphere. However, some radiation reaches the surface and is later given off as heat. The carbon dioxide in Venus's atmosphere traps heat so well that Venus has the hottest surface of any planet. At 460°C, its average surface temperature is hot enough to melt lead. This trapping of heat by the atmosphere is called the **greenhouse effect. Figure 4** shows how the greenhouse effect occurs.

Exploring Venus The first probe to land on Venus's surface and send back data, *Venera 7*, landed in 1970. It survived for only a few minutes because of the high temperature and pressure. Later probes were more durable and sent images and data back to Earth.

The *Magellan* probe reached Venus in 1990, carrying radar instruments. Radar works through clouds, so *Magellan* was able to map nearly the entire surface. The *Magellan* data confirmed that Venus is covered with rock. Venus's surface has more than 10,000 volcanoes. Lava flows from these volcanoes have formed plains.

More recent probes have included *Venus Express,* from the European Space Agency, as well as brief visits by space probes headed for other planets. Images from *Venus Express* have helped scientists understand how Venus's clouds form and change.

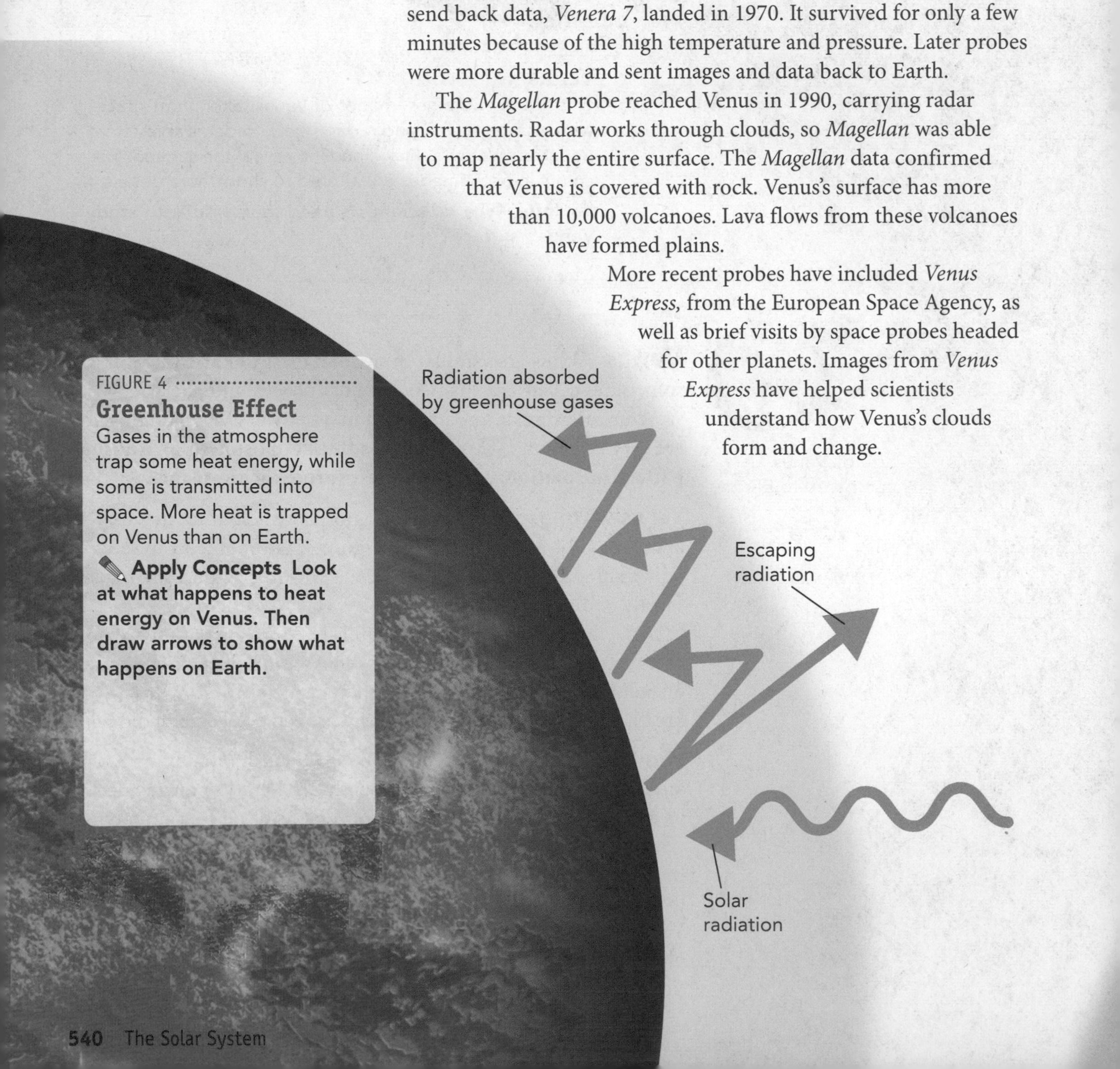

FIGURE 4 ·······························
Greenhouse Effect
Gases in the atmosphere trap some heat energy, while some is transmitted into space. More heat is trapped on Venus than on Earth.

✎ **Apply Concepts** Look at what happens to heat energy on Venus. Then draw arrows to show what happens on Earth.

Radiation absorbed by greenhouse gases

Escaping radiation

Solar radiation

Earth

There's only one planet in the solar system where you could live easily: Earth. ⬤ **Earth has liquid water and a suitable temperature range and atmosphere for living things to survive.**

The Water Planet Earth is unique in our solar system in having liquid water on its surface. In fact, most of Earth's surface, about 70 percent, is covered with water.

Earth's Temperature Scientists sometimes speak of Earth as having "Goldilocks" conditions—in other words, Earth is "just right" for life as we know it. Earth is not too hot and not too cold. If Earth were a little closer to the sun, it would be so hot that liquid water would evaporate. If it were a little farther away and colder, water would always be solid ice.

Earth's Atmosphere Earth has enough gravity to hold on to most gases. These gases make up Earth's atmosphere. Earth is the only planet with an atmosphere that is rich in oxygen. Oxygen makes up about 20 percent of Earth's atmosphere. Nearly all the rest is nitrogen, with small amounts of other gases such as argon, carbon dioxide, and water vapor.

Like Venus, Earth experiences a greenhouse effect. Earth's atmosphere traps heat, though less heat than Venus's atmosphere does. Without the atmosphere, Earth would be much colder.

FIGURE 5 ·······························
Earth's Structure

Earth has three main layers—a crust, a mantle, and a core. The crust includes the solid, rocky surface. Under the crust is the mantle, a layer of hot rock. Earth has a dense core made mainly of iron and nickel.

✎ **Relate Text and Visuals** Label the layer of Earth with the highest density.

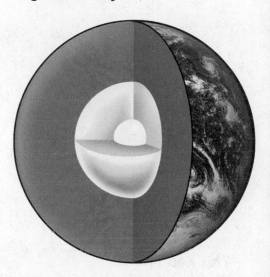

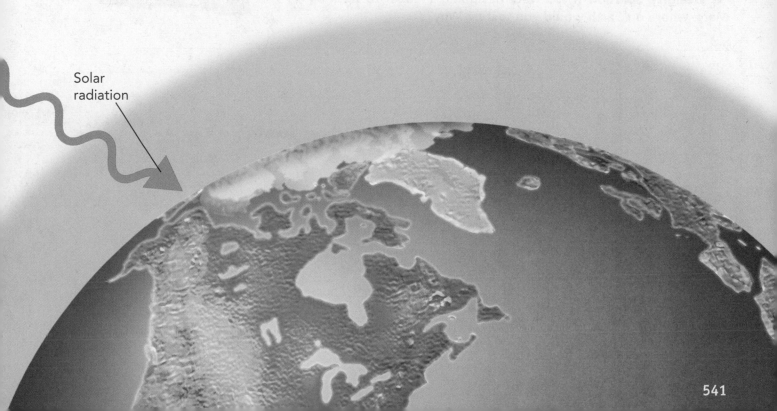

Solar radiation

541

Size of Mars
compared to Earth

Mars

Mars is called the "red planet." **Figure 6** shows why. This reddish color is due to the breakdown of iron-rich rocks, leaving a rusty dust behind. 🔑 **Though Mars is mostly too cold for liquid water, it does have water ice now and shows evidence of intermittent seasonal flowing water today as well as liquid water in the past.**

Mars's Atmosphere

The atmosphere of Mars is more than 95 percent carbon dioxide. You could walk around on Mars, but you would have to wear an airtight suit and carry your own oxygen. Mars has few clouds, and they are very thin compared to clouds on Earth. Temperatures on the surface range from $-140°C$ to $20°C$.

Water and Ice

Images of Mars taken from space show a variety of features that look as if they were made by ancient streams, lakes, or floods. Scientists think that more liquid water flowed on Mars's surface in the distant past. Scientists infer that Mars must have been much warmer and had a thicker atmosphere at that time.

Today, Mars's atmosphere is so thin that any liquid water would quickly turn into a gas. Some water is located in the planet's two polar ice caps, which are almost entirely made of frozen water. Observations from the *Mars Reconnaissance Orbiter* found evidence of flowing water in warmer areas today.

FIGURE 6 ···

The Red Planet

Remote-controlled landers such as *Phoenix*, *Spirit*, and *Opportunity* have sent back pictures of the surface of Mars.

✏️ **Design a Solution** If you were designing a lander to work on Mars, where on Earth would you test it? Why?

_____

_____

apply it!

Communicate Choose one of the inner planets other than Earth. Describe an alien that could live there. Include at least three features of your alien that make it well suited for the planet you chose. Draw your alien to the right.

_____

_____

_____

_____

_____

FIGURE 7 ·······································

Olympus Mons

This computer-generated image is based on data from the *Mars Global Surveyor* mission.

Volcanoes Some regions of Mars have giant volcanoes. There are signs that lava flowed from the volcanoes in the past, but the volcanoes are rarely active today. Olympus Mons, shown in **Figure 7,** is the largest volcano in the solar system. It is as large as Missouri and is nearly three times as tall as Mount Everest!

Mars's Moons Mars has two very small moons. Phobos, the larger moon, is about 22 kilometers across. Deimos is even smaller, about 13 kilometers across. Like Earth's moon, Phobos and Deimos are covered with craters.

Exploring Mars Many space probes have visited Mars, looking for signs of water and possible life. Rovers called *Spirit* and *Opportunity* found traces of salts and minerals that form in the presence of water. The *Phoenix* mission found frozen water near the north polar cap, and the *Mars Reconnaissance Orbiter* found evidence of flowing water in warmer areas. *Mars Express* has detected methane gas in Mars's atmosphere. This gas might be a clue that microscopic life forms exist on Mars, even today!

Lab zone ® Do the Quick Lab *Greenhouse Effect.*

Assess Your Understanding

1a. Name Which inner planet has the thickest

atmosphere? _____

b. Relate Cause and Effect Why is Venus hotter

than Mercury? _____

_____

got it?

○ **I get it!** Now I know that the inner planets

differ in _____

_____

○ **I need extra help with** _____

_____

The Outer Planets

UNLOCK
THE BIG

🔑 **What Do the Outer Planets Have in Common?**

🔑 **What Are the Characteristics of Each Outer Planet?**

MY PLANET DIARY

Predicting a Planet

In the 1840s, astronomers were puzzled.
Uranus didn't move as expected, based
on the theory of gravity. Astronomers John
Couch Adams and Urbain Leverrier
independently hypothesized that
Uranus was being affected by
another planet's gravity. They calculated where
this planet should be. Another astronomer,
Johann Galle, aimed his telescope at the place
Leverrier predicted. On September 23, 1846,
he discovered the new planet—Neptune.

DISCOVERY

✏️ **Communicate** Work with a partner to
answer the question.

What science skills did the astronomers use
when they discovered Neptune?

_____

_____

_____

_____

Lab zone Do the Inquiry Warm-Up
How Big Are the Planets?

What Do the Outer Planets Have in Common?

If you could visit the outer planets, you wouldn't have a solid place
to stand! 🔑 **The four outer planets are much larger and more
massive than Earth, and they do not have solid surfaces.** Because
these four planets are so large, they are often called **gas giants.**
Figure 1 summarizes some basic facts about the gas giants.

Composition Jupiter and Saturn are composed mainly of
hydrogen and helium. Uranus and Neptune contain some of these
gases, but also ices of ammonia and methane. Because they are so
massive, the gas giants exert a very strong gravitational force. This
gravity keeps gases from escaping, forming thick atmospheres.

Vocabulary
- gas giant
- ring

Skills
- Reading: Outline
- Inquiry: Pose Questions

Despite the name "gas giant," much of the material in these planets is actually liquid because the pressure inside the planets is so high. The outer layers are extremely cold because they are far from the sun. Temperatures increase greatly within the planets.

Moons and Rings

All the gas giants have many moons, ranging from 13 around Neptune to more than 60 around Jupiter! These moons vary from tiny balls of rock and ice barely a kilometer across to moons larger than Mercury. Some of these moons even have their own atmospheres!

In addition, each of the gas giants is surrounded by a set of rings. A **ring** is a thin disk of small particles of ice and rock. Saturn's rings are the largest and most complex.

As you visit each planet, don't forget to keep track of how many AU you've collected!

TOTAL AU:

SOL TOURS

INTERPLANETARY FREQUENT TRAVELER REWARDS PROGRAM

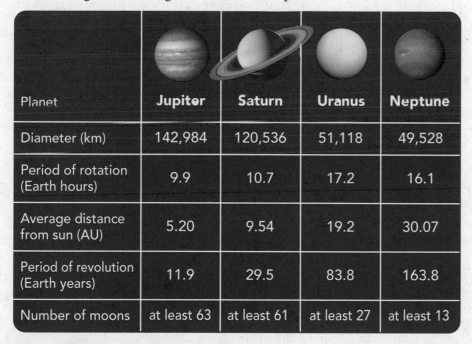

Planet	Jupiter	Saturn	Uranus	Neptune
Diameter (km)	142,984	120,536	51,118	49,528
Period of rotation (Earth hours)	9.9	10.7	17.2	16.1
Average distance from sun (AU)	5.20	9.54	19.2	30.07
Period of revolution (Earth years)	11.9	29.5	83.8	163.8
Number of moons	at least 63	at least 61	at least 27	at least 13

Note: Planets are not shown to scale.

FIGURE 1 ················

The Outer Planets
The table summarizes data about the outer planets.

✎ **Estimate** Earth's diameter is about 12,750 km. About how many times larger is Jupiter's diameter than Earth's?

_____

Lab zone® Do the Quick Lab *Density Mystery.*

🔑 Assess Your Understanding

got it? ···

○ **I get it!** Now I know that the gas giants all _____

_____

○ **I need extra help with** _____

_____

What Are the Characteristics of Each Outer Planet?

Since telescopes were first invented, scientists have studied the features of the outer planets and their moons. Today, space-based telescopes and space probes have revealed many details of these planets that are not visible from Earth. Because of engineering advances, such as space-based telescopes and space probes, scientists are constantly discovering new information about these planets and their moons. Engineering advances have led to important discoveries in the field of astronomy and space exploration and have helped to develop and expand the field of study.

Jupiter 🔑 **Jupiter is the largest and most massive planet.**
Jupiter's enormous mass dwarfs the other planets. In fact, its mass is about $2\frac{1}{2}$ times that of all the other planets combined!

Jupiter's Atmosphere Like all of the gas giants, Jupiter has a thick atmosphere made up mainly of hydrogen and helium. One notable feature of Jupiter's atmosphere is its Great Red Spot, a storm that is larger than Earth! The storm's swirling winds are similar to a hurricane, as you can see in **Figure 2.** Unlike hurricanes on Earth, however, the Great Red Spot shows no signs of going away.

Jupiter's Structure Astronomers think that Jupiter probably has a dense core of rock and iron at its center. A thick mantle of liquid hydrogen and helium surrounds this core. Because of the weight of Jupiter's atmosphere, the pressure at Jupiter's core is estimated to be about 30 million times greater than the pressure at Earth's surface.

Size of Jupiter compared to Earth

✏️ **Outline** As you read, make an outline about Jupiter.

I. Atmosphere

A. _____

_____

B. _____

_____

II. Structure

A. _____

_____

B. _____

_____

C. _____

_____

FIGURE 2 ·······································

The Great Red Spot
This storm is about 20,000 km long and 12,000 km wide. The largest tropical storm on Earth was 2,200 km across.

✏️ **Calculate** Think of the storm on Earth as a square and the Great Red Spot as a rectangle. How many Earth storms would fit inside the Great Red Spot?

_____

Jupiter's Moons The Italian astronomer Galileo Galilei discovered Jupiter's largest moons in 1610. These moons are shown in **Figure 3.** Since Galileo's time, astronomers have discovered dozens of additional moons orbiting Jupiter.

FIGURE 3 ·································

The Moons of Jupiter

Jupiter's four largest moons are larger than Earth's moon. Each has characteristics that set it apart from the others.

✎ **Relate Text and Visuals** Based on the photograph, match each description below to its moon.

❶ Ganymede is Jupiter's largest moon. It is larger than Mercury! Its surface is divided into dark and bright areas.

❷ Callisto is second to Ganymede in size, but has less ice. It has the most craters of any of Jupiter's moons.

❸ Io is not icy, unlike most of Jupiter's moons. It may have as many as 300 active volcanoes. The eruptions from those volcanoes constantly change the moon's surface.

❹ Europa is covered with ice. There may be liquid water below the ice—and if there's water, there might be life!

TOTAL AU:

SOL TOURS

INTERPLANETARY
FREQUENT TRAVELER
REWARDS PROGRAM

Titan This giant moon has a thick atmosphere.

TOTAL AU:

SOL 8 TOURS

INTERPLANETARY FREQUENT TRAVELER REWARDS PROGRAM

FIGURE 4 ···

The Saturn System

Recent space probes have shown details of Saturn and its moons.

✎ Answer the questions below.

1. **Make Judgments** Would it be easier to build a space colony on Saturn or on one of its moons? Why?

_____

_____

2. CHALLENGE Look at the photographs of Mimas and Tethys. What can you infer about the history of these moons?

_____

_____

Mimas A giant impact nearly broke Mimas apart, leaving the enormous crater shown here.

Iapetus This moon has light and dark areas.

✎ **Develop Hypotheses** What might the light areas be?

Saturn The second-largest planet in the solar system is Saturn. Saturn, like Jupiter, has a thick atmosphere made up mainly of hydrogen and helium. Saturn's atmosphere also contains clouds and storms, but they are less dramatic than those on Jupiter. The *Cassini* space probe found unusual six-sided cloud patterns around Saturn's north pole. Scientists aren't sure what causes these patterns.

Saturn's Rings 🔑 **Saturn has the most spectacular rings of any planet.** These rings are made of chunks of ice and rock, each traveling in its own orbit around Saturn. From Earth, it looks as though Saturn has only a few rings and that they are divided from each other by narrow, dark regions. Space probes have shown that each of these obvious rings is divided into many thinner rings. Saturn's rings are broad and thin, like a compact disc. Some rings are kept in place by gravity from tiny moons that orbit on either side of the ring.

Saturn's Moons Saturn's largest moon, Titan, is larger than the planet Mercury. It is also the only moon in the solar system that has a thick atmosphere. The atmosphere is composed mostly of nitrogen and methane. Some of these gases break down high in the atmosphere, forming a haze that is somewhat like smog on Earth. In 2005, the *Huygens* probe landed on Titan's surface. Photos from *Huygens* show features that may have been formed by flowing liquid. A few scientists think that Titan might support life.

Scientists have learned a great deal about Saturn's moons from the *Cassini* space probe. Giant craters and trenches cut cross Mimas (MY mus) and Tethys (TEE this). Ice and water erupt in geysers from the surface of Enccladus (en SEL uh dus). In 2009, scientists discovered a ring of material that may come from the outermost moon, Phoebe (FEE bee). **Figure 4** shows some of the members of the Saturn system.

Size of Saturn compared to Earth

did you know?

Saturn has the lowest density of any planet. If you could build a bathtub big enough, Saturn would float!

Tethys In this photo, you can just see a group of canyons that circle this moon.

Enceladus This photo shows faint bluish plumes erupting from the surface of Enceladus.

✎ **Make Generalizations** Eruptions from Enceladus form one of Saturn's rings. What is that ring most likely made of?

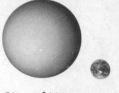

Size of Uranus
compared to Earth

Uranus

Although the gas giant Uranus (YOOR uh nus) is about four times the diameter of Earth, it is still much smaller than Jupiter and Saturn. Uranus is twice as far from the sun as Saturn, so it is much colder. Uranus looks blue-green because of traces of methane in its atmosphere. Like the other gas giants, Uranus is surrounded by a group of thin, flat rings, although they are much darker than Saturn's rings.

Uranus's Moons Photographs from *Voyager 2* show that Uranus's five largest moons have icy, cratered surfaces. The craters show that rocks from space have hit the moons. Uranus's moons also have lava flows on their surfaces, suggesting that material has erupted from inside each moon. *Voyager 2* images revealed 10 moons that had never been seen before. Recently, astronomers discovered several more moons, for a total of at least 27.

A Tilted Planet 🔑 **Uranus's axis of rotation is tilted at an angle of about 90 degrees from the vertical.** Viewed from Earth, Uranus rotates from top to bottom instead of from side to side, as other planets do. You can see the tilt in **Figure 5.** Uranus's rings and moons rotate around this tilted axis. Astronomers think that billions of years ago, an object hit Uranus and knocked it on its side. Images from the *Voyager 2* space probe allowed scientists to determine that Uranus rotates in about 17 hours.

FIGURE 5 ·······················
A Sideways Planet
✎ **Compare and Contrast** How do day and night at Uranus's equator change as Uranus revolves around the sun?

_____
_____
_____
_____
_____
_____
_____
_____

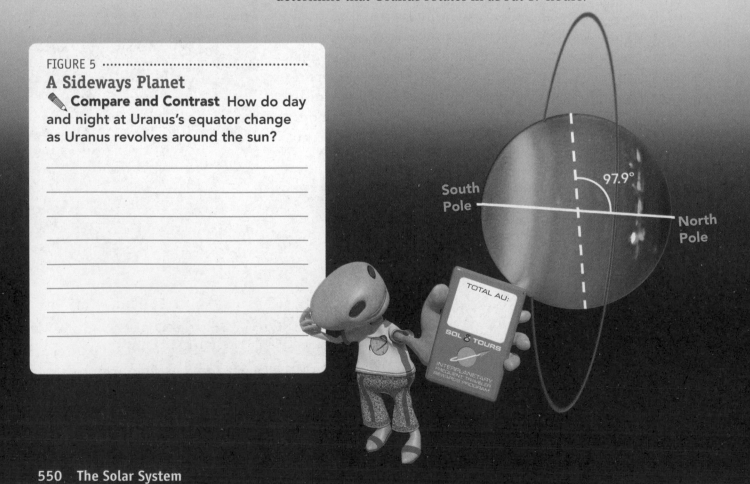

South Pole

97.9°

North Pole

TOTAL AU:

SOL 8 TOURS

INTERPLANETARY
FREQUENT TRAVELER
REWARDS PROGRAM

Neptune Neptune is similar in size and color to Uranus. 🔑 **Neptune is a cold, blue planet. Its atmosphere contains visible clouds.** The color comes from methane in the atmosphere. Neptune's interior is hot due to energy left over from its formation. As this energy rises, it produces clouds and storms in the atmosphere.

Size of Neptune compared to Earth

Neptune's Atmosphere In 1989, *Voyager 2* flew by Neptune and photographed a Great Dark Spot about the size of Earth. Like the Great Red Spot on Jupiter, the Great Dark Spot was probably a giant storm. But it didn't last long. Images taken five years later showed that the spot was gone.

Neptune's Moons Astronomers have discovered at least 13 moons orbiting Neptune. The largest moon is Triton, which has a thin atmosphere. *Voyager 2* images show that the area of Triton's south pole is covered by nitrogen ice.

FIGURE 6 ··

Changing Neptune
The photograph above was taken in 1989. The photograph below was taken in 2002.
✏️ **Interpret Photos** How did Neptune change?

_____

_____

_____

_____

apply it!

Congratulations! You've earned enough AU in your travels to qualify for a free mission to one planet or moon of your choice!

❶ **Make Judgments** Which planet or moon do you choose? List three reasons for your choice.

_____

_____

❷ **Pose Questions** What is one question you would want your mission to answer?

_____

Lab zone Do the Quick Lab
Make a Model of Saturn.

🔑 **Assess Your Understanding**

1. Describe Describe one feature of each outer planet that distinguishes it from the others.

_____

_____

_____

got it?

○ **I get it!** Now I know that the outer planets differ in _____

_____

○ **I need extra help with** _____

_____

Small Solar System Objects

🔑 **How Do Scientists Classify Small Objects in the Solar System?**

my pLaneT DiaRY

Posted by: Haley

Location: Constantia, New York

During the summer my dad and I go outside when it gets dark. We like to go stargazing. I have even seen shooting stars! Shooting stars are very hard to spot. You have to stare at the sky and sometimes you will see one shoot by. They only stick around for one split second, but it is really amazing to see one. This is my favorite thing to do when it gets dark during the summer!

✎ **Communicate** Discuss your answers to these questions with a partner.

1. What do you think shooting stars are?

_____

_____

_____

2. What do you like to observe in the night sky?

_____

_____

_____

Lab ® Do the Inquiry Warm-Up
zone *Collecting Micrometeorites.*

Vocabulary
- asteroid belt • Kuiper belt • Oort cloud
- comet • coma • nucleus • asteroid
- meteoroid • meteor • meteorite

Skills
- Reading: Summarize
- Inquiry: Classify

How Do Scientists Classify Small Objects in the Solar System?

The solar system contains many small objects that, like the planets, orbit the sun. **Scientists classify these objects based on their sizes, shapes, compositions, and orbits. The major categories include dwarf planets, comets, asteroids, and meteoroids.**

Areas of the Solar System Most of the small objects in the solar system are found in three areas: the asteroid belt, the Kuiper belt, and the Oort cloud. The **asteroid belt** is a region of the solar system between Mars and Jupiter. Beyond Neptune's orbit is a region called the **Kuiper belt** (KY per) which extends to about 100 times Earth's distance from the sun. Beyond the Kuiper belt, the **Oort cloud** (ort) stretches out more than 1,000 times the distance between the sun and Neptune. **Figure 1** shows these areas.

FIGURE 1 ....

Areas of the Solar System
The diagram below shows the relative positions of the asteroid belt, the Kuiper belt, and the Oort cloud.

✏️ **Relate Text and Visuals** As you read this lesson, write a C to show where a comet would most likely come from. Write a P to show where you would expect to find a plutoid. Write an A to show where you would expect to find an asteroid.

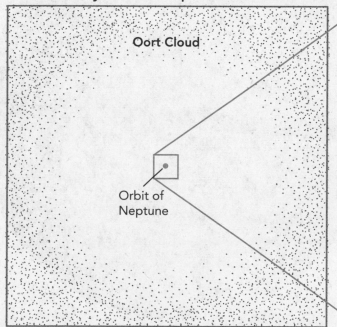

Oort Cloud

Orbit of Neptune

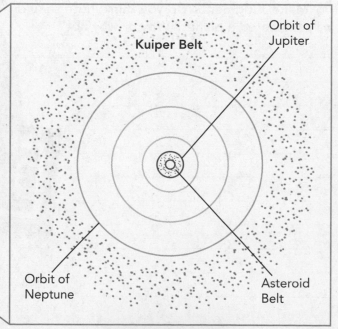

Kuiper Belt

Orbit of Jupiter

Orbit of Neptune

Asteroid Belt

Dwarf Planets

Dwarf Planets "What happened to Pluto?" You may have found yourself asking this question as you have learned about the solar system. For many years, Pluto was considered a planet. But then scientists discovered other objects that were at least Pluto's size. Some were even farther away than Pluto. Scientists began debating how to define a planet.

Defining Dwarf Planets In 2006, astronomers developed a new category of objects, called dwarf planets. These objects orbit the sun and have enough gravity to pull themselves into spheres, but they have other objects in the area of their orbits. As of 2009, scientists had identified five dwarf planets: Pluto, Eris, Makemake, Haumea, and Ceres. Eris is believed to be the largest dwarf planet so far. There are at least a dozen more objects that may turn out to be dwarf planets, once scientists are able to study them.

Like planets, dwarf planets can have moons. Pluto has three moons: Charon, Nix, and Hydra. Haumea has two and Eris has one.

Kuiper Belt Objects All the known dwarf planets except Ceres orbit beyond Neptune. (Ceres orbits in the asteroid belt.) A dwarf planet that orbits beyond Neptune is also called a plutoid. Most plutoids orbit the sun in the Kuiper belt, though Eris may be beyond it. The Kuiper belt also includes many other objects that are too small to be considered dwarf planets.

FIGURE 2 ···

Planet or Not?

This figure shows one artist's idea of what the surface of Pluto looks like.

Make Judgments Do you think Pluto should be considered a planet? Why or why not?

_____

_____

_____

_____

_____

_____

_____

Comets

A comet is one of the most dramatic objects you can see in the night sky. On a dark night, you can see its fuzzy white head and long, streaming tails. **Comets** are loose collections of ice, dust, and small rocky particles whose orbits can be very long, narrow ellipses. Some comets have smaller orbits that bring them near Earth regularly. Most comets originate in the Oort cloud.

A Comet's Head When a comet gets close to the sun, the energy in sunlight turns the ice into gas, releasing gas and dust. Clouds of gas and dust form a fuzzy outer layer called a **coma. Figure 3** shows the coma and the **nucleus,** the solid inner core of a comet. The nucleus is usually only a few kilometers across.

A Comet's Tail As a comet approaches the sun, it heats up and starts to glow. Some of its gas and dust stream outward, forming a tail. Most comets have two tails—a gas tail and a dust tail. The gas tail points away from the sun and the dust tail points along the path the comet has taken. A comet's tail can be more than 100 million kilometers long and from Earth, appears to stretch across most of the sky. The material is stretched out very thinly, however.

Summarize Write a few sentences to summarize the structure of a comet.

_____

_____

_____

_____

_____

_____

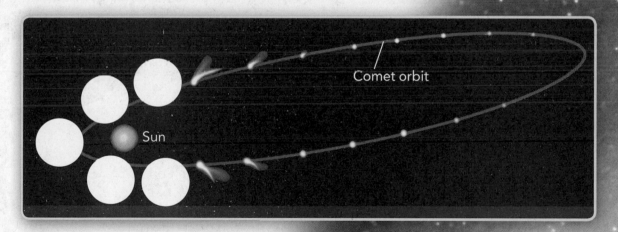

Comet orbit

Sun

FIGURE 3 ....

A Comet's Orbit
Comets, as shown here, have long, narrow orbits. Their tails tend to grow longer as they approach the sun.
Apply Concepts Complete the diagram above by adding the comet's tails.

Gas tail

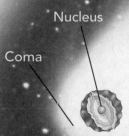

Nucleus

Coma

Dust tail

Asteroids

Asteroids Hundreds of small, irregular, rocky objects orbit the sun. These **asteroids** are rocky objects, most of which are too small and too numerous to be considered planets or dwarf planets. Astronomers have discovered more than 100,000 asteroids, and they are constantly finding more.

Small Bodies Most asteroids are small—less than a kilometer in diameter. Only Ceres, Pallas, Vesta, and Hygiea are more than 300 kilometers across. (Ceres is both a dwarf planet and the largest asteroid.) Most asteroids are not spherical. Scientists hypothesize that asteroids are leftover pieces of the early solar system that never came together to form a planet.

Asteroid Orbits Most asteroids orbit the sun in the asteroid belt. Some, however, have very elliptical orbits that bring them closer to the sun than Earth's orbit. Someday, an asteroid will hit Earth. One or more large asteroids did hit Earth about 65 million years ago, filling the atmosphere with dust and smoke and blocking out sunlight around the world. Scientists hypothesize that many species of organisms, including the dinosaurs, became extinct as a result.

apply it!

Classify For each description below, classify the object as a dwarf planet, comet, asteroid, or meteoroid.

1 This object is slightly smaller than Pluto. It orbits the sun beyond Neptune and is spherical. _____

2 This object is irregularly shaped. It orbits the sun just outside the orbit of Mars. _____

3 This object is a chunk of rock and metal. It was once part of another object that orbited the sun. _____

4 This object is composed of ice and rock. It orbits the sun in an elongated orbit, taking many years to complete one orbit.

_____

5 [CHALLENGE] Which two types of objects are hardest to tell apart? Why? _____

_____

_____

Meteoroids Chunks of rock or dust smaller than asteroids are called **meteoroids.** Meteoroids are generally less than 10 meters across. Some meteoroids form when asteroids collide. Others form when comets break up, creating dust clouds.

Meteors and Meteorites When a meteoroid enters Earth's atmosphere, friction with the air creates heat and produces a streak of light. This streak is a **meteor.** (People often call meteors shooting stars, but they are not stars.) Most meteors come from tiny bits of rock or dust that burn up completely. But some larger meteoroids do not burn up. Meteoroids that pass through the atmosphere and are found on Earth's surface are called **meteorites.** Meteorite impacts can leave craters, such as the one shown in **Figure 4.**

Meteor Showers Meteor showers occur when Earth passes through an area with many meteoroids. Some of these groups of meteoroids are bits of comets that broke up. These meteor showers occur every year as Earth passes through the same areas. Meteor showers are often named for the constellation from which they appear to come. The Perseids, Geminids, and Orionids are examples of meteor showers.

FIGURE 4 ....

Meteor Crater

Meteor Crater in Arizona formed about 50,000 years ago from the impact of a meteorite 50–100 meters wide. **Predict** How would a large meteorite impact affect Earth today?

_____

_____

_____

Approximate size of meteorite relative to crater

Lab zone® Do the Quick Lab *Changing Orbits.*

🗝 Assess Your Understanding

1a. Review (Comets/Asteroids) are rocky, while (comets/asteroids) are made of ice and dust.

b. Compare and Contrast What is the difference between a dwarf planet and an asteroid?

_____

_____

_____

c. Relate Cause and Effect How and why does a comet change as it approaches the sun?

_____

_____

_____

_____

got it? ....

○ **I get it!** Now I know that small solar system objects include _____

_____

_____

○ **I need extra help with** _____

_____

12 Study Guide

Objects in the solar system are different because they formed _____

LESSON 1 Models of the Solar System

🔑 In a geocentric model, Earth is at the center.

🔑 Copernicus worked out the arrangement of the known planets and how they orbit the sun.

🔑 Kepler found that planets' orbits are ellipses.

🔑 Evidence from Galileo Galilei convinced others that the heliocentric model was correct.

Vocabulary
• geocentric • heliocentric • ellipse

LESSON 2 Introducing the Solar System

🔑 Our solar system consists of the sun, the planets, their moons, and smaller objects.

🔑 The solar system formed about 4.6 billion years ago from a cloud of hydrogen, helium, rock, ice, and other materials pulled together by gravity.

Vocabulary
• solar system • astronomical unit • planet
• dwarf planet • planetesimal

LESSON 3 The Sun

🔑 The sun's interior consists of the core, the radiation zone, and the convection zone. The sun's atmosphere includes the photosphere, the chromosphere, and the corona.

🔑 Features on or just above the sun's surface include sunspots, prominences, and solar flares.

Vocabulary
• core • nuclear fusion • radiation zone
• convection zone • photosphere
• chromosphere • corona • solar wind
• sunspot • prominence • solar flare

LESSON 4 The Inner Planets

🔑 The inner planets are small and dense and have rocky surfaces.

🔑 Mercury is the smallest terrestrial planet and the planet closest to the sun. Venus has a thick atmosphere and the hottest surface of any planet. Earth has a suitable temperature range and atmosphere for living things to survive. Mars has ice and evidence of flowing liquid water.

Vocabulary
• terrestrial planet • greenhouse effect

LESSON 5 The Outer Planets

🔑 The outer planets are much larger than Earth and do not have solid surfaces.

🔑 Jupiter is the largest and most massive planet. Saturn has the most spectacular rings of any planet. Uranus's axis of rotation is tilted at an angle of about 90 degrees from the vertical. Neptune is a cold, blue planet with visible clouds.

Vocabulary
• gas giant • ring

LESSON 6 Small Solar System Objects

🔑 Scientists classify small objects based on their sizes, shapes, compositions, and orbits. The major categories include dwarf planets, comets, asteroids, and meteoroids.

Vocabulary
• asteroid belt • Kuiper belt • Oort cloud
• comet • coma • nucleus • asteroid
• meteoroid • meteor • meteorite

Review and Assessment

LESSON 1 Models of the Solar System

1. What object is at the center of a geocentric system?

   a. Earth   **b.** the moon

   c. a star   **d.** the sun

2. Kepler discovered that planets move in

_____

3. **Relate Cause and Effect** How did Tycho Brahe's work contribute to the development of the heliocentric model?

_____

_____

_____

4. [Write About It] Suppose you lived at the time of Copernicus. Write a letter to a scientific journal supporting the heliocentric model.

LESSON 2 Introducing the Solar System

5. Pluto is an example of a(n)

   a. dwarf planet.   **b.** inner planet.

   c. outer planet.   **d.** planetesimal.

6. An astronomical unit is equal to _____

_____

7. **Compare and Contrast** Compare the conditions that led to the formation of the inner planets with those that led to the formation of the outer planets.

_____

_____

_____

_____

LESSON 3 The Sun

8. In which part of the sun does nuclear fusion take place?

   a. chromosphere   **b.** convection layer

   c. core   **d.** corona

9. Relatively cool areas on the sun's surface are

called _____

10. **Explain** How can the solar wind affect life on

Earth? _____

_____

_____

11. **math!** The density of the sun's core is about 160 g/cm^3. The density of Earth's core is about 13.0 g/cm^3. About how many times denser is the sun's core than Earth's?

_____

LESSON 4 The Inner Planets

12. What feature is shared by all the inner planets?

   a. thick atmosphere   **b.** rocky surface

   c. ring system   **d.** liquid water

13. The inner planets are also called _____

_____

14. **Apply Concepts** Explain why Venus has the hottest surface of any planet.

_____

_____

_____

_____

15. [Write About It] Choose one inner planet. Write a news article describing a visit to that planet's surface. Include descriptive details.

12 Review and Assessment

The Outer Planets

16. Which planet's orbit is farthest from Earth's?

    a. Jupiter   **b.** Neptune

    c. Saturn   **d.** Uranus

17. All the gas giants are surrounded by _____

_____

Use the illustration to answer Question 18.

18. Interpret Diagrams What planet is shown above? What is unusual about it? What do scientists think caused that unusual feature?

_____

_____

_____

_____

_____

_____

19. Predict Do you think astronomers have found all the moons of the outer planets? Explain.

_____

_____

_____

_____

_____

Small Solar System Objects

20. Where are most dwarf planets found?

    a. asteroid belt   **b.** Kuiper belt

    c. Oort cloud   **d.** plutoid belt

21. A _____ is a meteoroid that reaches Earth's surface.

22. Compare and Contrast Compare and contrast asteroids, comets, and meteoroids.

_____

_____

_____

_____

_____

23. **Write About It** Suppose you could witness a large meteorite or asteroid striking Earth. Write a news report explaining the event.

APPLY THE BIG ? **Why are objects in the solar system different from each other?**

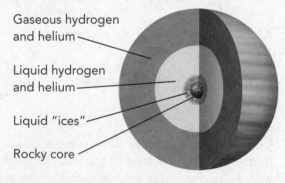

Gaseous hydrogen and helium

Liquid hydrogen and helium

Liquid "ices"

Rocky core

24. What type of planet is shown? Under what conditions would it most likely have formed?

_____

_____

_____

_____

Standardized Test Prep

Read each question and choose the best answer.

1. The table below shows data for five planets.

Planet	Period of Rotation (Earth days)	Period of Revolution (Earth years)	Average Distance from the Sun (million km)
Mars	1.03	1.9	228
Jupiter	0.41	12	779
Saturn	0.45	29	1,434
Uranus	0.72	84	2,873
Neptune	0.67	164	4,495

According to the table, which planet has a "day" that is most similar in length to a day on Earth?

A   Mars
B   Jupiter
C   Neptune
D   Uranus

2. What characteristic do all of the outer planets share?

A   They have rocky surfaces.
B   They are larger than the sun.
C   They have many moons.
D   They have thin atmospheres.

3. Which is the best description of our sun?

A   a small star
B   a mid-sized star
C   a large star
D   a supergiant star

4. Mercury has a daytime temperature of about 430°C and a nighttime temperature below −170°C. What is the best explanation for this?

A   Mercury has a greenhouse effect.
B   Mercury is the closest planet to the sun.
C   Mercury has little to no atmosphere.
D   Mercury has no liquid water.

5. From what region do most comets come?

A   asteroid belt
B   inner solar system
C   Kuiper belt
D   Oort cloud

Constructed Response

Use the diagram below to answer Question 6.

6. What model of the solar system is shown above? Give at least two pieces of evidence that support the model.

Mars Rovers

High school students came up with the names—*Spirit* and *Opportunity*—and scientists at the National Aeronautics and Space Administration (NASA) came up with the plan. Mars is too far away for humans to explore directly. So robot rovers would be dropped onto the surface of Mars and do the exploring for us. The rovers landed on Mars in January 2004. Their assignment was to collect images that would help answer the question: Was there ever water on Mars and could there have been life?

Chemical and physical data from the rovers suggested that there once was water on Mars. There is evidence of erosion as well as chemicals that would exist in an acidic lake or hot springs. Then, in 2015, *NASA's Mars Reconnaissance Orbiter* found evidence of flowing liquid water on Mars even today. It is still impossible to know for sure whether life ever existed on Mars.

Organize It Find three articles about the rover mission. Organize the information in the articles into a two-column chart. In one column, list any data about Mars described in the articles. In the second column, list any conclusions that scientists made about Mars based on that evidence. Circle any conclusions that were made by later Mars missions.

Elliptical, Predictable Orbits

Even the planets flying through the solar system have to obey the law! Gravitational forces determine the ways in which objects move throughout the solar system. In the early 1600s, Johannes Kepler proposed three laws to describe how these forces affect the motion of the planets in orbit around the sun. Kepler's first law of planetary motion states that all planets orbit the sun in a path that resembles an ellipse, with the sun located at one of the ellipse's two foci.

Kepler's second law uses a mathematical formula to describe the speed at which planets orbit the sun. Planets travel fastest when they are moving along the sun side of the ellipse. They travel more slowly along the opposite side of the ellipse. In his third law, Kepler was able to demonstrate that by knowing a planet's period of revolution, the planet's distance from the sun can be calculated. The formulas in Kepler's laws are still used to describe the motion of planets and other satellites.

▲ The two foci that anchor Earth's elliptical path are almost directly on top of each other. This makes Earth's orbit almost circular. The orbits of the outer planets are more strongly elliptical.

Model It You can make an ellipse using a pencil, a string, a sheet of paper, two pushpins, and a piece of cardboard. First, use two pushpins to fasten the sheet of paper to the cardboard. Next, tie the string into a loose loop around the two pins. The loop should have plenty of slack. Pull the string tight with your pencil tip. The string should form a triangle with the pencil and pins at its three corners. Then, trace out a path with the pencil, pulling the string along the farthest possible path from the pins. The resulting shape will be an ellipse.

WHAT CAN SHARKS TEACH THESE CAGED SCIENTISTS?

What does it mean to think like a scientist?

Would you ever go diving in a shark cage? If you were a marine biologist, this might be part of your job. To learn more about sharks, marine biologists study them in their natural environment. These Galápagos sharks were observed swimming off of the coast of Hawaii. Marine biologists have learned that a full-grown male Galápagos shark can grow to be 3.7 meters long and eat squid, octopus, and fish, including other sharks.

⚠️ **Infer** **What information could scientists learn by watching these sharks?**

_____

_____

_____

_____

Watch the **Untamed Science** video to learn more about science.

What Is Science?

1 Getting Started

Check Your Understanding

1. **Background** Read the paragraph below and then answer the question.

Andy is watching a movie when the television suddenly turns off. He decides to **investigate**. Andy turns on a lamp but nothing happens. He tries the radio, but it doesn't work either. Then, he looks out the window and **observes** that all the houses on his street are dark. Andy **concludes** that the electricity has gone out in the neighborhood. He hopes the power returns soon.

> To **investigate** is to observe or study closely.
>
> To **observe** is to see or notice.
>
> To **conclude** is to reach a decision.

• How did Andy investigate the problem?

_____

_____

Vocabulary Skill

Identify Related Word Forms Learning related forms of words increases your vocabulary. The table lists forms of words related to vocabulary terms.

Verb	Noun	Adjective
predict, *v.* to state what will happen in the future	prediction, *n.* a statement about what will happen in the future	predictable, *adj.* able to state what will happen in the future
vary, *v.* to make a partial change in something	variation, *n.* the amount of change in something; the result of a change	variable, *adj.* able to change

2. **Quick Check** Complete the sentence with the correct form of the word.

• Can you _____ how long it will take to do your homework?

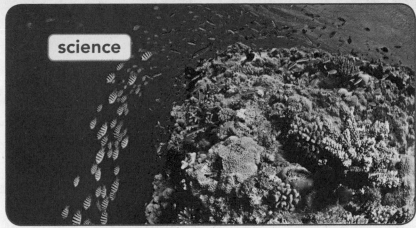

science

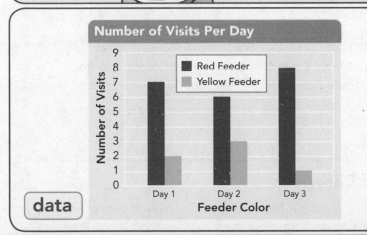

WHERE *I* COME FROM, WE DRINK A LOT OF *TEA,* SO I THINK IT'S OK IF WE DON'T HAVE *COFFEE* HERE.

cultural bias

Number of Visits Per Day

Red Feeder
Yellow Feeder

Number of Visits
9 8 7 6 5 4 3 2 1 0

Day 1   Day 2   Day 3
Feeder Color

data

scientific law

Part 1 Preview

LESSON 1
- science • observing
- quantitative observation
- qualitative observation • inferring
- predicting • classifying
- making models • evaluating
- scientific investigation

↻ **Sequence**
△ **Interpret Data**

LESSON 2
- skepticism • personal bias
- cultural bias • experimental bias
- ethics • objective • subjective
- deductive reasoning
- inductive reasoning

↻ **Ask Questions**
△ **Infer**

LESSON 3
- scientific inquiry • hypothesis
- variables • independent variable
- dependent variable
- controlled experiment
- data • scientific theory
- scientific law

↻ **Relate Cause and Effect**
△ **Control Variables**

Scenario Investigation

This Isn't Science!

Purpose To investigate how science relates to technology

Materials
- egg
- plastic foam cup
- five cotton balls
- four toothpicks
- blank paper
- scissors
- one foot of masking tape
- two rubber bands

Scenario

So far, your science class has been fun and interesting. Today's lesson involves building a container to protect a falling egg. This isn't science! Or is it?

When you asked why you are doing an egg-drop experiment in a science class, your teacher said that once scientific discoveries are confirmed, they can be useful. Your teacher knows the egg-drop experiment is an example of using scientific discoveries to design a successful technology to solve a problem. The more you apply scientific knowledge to your design, the better your results should be.

To show the class how they can use their knowledge of scientific discoveries to design useful technologies, your teacher is holding a contest. Groups will use their scientific knowledge to design egg carriers. The winner is the group whose egg carrier protects their egg from the highest drop.

Procedure

☑ 1. **Reading the Science** The box below contains a list of four scientific discoveries that may help you design a more successful egg-protection device. Each member of your team should read one of the discoveries and think about how it may influence the design of your egg carrier.

Scientific Discoveries

Force – Force is a push or pull. It can change the movement of an object by causing it to speed up, slow down, or change direction. Sir Isaac Newton discovered that force equals mass multiplied by acceleration.

Gravity – Newton also discovered that all objects are attracted to other objects by a force he called gravity. The more massive the objects, the greater the attraction. Every second an egg falls, gravity increases the egg's velocity.

Inertia – Newton also discovered that an object in motion stays in motion unless it encounters an opposing force. The greater the opposing force, the faster the moving object comes to a stop. If an egg stops too quickly, the force will break the egg.

Stress – Stress is force divided by area. This means that when a force is spread out over a larger area there is less stress. Stress on the egg will cause it to break.

Procedure *(continued)*

☑ **2. Explain the Science to Your Team** Take turns explaining to each other the scientific discovery you read. After each explanation, discuss how you can use the information to design a better egg carrier. Record this information in your notebook.

☑ **3. Building an Egg Carrier** Once you receive your egg, you will have 15 minutes to design a carrier that will protect it from the fall. Base each design choice on one or more of the scientific discoveries listed.

☑ **4. Recording Design Choices** As you build your carrier, record each design feature and any scientific reasons for including the feature. Count the total number of scientific reasons used in your design and record it in your notebook.

☑ **5. Testing Your Carrier** When everyone is ready, teams will take turns dropping their egg carriers from a height of one meter. After each drop, your teacher will check the egg for damage. If the egg is still intact, the team will drop its egg from one-quarter meter higher until it breaks. Record the highest successful drop for your team.

☑ **6. Declaring a Winner** If your egg survives the greatest height, you win! Be prepared to explain which scientific discovery was most helpful in designing your carrier.

Conclusion

Let's see what you learned about the difference between science and technology.

☑ **1.** Which field involves trying to understand how the natural world works?

☑ **2.** Which field involves designing a solution to a problem?

☑ **3.** How are science and technology related?

_____

_____

☑ **4.** What field involves using science and technological knowledge together to solve a problem?

_____

Now, you will prepare a final report that includes

> • a diagram of your finished carrier with each design feature labeled
>
> • a neat version of your chart stating the scientific discovery behind each feature
>
> • a paragraph that explains which science discovery was most helpful in designing your egg carrier

LESSON

1 The Skills of Science

🔑 **What Are the Skills of Science?**

UNLOCK
THE BIG
?

MY PLANET DiARY

Underwater Science

Imagine being an explorer who has truly gone where no one has gone before. Imagine seeing pale crabs as large as cats and tall spirals of bamboo coral that glow blue when touched. Imagine walking in the ocean nearly 380 meters below the surface or swimming so close to a whale you can touch it. Well, none of this is imaginary for Dr. Sylvia Earle!

Dr. Earle is a marine biologist, a scientist who studies ocean life. She has spent more than 7,000 hours underwater, studying everything from algae to humpback whales. She is also an inventor who developed submersibles (a type of submarine) so she could study life in the ocean close-up.

Dr. Sylvia Earle shows algae to an engineer in an underwater habitat.

CAREERS

Answer the questions below. Then discuss your answers with a classmate.

1. What is one advantage and one disadvantage of actually being in the ocean to study ocean life?

_____

_____

_____

_____

_____

_____

_____

2. What do you think is the most interesting part of being a marine biologist?

_____

_____

_____

Lab® Do the Inquiry Warm-Up
zone *Exploring Science.*

Vocabulary
- science • observing • quantitative observation
- qualitative observation • inferring • predicting
- classifying • making models • evaluating
- scientific investigation

Skills
↻ Reading: Sequence
△ Inquiry: Interpret Data

What Are the Skills of Science?

Dr. Earle is a scientist, or a person who practices science. Science is a way of learning about the natural world. Scientists gather information and explore the natural world using different science skills. ⊶ The skills of science include observing, inferring, predicting, classifying, evaluating, making models, and conducting scientific investigations.

Observing Scientists are always observing things. Observing means using one or more of your senses to gather information. It's the most important science skill. Dr. Earle, for example, has spent many hours observing ocean plants and animals, like those shown in Figure 1. By observing ocean life, she learned things such as which fish eat plants and which fish eat animals.

Observations can be either quantitative or qualitative. A quantitative observation deals with numbers, or amounts. For example, when you measure your height or your weight, or notice that there are 8 cars parked on your street, you are making a quantitative observation. A qualitative observation deals with descriptions that cannot be expressed in numbers. Noticing that a bird is blue or that a watermelon tastes sweet are qualitative observations.

FIGURE 1 ·······················

Observing Ocean Life

✎ Write at least one quantitative observation and one qualitative observation about these aquatic organisms. Discuss your observations with a classmate.

Inferring Unlike many ocean scientists, Dr. Earle has actually lived under water. She spent two weeks in an underwater habitat near the Virgin Islands. There she studied fish and their behavior. One thing Dr. Earle noticed was that different fish eat different things. For example, parrotfish eat seaweed that grows on dead coral, while the damselfish eat a certain type of algae. Dr. Earle also noticed that none of the fish in the area she was studying ate the feathery green leaves of a plant called *Caulerpa*. She reasoned that although the plant looked good, it probably didn't taste good to the fish in the area.

Dr. Earle was not observing when she reasoned that *Caulerpa* doesn't taste good to fish. She was inferring. When you explain or interpret the things you observe, you are **inferring,** or making an inference. Inferring is not guessing. Inferences are based on reasoning from what you already know. Inferences could also be based on assumptions you make about your observations. See **Figure 2.**

⟳ **Sequence**
What did Dr. Earle do after she made her observations?

_____
_____
_____
_____

FIGURE 2 ⋯⋯⋯⋯⋯⋯⋯

Inferring

Damselfish maintain and defend small "algal lawns" that they use for food, shelter, and nesting.

✎ **Complete these tasks.**

1. **Observe** Write one observation about the damselfish in the photo.

_____
_____
_____
_____

2. **Infer** Based on your observation, write one inference.

_____
_____
_____
_____

3. CHALLENGE What sources might you use to research your inference?

_____
_____

Predicting

Dr. Earle also followed humpback whales in the Hawaiian Islands. The more time she spent with the whales, the more she understood their behavior. Sometimes she could predict what a particular whale would do next. **Predicting** means making a statement or a claim about what will happen in the future based on past experience or evidence.

Inferences and predictions are closely related. While inferences are attempts to explain what is happening or *has* happened, predictions are statements or claims about what *will* happen. See what predictions you can make about the whales in **Figure 3**.

Classifying

On one expedition, Dr. Earle was part of a team gathering information about plants found in the Gulf of Mexico. Team members collected samples from different underwater areas, and took detailed notes about the temperature, salt content, and amount of light present. They then classified the information they collected to make it easier to understand. **Classifying** is the grouping together of items that are alike in some ways. For example, the team grouped together in a data table the type of algae found in each area.

FIGURE 3

Predicting Whale Behavior

Humpback whales eat krill, tiny shrimp-like animals. These panels show a sequence of humpback whale feeding behavior.

Predict Draw a picture in the empty panel to show what you think will happen next. Write your prediction on the lines.

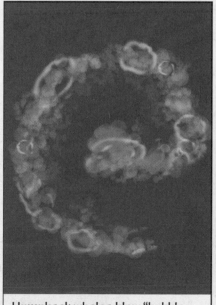

Humpback whales blow "bubble nets" when feeding.

The whales then move up through the center of the bubbles.

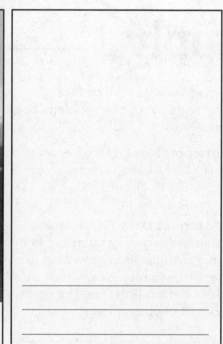

Making Models A data table is one way to present information. A model is another way. For example, Dr. Earle's team could have made a model showing the temperature and depth of the ocean at each algae collection point. **Making models** involves creating representations of complex objects or processes. Some models can be touched, such as a map. Others are in the form of mathematical equations or computer programs. Models help people study things that can't be observed directly. By using models, scientists can share information that would otherwise be difficult to explain.

Evaluating One of the reasons that Dr. Earle studied humpback whales was to see if she could determine if certain whale "songs"—a series of loud grunts and squeals repeated over and over—were associated with certain whale behaviors. Suppose she found that a whale sang a certain song each time it fed. What would this observation have told her about whale behavior? To reach a conclusion, Dr. Earle would first need to evaluate her observations and data. **Evaluating** involves comparing observations and data to reach a conclusion about them. For example, Dr. Earle would have needed to compare the whale's behaviors with those of the other whales in the group to reach a conclusion.

apply it!

This map shows ocean surface temperature along the Louisiana coast in January.

❶ **Interpret Maps** Mark the areas on the map that have a surface temperature of about 12°C.

❷ **Interpret Data** Phytoplankton are plantlike organisms that live in the ocean. Phytoplankton grow best in cold, nutrient-rich waters. Near which cities would you most likely find the greatest number of phytoplankton?

_____

_____

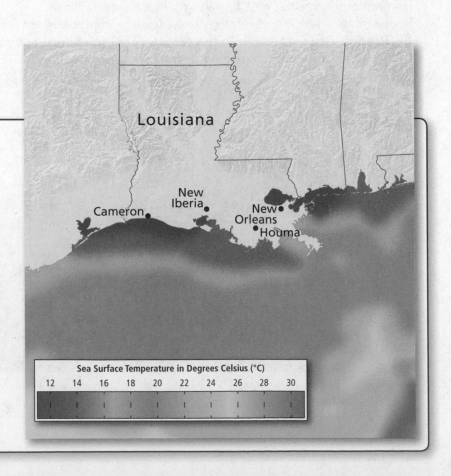

Louisiana

New Iberia
Cameron
New Orleans
Houma

Sea Surface Temperature in Degrees Celsius (°C)

12 14 16 18 20 22 24 26 28 30

Conducting Scientific Investigations

Science is a continuous cycle of asking questions about the natural world, looking for answers, solving problems, and forming new ideas. A **scientific investigation** is the way in which scientists study the natural world. First, you ask a question. Then, you figure out a way to find the answer. Finally, you perform the actions necessary to find the answer. Recall that Dr. Earle first observed that bamboo coral glowed blue when touched, as shown in the first photo of **Figure 4.** Then, other scientists began investigating how and why the coral glows. Scientific investigations may occur in different ways, but they usually involve most or all of the other science skills.

FIGURE 4 ....

Scientific Investigation

✎ **Pose Questions** For each image, write a question that could be answered by conducting a scientific investigation.

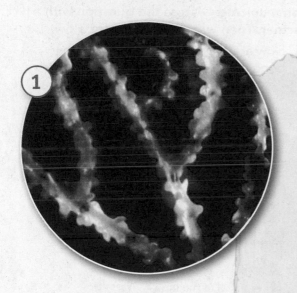

Try the Quick Lab
Practicing Science Skills.

🔑 Assess Your Understanding

1a. Review Why do scientists make models?

_____

_____

_____

b. Classify Identify each statement as an observation (*O*) or an inference (*I*).

The cat is fat. _____

The cat likes food. _____

got it?

○ **I get it!** Now I know that the skills of

science include _____

_____

_____

_____

○ **I need extra help with** _____

_____

_____

575

Scientific Thinking

UNLOCK
THE BIG
?

 What Are the Characteristics of Scientific Thinking?

 What Is Scientific Reasoning?

 How Does Scientific Knowledge Change?

MY PLANET DIARY

Inventor Extraordinaire

What does it take to be an extraordinary inventor like Elwood Haynes? Born in 1857 in Portland, Indiana, Haynes was recognized at an early age for his determination and curiosity. As a student and as a scientist, he overcame obstacles and went on to distinguish himself with many technological "firsts". He constructed our nation's first long-distance, high-pressure natural gas pipeline. He created stainless steel and other metal combinations. Haynes designed the first successful gasoline-powered car in America, the Pioneer, pictured here.

BIOGRAPHY

Communicate Discuss the question with a partner. Then write your answer below.

1. How are curiosity and determination beneficial to a scientist or an inventor?

_____

_____

_____

_____

_____

Lab zone® Do the Inquiry Warm-Up How to Think Scientifically.

What Are the Characteristics of Scientific Thinking?

Have you ever taken apart a flashlight just to see how it works? Or thought about whether a magician really sawed a person in half? Or told a teacher the truth about why your homework was late? If so, you've demonstrated some of the key characteristics of scientific thinking. **Scientific thinking involves characteristics such as curiosity, creativity, open-mindedness, skepticism, awareness of bias, honesty, and ethics.**

Vocabulary

- skepticism • personal bias • cultural bias
- experimental bias • ethics • objective
- subjective • deductive reasoning
- inductive reasoning

Skills

↻ **Reading:** Ask Questions

△ **Inquiry:** Infer

Curiosity and Creativity

Curiosity is one of the main characteristics that leads to new scientific knowledge. Scientists want to learn more about the topics they study. Curiosity helps them to make observations and ask questions.

In 1609, Galileo Galilei demonstrated his telescope, which would lead to many new astronomical observations. Although Galileo's curiosity inspired him to observe space, it was his creative thinking that allowed him to make improvements to the telescope. Creativity involves coming up with new sources and ways to help solve problems or produce new things.

Open-Mindedness and Skepticism

Scientists need to be open-minded, or capable of accepting new and different ideas. But open-mindedness should always be balanced by **skepticism,** which means having an attitude of doubt. Skepticism prevents scientists from accepting ideas that are presented without enough evidence or that may be untrue. Skeptics of scientific claims can help determine if something really exists. Practice using open-mindedness and skepticism in **Figure 1.**

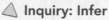

↻ **Ask Questions** If you were a scientist studying the organism pictured below, what would you be curious to know about it?

_____

_____

_____

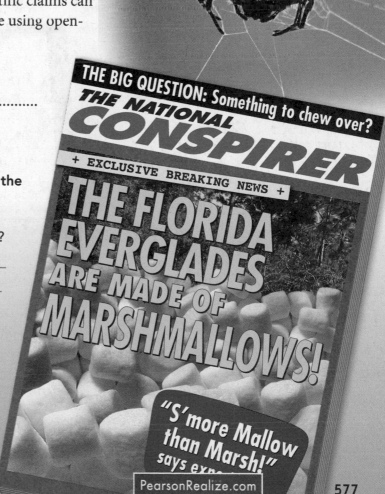

FIGURE 1 ·······························

Truth or Fiction?

This tabloid magazine is making a claim about the Florida Everglades.

✏ **Read the magazine's headline. Then answer the questions below.**

1. **Make Judgments** Would you respond to this headline with open-mindedness or skepticism?

_____

_____

2. **Explain** Why would you respond that way?

_____

_____

_____

_____

THE BIG QUESTION: Something to chew over?

THE NATIONAL CONSPIRER

+ EXCLUSIVE BREAKING NEWS +

THE FLORIDA EVERGLADES ARE MADE OF MARSHMALLOWS!

"S'more Mallow than Marsh!" says exp...

PearsonRealize.com

Awareness of Bias

What scientists expect to find can influence, or bias, what they observe and how they interpret their observations. There are several different kinds of bias.

Personal Bias If a person's likes and dislikes influence how he or she thinks about something, that is called **personal bias.** For instance, if you like the taste of milk, you might think everyone else likes it, too.

Cultural Bias When the culture in which a person grows up affects the way that person thinks, this is called **cultural bias.** For example, a culture that regards milk as a food just for babies might overlook the nutritional benefits of drinking milk in later life.

Experimental Bias A mistake in the design of an experiment that makes a certain result more likely is called **experimental bias.** For example, suppose you want to compare the health effects of drinking low-fat milk and regular milk. Your experiment consists of two groups of people. One group drinks low-fat milk for a month, and the other drinks regular milk for a month. If either group had been less healthy than the other group before the experiment, your results would be biased.

I REALLY LIKE WATCHING MOVIES, SO I'LL BET THAT EVERYONE LIKES WATCHING MOVIES!

WHERE *I* COME FROM, WE DRINK A LOT OF *TEA*, SO I THINK IT'S OK IF WE DON'T HAVE *COFFEE* HERE.

FIGURE 2 ....
Recognizing Bias
These people are making biased statements.

✎ **Answer the questions below.**

1. **Identify** On the lines provided, identify what type of bias each person is showing.

_____

_____

_____

2. **Design Experiments** How could one of these people correct his or her bias?

_____

_____

_____

_____

_____

Honesty and Ethics Good scientists always report their observations and results truthfully. Honesty is very important when a scientist's results go against previous ideas or predictions. For example, in 1912, a group of scientists in Britain announced that they found a fossil that was the "missing link" between humans and apes. The fossil had the skull of a man and the jaw of an orangutan. They called the fossil "Piltdown Man," as shown in **Figure 3**. About 40 years later, careful testing determined that the fossil was a fake!

Scientists also need a strong sense of **ethics,** which refers to the rules that enable people to know right from wrong. Scientists must consider all the effects their research may have on people and the environment. They make decisions only after considering the risks and benefits to living things and the environment.

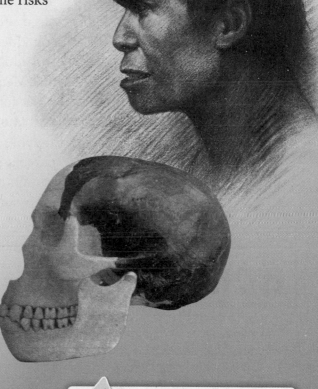

FIGURE 3 ·······················
The Piltdown Hoax
An artist has drawn what the Piltdown Man would have looked like, based on the fossilized skull parts.

✎ **Answer the questions below.**

1. **Name** What are two careers in which honesty and ethics are important?

_____

2. CHALLENGE How might a fake fossil affect the work of other scientists?

_____
_____
_____
_____

Lab® Do the Quick Lab
zone *Exploring Scientific Thinking.*

🗝 **Assess Your Understanding**

1a. Describe What is bias?

_____
_____

b. Infer How might creativity help scientists come up with new scientific knowledge?

_____
_____
_____
_____

got it?

○ I get it! Now I know that the characteristics of scientific thinking include _____

_____
_____
_____

○ I need extra help with _____

_____
_____

What Is Scientific Reasoning?

You use reasoning, or a logical way of thinking, when you solve problems. For example, you notice that water on a stove boils when the stove is turned on. Because the water doesn't boil when the stove is off, you might logically conclude that heat causes water to boil. 🔑 **Scientific reasoning requires a logical way of thinking based on gathering and evaluating evidence.**

Objective and Subjective Scientific reasoning involves being **objective,** which means that you make decisions and draw conclusions based on available evidence. For example, a paleontologist named Jack Horner and his partner, Robert Makela, discovered the nests of a dinosaur called *Maiasaura*. The nests contained fossilized eggs, newly hatched babies, young dinosaurs, and adults. Based on this evidence, Horner and Makela concluded that *Maiasaura* took care of their young.

In contrast, being **subjective** means that personal feelings affect how you make a decision or reach a conclusion. For example, suppose that a paleontologist thought that dinosaurs were bad parents. If she found a fossilized nest of eggs with no bones of parents nearby, she might ignore other evidence and conclude that dinosaurs did not care for their young.

PEDRO IS 1.7 M TALL.

NO ONE ELSE IN CLASS IS TALLER THAN 1.6 M.

Infer Read the comic above about measuring height. Write a conclusion and a title for the third picture. Is your conclusion based on subjective or objective reasoning? Explain.

_____

_____

Deductive and Inductive Reasoning There are two main types of scientific reasoning: deductive reasoning and inductive reasoning. **Deductive reasoning** is a way to explain things by starting with a general idea and then applying the idea to a specific observation. You can think about deductive reasoning as being a process. First, you state the general idea. Then you relate the general idea to the specific case you are investigating. Finally, you reach a conclusion. For instance, you know that water freezes at 0 degrees Celsius. You see a frozen puddle of water. You know that the water has frozen because it was at or below 0 degrees Celsius.

Inductive reasoning can be considered the opposite of deductive reasoning. **Inductive reasoning** uses specific observations to make generalizations. Suppose you notice that every time a puddle freezes, the temperature outside is at or below 0 degrees Celsius. You might conclude that water freezes at 0 degrees Celsius.

FIGURE 4 ···
What Goes Up . . .
Gene is playing with a basketball in his backyard.

✏️ **Apply Concepts** Read the comic below. Is Gene's thinking an example of deductive or inductive reasoning? Explain your answer.

_____

_____

_____

_____

THE LAW OF *GRAVITY* SAYS THAT OBJECTS ATTRACT ONE ANOTHER. SO IF I THROW THIS BALL *UP*, IT SHOULD COME *DOWN*.

I WAS *RIGHT!*

FIGURE 5 ················

Chat Room Controversy
You are chatting online with three friends who live in other states.

✎ **Communicate** In the space provided, explain to your friends why Jeff has shown faulty reasoning.

Faulty Reasoning

If you make a conclusion without gathering enough data, your reasoning might lead you to the wrong general idea. Incorrect reasoning such as this is called faulty reasoning. For example, suppose you saw a number of people walking their dogs and observed that every person who was walking a yellow retriever that day was a young girl. You might use inductive reasoning to say that only young girls own yellow retrievers. However, this conclusion would be wrong. Scientists must be careful not to use faulty reasoning, because it can lead to faulty conclusions.

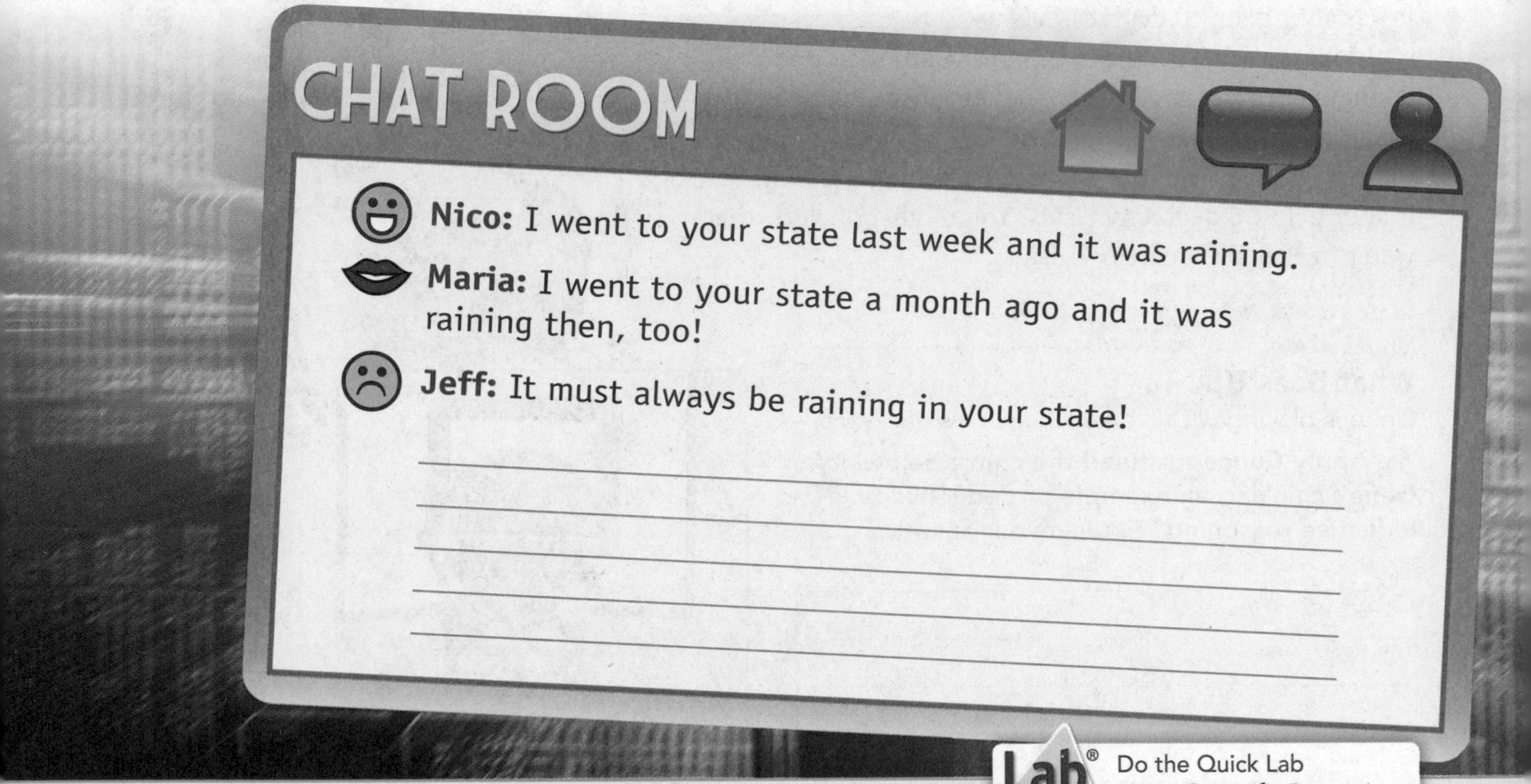

CHAT ROOM

😀 **Nico:** I went to your state last week and it was raining.

👄 **Maria:** I went to your state a month ago and it was raining then, too!

☹ **Jeff:** It must always be raining in your state!

_____
_____
_____
_____
_____

Lab zone® Do the Quick Lab
Using Scientific Reasoning.

🔑 Assess Your Understanding

2a. Summarize Why is subjective reasoning not an example of scientific thought?

_____
_____
_____

b. Relate Cause and Effect What is a cause of faulty reasoning?

_____
_____
_____

got it? ··

○ **I get it!** Now I know that scientific reasoning is _____
_____

○ **I need extra help with** _____
_____

How Does Scientific Knowledge Change?

Our understanding of the natural world is always growing and changing. New technologies expand the ways scientists gather and interpret data. This increases and changes scientific knowledge. Today, scientists know about topics ranging from matter's smallest particles to the deepest regions of space. But this wasn't always the case. **Scientific knowledge is based on an ever-growing collection of facts about the natural world, but it changes with new evidence or new interpretations.** For example, 2,300 years ago, ancient astronomers thought that all the observable objects in the sky revolved around Earth. Later scientists proposed that Earth and other planets actually revolve around the sun. However, there was no evidence of this until Galileo used his improved telescope and witnessed moons moving around Jupiter. Today, scientists know that Earth and all other planets in the solar system revolve around the sun.

FIGURE 6 ·····································

Life in the Deep

Scientists used to think nothing lived at the bottom of oceans. But, in 1977, tube worms were found living at a depth of 2,000 meters!

✏️ **Explain** How do you think scientists collected new evidence about deep oceans?

_____

_____

_____

_____

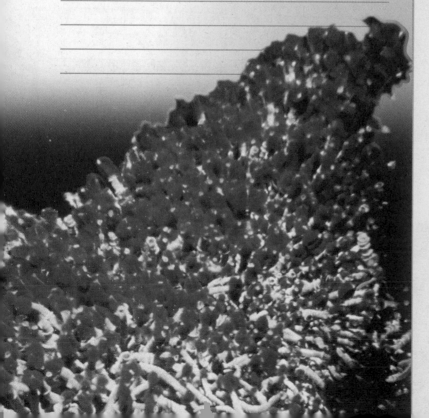

Lab zone ® Do the Quick Lab *Scientific Discovery.*

🗝 Assess Your Understanding

3a. Identify A telescope expanded which of Galileo's senses?

_____

b. Apply Concepts What kind of scientific knowledge has increased as a result of improvements to microscopes?

_____

_____

got it? ·····································

○ I get it! Now I know scientific knowledge

changes _____

_____

○ I need extra help with _____

_____

Answering Scientific Questions

🔑 **What Is Scientific Inquiry?**

🔑 **How Do You Design and Conduct an Experiment?**

🔑 **What Are Scientific Theories and Laws?**

MY PLANET DIARY

MYSTERY

Bittersweet

In 2007, scientists found they had a mystery on their hands. In some countries, commercial honeybees began dying off in very large numbers. Honeybees pollinate crops such as apples, nuts, celery, and squash. If the mystery went unsolved, basic foods might become scarce!

Scientists began to investigate. In 2009, they compared the genes in healthy honeybees to the genes in sick honeybees. They found evidence that certain viruses attack proteins in honeybees. The afflicted bees seem unable to produce proteins that can fight the viruses. So the bees die.

This study was one of the first to identify a cause for the mystery. But scientists still need to investigate further to find a cure for the sick bees.

Write your answers to the questions below. Then discuss your answers with a partner.

1. Why did scientists have to keep investigating even after they thought they had found a reason why honeybees were dying?

_____

_____

2. How might your life be affected if large numbers of honeybees kept dying?

_____

_____

_____

Lab zone® Do the Inquiry Warm-Up *Doing Science Is Asking Questions.*

Vocabulary

- scientific inquiry
- hypothesis
- variables
- independent variable
- dependent variable
- controlled experiment
- data
- scientific theory
- scientific law

Skills

↻ **Reading:** Relate Cause and Effect
△ **Inquiry:** Control Variables

What Is Scientific Inquiry?

You hear a small whirring noise and look up. A ruby-throated hummingbird darts by, its wings a blur. It hovers over red salvia in the garden and then moves to an orange flower. It doesn't seem to go near any yellow flowers. What attracts a hummingbird to a flower? Do hummingbirds prefer some flower colors to others? Thinking and questioning in this way are the start of the **scientific inquiry** process. 🔑 **Scientific inquiry refers to the diverse ways in which scientists study the natural world and propose explanations based on the evidence they gather.**

Posing Questions Scientific inquiry often begins with a question about an observation. Your observation about the hummingbird's feeding habits may lead you to ask a question: Do hummingbirds prefer red flowers to other flower colors? Questions come from your experiences, observations, and inferences. Curiosity plays a role, too. Because others may have asked similar questions, you should do research to find what information is already known about the topic before you go on with your investigation. Look at **Figure 1** to pose a scientific question about an observation.

FIGURE 1 ···

Posing Questions

The ruby-throated hummingbird is common in the eastern United States.

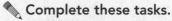 **Complete these tasks.**

1. **Pose Questions** Make an observation about this hummingbird. Then pose a question about this observation that you can study.

   _____

   _____

   _____

2. **Communicate** Share your questions with a group of classmates. Discuss which questions are the easiest and the most difficult to investigate.

Developing a Hypothesis
How could you answer your question about hummingbirds and flower color? In trying to answer the question, you are developing a hypothesis. A **hypothesis** (plural: *hypotheses*) is a possible answer to a scientific question. In this case, you may suspect that hummingbirds can see red better than yellow. Your hypothesis would be that hummingbirds are more attracted to red flowers than yellow flowers. Use **Figure 2** to practice developing a hypothesis.

A hypothesis is *not* a fact. In science, a fact is an observation that has been confirmed repeatedly. For example, it is a fact that hummingbirds have tiny hairs on the tip of the tongue that help lap up nectar. A hypothesis, on the other hand, is one possible answer to a question. For example, perhaps the hummingbirds only seem to be feeding more at red flowers because the garden has fewer other colors of flowers. In science, a hypothesis must be testable. Researchers must be able to carry out investigations and gather evidence that will either support or disprove the hypothesis.

FIGURE 2 ·······················
Developing a Hypothesis
You may form a hypothesis about an everyday event.

✎ **Develop Hypotheses** Why is the school bus always late? In the table, write two hypotheses for this question.

Hypothesis A	Hypothesis B

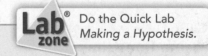
Do the Quick Lab
Making a Hypothesis.

🔑 Assess Your Understanding

1a. Explain Can you test a hypothesis that hummingbirds spend most of their waking hours feeding? Explain.

_____

_____

_____

b. Develop Hypotheses What is another hypothesis that might explain why hummingbirds seem to prefer red flowers?

_____

_____

_____

got it? ···

○ I get it! Now I know that scientific inquiry is _____

_____

○ I need extra help with _____

_____

How Do You Design and Conduct an Experiment?

After developing your hypothesis, you are ready to test it by designing an experiment. 🔑 **An experiment must follow sound scientific principles for its results to be valid.** The experiment needs to produce the kind of data that can answer your question. Also, the data collected need to be measurable. For example, to find out if the hummingbirds have a color preference, you could set up red and yellow feeders to test from which color, if any, the birds prefer to get food. Then you could collect data by counting how often hummingbirds feed from both the red and yellow feeders.

Controlling Variables To test your hypothesis, you will observe hummingbirds feeding from different colored feeders. All other **variables,** or factors that can change in an experiment, must be the same. This includes variables such as the type of food, the shape and size of the feeder, and even the time of day when you observe the hummingbirds. By keeping these variables the same, you will know that any difference in how often a hummingbird feeds is due to feeder color alone.

The one variable that is purposely changed to test a hypothesis is the **independent variable.** The independent variable here is feeder color. The factor that may change in response to the independent variable is the **dependent variable.** The dependent variable here is the number of times the hummingbird visits a feeder.

🖉

↪ **Relate Cause and Effect**
What is the effect of keeping all variables except the independent variable the same?

_____

_____

_____

_____

apply it!

A student performs an experiment to determine if adding 1 milliliter of salt to bubble solution made from soap and water affects bubble making.

❶ **Control Variables** Identify the independent variable and the dependent variable.

_____

_____

❷ **Identify** What are two other variables in this experiment?

_____

_____

❸ **Draw Conclusions** Write a hypothesis for this experiment.

_____

_____

Setting Up a Controlled Experiment You can test your hypothesis in a controlled experiment. A **controlled experiment** is an experiment in which only one variable is changed at a time. You decide to test the hummingbirds at two different colored feeders: red and yellow. All other variables are kept the same. The feeders should be the same size, shape, and height above the ground. They should be in the same general area and contain the same amount and concentration of sugar water. The amount of time you observe the feeders should also be the same. Otherwise, your experiment would have more than one independent variable. Then you would have no way to tell which variable affected your results. The more precisely an experiment's criteria and constraints can be defined, the more likely it is that the results or solution will be successful. Practice setting up a controlled experiment in **Figure 3.**

FIGURE 3 ···

A Controlled Experiment
The independent variable in this experiment is the color of the feeder.

✎ **Complete these tasks.**

1. **Design Experiments** On the lines below, write three variables for this experiment that must be kept the same. Then use the empty space to draw a picture of your experiment. Remember to include and label your variables.

   _____

   _____

   _____

   _____

   _____

2. **Compare and Contrast** With a group, discuss everyone's experiments and the different approaches that were used.

Collecting and Interpreting Data

Before you begin your experiment, decide what observations you will make and what data you will collect. **Data** are the facts, figures, and other evidence gathered through qualitative and quantitative observations. For the hummingbird experiment, you set up one feeder of each color. You decide to conduct three observations or trials because hummingbirds may behave differently from one trial to the next. You also decide to observe the feeders for 15 minutes at the same time for three days and count the number of visits to each feeder in that time period. You can use **Figure 4** to organize your hummingbird data.

After your data have been collected, they need to be interpreted. One tool that can help you interpret data is a graph. Graphs can reveal patterns or trends in data. You can use different graphs to present different types of information. Bar graphs are useful for comparing values across categories or treatments. Line graphs are used to show data points over time. Pie charts can be used to show the contribution of each item to the whole.

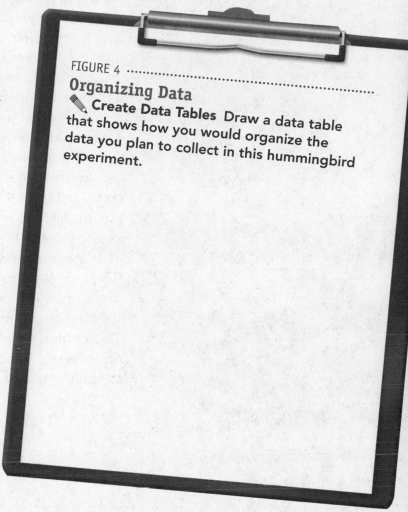

FIGURE 4 ......

Organizing Data

✎ **Create Data Tables** Draw a data table that shows how you would organize the data you plan to collect in this hummingbird experiment.

do the math!

Graphing the data collected in an experiment may reveal whether there are patterns to the data.

❶ **Read Graphs** Identify the independent variable and the dependent variable.

_____

_____

_____

❷ **Interpret Data** Do the data support the hypothesis that hummingbirds prefer red flowers? Explain your answer.

_____

_____

_____

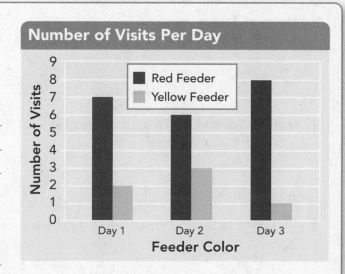

Number of Visits Per Day

■ Red Feeder
■ Yellow Feeder

(y-axis: Number of Visits, 0–9; x-axis: Feeder Color — Day 1, Day 2, Day 3)

Drawing Conclusions Now you can draw conclusions about your hypothesis. A conclusion is a summary of what you have learned from an experiment. To draw your conclusion, you must examine your data objectively to see if they support your hypothesis. You must also consider if you collected enough data or if there is more than one interpretation for the set of data.

In the case of the hummingbirds' color preference, the data show that the red feeder had a greater average number of visits than the yellow feeder. Thus, the data support your hypothesis. Now, you should repeat your experiment to see if you get the same results, as shown in **Figure 5**. A conclusion is unreliable if it comes from an experiment with results that cannot be repeated. Many trials are needed before a hypothesis can be accepted as true.

In some cases, your test results may not support your hypothesis. When this happens, check your experiment for things that went wrong or for improvements you can make. Then fix the problem and do the experiment again. If the experiment was done correctly the first time, your hypothesis was probably not correct. Propose a new hypothesis to test. Scientific inquiry usually doesn't end once an experiment is done. Often, one experiment leads to another.

FIGURE 5 ··
Drawing Conclusions
Sometimes the same experiment can produce very different data.
✎ **Use the table to answer the questions.**

1. **Interpret Tables** Suppose you retest your hypothesis. Do the new data in the table support your hypothesis? Explain.

_____

_____

2. **Analyze Sources of Error** If the data in this table were yours, what might you do next?

_____

_____

3. CHALLENGE Can you draw a conclusion from these data? Explain.

_____

_____

Number of Visits Per Day		
	Red Feeder	**Yellow Feeder**
Day 1	4	5
Day 2	9	9
Day 3	5	4
Average	6	6

Communicating Communicating is the sharing of ideas and results with others through writing and speaking. Scientists give talks at scientific meetings, exchange information on the Internet, or publish articles in scientific journals to communicate.

When scientists share the results of their research, they describe their procedures so that others can repeat their experiments. Scientists wait until an experiment has been repeated many times before accepting a result. This way, scientists know that the result is accurate. Therefore, scientists must keep accurate records of their methods and results. Before the results are published, other scientists review and evaluate the experiment systematically with respect to how well the results meet scientific principles and the criteria of the experiment. Scientists look for sources of error, such as bias, faulty data interpretation, and faulty conclusions. This review process helps prevent unreliable results from being published.

Sometimes, a scientific inquiry can be part of a huge project in which many scientists are working together around the world. On group projects, scientists share their ideas and results regularly. **Figure 6** asks you to come up with ideas for communicating the results of your hummingbird experiment.

FIGURE 6 ···
Communicating Results
Communicating results can lead to new questions, new hypotheses, and new investigations.

✎ **Communicate** With a group, write three ways to share the results of your hummingbird experiment.

_____

_____

_____

_____

_____

Lab ® Do the Lab Investigation
zone *Changing Pitch.*

🔑 **Assess Your Understanding**

2a. Name The _____ variable changes in response to the _____ variable in an experiment.

b. Summarize Why is it important for scientists to publish a description of their procedures with their results?

_____

_____

got it?

○ **I get it!** Now I know that an experiment must follow sound principles such as _____

_____

_____

_____

○ **I need extra help with** _____

_____

What Are Scientific Theories and Laws?

Have you ever had a theory that your friends were planning a surprise party for you? Everyday theories you might have are different from scientific theories.  **A scientific theory is a well-tested and widely accepted explanation of observations and experimental results.** Scientists are constantly testing scientific theories. If new observations or experiments do not support a theory, then the theory is changed or thrown out.

In a community, people make rules to help them live together. These rules are called laws. Science has laws, too. A **scientific law** is a statement that describes what scientists expect to happen every time under a particular set of conditions. **Scientific laws describe observed patterns in nature without trying to explain those patterns.** For example, according to the law of gravity, all objects in the universe attract each other. Learn about another scientific law in **Figure 7.**

FIGURE 7 ···

Scientific Laws

The law of superposition states that, in layers of rock, the oldest layer is at the bottom. The layers above it are younger.

✎ Complete these tasks.

1. **Predict** Draw an arrow pointing to the rock layer that you think would contain the oldest fossils.

2. **Evaluate Scientific Claims** How could it be possible for a younger layer of rock to be below an older layer?

_____

_____

3. **Communicate** Explain to a classmate why the law of superposition is a scientific law.

EXPLORE THE BIG ?

In a Scientist's Shoes

What does it mean to think like a scientist?

FIGURE 8 ··

When you think like a scientist, you conduct scientific investigations.

✎ **Apply Concepts** Think like a scientist to find out about whale songs. Answer these questions.

1. What question would you ask about whale songs?

_____

2. What is a hypothesis that might answer your question?

_____

_____

3. What three types of data could you collect to test your hypothesis?

_____

_____

_____

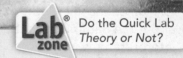
Do the Quick Lab
Theory or Not?

🔑 Assess Your Understanding

3a. Review Why are multiple experiments necessary before a theory is accepted?

_____

b. Compare and Contrast How are scientific theories and scientific laws different?

_____

_____

 c. What does it mean to think like a scientist?

_____

_____

_____

_____

_____

got**it?** ···

○ **I get it!** Now I know that scientific theories and laws are _____

_____

○ **I need extra help with** _____

_____

Study Guide

To think like a scientist, you make _____ , develop _____ , design _____ , and collect data.

LESSON 1 The Skills of Science

🔑 The skills of science include observing, inferring, predicting, classifying, evaluating, making models, and conducting scientific investigations.

Vocabulary
- science • observing
- quantitative observation
- qualitative observation
- inferring • predicting
- classifying • making models
- evaluating • scientific investigation

LESSON 2 Scientific Thinking

🔑 Scientific thinking involves characteristics such as curiosity, creativity, open-mindedness, skepticism, awareness of bias, honesty, and ethics.

🔑 Scientific reasoning requires a logical way of thinking based on gathering and evaluating evidence.

🔑 Scientific knowledge is based on an ever-growing collection of facts about the natural world, but it changes with new evidence or new interpretations.

Vocabulary
- skepticism • personal bias • cultural bias • experimental bias
- ethics • objective • subjective • deductive reasoning • inductive reasoning

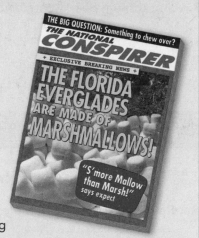

LESSON 3 Answering Scientific Questions

🔑 Scientific inquiry refers to the ways in which scientists study the natural world and propose explanations based on the evidence they gather.

🔑 An experiment must follow sound scientific principles for its results to be valid.

Vocabulary • scientific inquiry • hypothesis
- variables • independent variable
- dependent variable • controlled experiment
- data • scientific theory • scientific law

Review and Assessment

LESSON 1 **The Skills of Science**

1. An observation that deals with numbers is a(n)

  a. prediction.

  b. quantitative observation.

  c. inference.

  d. qualitative observation.

2. Review When a scientist is evaluating, he or she is _____

_____

_____

3. Apply Concepts A mother comes home to find her son holding a tennis racquet behind him, with a worried look on his face. A broken vase is on the floor next to him. What inference can you make about this situation?

_____

_____

_____

4. A scientific investigation is _____

_____

_____

5. Compare and Contrast How are the skills of inferring and predicting alike? How are they different?

_____

_____

_____

_____

6. Explain Choose one scientific skill. Explain how it is useful in a scientific investigation.

_____

_____

_____

_____

LESSON 2 **Scientific Thinking**

7. A conclusion based on too little data is called

  a. cultural bias.   **b.** deductive reasoning.

  c. personal bias.   **d.** faulty reasoning.

8. An attitude of doubt, or _____ can lead to new understanding.

9. Review Experimental bias is _____

_____

_____

10. Why do scientists need a strong sense of ethics?

_____

_____

_____

_____

11. _____ reasoning uses specific observations to make generalizations.

12. Draw Conclusions Why is it important that scientific reasoning be objective?

_____

_____

_____

_____

_____

_____

13. Write About It Scientific knowledge changes with new evidence and new interpretations. Think of a scientific question you would like to answer, and then describe how you could collect evidence to answer it.

LESSON 3 Answering Scientific Questions

14. Before you conduct an experiment, you must

    a. collect data.

    b. communicate your results.

    c. develop a hypothesis.

    d. draw conclusions.

15. A variable is _____

_____

16. Pose Questions Write a question about magnolia plants that you could test in a scientific investigation.

_____

_____

17. Summarize What is a scientific theory and a scientific law?

_____

_____

_____

_____

_____

18. Communicate Why do scientists review each other's work?

_____

_____

_____

_____

_____

19. Write About It You're part of a research team that wants to determine the most popular type of cereal in your school. What type of scientific investigation would you conduct? How would you collect data and communicate the results?

APPLY THE BIG ? **What does it mean to think like a scientist?**

20. People worldwide eat different kinds of tuna. One of the most popular types is the bluefin tuna. In fact, so many people eat bluefin tuna that the population has changed. Now only small bluefin are caught. You've been asked to investigate the cause of the decline in size of the bluefin tuna.

Think about the problem scientifically. What is a possible hypothesis? Could you test it? Mention how you would use at least one science skill in your investigation. Compare methods with a partner.

_____

_____

_____

_____

_____

_____

_____

_____

_____

_____

_____

_____

Standardized Test Prep

Read each question and choose the best answer.

1. A scientist tested how long some modes of transportation took to travel between the two same cities. The data table shows the average amount of time each mode took.

Mode of Transportation	Average Time (minutes)
Airplane	80
Car	367
High-speed train	275
Maglev train	174

Which conclusion communicates the results of the investigation?

A The car was the most efficient mode of transportation

B The airplane traveled faster than the car

C The maglev train is the world's fastest transportation

D The speed of the high-speed train was variable

2. Which of the following is a characteristic of a scientific theory?

A It is an explanation of observations and results

B It is constantly being tested by scientists

C It is well supported and widely accepted

D All of the above

3. Abbie took a trip to the beach. Which is a quantitative observation she may have made?

A There were two lifeguards

B Everyone was wearing bathing suits

C It was a hot day

D The waves were big

4. Which describes an independent variable in a controlled experiment?

A the factor that is purposely changed

B the factor that changes in response

C the factor that is kept the same

D the factor that does not change

Constructed Response

Write your answer to Question 5 on the lines below.

5. How does scientific knowledge change?

_____

_____

_____

_____

Write your answer to Question 6 on another sheet of paper.

6. A scientist concludes that people prefer the smell of cinnamon more than any other scent. You find out that her data comes from the opinions of only three people. What is wrong with her conclusion? How might you improve her experiment?

Sandy Habitats

Do you enjoy taking field trips to natural places? Back in 1896, Dr. Henry Cowles, a botanist from the University of Chicago, visited the shores of Lake Michigan, now known as the Indiana Dunes.

Dr. Cowles set out to study plant species on the dunes. But he was fascinated by how many kinds of life he found. He noticed that the dunes supported greater varieties of life the farther away they were from the shore. He observed that interactions among organisms and between organisms and the environment changed over time.

Cowles looked at how factors such as rain, wind, and human development caused changes in the dunes. He also saw that these changes affected plant and animal life. Cowles noticed there was a connection between the diversity of species and environmental conditions.

Cowles's research contributed to the development of the science of ecology, the study of the relationships among organisms and between organisms and their environment. His study of the changes over time in organisms and the places they live became known as succession.

▲ The Indiana Dunes is now a national park that attracts more than 2 million visitors each year.

Research the public efforts to protect the Indiana Dunes from human development. Write a persuasive letter to a public official giving your opinion as to whether public funds should be used to protect the dunes. Support your opinion with facts and details from your research.

Healing With MAGNETISM?

Magnetism is a powerful force with many uses. One claim is that it can relieve pain. The idea is that the magnetic field of a copper bracelet ionizes blood traveling through the wearer's wrist. This is supposed to change the electronic charge in the molecules of the blood. Supporters claim that the newly ionized blood improves circulation and oxygen flow. But what is really going on?

Doctors have done studies to test the claims made about these bracelets. A placebo is a control substance in experiments—something that looks like the material being tested, but doesn't do anything to the subject. In these studies, some patients wore ionic bracelets and others wore placebo bracelets, which looked the same but were not ionic. Doctors found no statistical difference in the pain relief from wearing an ionic bracelet versus a placebo bracelet. That means the bracelets don't work, but people experience pain relief because they believe the bracelets work. It's mind over matter!

Find several sources presenting claims about magnetic bracelets. Write a letter to a friend who is considering buying one of these bracelets. Evaluate the claims made in the ads, and help your friend make an informed decision.

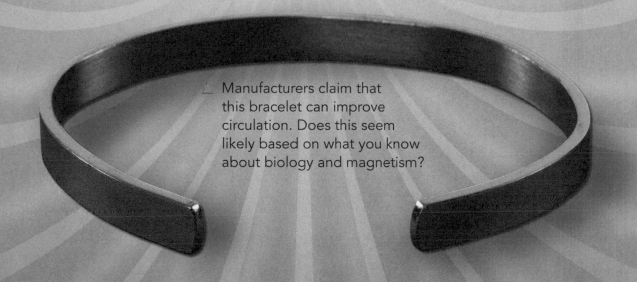

Manufacturers claim that this bracelet can improve circulation. Does this seem likely based on what you know about biology and magnetism?

WHAT MIGHT A CRAB'S SHELL SIZE TELLA SCIENTIST?

What tools do scientists use to understand the natural world?

This Dungeness crab's shell is being measured using a specialized tool. A crab ruler measures the shell at its widest point and is often used by fishermen to see if a crab is big enough to keep. For example, in Washington state, male crabs must be at least 15.9 cm (6 1/4 in) wide. Scientists studying this crab may record its shell size, weight, and the number of crabs that were found in the same area.

⚠️ **Infer** Why might a scientist measure a crab's size and record information about its surroundings?

Watch the **Untamed Science** video to learn more about how tools help scientists.

_____

_____

_____

_____

Female

Check Your Understanding

1. Background Read the paragraph below and then answer the question.

Emi studied hard to prepare for her science lab investigation. Emi was concerned because her investigation was **complex**. She had been earning high marks all year and wanted to maintain this **trend**. Emi also wanted to use her lab report as a **sample** of her science work.

> To be **complex** is to have many parts.
>
> A **trend** is the general direction that something tends to move.
>
> A **sample** is a portion of something that is used to represent the whole thing.

• Why would preparing help Emi maintain her high marks?

_____

_____

Vocabulary Skill

Identify Multiple Meanings Some words have more than one meaning. The table below lists multiple meaning words used in science and in daily life.

Word	Everyday Meaning	Scientific Meaning
mean	*v.* to indicate; to intend **Example:** They didn't *mean* to hurt her.	*n.* the numerical average **Example:** The *mean* of 11, 7, 5, and 9 is 8.
volume	*n.* the loudness of a sound **Example:** Turn up the *volume* so we can hear the song.	*n.* the amount of space an object or substance takes up **Example:** Record the *volume* of water in the graduated cylinder.

2. Quick Check In the table above, circle the meaning of the word *volume* that is used in the following sentence.

• The *volume* of juice in the container is 1.89 liters.

density

estimate

model

safety symbol

Part 2 Preview

Out of the Corner of Your Eye

Have you ever seen something out of the corner of your eye? You were using your peripheral vision. Your peripheral vision is your ability to detect objects that you are not looking at directly.

Visual perception, or sight, occurs when light bounces off objects and enters the eye. The direction of your line of sight is called your focal point. Receptor cells in your eyes, called rods and cones, detect this light. Cones are concentrated toward the back of your eyes. They receive light most directly from your focal point, straight ahead. Rods surround the region of cones. They receive the light from angles other than your direct, or straight forward, gaze.

In bright enough light, you see images at your focal point in clear detail and color. Peripheral vision is most sensitive to motion and in dim light. The locations of objects in peripheral vision tests are identified by the degrees of angles. The focal point (straight ahead of the viewer) is at 90°; the direct left and right of the viewer are at 0°.

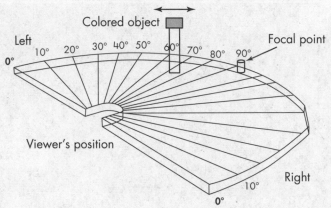

In this activity, you will design, build, and use a peripheral vision tester.

Identify the Problem

1. Suppose you are in charge of screening drivers for a top auto racing team. A racecar driver must be able to see other cars approaching at high speeds from all directions. You need a device that will help you test whether a driver will be able to function well on the speedway. What problem(s) will your designs help solve?

_____

_____

_____

_____

Do Research

Examine the diagrams of the human eye provided by your teacher.

☑ **2.** Where are the receptor cells located? _____

_____

_____

☑ **3.** How does the location of receptor cells relate to the two types of sight, direct gaze and peripheral vision? _____

_____

_____

☑ **4.** On a separate sheet of paper, draw a diagram of a cross section of an eye. Label the predominant locations of rods and cones. Show the angles from which light must enter the eye to strike the different types of receptor cells.

Go to the materials station(s). Examine the materials. Think about how each one may or may not be useful in the design for a peripheral vision tester. Leave the materials where they are.

☑ **5.** What are your design constraints? _____

_____

_____

Develop Possible Solutions

☑ **6.** Describe ways in which you could use the materials to build a peripheral vision tester. Identify at least two problems that your peripheral vision tester will address.

_____

_____

_____

Choose One Solution

Answer the following questions on a separate sheet of paper.

☑ **7.** List the material(s) you will use in your peripheral vision tester prototype.

☑ **8.** Draw your design and label all the materials and parts.

☑ **9.** Describe how you will build your peripheral vision tester.

☑ **10.** Describe the procedure you will use to test your classmates' peripheral vision.

Design and Construct a Prototype

Have your teacher review and approve your designs. Then, gather the materials you need. Build a prototype, the first working version of your design. If you can, document your construction process by taking photos or recording video as you go.

☑ **11.** On a separate sheet of paper, draw a diagram to scale of your completed prototype. Label the features and note the scale of the dimensions.

Test the Prototypes

☑ **12.** Three of your classmates will act as potential racecar drivers. Use your prototype to test their peripheral vision. Identify the people that you test as *Driver A, Driver B,* and *Driver C.* Record your observations (in degrees from the center) on the table below or a separate sheet of paper.

Driver	Direction	Object First Detected	Color Detected	Object Identified
A	From left			
	From right			
B	From left			
	From right			
C	From left			
	From right			

☑ **13.** Use a protractor to make diagrams on which to plot your observations. Make a separate diagram for each driver you test.

Communicate Results

14. Collect the materials that document the design, construction, and testing of your prototype. Assemble a portfolio that includes your diagrams, your photographs or video of the process, and the diagrams of your test results. Make and display a poster or a computer slide show that summarizes how your prototype worked and the test results for Drivers A, B, and C.

Evaluate and Redesign

15. Evaluate how well your prototype worked in testing the peripheral vision of prospective racecar drivers. Check one answer for each question.

Does the prototype...	Very Much	Somewhat	Not At All
fit within the size constraint?			
allow for reassembly in a new location?			
use degrees from center?			
block the driver's focal point?			
evaluate ability to detect the location?			
evaluate ability to detect color?			
evaluate ability to identify details?			

16. Compare your results with your classmates. Did your prototypes function in similar ways? Explain.

_____

_____

_____

_____

17. What changes could you make to your prototype to make it more effectively test peripheral vision of a racecar driver?

_____

_____

_____

_____

Measurement in Science

UNLOCK THE BIG **?**

🔑 **Why Is a Standard Measurement System Important?**

🔑 **What Are Some SI Units of Measure?**

MY PLANET DIARY

Measurements have helped people record and share information about some pretty amazing moments!

- In 2006 in Maui, Hawaii, a surfer rode the biggest wave on record: a 21-meter-tall wall of water!

- Growers compete every year for the heaviest pumpkin in the United States. The 2009 winner weighed more than 725 kilograms.

- In the winter of 1909 a severe cold front hit the East Coast, including Florida. Tallahassee holds the record for the coldest temperature in the state: -19°C.

FUN FACTS

Read the following questions. Write your answers below.

1. What unit of measure is used to find both length and height?

_____

2. What problems could arise if scientists used different units to measure height?

_____

_____

_____

Lab zone® Do the Inquiry Warm-Up *Taking Measurements.*

Why Is a Standard Measurement System Important?

Suppose you wanted to measure the width of a book. If you used your finger, the book might be 3 fingers wide. If you used paper clips, the book might be 5 paper clips wide. And if you used a ruler, the book might be 22 centimeters wide. These are three different ways of measuring the same thing.

Vocabulary

- metric system
- International System of Units (SI)
- mass
- weight
- volume
- density

Skills

↪ Reading: Compare and Contrast

△ Inquiry: Predict

To avoid the problem of using different units of measurement, standard measurement systems were developed. ☞ **A standard measurement system is important because it allows scientists to compare data and communicate with each other about their results.**

In the 1790s, scientists developed the metric system of measurement. The **metric system** is a measurement system based on the number 10. Modern scientists use a version of the metric system called the **International System of Units,** or SI (from the French, *Système International d'Unités*). Prefixes are used to identify larger and smaller units. The prefixes used in the SI system are shown in **Figure 1.**

FIGURE 1 ··

SI Prefixes

The metric system is used to measure things like length, mass, and volume.

✎ **Identify Complete the tasks below.**

1. Fill in the blanks to complete the chart of SI prefixes.

2. Identify something you would measure in each of the following:

Millimeters _____

Kilometers _____

Common SI Prefixes

Prefix	Meaning		Units
_____	1,000		kilometer
_____	100		hectometer
deka- (da)	10		dekameter
no prefix	1		meter
deci- (d)	_____	(one tenth)	decimeter
centi- (c)	_____	(one hundredth)	centimeter
milli- (m)	0.001 (one thousandth)		_____

Lab zone® Do the Quick Lab *Measurement Systems.*

☞ Assess Your Understanding

got it? ··

○ **I get it!** Now I know that a standard measurement system is important because _____

_____

○ **I need extra help with** _____

_____

What Are Some SI Units of Measure?

Scientists regularly measure properties such as length, mass, volume, density, temperature, and time. Each property can be measured using an SI unit.

Length Length is the distance from one point to another. 🔑 **A meter (m) is the basic SI unit used for measuring length.** One meter is about the distance from the floor to a doorknob. One tool used to measure length is a metric ruler.

Many distances can be measured in meters. For example, you can measure your height or a soccer kick in meters. For measuring lengths smaller than a meter, you use the centimeter (cm) and millimeter (mm). For example, the length of a piece of binder paper is about 29 centimeters. For measuring a long distance, such as the distance between cities, you use kilometers. The table at the left shows you how to convert between different metric length units. Try measuring the green anole in **Figure 2**.

Conversions for Length		
1 km	=	1,000 m
1 m	=	100 cm
1 m	=	1,000 mm
1 cm	=	10 mm

FIGURE 2 ··

Measuring Length

The green anole is a small lizard native to southeastern parts of the United States.

✎ **Measure** Do the activities at the right.

1. How long is the anole:

   In centimeters? _____

   In millimeters? _____

2. Choose three small items on or near your desk such as your pencil, finger, or eraser. Record their lengths below. How do your measurements compare with those of your classmates?

   _____

   _____

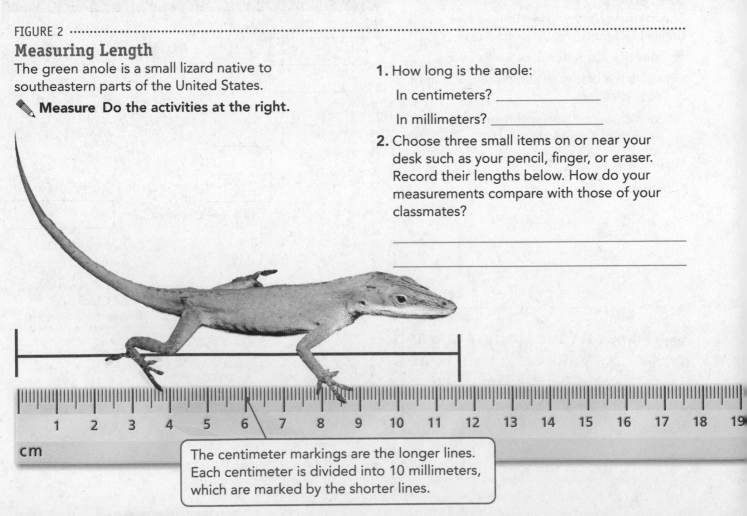

The centimeter markings are the longer lines. Each centimeter is divided into 10 millimeters, which are marked by the shorter lines.

cm

Mass

Mass is a measure of the amount of matter in an object. **In SI, the basic unit for measuring mass is the kilogram (kg).** The mass of cars, bicycles, and people is measured in kilograms. If you want to measure smaller masses, you would use grams (g) or milligrams (mg). The table at the right shows how to convert between kilograms, grams, and milligrams. The balance shown in **Figure 3** is used to measure mass. A balance compares the mass of an object to a known mass.

Weight is different than mass. **Weight** is a measure of the force of gravity acting on an object. A scale is used to measure weight. When you stand on a scale, gravity pulls you downward. This compresses springs inside the scale. The more you weigh, the more the springs compress.

Although mass and weight are related, they are not the same. The mass of an object is constant—it stays the same. The weight of the object is not constant. It can change because the force of gravity can change. For instance, on the moon, the force of gravity is weaker than it is on Earth. So you weigh less on the moon than you do on Earth. But your mass is the same no matter where you are.

✏ **Compare and Contrast**
In the space below, compare and contrast mass and weight. How are they similar? How are they different?

_____

_____

_____

_____

_____

_____

Conversions for Mass

1 kg	=	1,000 g
1 g	=	1,000 mg

FIGURE 3 ···

Measuring Mass

✏ **Use the triple-beam balance to complete this activity.**

1. **Review** What does a triple-beam balance measure? _____

2. **Identify** What SI unit is used to measure mass?

_____

3. **Measure** What is the mass of the toy car? _____

1 Place an object on the pan.

2 Shift the riders on the beams until they balance the object and the pointer hits 0.

3 Add up the grams shown on all three beams to find the mass.

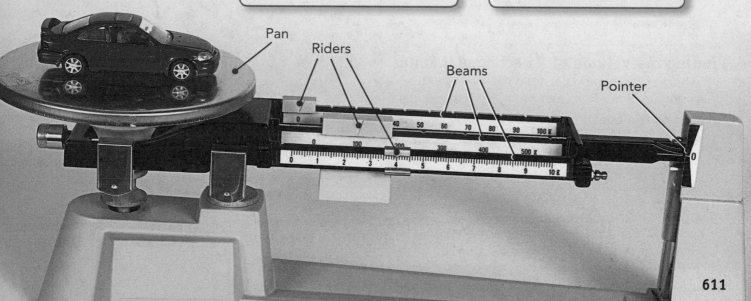

Pan

Riders

Beams

Pointer

611

Conversions for Volume

1 m³	=	1,000,000 cm³
1 cm³	=	1 mL
1 L	=	1,000 mL
1 L	=	1,000 cm³

Volume Have you ever looked at a box of your favorite food and seen the following line: "This package sold by weight, not by volume"? **Volume** is the amount of space an object or substance takes up. All objects with mass—whether they are solids, liquids, or gases—have volume. 🔑 **In SI, the basic unit for measuring volume is the cubic meter (m³).** Cubic meters and cubic centimeters (cm³) are used to measure the volume of solids. The unit for measuring the volume of liquids or gases is the liter (L). The table at the left shows how to convert between these units.

Calculating the Volume of Rectangular Solids

Suppose you want to know the volume of a rectangular solid, such as the gift box in **Figure 4**. To find this volume, you would first measure the length, width, and height of the box. Then you would multiply length times width times height. When you use this formula, you must use the same units for all the measurements.

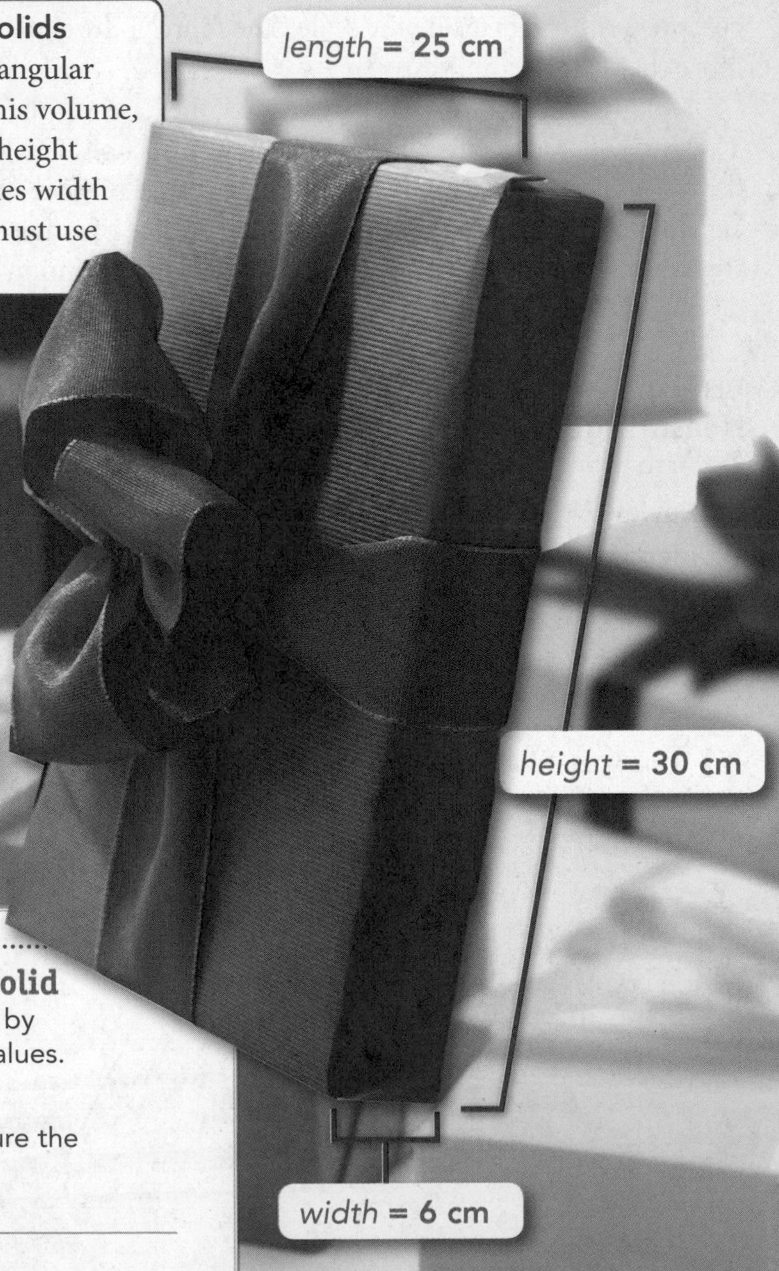

length = 25 cm

height = 30 cm

width = 6 cm

FIGURE 4 ....

Finding the Volume of a Rectangular Solid
The volume of a rectangular solid can be found by measuring its dimensions and multiplying the values.

✏️ **Answer the questions below.**

1. **Review** What unit should you use to measure the volume of a rectangular solid?

   _____

2. **Calculate** What is the volume of this gift box?

   _____

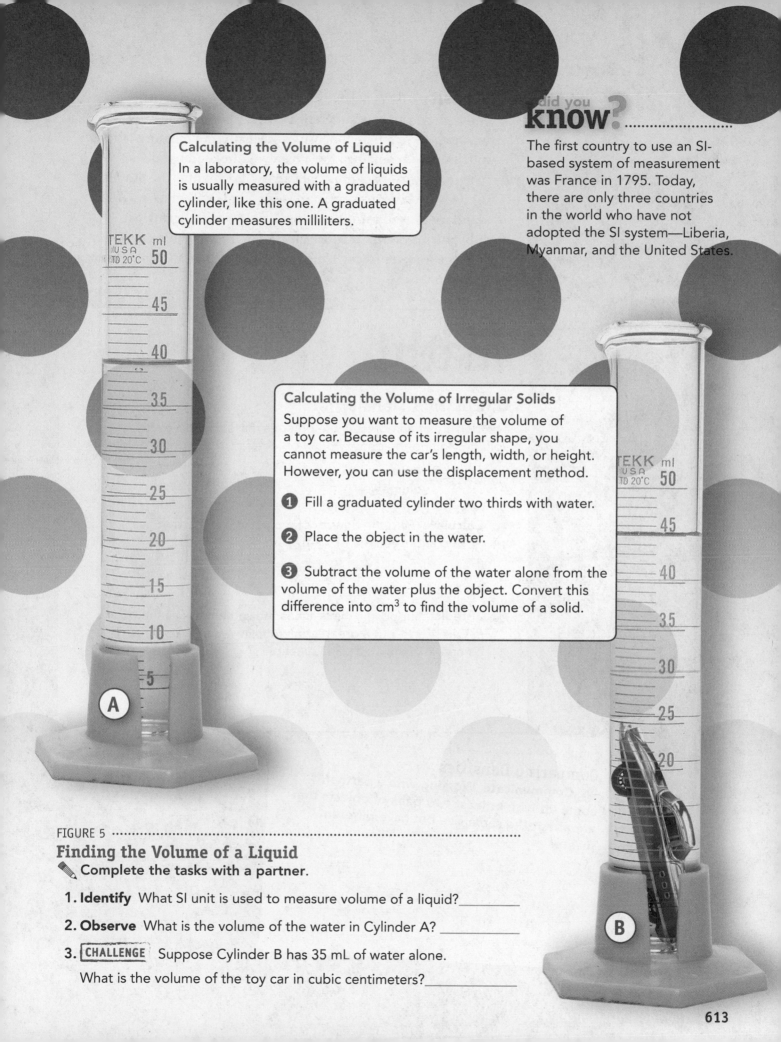

Calculating the Volume of Liquid

In a laboratory, the volume of liquids is usually measured with a graduated cylinder, like this one. A graduated cylinder measures milliliters.

Calculating the Volume of Irregular Solids

Suppose you want to measure the volume of a toy car. Because of its irregular shape, you cannot measure the car's length, width, or height. However, you can use the displacement method.

❶ Fill a graduated cylinder two thirds with water.

❷ Place the object in the water.

❸ Subtract the volume of the water alone from the volume of the water plus the object. Convert this difference into cm^3 to find the volume of a solid.

FIGURE 5 ···

Finding the Volume of a Liquid

✎ Complete the tasks with a partner.

1. **Identify** What SI unit is used to measure volume of a liquid?_____

2. **Observe** What is the volume of the water in Cylinder A? _____

3. **CHALLENGE** Suppose Cylinder B has 35 mL of water alone.

   What is the volume of the toy car in cubic centimeters?_____

613

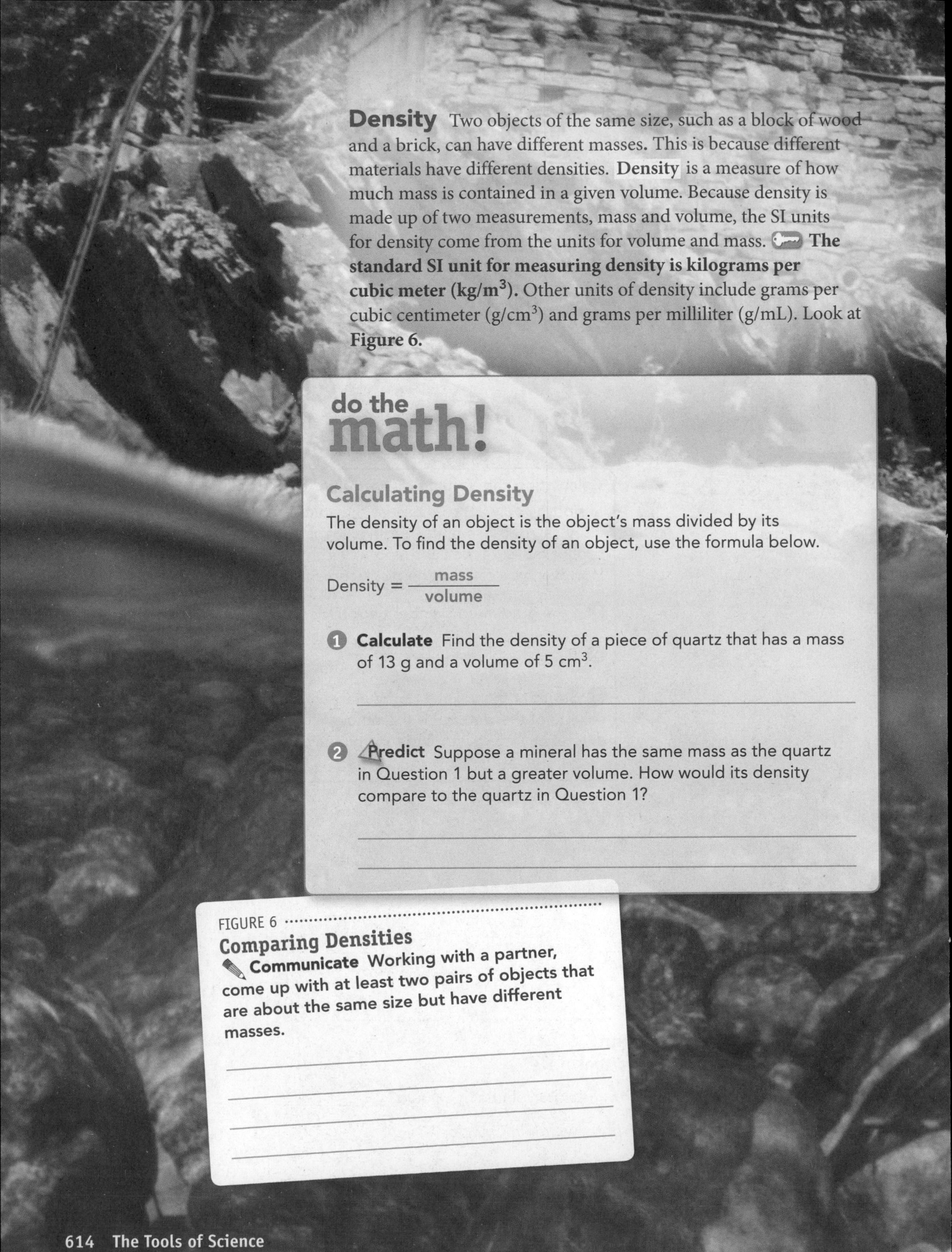

Density Two objects of the same size, such as a block of wood and a brick, can have different masses. This is because different materials have different densities. **Density** is a measure of how much mass is contained in a given volume. Because density is made up of two measurements, mass and volume, the SI units for density come from the units for volume and mass. 🔑 **The standard SI unit for measuring density is kilograms per cubic meter (kg/m^3).** Other units of density include grams per cubic centimeter (g/cm^3) and grams per milliliter (g/mL). Look at **Figure 6.**

do the math!

Calculating Density

The density of an object is the object's mass divided by its volume. To find the density of an object, use the formula below.

$$\text{Density} = \frac{\text{mass}}{\text{volume}}$$

1 Calculate Find the density of a piece of quartz that has a mass of 13 g and a volume of 5 cm^3.

_____

2 Predict Suppose a mineral has the same mass as the quartz in Question 1 but a greater volume. How would its density compare to the quartz in Question 1?

_____

_____

FIGURE 6 ·······················

Comparing Densities

✎ **Communicate** Working with a partner, come up with at least two pairs of objects that are about the same size but have different masses.

_____

_____

_____

_____

Density of Substances Different substances have different densities. Very dense materials contain a lot of matter in a given space or volume, while less dense materials contain smaller amounts of matter in the same space or volume. The density of a particular substance is the same for all samples of that substance, no matter how large or small. For example, a ring made of pure gold has the same density as a brick made of pure gold. The table in **Figure 7** lists the densities of some common substances.

Using Density If you know an object's density, you can determine whether the object will float in a given liquid. An object will float if it is less dense than the surrounding liquid. For example, the density of water is 1 g/cm³. A piece of wood with a density of 0.8 g/cm³ will float in water. However, a piece of copper, which has a density of 8.9 g/cm³, will sink. Use the table to answer the question about using density in **Figure 7**.

Densities of Some Common Substances

Substance	Density (g/cm³)
Air	0.001
Ice	0.9
Water	1.0
Aluminum	2.7
Lead	11.35

FIGURE 7 ···

Understanding Density

People who fish put small weights on their fishing line so the hook and bait sink below the surface of the water.

✎ **Complete the activities with a partner.**

1. **Identify** According to the chart, which substances will float in water?

_____

3. **Investigate** You need a lead weight for your fishing line, but your tackle box is unorganized. You have small weights of aluminum and lead but they look the same. How would you determine which weights are lead?

_____

_____

_____

_____

Lead fishing weight

Conversions for Temperature

0°C	=	273 K
100°C	=	373 K

Temperature Is it hot or cold outside today? You can answer this questions by measuring the temperature of the air.

Temperature is measured using a thermometer. A thermometer has numbers and units, or a temperature scale on it. When you place a liquid thermometer in a substance, the liquid inside will increase or decrease in volume. This makes the level rise or fall. To determine the temperature, you read the number next to the top of the liquid in the thermometer.

There are two temperature scales that are used in science—the Celsius scale and the Kelvin scale. On the Celsius scale, water freezes at 0°C and boils at 100°C. On the Kelvin scale, the lowest possible temperature is 0 K, or absolute zero. There are no negative numbers on this scale. ⌐ **The Kelvin scale is the basis for the SI temperature units, and the kelvin (K) is the SI unit for temperature. Figure 8** shows a comparison of the Celsius and Kelvin scales. The table shows how to convert between the two scales.

FIGURE 8 ·······························

Temperature Scales

✎ **Read the text and then complete the activity.**

1. **Identify** Determine which thermometer is Kelvin and which is Celsius. Label them above the diagram.

2. **Interpret Diagrams** Find and shade in the freezing point on the Kelvin thermometer.

3. **Review** Identify one way the Kelvin and Celsius scales differ.

_____

_____

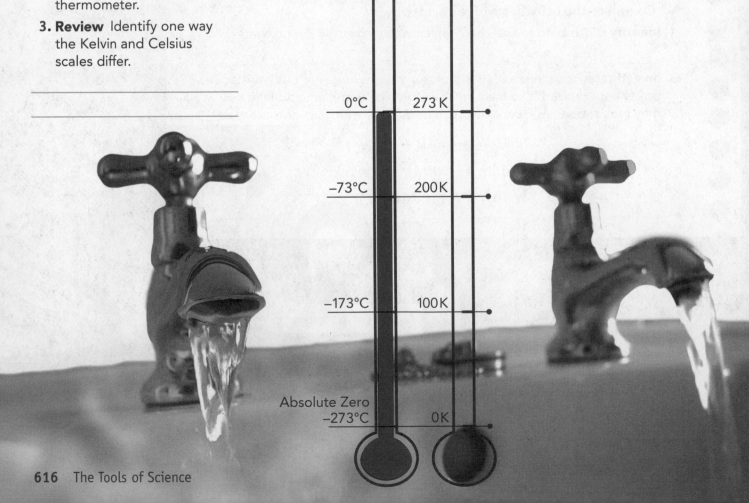

Time The race is on, and the finish line is in sight. But an opponent is catching up. Just one second can mean the difference between winning and losing. But what is a second?

Time is a measurement of the period between two events. 🔑 **The second (s) is the SI unit used to measure time.** In one second, light can travel about seven and a half times around Earth at the equator. Just like all SI units, the second can be divided into smaller units based on the number 10. For example, a millisecond (ms) is one thousandth of a second. However, for longer periods of time, minutes or hours are typically used. There are 60 seconds in a minute, and 60 minutes in an hour.

Clocks and watches are used to measure time. Some clocks are more accurate than others. Most digital stopwatches measure time accurately to one hundredth of a second, as shown in **Figure 9.** Devices used for timing Olympic events measure time to a thousandth of a second or less.

FIGURE 9 ⋯⋯⋯⋯⋯⋯⋯⋯⋯⋯⋯
Measuring Time
✏ **Review** Identify and record the minutes, seconds, and hundredths on the stopwatch.

Lab® zone   Do the Quick Lab *Measuring Volume in Metric.*

🔑 **Assess Your Understanding**

1a. Identify What tool would you use to measure the mass of an egg?

_____

b. Sequence What steps would you take to determine the density of an egg?

_____

_____

_____

got it?

○ **I get it!** Now I know that the basic SI units of measurement are _____

_____

_____

○ **I need extra help with** _____

_____

_____

_____

Math in Science

UNLOCK THE ESSENTIAL Q?

🔑 **What Are Some Math Skills Used in Science?**

🔑 **What Are Some Math Tools Used in Science?**

MY PLANET DIARY

BLOG

Write your answer to the question below.
How do you use math during a typical day?

_____

_____

_____

_____

_____

Lab zone® Do the Inquiry Warm-Up *Making Models.*

Posted by: Nikos

Location: Monrovia, Indiana

I was planning my birthday party when I realized that I needed to buy the tickets to the movie that my friends and I were going to see. Since it was my party, I thought I should pay for my friends' admission. I had three friends going, and each ticket was about 9 dollars. So I figured I should bring 40 dollars to be safe. This all happened within a minute, and I realized just how much we use math every day.

SP
EVENT CODE

Q ROW / BOX   15 SEAT

X8 SECTION

SCREEN 4: HAPPY BIRTHDAY!

Q ROW / BOX

15 SEAT

$8.95 PRICE

Vocabulary
- estimate • accuracy • precision • significant figures
- percent error • mean • median • mode • range
- anomalous data

Skills
↺ Reading: Ask Questions
△ Inquiry: Calculate

What Are Some Math Skills Used in Science?

Scientists in different fields use math to different degrees, but all use some math in their work. Scientists use math to collect, organize, analyze, and present data. 🔑 **Some math skills used in science when working with data include estimation, accuracy and precision, and significant figures.**

Estimation How could you measure the length of a book without using a measuring device? You might estimate the length by comparing it with a book you had already measured. An **estimate** is an approximation of a number based on reasonable assumptions. An estimate is not a guess. It is always based on known information.

Scientists often rely on estimates when they cannot obtain exact numbers. The estimates might be based on indirect measurements, calculations, models, or samples. For example, a scientist might estimate the number of insects living in an area based on a sample count in one part of the total area.

do the math!

Estimation

Estimating from a sample is a quick way to determine the large number of insects in this photo.

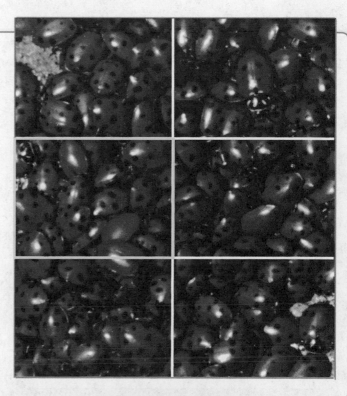

1. **Interpret Photos** How many insects are in the yellow square? This number is your sample.

_____

2. **Explain** By what number should you multiply the sample to find an estimate for the total number of insects in the area? Explain your answer.

_____

_____

3. △ **Calculate** Calculate your estimate for the total number of insects. Show your work.

_____

FIGURE 1 ··

Accuracy and Precision

In a dart game, accurate throws land close to the bull's-eye. Precise throws land close together. ✎ **Identify** Are the darts thrown accurately or precisely? Explain.

_____

_____

_____

FIGURE 2 ··

Significant Figures

When combining measurements with different degrees of accuracy and precision, the accuracy of the final answer can be no greater than the *least* accurate measurement.

✎ **Calculate** Read about working with significant figures. Then complete the activities in the boxes.

Accuracy and Precision

People often use the words *accuracy* and *precision* to describe the same idea. In science, these words have different meanings. **Accuracy** refers to how close a measurement is to the true or accepted value. **Precision** refers to how close a group of measurements are to each other.

How can you be sure that a measurement is both accurate and precise? First, use a high-quality measurement tool. Next, measure carefully. Finally, repeat the measurement a few times. If your measurement is the same each time, you can assume that it is reliable. A reliable measurement is both accurate and precise. Look at **Figure 1**.

Significant Figures

The precision of a measurement depends on the instrument you use to take the measurement. For example, if the smallest unit on a ruler is centimeters, then the most precise measurement you can make will be in centimeters. **Significant figures** communicate how precise measurements are. The significant figures in a measurement include all digits measured exactly, plus one estimated digit. If the measurement has only one digit, you must assume it is estimated. Use **Figure 2** to learn more about significant figures.

2

Adding and Subtracting Significant Figures

When measurements are added or subtracted, the answer can contain no more decimal places than the least accurate measurement.

Suppose you wanted to decorate a frame with shells. If a shell 2.3 centimeters long is added to a row of shells 10.23 centimeters long, what is the new length of the row? How many significant figures are in this measurement? Why?

_____

_____

_____

_____

1

Finding Significant Figures

What is length of the shell in centimeters? How many significant figures are in your measurement?

_____

3

Multiplying and Dividing Significant Figures

When measurements are multiplied or divided, the answer can contain no more significant figures than the least accurate measurement.

Suppose you have framed artwork that measures 1.25 meters by 2 meters. What is the area of the artwork? How many significant figures are in this measurement? Why?

_____

_____

_____

Lab® zone Try the Quick Lab *Understanding Significant Figures.*

🔑 Assess Your Understanding

1a. Compare and Contrast How does accuracy differ from precision?

_____

_____

_____

_____

_____

_____

_____

b. Measuring A tortoise shell, measured with a meterstick divided into 0.01-m intervals, is 0.61 m long. How many significant figures are in this measurement?

_____

got it?..

○ **I get it!** Now I know that some of the math skills used in science include _____

_____

_____

○ **I need extra help with** _____

_____

_____

cm
1 2 3 4 5 6 7 8 9 10 11 12 13 14 15

What Are Some Math Tools Used in Science?

Scientists also use certain math tools to analyze data. 🔑 **Some math tools used in science include calculating percent error; finding the mean, median, mode, and range; and checking the reasonableness of data.**

Percent Error Individual measurements can be accurate or inaccurate. For example, suppose you measure the temperature of boiling water and find the thermometer reads 100.6°C. You know that the accepted, or true, value for the boiling point of water is 100.0°C. Therefore, your measurement is not accurate. But how inaccurate is it? **Percent error** calculations are a way to determine how accurate an experimental value is. A low percent error means that the result you obtained was accurate. A high percent error means that your result was not accurate. It may not be accurate because you did not measure carefully or because something was wrong with your measurement tool.

Percent Error

The experimental value you obtained for the boiling point of water is 100.6°C. The true value is 100.0°C. Calculate percent error using the formula below. Substitute in the experimental and true values.

$$\text{Percent error} = \frac{\text{Difference between experimental value and true value}}{\text{True value}} \times 100\%$$

$$\text{Percent error} = \frac{100.6°C - 100.0°C}{100.0°C} \times 100\% = 0.6\%$$

The percent error in the calculation of the boiling point of water was 0.6%.

❶ Calculate Suppose you measure the density of copper to be 9.37 g/cm³, but you know the true value for the density of copper is 8.92 g/cm³. Find the percent error for the density you measured.

_____

_____

❷ Explain What is a possible source of the error in the density measurement?

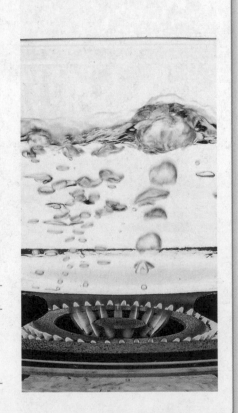

Mean, Median, Mode, and Range

On a sight-seeing trip through the Florida Everglades, the sound of your boat startles a crocodile. The crocodile runs into the water, leaving behind its nest of eggs in the dirt. When you spot the nest, you get curious. How many eggs are there? Is this the typical number of eggs in a nest? What is the range of eggs in a group of nests? Scientists ask questions like these, too. Their answers come from analyzing data. Use **Figure 3** to analyze crocodile egg data yourself.

FIGURE 3 ···

American Crocodile Egg Data

You can use math to analyze the data in the table at the right about the number of American crocodile eggs in seven nests.

✎ **Calculate** Fill in the boxes with the mean, median, mode, and range of the crocodile egg data.

Nest	Number of Eggs
A	40
B	32
C	24
D	40
E	37
F	40
G	39

Mean

The **mean** is the numerical average of a set of data. To find the mean, add up the numbers in the data set. Then divide the sum by the total number of items you added.
Find the mean for the egg data.

_____

Median

The **median** is the middle number in a set of data. To find the median, list all the numbers in order from least to greatest. The median is the middle entry. If a list has an even number of entries, add the two middle numbers together and divide by two to find the median.
Find the median for the egg data.

_____

_____

Mode

The **mode** is the number that appears most often in a list of numbers.
Find the mode for the egg data.

_____

Range

The **range** of a set of data is the difference between the greatest value and the least value in the set.
Find the range for the egg data.

_____

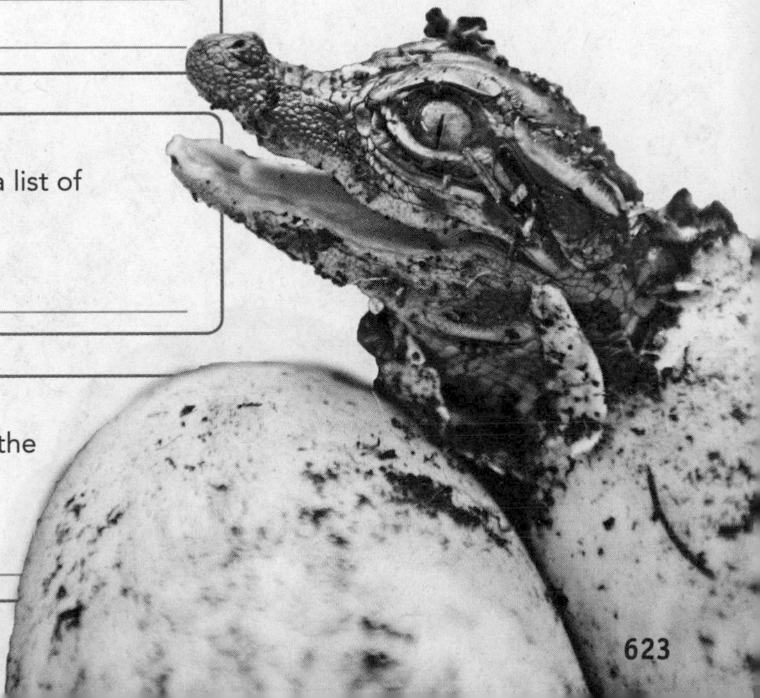

623

Ask Questions Before
you read this section, pose a
question about the topic. After
you read, try to answer it.

_____

_____

_____

_____

Reasonable and Anomalous Data

An important part of analyzing any set of data is to ask, "Do they make sense? Are these data reasonable?" Suppose a scientist studying American crocodiles measures the air temperature near a nesting spot each night for five nights. The data for the first four nights are 20°C, 19°C, 21°C, and 22°C. On the last night, a student is asked to make the measurement. The student records 69°C in the data book.

Are the data reasonable? The reading on Day 5 is very different. Some variation in air temperature makes sense within a small range. But it doesn't make sense for the air temperature to rise 47°C in one day, from 22°C to 69°C. The 69°C does not fit with the rest of the data. Data that do not fit with the rest of a data set are **anomalous data.** In this case, the anomalous datum is explainable. The student measured temperature in °F instead of °C. Sometimes asking whether data are reasonable can uncover sources of error. Investigating the reason for anomalous data can lead to new information and discoveries. See **Figure 4.**

FIGURE 4 ···

American Crocodile Nest Data

Researchers have been tracking the number of crocodile nests in the Everglades for years. The table shows approximate nest data from 1996 to 2000. During these years, the population of American crocodiles in the region increased.

Analyze Experimental Results What variable could have affected the number of nests?

_____

_____

_____

_____

Year	Number of Nests
1996	10
1997	8
1998	11
1999	18
2000	22

apply it!

Until recently, the American crocodile was considered an endangered species. Even today, there are only about 2,000 in the United States. Most of these are in Florida. Studying crocodiles and their nesting habits have helped scientists better understand what affects the crocodile population.

1 Design Experiments How would you collect accurate and precise crocodile nest data?

_____

_____

_____

2 Explain How could you estimate the total number of nests in Florida?

_____

_____

_____

_____

_____

3 CHALLENGE How might a hurricane in Florida cause anomalous nest data?

_____

_____

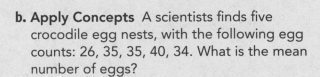
Try the Quick Lab
Math Tools in Science.

🔑 Assess Your Understanding

2a. Explain Why is it important for scientists to calculate percent error?

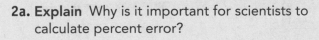

_____

b. Apply Concepts A scientists finds five crocodile egg nests, with the following egg counts: 26, 35, 35, 40, 34. What is the mean number of eggs?

_____

got it? ....

○ **I get it!** Now I know that some math skills used in science include _____

_____

○ I need extra help with _____

_____

🔑 **What Kinds of Data Do Graphs Display?**

🔑 **How Are Different Graphs Used to Display Data?**

my planet DiaRY

SCIENCE STATS

Snow Day!

Brrr! Winters in Indiana can be cold. Snow emergencies can even cancel school! Average temperatures in January vary between −8°C and 2°C. The average annual snowfall for the entire state is about 56 centimeters. The bar graph shows the snowfall totals for each winter from 2003 to 2008 for Bloomington, Indiana.

Answer the question below.

What are the benefits of displaying this data in a graph rather than as a list of years and snowfall amounts?

_____

_____

_____

Lab® Do the Inquiry
zone Warm-Up *Picturing Information.*

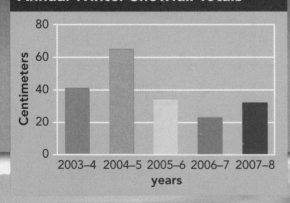

Annual Winter Snowfall Totals

Centimeters

80
60
40
20
0

2003–4 2004–5 2005–6 2006–7 2007–8
years

What Kinds of Data Do Graphs Display?

Suppose you conduct an experiment about the number of calories burned in 30 minutes when bike riding, playing basketball, and watching television. You could simply list your results. This data would be difficult to analyze because it's only a summary of your results in word form.

Vocabulary
- graph • linear graph
- nonlinear graph

Skills
🔄 Reading: Compare and Contrast
△ Inquiry: Graph

Instead, you could use a graph to organize your data. A **graph** is a picture of your data that allows you to visually analyze and compare information.

Kinds of Data

Scientists frequently use graphs to display and analyze results of surveys and experiments. 🔑 **Graphs can display categorical and numerical data.** Categorical data are information that can be grouped into categories. For example, you might take a survey of your classmates to find out their favorite sports. You would then group the results of your survey by type: basketball, football, baseball, tennis, soccer, and so on. Or you might test a rock to determine its mineral composition. You would group the data by the types of minerals in the sample. Numerical data, such as time, temperature, and weight, are continuous, ranging from small to large amounts. Different kinds of graphs are used to display these different kinds of data.

The Martian atmosphere is very thin, which prevents liquid water from forming on the planet's surface.

FIGURE 1 ....
Analyzing Data

The graph shows the amounts of different gases that make up the atmosphere of the planet Mars. By displaying this information visually, you can analyze and compare the data even in the absence of actual figures.

✏️ **Read Graphs** Use the graph to answer the questions below.

1. Estimate the percentage of carbon dioxide that makes up the Martian atmosphere.

_____

2. **Identify** Which two gases in the graph occur in almost equal amounts in the Martian atmosphere?

_____

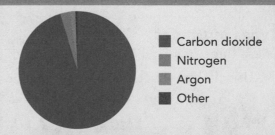

Composition of Martian Atmosphere

- ■ Carbon dioxide
- ■ Nitrogen
- ■ Argon
- ■ Other

Lab® Do the Quick Lab
zone *Making Graphs.*

🔑 Assess Your Understanding

got**it?** ....

○ **I get it!** Now I know that graphs display both _____

_____

○ **I need extra help with** _____

_____

What Are the Different Types of Graphs and How Are They Used?

The most commonly used graphs in science include bar graphs, circle graphs, and line graphs. **Bar graphs and circle graphs are suitable for displaying categorical data, and line graphs and bar graphs are appropriate for displaying numerical data.**

Bar Graphs A bar graph uses vertical or horizontal bars to display data for separate categories. Bar graphs are most often used when you want to show the amount of something in each category. Each bar in the graph represents the data for a single category and lets you compare data with the other categories.

Circle Graphs Like a bar graph, a circle graph displays data in a number of separate categories. However, circle graphs can only be used when you have data for all the categories in your survey or experiment. A circle graph is sometimes called a pie chart. Each "slice" in the pie chart represents an individual category. The size of the slice indicates what percentage of the whole a particular category makes up.

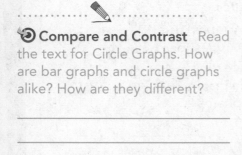

Compare and Contrast Read the text for Circle Graphs. How are bar graphs and circle graphs alike? How are they different?

_____

_____

_____

_____

_____

FIGURE 2

Types of Graphs

These three graphs show different kinds of data about amphibians.

✎ **Use the graphs to answer the questions.**

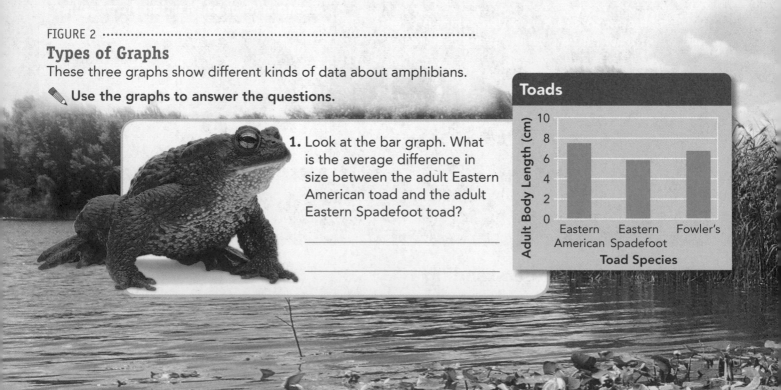

1. Look at the bar graph. What is the average difference in size between the adult Eastern American toad and the adult Eastern Spadefoot toad?

_____

_____

Toads

(Bar graph: Adult Body Length (cm) vs. Toad Species — Eastern American, Eastern Spadefoot, Fowler's)

Line Graphs

Line graphs are among the most common types of graphs used in science. Line graphs display data that show how one variable changes in response to another variable. Line graphs are useful for recording the results of many experiments.

Line Graphs in Experiments

In experiments, scientists make changes to one variable, called the independent variable. The data they collect shows how a second variable responds to these changes. This second variable is called the dependent variable. A line graph is used when an independent variable is continuous. A continuous variable has other points between the tested points. Temperature and time are examples of continuous variables.

For example, to see whether a relationship exists between a person's body mass and the number of calories burned when jogging, you could use a line graph. Body mass is a continuous variable because within the range of body masses you are studying, any value is possible.

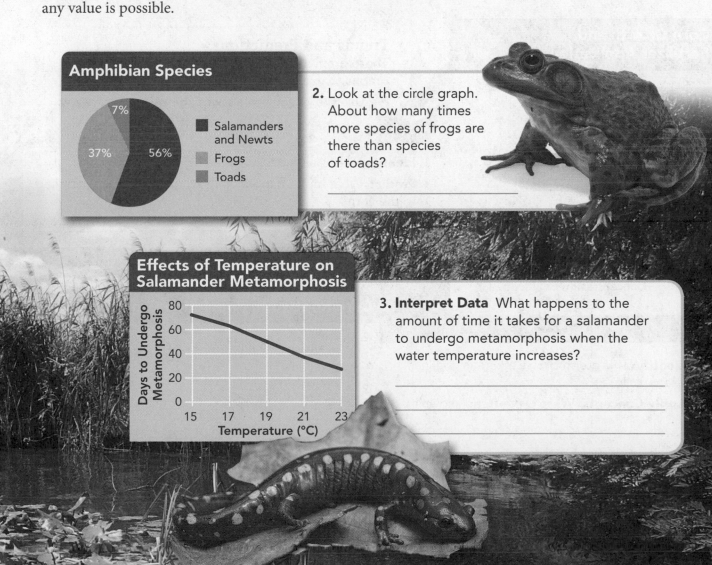

Amphibian Species

- 7%
- 37%
- 56%

■ Salamanders and Newts
■ Frogs
■ Toads

2. Look at the circle graph. About how many times more species of frogs are there than species of toads?

_____

Effects of Temperature on Salamander Metamorphosis

Days to Undergo Metamorphosis

80
60
40
20
0

15   17   19   21   23

Temperature (°C)

3. **Interpret Data** What happens to the amount of time it takes for a salamander to undergo metamorphosis when the water temperature increases?

_____

_____

Using Line Graphs A line graph in which the data points form a straight line is a **linear graph.** A line graph in which the data points do not fall along a straight line, is called a **nonlinear graph.** If the data points form a jagged line, or no line at all, the variables may not have any clear relationship.

Line graphs are powerful tools in science because they allow you to identify trends and make predictions about those trends. Both linear and nonlinear graphs can show trends. A trend is the general direction in which a graph is changing. You can use lines on these graphs to predict the values of points that you have not measured. Use the graphs in **Figure 3** to explore trends and make predictions about the data that are shown.

Corn Growth and Fertilizer Application

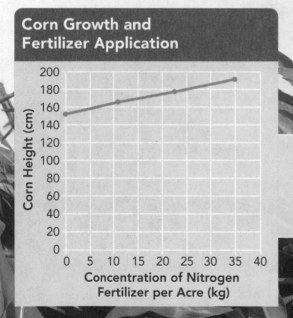

FIGURE 3 ···

Trends and Predictions

These graphs are fit from data. You can use these graphs to make predictions or identify trends.

✎ **Use the graphs to answer the questions below.**

1. **Identify** This is a (linear/nonlinear) graph.

2. **Predict** What might happen if 40 kg of fertilizer was applied to the corn?

   _____

3. **Identify** This graph shows a (linear/nonlinear) relationship.

4. **Apply Concepts** What is the trend shown in this graph?

   _____
   _____
   _____
   _____
   _____

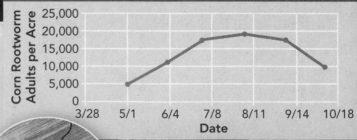

Cell phones have changed the way we communicate.

1 ✎ **Graph** Use the data to make a line graph.

2 **Describe** Does the graph show a linear or nonlinear relationship? Explain.

_____

_____

_____

_____

_____

3 **CHALLENGE** Based on the data, predict the number of cell phone subscribers in 2009.

_____

_____

_____

_____

Year	U.S. Subscribers
2002	140,000,000
2003	159,000,000
2004	182,000,000
2005	208,000,000
2006	233,000,000
2007	255,000,000
2008	263,000,000

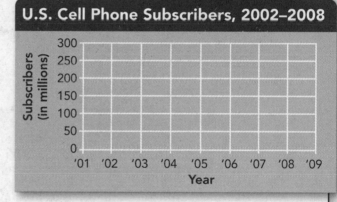

U.S. Cell Phone Subscribers, 2002–2008

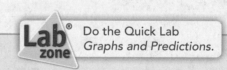

Do the Quick Lab
Graphs and Predictions.

🔑 Assess Your Understanding

1a. Review You are observing a _____ when you notice that the height of corn increases with increasing concentrations of fertilizer.

b. Summarize Why is it often possible to make predictions from data in a line graph?

_____

_____

_____

_____

_____

got it?

○ **I get it!** Now I know that bar graphs and circle graphs are used for _____ data and line graphs and bar graphs are used for _____ data.

○ **I need extra help with** _____

_____

_____

_____

_____

Using Models

UNLOCK THE BIG Q?

🔑 Why Do Scientists Use Models?

🔑 What Is a System?

🔑 How Are Models of Systems Used?

MY PLANET DIARY

BLOG

Posted by: Maddie
Location: Monrovia, Indiana

One day in third grade my teacher said that the class was going to construct a model of the water cycle. At that time I had no idea what the water cycle was or how it worked. When I saw how the water cycle functioned in the model, it gave me a better perspective of how the water cycle worked than a book. Models can give a person a view of something that no book or website can give.

Write your answer to the question below. Describe a time you used a model to help accomplish a task.

_____

_____

_____

_____

_____

Lab zone® Do the Inquiry Warm-Up *Models and Science.*

Vocabulary
- model • system • input • process
- output • feedback

Skills
↪ Reading: Sequence
△ Inquiry: Classify

Why Do Scientists Use Models?

So what exactly is a model? A **model** is a representation of a simple or complex object or process. Models can be pictures, diagrams, three-dimensional objects, mathematical equations, chemical equations, computer programs, or even written descriptions. **Scientists use models to understand things that they cannot observe directly.** Models help scientists to understand things that are very large, such as the universe, or things that are very small, such as an atom. Models can also help scientists to understand processes, such as weather systems. **Figure 1** shows how models can be used to predict earthquake damage.

FIGURE 1 ·····························

Shake, Rattle, and Roll

Look at how these two models of houses, built with different materials, react to an "earthquake" simulated by a shaking table.

✎ **Apply Concepts** How might scientists use the information from how the models reacted to the "earthquake"?

_____

_____

_____

_____

_____

Lab zone
Do the Lab Investigation
Super Models.

⊂⊃ Assess Your Understanding

got it? ···

○ **I get it!** Now I know scientists use models because _____

_____

○ **I need extra help with** _____

_____

What Is a System?

What happens when you touch a hot stove? Your nervous system sends a signal to your muscles to pull your hand away from the hot surface. Your response to the hot stove is an example of a system in action. 🗝️ **A system is a group of parts that work together to perform a function or produce a result.**

Every system has an input, process, and output. **Input** is the material or energy that goes into the system. **Process** is what happens in the system. **Output** is the material or energy that comes out of the system. When you touch a hot stove, your skin sends a message to your nervous system. This is the input. Your nervous system understands that you are touching something hot. This is the process. The output is when your nervous system sends a signal to your muscles to pull your hand back. **Feedback** is output that changes the system in some way. For example, when you pull your hand back from the hot stove, your nervous system sends a message that your hand is no longer touching a hot object, so you can relax.

↻ **Sequence**
Underline and number the steps that happen in your nervous system when you touch a hot stove.

apply it!

Classify You and your friends are sitting at the lunch table enjoying your food. You begin to eat an apple. In the chart below, fill in the input, process, and output of the digestive system. Circle and label the input and process on the diagram.

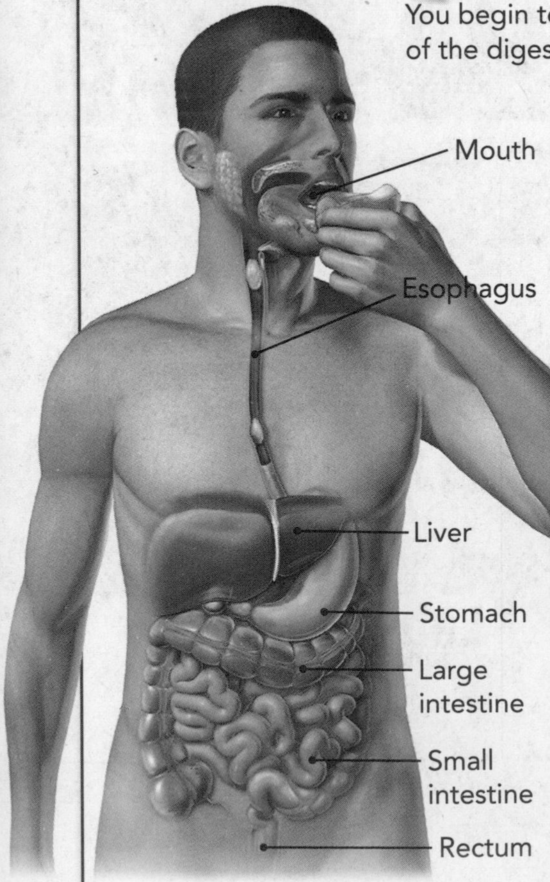

— Mouth

— Esophagus

— Liver

— Stomach

— Large intestine

— Small intestine

— Rectum

Input	
Process	
Output	
Feedback	

Mechanical Systems
People have designed many mechanical systems to keep them comfortable or to help them do work. Heating and air conditioning systems, elevators, and engines are examples of mechanical systems. **Figure 2** shows an example of a basic mechanical system.

FIGURE 2

A System on Wheels
This skateboarder may be having too much fun to realize it, but his skateboard is a mechanical system.

✎ **Apply Concepts** Describe the input, process, and output of this system in the spaces provided. Then, in the empty space, draw an example of a mechanical system you use.

Input	
Process	
Output	

Vocabulary Prefixes The prefix *in-* can mean "into" or "within," such as in the word *input*. It can also mean "not." What do you think the word *inability* means?

_____

_____

_____

635

FIGURE 3 ·······························

Cloud Formation

Clouds form when warm, moist air rises and cools. Water vapor condenses onto tiny particles in the air.

✎ **On the lines provided, write the input, process, and output of this system.**

1. **Identify** What is the input of this system?

_____

_____

_____

2. **Predict** What would happen if there was no input?

_____

_____

_____

_____

_____

Environmental Systems   There are many systems in nature. Environmental systems may involve biological, geological, and physical parts. The process that forms soil is one environmental system. Another is how a cloud forms, shown in **Figure 3.**

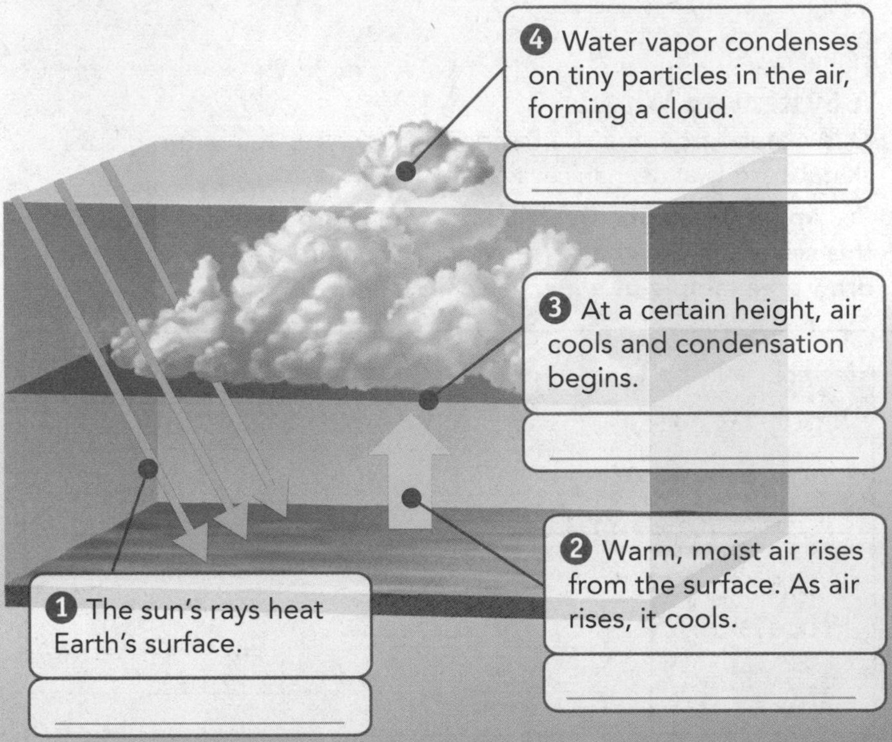

❹ Water vapor condenses on tiny particles in the air, forming a cloud.

_____

❸ At a certain height, air cools and condensation begins.

_____

❷ Warm, moist air rises from the surface. As air rises, it cools.

_____

❶ The sun's rays heat Earth's surface.

_____

Lab ® zone   Do the Quick Lab *Systems of Science.*

⚷ Assess Your Understanding

1a. Name _____ is the material or energy that comes out of a system.

b. Explain Why is a computer a system?

_____

_____

_____

c. CHALLENGE   What are the input, process, and output of an automatic paper towel dispenser?

_____

_____

_____

_____

got it? ·······························

○ **I get it!** Now I know that a system is _____

_____

_____

○ **I need extra help with** _____

_____

How Are Models of Systems Used?

Many systems are complex. Scientists cannot always observe all the inputs, processes, and outputs of a complex system. 🔑 **Scientists often use models of systems to understand how systems work.** These models can help scientists to predict changes in a system as a result of a change in input or system feedback.

Using Basic Models Sometimes basic models of complex systems allow scientists, students, or the public to get a general knowledge of the system. These models do not show all the details of the system. However, they still show the major parts, processes, and relationships in the system. **Figure 4** shows a model of a basic system, the tick life cycle.

FIGURE 4 ···

Life Cycle of the American Dog Tick

American dog ticks are a common pest. They can spread diseases such as Rocky Mountain spotted fever to humans.

✏️ **Interpret Diagrams** Read the model of the life cycle of the American dog tick below. Then, fill in the sign with a title and information that could help you avoid ticks.

WARNING!

Title: _____

Warning:

- _____
  _____

- _____
  _____

- _____
  _____

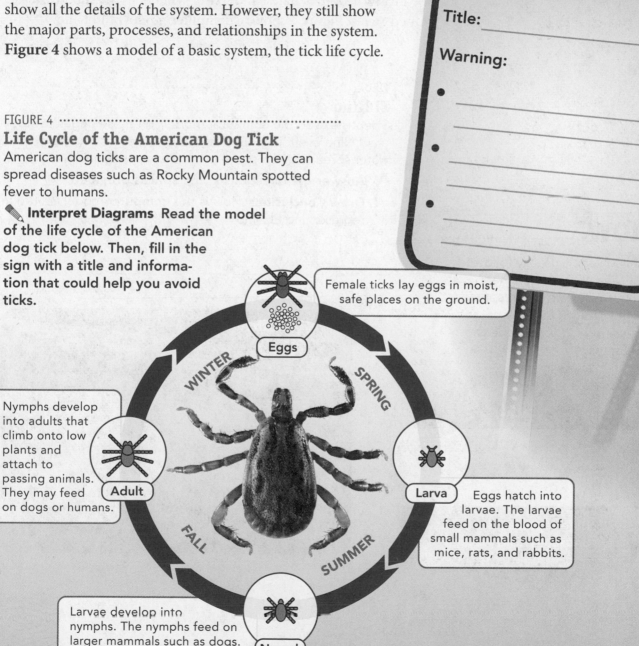

Female ticks lay eggs in moist, safe places on the ground.

Eggs

WINTER

SPRING

Nymphs develop into adults that climb onto low plants and attach to passing animals. They may feed on dogs or humans.

Adult

Larva

Eggs hatch into larvae. The larvae feed on the blood of small mammals such as mice, rats, and rabbits.

FALL

SUMMER

Larvae develop into nymphs. The nymphs feed on larger mammals such as dogs.

Nymph

Using Complex Models Some systems are complex, with many interactions. Scientists cannot understand these systems by using simple models. Scientists often use computer programs to represent all the interactions in a complex system.

The El Niño weather event is an example of a complex system because it involves both air and water. During some years, the difference in air pressure decreases across the tropical Pacific Ocean. You can think of this as the input of the system. It causes the trade winds to relax. Warm water spreads eastward toward the west coast of South America. The output of this system is thunderstorms, extra rainfall, and flooding in the southwestern United States. El Niño also causes warmer winters in the northeastern United States, and wetter winters in the southeastern United States. **Figure 5** shows a computer model of El Niño.

FIGURE 5 ···

El Niño
Scientists used the computer models on these pages to study an El Niño event in 1997. The red color represents warm water spreading across the ocean between January and June.

✎ **Answer the questions in the spaces provided.**

1. **Draw Conclusions** How is this computer model limited in representing El Niño?

_____

_____

_____

Blue represents unusually cold water.

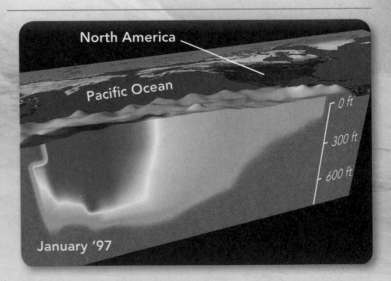

North America

Pacific Ocean

0 ft

300 ft

600 ft

January '97

do the math!

Although El Niño occurs in the Pacific Ocean, it also affects the weather patterns on the east coast of the United States.

Type of Year	Average Number of Hurricanes
Normal Year	5.8
El Niño Year	4

1 Interpret Tables Use the data table to make a bar graph in the space provided.

2 Graph Label the x- and y-axes. Write a title for the graph.

3 Interpret Data How did El Niño affect the average number of hurricanes?

_____

_____

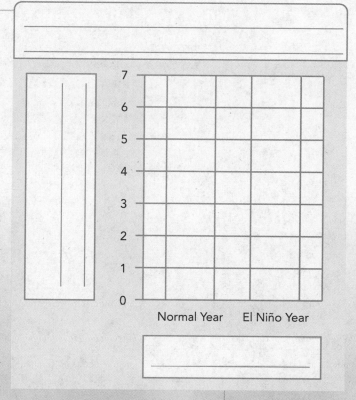

7
6
5
4
3
2
1
0

Normal Year   El Niño Year

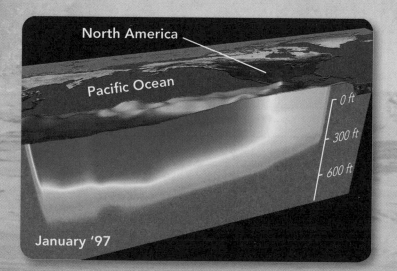

North America
Pacific Ocean

0 ft
300 ft
600 ft

January '97

2. Summarize How does the output of the El Niño system affect different areas of the United States?

_____

_____

_____

_____

_____

Out in Space

What tools do scientists use to understand the natural world?

FIGURE 6 ·······················
Scientists use models and math tools to study the solar system. The planets' distances are measured in units called astronomical units (AU). The time for one orbit of a planet is measured in Earth years. In this model, the planets' sizes and their distances from the sun are not shown to scale.

✏ **Complete the tasks in the boxes.**

Sun

Mars
1.5 AU
1.9 Earth years

Earth
1 AU
1 Earth year

Venus
0.7 AU
0.6 Earth year

Mercury
0.4 AU
0.2 Earth year

1. **Graph** Complete the graph using the data points for Jupiter, Saturn, Uranus, and Neptune. The inner planets— Mercury, Venus, Earth, and Mars—have been done for you.

2. **Interpret Data** What does the trend of the graph show?

_____
_____
_____
_____
_____

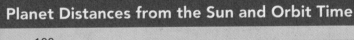

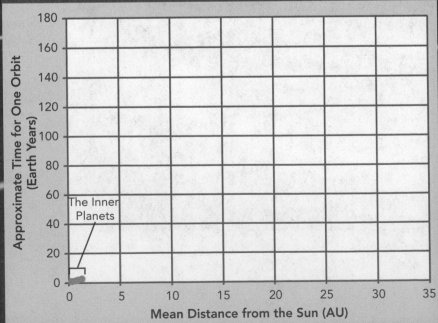

Planet Distances from the Sun and Orbit Time

Approximate Time for One Orbit (Earth Years)

The Inner Planets

Mean Distance from the Sun (AU)

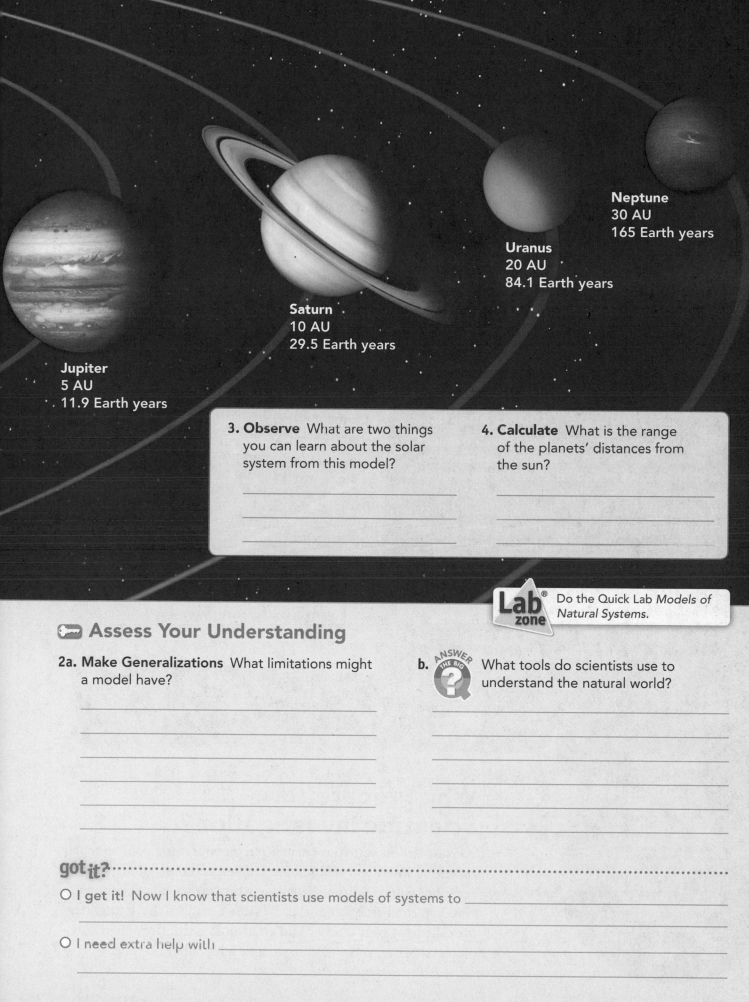

Neptune
30 AU
165 Earth years

Uranus
20 AU
84.1 Earth years

Saturn
10 AU
29.5 Earth years

Jupiter
5 AU
11.9 Earth years

3. Observe What are two things you can learn about the solar system from this model?

_____

_____

_____

4. Calculate What is the range of the planets' distances from the sun?

_____

_____

_____

Lab® zone Do the Quick Lab *Models of Natural Systems.*

🔑 Assess Your Understanding

2a. Make Generalizations What limitations might a model have?

_____

_____

_____

_____

_____

b. ANSWER THE BIG ? What tools do scientists use to understand the natural world?

_____

_____

_____

_____

_____

got it? ....

○ **I get it!** Now I know that scientists use models of systems to _____

_____

○ I need extra help with _____

_____

Safety in the Science Laboratory

UNLOCK THE BIG ?

🗝 **Why Prepare for a Scientific Investigation?**

🗝 **What Should You Do if an Accident Occurs?**

MY PLANET DIARY

Staying Safe Among Snakes

What would you do if you saw a banded snake of black, red, and yellow slithering on the path in front of you? It could be the eastern coral snake, a venomous snake found in the southern United States. First, you should stop. Then walk away slowly. Often, a venomous snake will only bite if it feels threatened.

If you plan on hiking, take precautions to avoid snakebites. Always go with someone else. Once you are there, watch where you place your feet when you walk.

If you see a snake, leave it alone!

FUN FACT

Communicate Discuss the question with a partner. Then write your answer below.

What are two other precautions you can take to avoid snakebite if you go hiking?

_____

_____

_____

_____

 Lab zone® Do the Inquiry Warm-Up *Is Science Safe?*

Why Prepare for a Scientific Investigation?

As you start the test your teacher put on your desk, your stomach sinks. You knew you should have studied and then gone to bed early. But you couldn't resist going with your friends to a movie. Now you can barely keep your eyes open, and you have forgotten the calculator your teacher said you would need. If you had only prepared better, you would have done a lot better on the test.

Vocabulary
- safety symbol
- field

Skills
- 🔄 Reading: Summarize
- △ Inquiry: Infer

Investigation Preparation Just like preparing for a test, you must prepare before you begin a science investigation. 🔑 **Good preparation helps you stay safe when doing science investigations in a laboratory or in the field.** If you do not stay safe, you may not be able to finish the investigation or you may not obtain good results. To prepare for an investigation, first read through any procedures carefully and make sure you understand all the directions. Then, if anything is unclear, ask your teacher about it before you begin. Finally, use the safety equipment required, as indicated by an investigation's safety symbols. Also, observe the cautions of the other safety symbols. **Safety symbols** are signs that alert you to possible sources of accidents in a laboratory.

Safety Symbols

 Safety Goggles

 Lab Apron

 Breakage

 Heat-Resistant Gloves

 Heating

 Poison

 Physical Safety

 Flames

 Electric Shock

apply it!

You will perform different tasks in a science investigation.

1 △ **Infer** For each laboratory task below, list the safety symbols that best match the task. Each task has more than one safety symbol.

Task 1: adding food coloring to a liquid

_____

_____

Task 2: measuring the temperature of hot water

_____

_____

Task 3: dissolving a solid material in alcohol

_____

_____

Task 4: heating a liquid on a hot plate

_____

_____

_____

2 [CHALLENGE] Electrical appliances in the laboratory can cause shocks. What is another safety issue that all electrical appliances have?

_____

_____

_____

Performing an Investigation Whenever you are in a laboratory, your main concern must be the safety of you, your teacher, and your classmates. One safety rule is the most important. *Always follow your teacher's instructions and the investigation directions exactly.* Never try anything on your own without asking your teacher first.

When performing an investigation, you can do many things to make your laboratory experience safe and successful. In **Figure 1**, the students are not following many of the rules listed.

FIGURE 1 ·················

Laboratory Safety
Recognizing and avoiding safety hazards are important lab skills.

✎ **Read the rules on the notebook below. Then complete these tasks.**

1. **Interpret Photos** Identify two safety hazards shown in each picture, and list them on the lines provided.

2. **Identify** Explain why it is important to wear plastic gloves when handling plants.

_____

_____

_____

Rules

- Wear safety goggles to protect your eyes from chemical splashes, glass breakage, and sharp objects.
- Wear an apron to protect yourself and your clothes from chemicals.
- Use heat-resistant gloves when handling hot objects.
- Keep your work area clean and organized.
- Tie back long hair to keep it away from flames, chemicals, or equipment.
- Provide appropriate care for live animals.
- Handle live animals and plants with care.
- Wear plastic gloves to protect your skin when handling animals, plants, or chemicals.
- Make sure electric cords are untangled and out of the way.
- Wear closed-toe shoes when working in the laboratory.

End-of-Investigation Procedures Just because you have completed an investigation does not mean you are finished. You still need to clean up your work area. Also, turn off and unplug any electrical equipment and return it to its proper place. Dispose of any waste materials properly. Some wastes should not be thrown in the trash or poured down the drain. Follow your teacher's instructions about proper disposal. Finally, always be sure to wash your hands thoroughly after working in the laboratory.

Working Safely in the Field Some of your science investigations may be done in the **field,** which is any area outside a science laboratory. Just as in the laboratory, good preparation helps you stay safe because there can be many safety hazards outdoors. You could encounter severe weather, traffic, wild animals, or poisonous plants. Whenever you set out to work in the field, you should always tell an adult where you will be. Never carry out a field investigation alone. Wear appropriate clothing. Use common sense to avoid any potentially dangerous situations. You can see some scientists working in the field in **Figure 2.**

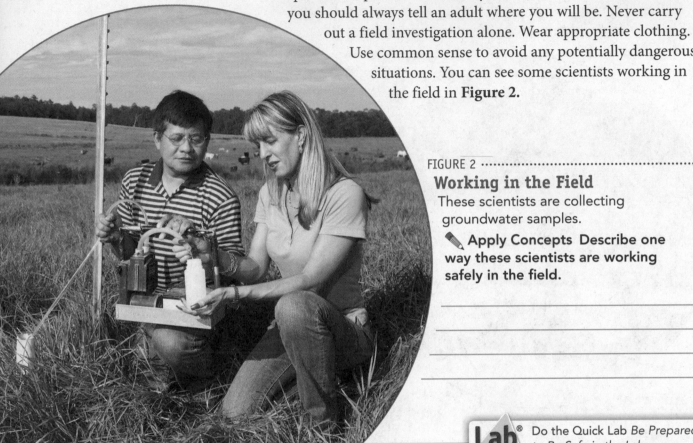

FIGURE 2 ....
Working in the Field
These scientists are collecting groundwater samples.

✎ **Apply Concepts** Describe one way these scientists are working safely in the field.

_____

_____

_____

_____

Lab® Do the Quick Lab *Be Prepared*
zone *to Be Safe in the Lab.*

🔑 Assess Your Understanding

1a. Describe Suppose a student holds an insect by its wings during an investigation. How should the student observe the insect instead?

_____

_____

_____

b. Relate Cause and Effect What might happen if you were to wear open-toed shoes on a field investigation?

_____

_____

_____

got it? ....

○ **I get it!** Now I know that preparing for a science investigation is important because _____

_____

_____

○ **I need extra help with** _____

_____

What Should You Do if an Accident Occurs?

Although you may have prepared carefully, an accident may occur at some point. **When any accident occurs, no matter how minor, tell your teacher or another adult immediately. Then listen to their directions and carry them out quickly.** Make sure you know the location and the proper use of all the emergency equipment in your laboratory. **Figure 3** shows a lab that contains some emergency equipment.

FIGURE 3 ···

Safety Equipment

In case of an emergency in the lab, you should recognize some basic safety equipment and know how to use it.

✎ **Observe** Circle all the lab safety equipment shown in the picture.

FIRE BLANKET

EXIT

FIRE EXTINGUISHER

FIRE

Lab zone® Do the Quick Lab *In Case of an Emergency.*

⚷ Assess Your Understanding

got it? ···

○ **I get it!** Now I know that if an accident occurs, I should _____

_____

_____

○ **I need extra help with** _____

_____

_____

Study Guide

Scientists use _____ of systems and _____ tools, such as calculating percent error, to study the natural world.

LESSON 1 Measurement in Science

🔑 A standard measurement allows scientists to compare data and communicate results.

🔑 SI measurement units include the meter (length), kilogram (mass), cubic meter (volume), kilograms per cubic meter (density), kelvin (temperature), and seconds (time).

Vocabulary
• metric system • International System of Units (SI)
• mass • weight • volume • density

LESSON 2 Math in Science

🔑 Math skills used in science when working with data include estimation, accuracy and precision, and significant figures.

🔑 Math tools include calculating percent error; finding the mean, median, mode, and range; and checking the reasonableness of data.

Vocabulary
• estimate • accuracy • precision
• significant figures • percent error • mean
• median • mode • range • anomalous data

LESSON 3 Graphs

🔑 Graphs can display categorical and numerical data.

🔑 Bar graphs and circle graphs are suitable for displaying categorical data and line graphs and bar graphs are appropriate for displaying numerical data.

Vocabulary
• graph • linear graph • nonlinear graph

Corn Rootworm Population Growth

LESSON 4 Using Models

🔑 Scientists use models to understand things that they cannot observe directly.

🔑 A system is a group of parts that work together to perform a function or produce a result.

🔑 Scientists often use models to understand systems.

Vocabulary
• model • system • input • process • output
• feedback

LESSON 5 Safety in the Science Laboratory

🔑 Good preparation helps you stay safe when doing science investigations in a laboratory or in the field.

🔑 When any accident occurs, no matter how minor, tell your teacher or another adult immediately. Then listen to their directions and carry them out quickly.

Vocabulary
• safety symbol • field

Review and Assessment

LESSON 1 **Measurement in Science**

1. The metric system is a measurement system based on the number
   - **a.** 1.
   - **b.** 10.
   - **c.** 100.
   - **d.** 1,000.

2. **Review** The basic SI unit of time is _____ _____

3. **Calculate** If your calculator is 5 centimeters wide, what is its width in millimeters?

   _____

4. **Compare and Contrast** How do you find the volume of a regular solid? An irregular solid?

   _____
   _____
   _____
   _____

LESSON 2 **Math in Science**

5. An estimate is a(n)
   - **a.** guess.
   - **b.** observation.
   - **c.** precise number.
   - **d.** approximation.

6. _____ do not fit with the rest of a data set.

7. **Interpret Data** Suppose you have a row of tiles that is 26.7 cm long. How many significant figures are in this measurement? Which digit is estimated?

   _____
   _____

8. **math!** Find the mean, median, mode, and range for these data: 24, 16, 11, 10, 16, 4, 17.

LESSON 3 **Graphs**

9. The factor that scientists change is called a(n)
   - **a.** independent variable.
   - **b.** prediction.
   - **c.** dependent variable.
   - **d.** trend.

10. _____ data are information that can be grouped into categories.

11. You want to include a graph showing the different species of animals on display at a local zoo. What is the most appropriate type of graph to use?

    _____
    _____
    _____

Use the graph to answer Questions 12 and 13.

Time vs. Number of Pages

12. **Interpret Graphs** The graph shows how many pages Sarah read over time. Describe the relationship that the data have.

    _____
    _____
    _____

13. **Predict** How many pages do you expect Sarah to have read after 10 minutes? Explain.

    _____
    _____
    _____
    _____

LESSON 4 Using Models

14. A representation of a simple or complex object or process is a

    a. theory.   **b.** system.

    c. model.   **d.** output.

15. A _____ is a group of parts that work together to perform a function or produce a result.

16. **Explain** You are a scientist studying the energy given off by a distant star. Why might you use a computer model to study this star?

_____

_____

_____

_____

_____

17. **Make Generalizations** Why would a complex model make more accurate predictions about a system than a basic model?

_____

_____

_____

_____

_____

_____

_____

_____

_____

LESSON 5 Safety in the Science Laboratory

18. To protect your eyes from chemical spills, wear

    a. plastic gloves.   **b.** safety goggles.

    c. an apron.   **d.** closed-toe shoes.

19. Signs that alert you to possible sources of accidents are _____

20. **Sequence** You accidentally cut yourself during an investigation. What are the first two steps you should take?

_____

_____

21. **Write About It** Suppose you observe animals in their habitats as part of a field investigation. Give at least three examples of how you would keep yourself and the animals safe.

APPLY THE BIG ?

What tools do scientists use to understand the natural world?

22. Suppose you are studying the energy use in your school. What math tools might you use to help collect data? How might you use a model?

_____

_____

_____

_____

_____

_____

_____

_____

Standardized Test Prep

Read each question and choose the best answer.

1. **What is this tool used to measure?**

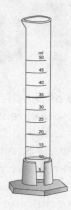

A weight
B length
C volume
D mass

2. **In the event that a glass beaker breaks in the laboratory, the first thing you should do is**

A alert your teacher.
B clean up the broken glass.
C obtain another beaker.
D wash your hands.

3. **The data points on a linear graph form**

A a straight line.
B a curve.
C a jagged line.
D no line.

4. **Find the range for this set of data: 22, 36, 7, 19, 56.**

A 28
B 49
C 7
D 22

Constructed Response

Write your answer to Question 5 on the lines below.

5. **You have recorded data about the height of a seedling each day for a month. What is the best type of graph to use to display your data? Explain your choice.**

_____
_____
_____
_____
_____
_____

Write your answer to Question 6 on another sheet of paper.

6. **You are finding the density of a substance. Write the steps you would follow. What metric units would you use? What is a possible source of error in your measurement?**

BAKELITE®: Molding the Future

In 1907, Dr. Leo Baekeland created the first artificial plastic. Bakelite, as he called it, was an instant hit. It was strong and didn't easily melt. It could be molded into any shape in any color. At the time, more and more people were using electricity. Bakelite did not conduct electricity, so it was an excellent insulator. It was used to make electric plugs and cases for electronic devices like telephones.

Soon, Bakelite was everywhere. People found a lot of uses for such a valuable yet inexpensive material. It was used to make everything from engine parts to jewelry. And that was just the beginning.

Later, chemists created other, more useful types of plastic. Now over a century later, can you imagine life without plastic?

The benefits of plastic are obvious. But what are the downfalls? Plastics do not break down easily in landfills. They are not easily recycled, either. The production of plastic can release chemical pollutants into the environment. Companies are developing technologies to solve these problems, but doing so can be costly. The history of plastic shows that sometimes a new technology can create unforeseen challenges for society.

Analyze It Working with a partner, choose a new technology. Learn about the benefits and drawbacks of this technology. Then, do a cost-benefit analysis.

CAFFEINE CAUSES HALLUCINATIONS!

A new study reports that the equivalent of seven cups of coffee a day could cause people to see "ghosts."

Reading Between the Lines

Headlines grab your attention. That's their job—to get you to read more. Sometimes, though, when headlines promise interesting news, the report doesn't deliver accurate scientific data.

Recently, some newspapers reported that caffeine caused people to hallucinate. The report cited a study that showed that people who drank seven or more cups of coffee in a day saw things that weren't really there.

The newspapers reported the results of the study because a lot of people drink coffee and tea, which both have caffeine. So, a lot of people would find the study interesting. However, the study had some flaws.

It had a small sample of only 219 people. Also, the sample came from a specific group of people—university students. The study took the form of a survey, which means the researchers did not directly observe the subjects. Finally, the researchers did not have a control group. There was no way for them to determine if other factors, besides the caffeine, had affected the subjects. Many scientists later agreed that more tests still needed to be done.

Science doesn't always make for interesting news. Most scientific discoveries happen slowly. They are the result of many trials performed over long periods of time. So be critical of catchy headlines that promise an interesting story. You may not be reading accurate science.

Analyze It Compare articles about science in two or three news sources. Are the headlines more eye-catching in one source? Identify the science claims that the articles make. Identify the evidence that supports these claims. Which source provides the clearest evidence? Which source relies mostly on opinions and assumptions? Create a table to compare the reporting in your sources.

APPENDIX A
Star Charts

Use these star charts to locate bright stars and major constellations in the night sky at different times of year. Choose the appropriate star chart for the current season.

Autumn Sky This chart works best at the following dates and times: September 1 at 10:00 P.M., October 1 at 8:00 P.M., or November 1 at 6:00 P.M. Look for the constellations Ursa Minor (the Little Dipper) and Cassiopeia in the northern sky, and for the star Deneb, which is nearly overhead in autumn.

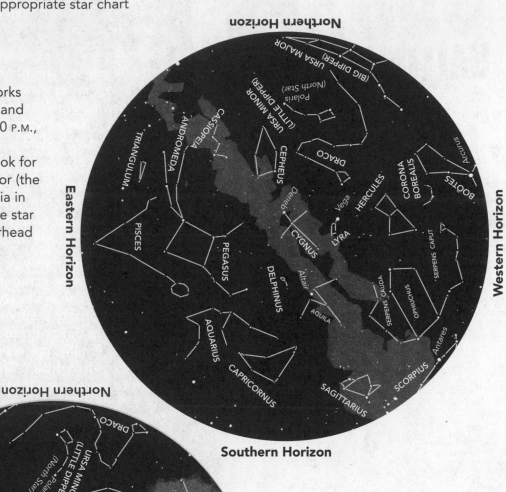

Winter Sky This chart works best at the following dates and times: December 1 at 10:00 P.M., January 1 at 8:00 P.M., or February 1 at 6:00 P.M. Look for the constellations Orion and Gemini; the bright star Sirius; and the Pleiades, a star cluster, in the winter sky.

How to Use the Star Charts

Using a flashlight and a compass, hold the appropriate chart and turn it so that the direction you are facing is at the bottom of the chart. These star charts work best at 34° north latitude, but can be used at other central latitudes.

Spring Sky This chart works best at the following dates and times: March 1 at 10:00 P.M., March 15 at 9:00 P.M., or April 1 at 8:00 P.M. Look for the constellations Ursa Major (which contains the Big Dipper), Boötes, and Leo in the spring sky. The bright stars Arcturus and Spica can be seen in the east.

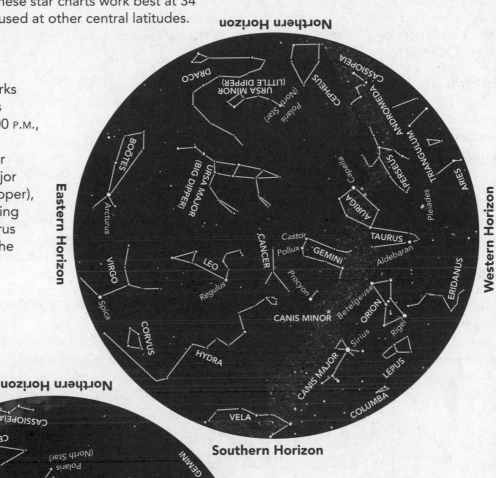

Summer Sky This chart works best at the following dates and times: May 15 at 11:00 P.M., June 1 at 10:00 P.M., or June 15 at 9:00 P.M. Look for the bright star Arcturus in the constellation Boötes overhead in early summer. Toward the east, look for the bright stars Vega, Altair, and Deneb, which form a triangle.

APPENDIX B

Using a Laboratory Balance

The laboratory balance is an important tool in scientific investigations. Different kinds of balances are used in the laboratory to determine the masses and weights of objects. You can use a triple-beam balance to determine the masses of materials that you study or experiment with in the laboratory. An electronic balance, unlike a triple-beam balance, is used to measure the weights of materials.

The triple-beam balance that you may use in your science class is probably similar to the balance illustrated in this Appendix. **To use the balance properly, you should learn the name, location, and function of each part of the balance you are using. What kind of balance do you have in your science class?**

The Triple-Beam Balance

The triple-beam balance is a single-pan balance with three beams calibrated in grams. The back, or 100-gram, beam is divided into ten units of 10 grams each. The middle, or 500-gram, beam is divided into five units of 100 grams each. The front, or 10-gram, beam is divided into ten units of 1 gram each. Each of the units on the front beam is further divided into units of 0.1 gram. What is the largest mass you could find with a triple-beam balance?

The following procedure can be used to find the mass of an object with a triple-beam balance:

1. Place the object on the pan.
2. Move the rider on the middle beam notch by notch until the horizontal pointer on the right drops below zero. Move the rider back one notch.
3. Move the rider on the back beam notch by notch until the pointer again drops below zero. Move the rider back one notch.
4. Slowly slide the rider along the front beam until the pointer stops at the zero point.
5. The mass of the object is equal to the sum of the readings on the three beams.

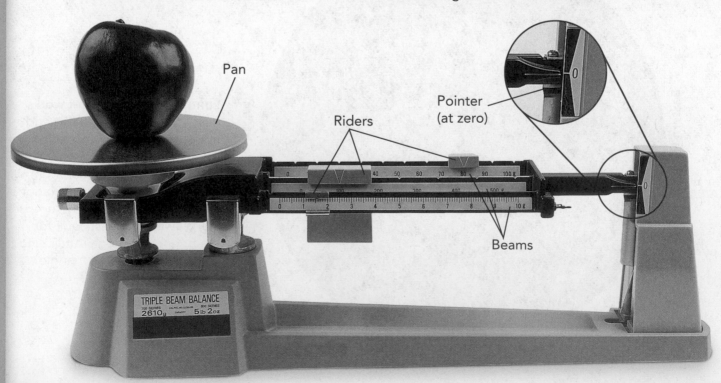

Pan

Riders

Pointer (at zero)

Beams

TRIPLE BEAM BALANCE
700 SERIES   U.S. PAT. AND CLAIM FOR   900 SERIES
2610g   CAPACITY   5 lb 2 oz

APPENDIX C
List of Chemical Elements

Name	Symbol	Atomic Number	Atomic Mass†
Actinium	Ac	89	(227)
Aluminum	Al	13	26.982
Americium	Am	95	(243)
Antimony	Sb	51	121.75
Argon	Ar	18	39.948
Arsenic	As	33	74.922
Astatine	At	85	(210)
Barium	Ba	56	137.33
Berkelium	Bk	97	(247)
Beryllium	Be	4	9.0122
Bismuth	Bi	83	208.98
Bohrium	Bh	107	(264)
Boron	B	5	10.81
Bromine	Br	35	79.904
Cadmium	Cd	48	112.41
Calcium	Ca	20	40.08
Californium	Cf	98	(251)
Carbon	C	6	12.011
Cerium	Ce	58	140.12
Cesium	Cs	55	132.91
Chlorine	Cl	17	35.453
Chromium	Cr	24	51.996
Cobalt	Co	27	58.933
Copernicium	Cn	112	(277)
Copper	Cu	29	63.546
Curium	Cm	96	(247)
Darmstadtium	Ds	110	(269)
Dubnium	Db	105	(262)
Dysprosium	Dy	66	162.50
Einsteinium	Es	99	(252)
Erbium	Er	68	167.26
Europium	Eu	63	151.96
Fermium	Fm	100	(257)
Flerovium	Fl	114	(289)
Fluorine	F	9	18.998
Francium	Fr	87	(223)
Gadolinium	Gd	64	157.25
Gallium	Ga	31	69.72
Germanium	Ge	32	72.59
Gold	Au	79	196.97
Hafnium	Hf	72	178.49
Hassium	Hs	108	(265)
Helium	He	2	4.0026
Holmium	Ho	67	164.93
Hydrogen	H	1	1.0079
Indium	In	49	114.82
Iodine	I	53	126.90
Iridium	Ir	77	192.22
Iron	Fe	26	55.847
Krypton	Kr	36	83.80
Lanthanum	La	57	138.91
Lawrencium	Lr	103	(262)
Lead	Pb	82	207.2
Lithium	Li	3	6.941
Livermorium	Lv	116	(292)
Lutetium	Lu	71	174.97
Magnesium	Mg	12	24.305
Manganese	Mn	25	54.938
Meitnerium	Mt	109	(268)

Name	Symbol	Atomic Number	Atomic Mass†
Mendelevium	Md	101	(258)
Mercury	Hg	80	200.59
Molybdenum	Mo	42	95.94
Moscovium	Mc	115	(289)
Neodymium	Nd	60	144.24
Neon	Ne	10	20.179
Neptunium	Np	93	(237)
Nickel	Ni	28	58.71
Nihonium	Nh	113	(286)
Niobium	Nb	41	92.906
Nitrogen	N	7	14.007
Nobelium	No	102	(259)
Oganesson	Og	118	(294)
Osmium	Os	76	190.2
Oxygen	O	8	15.999
Palladium	Pd	46	106.4
Phosphorus	P	15	30.974
Platinum	Pt	78	195.09
Plutonium	Pu	94	(244)
Polonium	Po	84	(209)
Potassium	K	19	39.098
Praseodymium	Pr	59	140.91
Promethium	Pm	61	(145)
Protactinium	Pa	91	231.04
Radium	Ra	88	(226)
Radon	Rn	86	(222)
Rhenium	Re	75	186.21
Rhodium	Rh	45	102.91
Roentgenium	Rg	111	(272)
Rubidium	Rb	37	85.468
Ruthenium	Ru	44	101.07
Rutherfordium	Rf	104	(261)
Samarium	Sm	62	150.4
Scandium	Sc	21	44.956
Seaborgium	Sg	106	(263)
Selenium	Se	34	78.96
Silicon	Si	14	28.086
Silver	Ag	47	107.87
Sodium	Na	11	22.990
Strontium	Sr	38	87.62
Sulfur	S	16	32.06
Tantalum	Ta	73	180.95
Technetium	Tc	43	(98)
Tellurium	Te	52	127.60
Tennessine	Ts	117	(294)
Terbium	Tb	65	158.93
Thallium	Tl	81	204.37
Thorium	Th	90	232.04
Thulium	Tm	69	168.93
Tin	Sn	50	118.69
Titanium	Ti	22	47.90
Tungsten	W	74	183.85
Uranium	U	92	238.03
Vanadium	V	23	50.941
Xenon	Xe	54	131.30
Ytterbium	Yb	70	173.04
Yttrium	Y	39	88.906
Zinc	Zn	30	65.38
Zirconium	Zr	40	91.22

†Numbers in parentheses give the mass number of the most stable isotope.

APPENDIX D
Periodic Table of the Elements

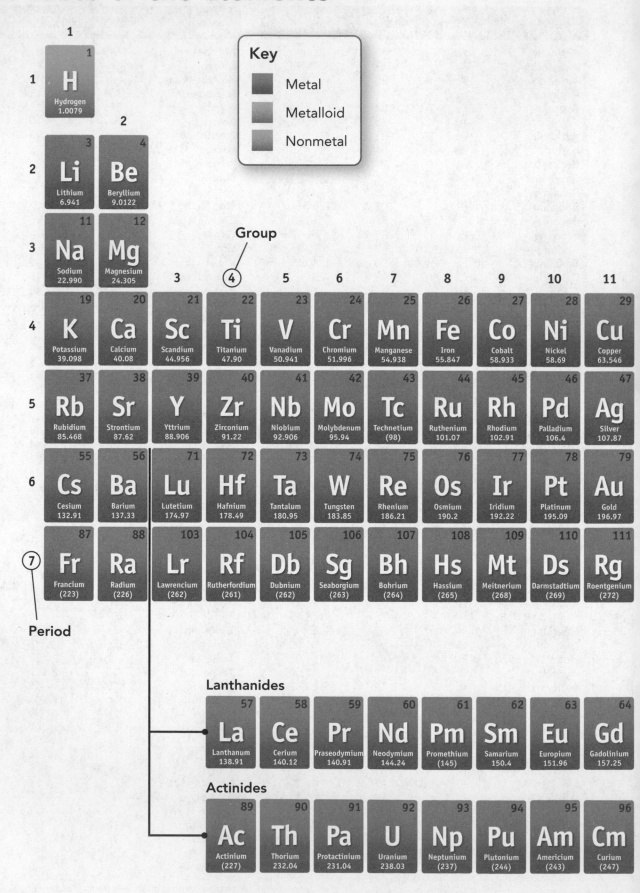

Key
- Metal
- Metalloid
- Nonmetal

Group

Period

1										
1 H Hydrogen 1.0079										

2									
3 Li Lithium 6.941	4 Be Beryllium 9.0122								

		3	4	5	6	7	8	9	10	11
11 Na Sodium 22.990	12 Mg Magnesium 24.305									
19 K Potassium 39.098	20 Ca Calcium 40.08	21 Sc Scandium 44.956	22 Ti Titanium 47.90	23 V Vanadium 50.941	24 Cr Chromium 51.996	25 Mn Manganese 54.938	26 Fe Iron 55.847	27 Co Cobalt 58.933	28 Ni Nickel 58.69	29 Cu Copper 63.546
37 Rb Rubidium 85.468	38 Sr Strontium 87.62	39 Y Yttrium 88.906	40 Zr Zirconium 91.22	41 Nb Niobium 92.906	42 Mo Molybdenum 95.94	43 Tc Technetium (98)	44 Ru Ruthenium 101.07	45 Rh Rhodium 102.91	46 Pd Palladium 106.4	47 Ag Silver 107.87
55 Cs Cesium 132.91	56 Ba Barium 137.33	71 Lu Lutetium 174.97	72 Hf Hafnium 178.49	73 Ta Tantalum 180.95	74 W Tungsten 183.85	75 Re Rhenium 186.21	76 Os Osmium 190.2	77 Ir Iridium 192.22	78 Pt Platinum 195.09	79 Au Gold 196.97
87 Fr Francium (223)	88 Ra Radium (226)	103 Lr Lawrencium (262)	104 Rf Rutherfordium (261)	105 Db Dubnium (262)	106 Sg Seaborgium (263)	107 Bh Bohrium (264)	108 Hs Hassium (265)	109 Mt Meitnerium (268)	110 Ds Darmstadtium (269)	111 Rg Roentgenium (272)

Lanthanides

57 La Lanthanum 138.91	58 Ce Cerium 140.12	59 Pr Praseodymium 140.91	60 Nd Neodymium 144.24	61 Pm Promethium (145)	62 Sm Samarium 150.4	63 Eu Europium 151.96	64 Gd Gadolinium 157.25

Actinides

89 Ac Actinium (227)	90 Th Thorium 232.04	91 Pa Protactinium 231.04	92 U Uranium 238.03	93 Np Neptunium (237)	94 Pu Plutonium (244)	95 Am Americium (243)	96 Cm Curium (247)

Many periodic tables include a zigzag line that separates the metals from the nonmetals. Metalloids, found on either side of the line, share properties of both metals and nonmetals.

13	14	15	16	17	18
					2 **He** Helium 4.0026
5 **B** Boron 10.81	6 **C** Carbon 12.011	7 **N** Nitrogen 14.007	8 **O** Oxygen 15.999	9 **F** Fluorine 18.998	10 **Ne** Neon 20.179
13 **Al** Aluminum 26.982	14 **Si** Silicon 28.086	15 **P** Phosphorus 30.974	16 **S** Sulfur 32.06	17 **Cl** Chlorine 35.453	18 **Ar** Argon 39.948

12

30 **Zn** Zinc 65.38	31 **Ga** Gallium 69.72	32 **Ge** Germanium 72.59	33 **As** Arsenic 74.922	34 **Se** Selenium 78.96	35 **Br** Bromine 79.904	36 **Kr** Krypton 83.80
48 **Cd** Cadmium 112.41	49 **In** Indium 114.82	50 **Sn** Tin 118.69	51 **Sb** Antimony 121.76	52 **Te** Tellurium 127.60	53 **I** Iodine 126.90	54 **Xe** Xenon 131.30
80 **Hg** Mercury 200.59	81 **Tl** Thallium 204.37	82 **Pb** Lead 207.2	83 **Bi** Bismuth 208.98	84 **Po** Polonium (209)	85 **At** Astatine (210)	86 **Rn** Radon (222)
112 **Cn** Copernicium (277)	113 **Nh** Nihonium (284)	114 **Fl** Flerovium (289)	115 **Mc** Moscovium (288)	116 **Lv** Livermorium (292)	117 **Ts** Tennessine (294)	118 **Og** Oganesson (294)

Atomic masses in parentheses are those of the most stable isotopes.

65 **Tb** Terbium 158.93	66 **Dy** Dysprosium 162.50	67 **Ho** Holmium 164.93	68 **Er** Erbium 167.26	69 **Tm** Thulium 168.93	70 **Yb** Ytterbium 173.04
97 **Bk** Berkelium (247)	98 **Cf** Californium (251)	99 **Es** Einsteinium (252)	100 **Fm** Fermium (257)	101 **Md** Mendelevium (258)	102 **No** Nobelium (259)

APPENDIX E

The Design Process

Engineers are people who use scientific and technological knowledge to solve practical problems. To design new products, engineers usually follow the process described here, even though they may not follow these steps in the same order each time.

Identify a Need

Before engineers begin designing a new product, they must first identify the need they are trying to meet or the problem they want to solve. For example, suppose you are a member of a design team in a company that makes model cars. Your team has identified a need: a model car that is inexpensive and easy to assemble.

Research the Problem

Engineers often begin by gathering information that will help them with their new design. This research may include finding articles in books, magazines, or on the Internet. It may also involve talking to other engineers who have solved similar problems. Engineers often perform experiments related to the product they want to design.

For your model car, you could look at cars that are similar to the one you want to design. You might do research on the Internet. You could also test some materials to see whether they will work well in a model car.

Design a Solution

Brainstorm Ideas When engineers design new products, they usually work in teams. Design teams often hold brainstorming meetings in which any team member can contribute ideas. Brainstorming is a creative process in which one team member's suggestions often spark ideas in other group members. Brainstorming can lead to new approaches to solving a design problem.

Document the Process As the design team works, its members document, or keep a record of, the process. Having access to documentation enables others to repeat, or replicate, the process in the future. Design teams document their research sources, ideas, lists of materials, and so on because any part of the process may be a helpful resource later.

Identify Constraints During brainstorming, a design team may come up with several possible designs. To better focus their ideas, team members consider constraints. A constraint is a factor that limits a product design. Physical characteristics, such as the properties of materials used to make your model car, are constraints. Money and time are also constraints. If the materials in a product cost a lot or if the product takes a long time to make, the design may be impractical.

Make Trade-offs Design teams usually need to make trade-offs. In a trade-off, engineers give up one benefit of a proposed design in order to obtain another. In designing your model car, you might have to make trade-offs. For example, you might decide to give up the benefit of sturdiness in order to obtain the benefit of lower cost.

Select a Solution After considering the constraints and trade-offs of the possible designs, engineers then select one idea to develop further. That idea represents the solution that the team thinks best meets the need or solves the problem that was identified at the beginning of the process. The decision includes selecting the materials that will be used in the first attempt to build a product.

Create, Test, and Evaluate a Prototype

Once the team has chosen a design plan, the engineers build a prototype. A prototype is a working model used to test a design. Engineers evaluate the prototype to see whether it meets the goal. They must determine whether it works well, is easy to operate, is safe to use, and holds up to repeated use.

Part of the evaluation includes collecting data in the form of measurements. For example, think of your model car. Once you decide how to build your prototype, what would you want to know about it? You might want to measure how much baggage it could carry or how its shape affects its speed.

Troubleshoot and Redesign

Few prototypes work perfectly, which is why they need to be tested. Once a design team has tested a prototype, the members analyze the results and identify any problems. The team then tries to troubleshoot, or fix the design problems. Troubleshooting allows the team to redesign the prototype to improve on how well the solution meets the need.

Communicate the Solution

A team needs to communicate the final design to the people who will manufacture and use the product. To do this, teams may use sketches, detailed drawings, computer simulations, and word descriptions. The team may also present the evidence that was collected when the prototype was tested. This evidence may include mathematical representations, such as graphs and data tables, that support the choice for the final design.

GLOSSARY

A

abiotic factor A nonliving part of an organism's habitat.
factor abiótico La parte sin vida del hábitat de un organismo.

abrasion The grinding away of rock by other rock particles carried in water, ice, or wind.
abrasión Tipo de desgaste de la roca por otras partículas de roca transportadas por el agua, el viento o el hielo.

absolute age The age of a rock given as the number of years since the rock formed.
edad absoluta Edad de una roca basada en el número de años de su formación.

absolute brightness The brightness a star would have if it were at a standard distance from Earth.
magnitud absoluta Brillo que tendría una estrella si estuviera a una distancia estándar de la Tierra.

absolute zero The temperature at which no more energy can be removed from matter.
cero absoluto Temperatura a cuyo punto ya no se puede extraer energía de la materia.

absorption 1. The process by which nutrient molecules pass through the wall of the digestive system into the blood. **2.** The process by which an object takes in, or absorbs, light.
absorción 1. Proceso en el cual las moléculas de nutrientes pasan a la sangre a través de las paredes del sistema digestivo. **2.** Proceso en el cual un objeto recibe, o absorbe, luz.

abyssal plain A smooth, nearly flat region of the deep ocean floor.
llanura abisal Región llana, casi plana, de la cuenca oceánica profunda.

acceleration The rate at which velocity changes.
aceleración Ritmo al que cambia la velocidad.

accuracy How close a measurement is to the true or accepted value.
exactitud Cuán cerca está una medida del valor verdadero o aceptado.

acid A substance that tastes sour, reacts with metals and carbonates, and turns blue litmus paper red.
ácido Sustancia de sabor agrio que reacciona con metales y carbonatos, y que vuelve rojo el papel de tornasol azul.

acid rain Rain or another form of precipitation that is more acidic than normal, caused by the release of molecules of sulfur dioxide and nitrogen oxide into the air.

lluvia ácida Lluvia u otra forma de precipitación que es más ácida de lo normal, debido a la contaminación del aire con moléculas de dióxido de azufre y óxido de nitrógeno.

activation energy The minimum amount of energy needed to start a chemical reaction.
energía de activación Cantidad mínima de energía que se necesita para iniciar una reacción química.

active immunity Immunity that occurs when a person's own immune system produces antibodies in response to the presence of a pathogen.
inmunidad activa Inmunidad que ocurre cuando el sistema inmunológico de una persona produce anticuerpos en respuesta a la presencia de un patógeno.

active transport The movement of materials across a cell membrane using cellular energy.
transporte activo Proceso que usa la energía celular para mover materiales a través de la membrana celular.

adaptation An inherited behavior or physical characteristic that helps an organism survive and reproduce in its environment.
adaptación Comportamiento o característica física hereditaria que le permite a un organismo sobrevivir y reproducirse en su ambiente.

aerosols Solid particles or liquid droplets in the atmosphere.
aerosoles Partículas sólidas o gotas de líquido en la atmósfera.

AIDS (acquired immunodeficiency syndrome) A disease caused by a virus that attacks the immune system.
SIDA (síndrome de inmunodeficiencia adquirida) Enfermedad causada por un virus que ataca el sistema inmunológico.

air mass A huge body of air that has similar temperature, humidity, and air pressure at any given height.
masa de aire Gran cuerpo de aire que tiene temperatura, humedad y presión similares en todos sus puntos.

air pressure The pressure caused by the weight of a column of air pushing down on an area.
presión de aire Presión causada por el peso de una columna de aire en un area.

algae Plantlike protists.
algas Protistas con características vegetales.

alleles The different forms of a gene.
alelos Diferentes formas de un gen.

allergen A substance that causes an allergy.
alérgeno Sustancia que causa la alergia.

allergy A disorder in which the immune system is overly sensitive to a foreign substance.
alergia Trastorno fisiológico en el cual el sistema inmunológico es extremadamente sensible a sustancias externas.

alloy A mixture of two or more elements, at least one of which is a metal.
aleación Mezcla de dos o más elementos, uno de los cuales es un metal.

alluvial fan A wide, sloping deposit of sediment formed where a stream leaves a mountain range.
abanico aluvial Depósito de sedimento ancho e inclinado que se forma donde un arroyo sale de una cordillera.

alternating current Current consisting of charges that move back and forth in a circuit.
corriente alterna Corriente de cargas eléctricas que se mueven hacia delante y hacia atrás en un circuito.

altitude Elevation above sea level.
altitud Elevación sobre el nivel del mar.

alveoli Tiny sacs of lung tissue specialized for the movement of gases between air and blood.
alvéolos Sacos diminutos de tejido pulmonar que se especializan en el intercambio de gases entre el aire y la sangre.

amniotic egg An egg with a shell and internal membranes that keep the embryo moist; a major adaptation to life on land characteristic of reptiles, birds, and egg-laying mammals.
huevo amniótico Huevo con cáscara y membranas internas que mantiene al embrión húmedo; adaptación principal a la vida en la tierra, característica de los reptiles, las aves y los mamíferos que ponen huevos.

amniotic sac A fluid-filled sac that cushions and protects a developing embryo or fetus in the uterus.
saco amniótico Saco lleno de líquido que acojina y protege al embrión o feto dentro del útero.

amorphous solid A solid made up of particles that are not arranged in a regular pattern.
sólido amorfo Sólido constituido por partículas que no están dispuestas en un patrón regular.

amphibian A vertebrate whose body temperature is determined by the temperature of its environment, and that lives its early life in water and its adult life on land.

anfibio Animal vertebrado cuya temperatura corporal depende de la temperatura de su entorno, y que vive la primera etapa de su vida en el agua y su vida adulta en la tierra.

amplitude 1. The height of a transverse wave from the center to a crest or trough. **2.** The maximum distance the particles of a medium move away from their rest positions as a longitudinal wave passes through the medium.
amplitud 1. Altura de una onda transversal desde el centro a una cresta o un valle. **2.** Máxima distancia del desvío de las partículas de un medio, desde sus posiciones de reposo, al ser atravesado por una onda longitudinal.

amplitude modulation A method of transmitting signals by changing the amplitude of a radio wave.
amplitud modulada Método de transmisión de señales al cambiar la amplitud de una onda de radio.

analyzing Evaluating data to reach a conclusion about an experiment.
analizar Evaluar datos para llegar a una conclusion acerca de un experimento.

anemometer An instrument used to measure wind speed.
anemómetro Instrumento que se usa para medir la velocidad del viento.

aneroid barometer An instrument that measures changes in air pressure without using a liquid.
barómetro aneroide Instrumento que mide los cambios en la presión del aire sin usar líquidos.

angiosperm A flowering plant that produces seeds enclosed in a protective fruit.
angiosperma Planta con flores que produce semillas encerradas en una fruta protectora.

annual A flowering plant that completes its life cycle in one growing season.
anual Planta con flores que completa su ciclo de vida en una sola temporada de crecimiento.

anomalous data Data that do not fit with the rest of a data set.
datos anómalos Información que no encaja con los otros datos de un conjunto de datos.

antibiotic A chemical that kills bacteria or slows their growth without harming body cells.
antibiótico Sustancia química que mata las bacterias o disminuye la velocidad de su crecimiento sin dañar las células del cuerpo humano.

GLOSSARY

antibiotic resistance The ability of bacteria to withstand the effects of an antibiotic.
resistencia a los antibióticos Capacidad de la bacteria de resistir los efectos de los antibióticos.

antibody A protein produced by a B cell of the immune system that destroys pathogens.
anticuerpo Proteína producida por una célula B del sistema inmunológico que destruye patógenos.

anticyclone A high-pressure center of dry air.
anticiclón Centro de aire seco de alta presión.

antigen A molecule that the immune system recognizes either as part of the body or as coming from outside the body.
antígeno Molécula que el sistema inmunológico puede reconocer como parte del cuerpo o como un agente extraño.

antinode A point of maximum amplitude on a standing wave.
antinodo Punto de máxima amplitud de una onda estacionaria.

aorta The largest artery in the body; receives blood from the left ventricle.
aorta La arteria más grande del cuerpo; recibe sangre del ventrículo izquierdo.

apparent brightness The brightness of a star as seen from Earth.
magnitud aparente Brillo de una estrella vista desde la Tierra.

aquifer An underground layer of rock or sediment that holds water.
acuífero Capa subterránea de roca o sedimento que retiene agua.

artery A blood vessel that carries blood away from the heart.
arteria Vaso sanguíneo que transporta la sangre que sale del corazón.

artesian well A well in which water rises because of pressure within the aquifer.
pozo artesiano Pozo por el que el agua se eleva debido a la presión dentro del acuífero.

arthropod An invertebrate that has an external skeleton, a segmented body, and jointed appendages.
artrópodo Invertebrado que tiene un esqueleto externo, un cuerpo segmentado y apéndices articulados.

asexual reproduction A reproductive process that involves only one parent and produces offspring that are genetically identical to the parent.

reproducción asexual Proceso reproductivo que consiste de un solo reproductor y que produce individuos que son genéticamente idénticos al reproductor.

asteroid One of the rocky objects revolving around the sun that are too small and numerous to be considered planets.
asteroide Uno de los cuerpos rocosos que se mueven alrededor del Sol y que son demasiado pequeños y numerosos como para ser considerados planetas.

asteroid belt The region of the solar system between the orbits of Mars and Jupiter, where many asteroids are found.
cinturón de asteroides Región del sistema solar entre las órbitas de Marte y Júpiter, donde se encuentran muchos asteroides.

asthenosphere The soft layer of the mantle on which the lithosphere floats.
astenósfera Capa suave del manto en la que flota la litósfera.

asthma A disease in which the airways in the lungs narrow significantly.
asma Enfermedad en la que las vías respiratorias de los pulmones se estrechan considerablemente.

astronomical unit A unit of distance equal to the average distance between Earth and the sun, about 150 million kilometers.
unidad astronómica Unidad de medida equivalente a la distancia media entre la Tierra y el Sol, aproximadamente 150 millones de kilómetros.

atmosphere The relatively thin layer of gases that form Earth's outermost layer.
atmósfera Capa de gases relativamente delgada que forma la capa exterior de la Tierra.

atom The basic particle from which all elements are made; the smallest particle of an element that has the properties of that element.
átomo Partícula básica de la que todos los elementos están formados; partícula más pequeña de un elemento, que tiene las propiedades de ese elemento.

atrium An upper chamber of the heart that receives blood.
aurícula Cavidad superior del corazón que recibe la sangre.

autotroph An organism that is able to capture energy from sunlight or chemicals and use it to produce its own food.

autótrofo Organismo capaz de capturar y usar la energía del Sol o de las sustancias químicas para producir su propio alimento.

auxin A plant hormone that speeds up the rate at which a plant's cells grow and controls a plant's response to light.
auxina Hormona vegetal que acelera la velocidad del crecimiento de las células de una planta y que controla la respuesta de la planta a la luz.

average speed The overall rate of speed at which an object moves; calculated by dividing the total distance an object travels by the total time.
velocidad media Índice de velocidad general de un objeto en movimiento; se calcula dividiendo la distancia total recorrida por el tiempo total empleado.

axis An imaginary line that passes through a planet's center and its north and south poles, about which the planet rotates.
eje Línea imaginaria alrededor de la cual gira un planeta, y que atraviesa su centro y sus dos polos, norte y sur.

B

B cell A lymphocyte that produces proteins that help destroy pathogens.
célula B Linfocito que produce proteínas que ayudan a destruir patógenos.

bacteria Single-celled organisms that lack a nucleus; prokaryotes.
bacteria Organismos unicelulares que no tienen un núcleo; procariotas.

barometer An instrument used to measure changes in air pressure.
barómetro Instrumento que se usa para medir cambios de la presión del aire.

basalt A dark, dense, igneous rock with a fine texture, found in oceanic crust.
basalto Roca ígnea, oscura y densa, de textura lisa, que se encuentra en la corteza oceánica.

base A substance that tastes bitter, feels slippery, and turns red litmus paper blue.
base Sustancia de sabor amargo, escurridiza y que vuelve azul el papel de tornasol rojo.

batholith A mass of rock formed when a large body of magma cools inside the crust.
batolito Masa de roca formada cuando una gran masa de magma se enfría dentro de la corteza terrestre.

beach Wave-washed sediment along a coast.
playa Sedimento depositado por las olas a lo largo de una costa.

bedrock Rock that makes up Earth's crust; also the solid rock layer beneath the soil.
lecho rocoso Roca que compone la corteza terrestre; también, la capa sólida de roca debajo del suelo.

bias A subjective belief that affects a person's attitude toward something; an error in the design of an experiment that affects the results of the experiment.
predisposición Creencia subjetiva que afecta la actitud de una persona acerca de algo; un error en el diseño de un experimento que afecta los resultados del experimento.

biennial A flowering plant that completes its life cycle in two years.
bienal Planta con flores que completa su ciclo de vida en dos años.

big bang The initial explosion that resulted in the formation and expansion of the universe.
Big bang Explosión inicial que resultó en la formación y expansión del universo.

bilateral symmetry A body plan in which a single imaginary line divides the body into left and right sides that are mirror images of each other.
simetría bilateral Esquema del cuerpo en el que una línea imaginaria divide el cuerpo en dos partes, izquierda y derecha, que son el reflejo la una de la otra.

binary fission A form of asexual reproduction in which one cell divides, forming two identical cells.
fisión binaria Forma de reproducción asexual en la que una célula se divide y forma dos células idénticas.

binary star A star system with two stars.
estrella binaria Sistema estelar de dos estrellas.

binomial nomenclature The classification system in which each organism is given a unique, two-part scientific name indicating its genus and species.
nomenclatura binaria Sistema de clasificación en el que cada organismo tiene un nombre científico específico de dos partes que indica el género y la especie.

GLOSSARY

biodegradable Capable of being broken down by bacteria and other decomposers.
biodegradable Sustancia que las bacterias y otros descomponedores pueden descomponer.

biodiversity The total number of different species on Earth, including those on land, in the water, and in the air.
biodiversidad Número total de especies diferentes que habitan la Tierra, incluyendo especies terrestres, marinas y del aire.

biogeography The study of where organisms live and how they got there.
biogeografía Estudio del hábitat de los organismos y de cómo han llegado a ese hábitat.

biomass fuel Fuel made from living things.
combustible de biomasa Combustible creado a partir de seres vivos.

biome A group of ecosystems with similar climates and organisms.
bioma Grupo de ecosistemas con organismos y climas parecidos.

biosphere The parts of Earth that contain living organisms.
biósfera Partes de la Tierra que contienen organismos vivos.

biotic factor A living or once living part of an organism's habitat.
factor biótico Parte viva, o que alguna vez tuvo vida, del hábitat de un organismo.

bird A vertebrate whose body temperature is regulated by its internal heat, lays eggs, and has feathers and a four-chambered heart.
ave Vertebrado cuya temperatura corporal es regulada por su calor interno, que produce huevos y que tiene plumas y un corazón de cuatro cavidades.

birth rate The number of births per 1,000 individuals for a certain time period.
tasa de natalidad Número de nacimientos por 1,000 individuos durante un período de tiempo determinado.

black hole An object whose gravity is so strong that nothing, not even light, can escape.
agujero negro Cuerpo cuya gravedad es tan fuerte que nada, ni siquiera la luz, puede escapar.

boiling Vaporization that occurs at and below the surface of a liquid.
ebullición Evaporación que ocurre en y bajo la superficie de un líquido.

boiling point The temperature at which a liquid boils.
punto de ebullición Temperatura a la cual hierve un líquido.

boreal forest Dense forest of evergreens located in the upper regions of the Northern Hemisphere.
bosque boreal Bosque denso donde abundan las plantas coníferas y que se encuentra en las regiones más al norte del Hemisferio Norte.

Boyle's law A principle that describes the relationship between the pressure and volume of a gas at constant temperature.
ley de Boyle Principio que describe la relación entre la presión y el volumen de un gas a una temperatura constante.

brain 1. An organized grouping of neurons in the head of an animal with bilateral symmetry. **2.** The part of the central nervous system that is located in the skull and controls most functions in the body.
encéfalo 1. Conjunto organizado de neuronas ubicado en la cabeza de animales con simetría bilateral. **2.** Parte del sistema nervioso ubicada en el cráneo y que controla la mayoría de las funciones del cuerpo.

branching tree diagram A diagram that shows probable evolutionary relationships among organisms and the order in which specific characteristics may have evolved.
árbol ramificado Diagrama que muestra las relaciones evolucionarias probables entre los organismos y el orden en que ciertas características específicas podrían haber evolucionado.

bronchi The passages that direct air into the lungs.
bronquios Conductos que dirigen el aire hacia los pulmones.

budding A form of asexual reproduction in which a new organism grows out of the body of a parent.
gemación Forma de reproducción asexual en la que una porción del cuerpo de un reproductor se separa y forma un nuevo organismo.

C

caldera The large hole at the top of a volcano formed when the roof of a volcano's magma chamber collapses.
caldera Gran agujero en la parte superior de un volcán que se forma cuando la tapa de la cámara magmática de un volcán se desploma.

calendar A system of organizing time that defines the beginning, length, and divisions of a year.
calendario Sistema de organización del tiempo que define el principio, la duración y las divisiones de un año.

calorie The amount of energy needed to raise the temperature of one gram of water by 1°C.
caloría Cantidad de energía que se necesita para elevar en 1°C la temperatura de un gramo de agua.

cambium A layer of cells in a plant that produces new phloem and xylem cells.·
cámbium Una capa de células de una planta que produce nuevas células de floema y xilema.

camera An optical instrument that uses lenses to focus light, and film or an electronic sensor to record an image of an object.
cámara Instrumento óptico que usa lentes para enfocar la luz, y película o un sensor electrónico para grabar la imagen de un objeto.

cancer A disease in which some body cells grow and divide uncontrollably, damaging the parts of the body around them.
cáncer Enfermedad en la que algunas células del cuerpo crecen y se dividen sin control, y causan daño a las partes del cuerpo que las rodean.

canopy A leafy roof formed by tall trees in a rain forest.
dosel Techo de hojas que forman los árboles en la selva tropical.

capillary A tiny blood vessel where substances are exchanged between the blood and the body cells.
capilar Vaso sanguíneo diminuto donde se intercambian sustancias entre la sangre y las células del cuerpo.

captive breeding The mating of animals in zoos or wildlife preserves.
reproducción en cautiverio Apareamiento de animales en zoológicos y reservas naturales.

carbohydrate An energy-rich organic compound, such as a sugar or a starch, that is made of the elements carbon, hydrogen, and oxygen.
carbohidrato Compuesto orgánico rico en energía, como un azúcar o almidón, formado por los elementos carbono, hidrógeno y oxígeno.

carbon film A type of fossil consisting of an extremely thin coating of carbon on rock.
película de carbono Tipo de fósil que consiste en una capa de carbono extremadamente fina que recubre la roca.

carcinogen A substance or a factor in the environment that can cause cancer.
carcinógeno Sustancia o factor ambiental que puede causar cáncer.

cardiac muscle Involuntary muscle tissue found only in the heart.
músculo cardiaco Tejido de músculo involuntario, que sólo se encuentra en el corazón.

carnivore A consumer that obtains energy by eating only animals.
carnívoro Consumidor que adquiere su energía al alimentarse de animales solamente.

carrier A person who has one recessive allele and one dominant allele for a trait.
portador Persona que tiene un alelo recesivo y un alelo dominante para un rasgo.

carrying capacity The largest population that a particular environment can support.
capacidad de carga Población mayor que un ambiente en particular puede mantener.

cartilage A connective tissue that is more flexible than bone and that protects the ends of bones and keeps them from rubbing together.
cartílago Tejido conector más flexible que el hueso, que protege los extremos de los huesos y evita que se rocen.

cast A fossil that is a solid copy of an organism's shape, formed when minerals seep into a mold.
vaciado Fósil que es una copia sólida de la forma de un organismo y que se forma cuando los minerales se filtran y crean un molde.

catalyst A material that increases the rate of a reaction by lowering the activation energy.
catalizador Material que aumenta la velocidad de una reacción al disminuir la energía de activación.

cell The basic unit of structure and function in living things.
célula Unidad básica de la estructura y función de todos los seres vivos.

cell cycle The series of events in which a cell grows, prepares for division, and divides to form two daughter cells.
ciclo celular Serie de sucesos en los que una célula crece, se prepara para dividirse y se divide para formar dos células hijas.

cell membrane A thin, flexible barrier that surrounds a cell and controls which substances pass into and out of a cell.
membrana celular Barrera delgada y flexible alrededor de la célula que controla lo que entra y sale de la célula.

cell theory A widely accepted explanation of the relationship between cells and living things.
teoría celular Explicación ampliamente aceptada sobre la relación entre las células y los seres vivos.

cell wall A rigid supporting layer that surrounds the cells of plants and some other organisms.
pared celular Capa fuerte de apoyo alrededor de las células de las plantas y algunos otros organismos.

cellular respiration The process in which oxygen and glucose undergo a complex series of chemical reactions inside cells, releasing energy.
respiración celular Proceso en el cual el oxígeno y la glucosa pasan por una serie compleja de reacciones químicas dentro de las células y así liberan energía.

Celsius scale The temperature scale on which water freezes at 0°C and boils at 100°C.
escala Celsius Escala de temperatura en la que el punto de congelación del agua es 0°C y el punto de ebullición es 100°C.

cementation The process by which dissolved minerals crystallize and glue particles of sediment together into one mass.
cementación Proceso mediante el cual minerales disueltos se cristalizan y forman una masa de partículas de sedimento.

central nervous system The division of the nervous system consisting of the brain and spinal cord.
sistema nervioso central División del sistema nervioso formada por el cerebro y la médula espinal.

centripetal force A force that causes an object to move in a circle.
fuerza centrípeta Fuerza que hace que un objeto se mueva circularmente.

Charles's law A principle that describes the relationship between the temperature and volume of a gas at constant pressure.
ley de Charles Principio que describe la relación entre la temperatura y el volumen de un gas a una presión constante.

chemical bond The force of attraction that holds two atoms together.
enlace químico Fuerza de atracción que mantiene juntos a dos átomos.

chemical change A change in which one or more substances combine or break apart to form new substances.
cambio químico Cambio en el cual una o más sustancias se combinan o se descomponen para formar sustancias nuevas.

chemical energy A form of potential energy that is stored in chemical bonds between atoms.
energía química Forma de energía potencial almacenada en los enlaces químicos de los átomos.

chemical equation A short, easy way to show a chemical reaction using symbols.
ecuación química Forma corta y sencilla de mostrar una reacción química usando símbolos.

chemical formula Symbols that show the elements in a compound and the ratio of atoms.
fórmula química Símbolos que muestran los elementos de un compuesto y la cantidad de átomos.

chemical property A characteristic of a substance that describes its ability to change into different substances.
propiedad química Característica de una sustancia que describe su capacidad de convertirse en sustancias diferentes.

chemical rock Sedimentary rock that forms when minerals crystallize from a solution.
roca química Roca sedimentaria que se forma cuando los minerales de una solución se cristalizan.

chemical weathering The process that breaks down rock through chemical changes.
desgaste químico Proceso que erosiona la roca mediante cambios químicos.

chemistry The study of the properties of matter and how matter changes.
química Estudio de las propiedades de la materia y de sus cambios.

chemotherapy The use of drugs to treat diseases such as cancer.
quimioterapia Uso de medicamentos para tratar enfermedades como el cáncer.

chlorofluorocarbons Human-made gases containing chlorine and fluorine (also called CFCs) that are the main cause of ozone depletion.
clorofluorocarbonos Gases generados por el hombre, que contienen cloro y flúor (también llamados CFC) y que son la causa principal del deterioro de la capa de ozono.

chlorophyll A green photosynthetic pigment found in the chloroplasts of plants, algae, and some bacteria.
clorofila Pigmento verde fotosintético de los cloroplastos de las plantas, algas y algunas bacterias.

chloroplast An organelle in the cells of plants and some other organisms that captures energy from sunlight and changes it to an energy form that cells can use in making food.
cloroplasto Orgánulo de las células vegetales y otros organismos que absorbe energía de la luz solar y la convierte en una forma de energía que las células pueden usar para producir alimentos.

chordate An animal that has a notochord, a nerve cord, and throat pouches at some point in its life.
cordado Animal que tiene un notocordio, un cordón nervioso y bolsas en la garganta en determinada etapa de su vida.

chromosome A threadlike structure within a cell's nucleus that contains DNA that is passed from one generation to the next.
cromosoma Estructura filamentosa en el núcleo celular que contiene el ADN que se transmite de una generación a la siguiente.

chromosphere The middle layer of the sun's atmosphere.
cromósfera Capa central de la atmósfera solar.

cilia Tiny, hairlike projections on the outside of cells that move in a wavelike manner.
cilio Estructuras diminutas parecidas a pelos, ubicadas en el exterior de las células y que ondulan.

cinder cone A steep, cone-shaped hill or small mountain made of volcanic ash, cinders, and bombs piled up around a volcano's opening.
cono de escoria Colina o pequeña montaña escarpada en forma de cono que se forma cuando ceniza volcánica, escoria y bombas se acumulan alrededor del cráter de un volcán.

circuit breaker A reusable safety switch that breaks the circuit when the current becomes too high.
interruptor de circuito Interruptor de seguridad reutilizable que corta un circuito cuando la corriente es demasiado alta.

circulatory system An organ system that transports needed materials to cells and removes wastes.
sistema circulatorio Sistema de órganos que transporta los materiales que la célula necesita y elimina los desechos.

cirrus Wispy, feathery clouds made of ice crystals that form at high levels.

cirros Nubes que parecen plumas o pinceladas y que están formadas por cristales de hielo que se crean a grandes alturas.

classification The process of grouping things based on their similarities.
clasificación Proceso de agrupar cosas según sus semejanzas.

classifying The process of grouping together items that are alike in some way.
clasificar Proceso de agrupar objetos con algún tipo de semejanza.

clastic rock Sedimentary rock that forms when rock fragments are squeezed together under high pressure.
roca clástica Roca sedimentaria que se forma cuando fragmentos de roca se unen bajo gran presión.

cleavage A mineral's ability to split easily along flat surfaces.
exfoliación Facilidad con la que un mineral se divide en capas planas.

climate The average annual conditions of temperature, precipitation, winds, and clouds in an area.
clima Condiciones promedio anuales de temperatura, precipitación, viento y nubosidad de un área.

clone An organism that is genetically identical to the organism from which it was produced.
clon Organismo genéticamente idéntico al organismo del que proviene.

closed system A system in which no matter is allowed to enter or leave.
sistema cerrado Sistema en el cual la materia no puede entrar ni salir.

cnidarian A radially symmetrical invertebrate that uses stinging cells to capture food and defend itself.
cnidario Invertebrado de simetría radiada que usa células urticantes para obtener alimentos y defenderse.

cochlea A snail-shaped tube in the inner ear that is lined with receptor cells that respond to sound.
cóclea Conducto en forma de caracol del oído interno que está cubierto de células receptoras que responden al sonido.

codominance A situation in which both alleles for a gene are expressed equally.
codominancia Situación en la que ambos alelos de un gen se manifiestan de igual manera.

GLOSSARY

coefficient A number in front of a chemical formula in an equation that indicates how many molecules or atoms of each reactant and product are involved in a reaction.
coeficiente En un ecuación, número delante de una fórmula química que indica cuántas moléculas o átomos de cada reactante y producto intervienen en una reacción.

colloid A mixture containing small, undissolved particles that do not settle out.
coloide Mezcla que contiene partículas pequeñas y sin disolver que no se depositan.

coma The fuzzy outer layer of a comet.
coma Capa exterior y difusa de un cometa.

comet A loose collection of ice and dust that orbits the sun, typically in a long, narrow orbit.
cometa Cuerpo poco denso de hielo y polvo que orbita alrededor del Sol. Generalmente su órbita es larga y estrecha.

commensalism A type of symbiosis between two species in which one species benefits and the other species is neither helped nor harmed.
comensalismo Tipo de relación simbiótica entre dos especies en la cual una especie se beneficia y la otra especie ni se beneficia ni sufre daño.

community All the different populations that live together in a particular area.
comunidad Todas las poblaciones distintas que habitan en un área específica.

compact bone Hard and dense, but not solid, bone tissue that is beneath the outer membrane of a bone.
hueso compacto Tejido de hueso denso y duro, pero no sólido, que se encuentra debajo de la membrana externa de un hueso.

compaction The process by which sediments are pressed together under their own weight.
compactación Proceso mediante el cual los sedimentos se unen por la presión de su propio peso.

compass A device with a magnetized needle that can spin freely; a compass needle always points north.
brújula Instrumento con una aguja imantada que puede girar libremente; la aguja siempre apunta hacia el norte.

competition The struggle between organisms to survive as they attempt to use the same limited resources in the same place at the same time.
competencia Lucha por la supervivencia entre organismos que se alimentan de los mismos recursos limitados en el mismo lugar y al mismo tiempo.

complementary colors Any two colors that combine to form white light.
colores complementarios Dos colores cualesquiera que se combinan para crear luz blanca.

complete metamorphosis A type of metamorphosis with four distinct stages: egg, larva, pupa, and adult.
metamorfosis completa Tipo de metamorfosis de cuatro etapas: huevo, larva, pupa y adulto.

composite volcano A tall, cone-shaped mountain in which layers of lava alternate with layers of ash and other volcanic materials.
volcán compuesto Montaña alta en forma de cono en la que las capas de lava se alternan con capas de ceniza y otros materiales volcánicos.

compound A substance made of two or more elements chemically combined in a specific ratio, or proportion.
compuesto Sustancia formada por dos o más elementos combinados químicamente en una razón o proporción específica.

compound machine A device that combines two or more simple machines.
máquina compuesta Dispositivo que combina dos o más máquinas simples.

compression 1. Stress that squeezes rock until it folds or breaks. 2. The part of a longitudinal wave where the particles of the medium are close together.
compresión 1. Fuerza que oprime una roca hasta que se pliega o se rompe. 2. Parte de una onda longitudinal en la que las partículas del medio están más cerca.

concave lens A lens that is thinner in the center than at the edges.
lente cóncava Lente que es más fina en el centro que en los extremos.

concave mirror A mirror with a surface that curves inward.
espejo cóncavo Espejo cuya superficie se curva hacia dentro.

concentrated solution A mixture that has a lot of solute dissolved in it.
solución concentrada Mezcla que tiene muchos solutos disueltos en ella.

concentration The amount of one material in a certain volume of another material.
concentración Cantidad de un material en cierto volumen de otro material.

condensation The change in state from a gas to a liquid.
condensación Cambio del estado gaseoso al estado líquido.

conduction 1. The transfer of thermal energy from one particle of matter to another. **2.** A method of charging an object by allowing electrons to flow from one object to another object through direct contact.
conducción 1. Transferencia de energía térmica de una partícula de materia a otra. **2.** Método de transferencia de electricidad que consiste en permitir que los electrones fluyan por contacto directo de un cuerpo a otro.

conductor 1. A material that conducts heat well. **2.** A material that allows electric charges to flow.
conductor 1. Material que puede conducir bien el calor. **2.** Material que permite que las cargas eléctricas fluyan.

cone The reproductive structure of a gymnosperm.
cono Estructura reproductora de una gimnosperma.

cones Cells in the retina that respond to and detect color.
conos Células en la retina que responden y detectan el color.

coniferous tree A tree that produces its seeds in cones and that has needle-shaped leaves coated in a waxy substance to reduce water loss.
árbol conífero Árbol que produce sus semillas en piñones y que tiene hojas en forma de aguja y cubiertas por una sustancia cerosa que reduce la pérdida de agua.

conjugation A form of sexual reproduction in which a unicellular organism transfers some of its genetic material to another unicellular organism.
conjugación Forma de reproducción sexual en la que un organismo unicelular transfiere su material genético a otro organismo unicelular.

connective tissue A body tissue that provides support for the body and connects all its parts.
tejido conector Tejido del cuerpo que mantiene la estructura del cuerpo y une todas sus partes.

conservation The practice of using less of a resource so that it can last longer.
conservación Práctica que consiste en reducir el uso de un recurso para prolongar su duración.

conservation of charge The law that states that charges are neither created nor destroyed.
conservación de carga eléctrica Ley que establece que las cargas no se crean ni se destruyen.

conservation plowing Soil conservation method in which weeds and dead stalks from the previous year's crop are plowed into the ground.

arado de conservación Método de conservación de la tierra en el que las plantas y los tallos muertos de la cosecha del año anterior se dejan en la tierra al ararla.

constellation A pattern or grouping of stars that people imagine to represent a figure or object.
constelación Patrón de estrellas que se dice se asemeja a una figura u objeto.

constructive force Any natural process that builds up Earth's surface.
fuerza constructiva Proceso natural que incrementa la superficie de la Tierra.

constructive interference The interference that occurs when two waves combine to make a wave with an amplitude larger than the amplitude of either of the individual waves.
interferencia constructiva Interferencia que ocurre cuando se combinan ondas para crear una onda con una amplitud mayor a la de cualquiera de las ondas individuales.

consumer An organism that obtains energy by feeding on other organisms.
consumidor Organismo que obtiene energía al alimentarse de otros organismos.

continental (air mass) A dry air mass that forms over land.
masa de aire continental Masa de aire seco que se forma sobre la Tierra.

continental climate The climate of the centers of continents, with cold winters and warm or hot summers.
clima continental Clima del centro de los continentes, con inviernos fríos y veranos templados o calurosos.

continental drift The hypothesis that the continents slowly move across Earth's surface.
deriva continental Hipótesis que sostiene que los continentes se desplazan lentamente sobre la superficie de la Tierra.

continental glacier A glacier that covers much of a continent or large island.
glaciar continental Glaciar que cubre gran parte de un continente o una isla grande.

continental shelf A gently sloping, shallow area of the ocean floor that extends outward from the edge of a continent.
plataforma continental Área poco profunda con pendiente suave en la cuenca oceánica que se extiende desde los márgenes de un continente.

GLOSSARY

continental slope A steep incline of the ocean floor leading down from the edge of the continental shelf.
talud continental Región de la cuenca oceánica con pendiente empinada que baja del borde de la plataforma continental.

contour plowing Plowing fields along the curves of a slope to prevent soil loss.
arado en contorno Arar los campos siguiendo las curvas de una pendiente para evitar la pérdida del suelo.

contractile vacuole The cell structure that collects extra water from the cytoplasm and then expels it from the cell.
vacuola contráctil Estructura celular que recoge el agua sobrante del citoplasma y luego la expulsa de la célula.

control rod A cadmium rod used in a nuclear reactor to absorb neutrons from fission reactions.
varilla de control Varilla de cadmio que se usa en un reactor nuclear para absorber los neutrones emitidos por reacciones de fisión.

controlled experiment An experiment in which only one variable is manipulated at a time.
experimento controlado Experimento en el cual sólo se manipula una variable a la vez.

convection The transfer of thermal energy by the movement of a fluid.
convección Transferencia de energía térmica por el movimiento de un líquido.

convection current The movement of a fluid, caused by differences in temperature, that transfers heat from one part of the fluid to another.
corriente de convección Movimiento de un líquido ocasionado por diferencias de temperatura y que transfiere calor de un área del líquido a otra.

convection zone The outermost layer of the sun's interior.
zona de convección Capa más superficial del interior del Sol.

convergent boundary A plate boundary where two plates move toward each other.
borde convergente Borde de una placa donde dos placas se deslizan una hacia la otra.

convergent evolution The process by which unrelated organisms evolve similar characteristics.
evolución convergente Proceso por el cual organismos no relacionados exhiben una evolución de características similares.

convex lens A lens that is thicker in the center than at the edges.
lente convexa Lente que es más gruesa en el centro que en los extremos.

convex mirror A mirror with a surface that curves outward.
espejo convexo Espejo cuya superficie se curva hacia fuera.

core The central region of the sun, where nuclear fusion takes place.
núcleo Región central del Sol, donde ocurre la fusión nuclear.

Coriolis effect The effect of Earth's rotation on the direction of winds and currents.
efecto Coriolis Efecto de la rotación de la Tierra sobre la dirección de los vientos y las corrientes.

cornea The transparent tissue that covers the front of the eye.
córnea Tejido transparente que cubre la parte delantera del ojo.

corona The outer layer of the sun's atmosphere.
corona Capa externa de la atmósfera solar.

corrosive The way in which acids react with some metals so as to wear away the metal.
corrosivo Forma en que los ácidos reaccionan con algunos metales y los desgastan.

cosmic background radiation The electromagneticradiationleft over from the big bang.
radiación cósmica de fondo Radiaciónelectromagnética que quedó del Big bang.

cotyledon A leaf produced by an embryo of a seed plant; sometimes stores food.
cotiledón Hoja producida por el embrión de una planta fanerógama; a veces almacena alimentos.

covalent bond A chemical bond formed when two atoms share electrons.
enlace covalente Enlace químico que se forma cuando dos átomos comparten electrones.

crater 1. A large round pit caused by the impact of a meteoroid. 2. A bowl-shaped area that forms around a volcano's central opening.
cráter 1. Gran hoyo redondo que se forma por el impacto de un meteorito. 2. Área en forma de tazón que se forma en la abertura central de un volcán.

crest The highest part of a transverse wave.
cresta Parte más alta de una onda transversal.

critical night length The number of hours of darkness that determines whether or not a plant will flower.
duración crítica de la noche El número de horas de oscuridad que determina si florecerá una planta o no.

crop rotation The planting of different crops in a field each year to maintain the soil's fertility.
rotación de las cosechas Cultivo anual de cosechas diferentes en un campo para mantener la fertilidad del suelo.

crust The layer of rock that forms Earth's outer surface.
corteza terrestre Capa de rocas que forma la superficie externa de la Tierra.

crystal A solid in which the atoms are arranged in a pattern that repeats again and again.
cristal Cuerpo sólido en el que los átomos siguen un patrón que se repite una y otra vez.

crystalline solid A solid that is made up of crystals in which particles are arranged in a regular, repeating pattern.
sólido cristalino Sólido constituido por cristales en los que las partículas están colocadas en un patrón regular repetitivo.

crystallization The process by which atoms are arranged to form a material with a crystal structure.
cristalización Proceso mediante el cual los átomos se distribuyen y forman materiales con estructura de cristal.

cultural bias An outlook influenced by the beliefs, social forms, and traits of a group.
prejuicio cultural Opinión influenciada por las creencias, costumbres sociales y características de un grupo.

cumulus Fluffy, white clouds, usually with flat bottoms, that look like rounded piles of cotton.
cúmulos Nubes blancas, normalmente con la parte inferior plana, que parecen grandes masas de algodón esponjosas y redondas.

current A large stream of moving water that flows through the oceans.
corriente Gran volumen de agua que fluye por los océanos.

cuticle The waxy, waterproof layer that covers the leaves and stems of most plants.
cutícula Capa cerosa e impermeable que cubre las hojas y los tallos de la mayoría de las plantas.

cyclone A swirling center of low air pressure.
ciclón Centro de un remolino de aire de baja presión.

cytokinesis The final stage of the cell cycle, in which the cell's cytoplasm divides, distributing the organelles into each of the two new daughter cells.
citocinesis Última etapa del ciclo celular en la que se divide el citoplasma y se reparten los orgánulos entre las dos células hijas nuevas.

cytoplasm The thick fluid region of a cell located inside the cell membrane (in prokaryotes) or between the cell membrane and nucleus (in eukaryotes).
citoplasma egión celular de líquido espeso ubicada dentro de la membrana celular (en las procariotas) o entre la membrana celular y el núcleo (en las eucariotas).

D

dark energy A mysterious force that appears to be causing the expansion of the universe to accelerate.
energía negra Misteriosa fuerza que parece acelerar la expansión del universo.

dark matter Matter that does not give off electromagnetic radiation but is quite abundant in the universe.
materia negra Materia que es muy abundante en el universo y no despide radiación electromagnética.

data Facts, figures, and other evidence gathered through observations.
dato Hechos, cifras u otra evidencia reunida por medio de observaciones.

day-neutral plant A plant with a flowering cycle that is not sensitive to periods of light and dark.
planta de día neutro Planta con un ciclo de floración que no es sensible a la luz o la oscuridad.

death rate The number of deaths per 1,000 individuals for a certain time period.
tasa de mortalidad Número de muertes por 1,000 individuos durante un período de tiempo determinado.

decibel (dB) A unit used to compare the loudness of different sounds.
decibelio (dB) Unidad usada para comparar el volumen de distintos sonidos.

deciduous tree A tree that sheds its leaves during a particular season and grows new ones each year.
árbol caducifolio Árbol que pierde las hojas durante una estación específica y al que le salen hojas nuevas cada año.

GLOSSARY

decomposer An organism that gets energy by breaking down biotic wastes and dead organisms, and returns raw materials to the soil and water.
descomponedor Organismo que obtiene energía al descomponer desechos bióticos y organismos muertos, y que devuelve materia prima al suelo y al agua.

decomposition A chemical reaction that breaks down compounds into simpler products.
descomposición Reacción química que descompone los compuestos en productos más simples.

deductive reasoning A way to explain things by starting with a general idea and then applying the idea to a specific observation.
razonamiento deductivo Manera de explicar las cosas en la que se aplica una idea general a una observación específica.

deep-ocean trench A deep valley along the ocean floor beneath which oceanic crust slowly sinks toward the mantle.
fosa oceánica profunda Valle profundo a lo largo del suelo oceánico debajo del cual la corteza oceánica se hunde lentamente hacia el manto.

deflation The process by which wind removes surface materials.
deflación Proceso por el cual el viento se lleva materiales de la superficie.

delta A landform made of sediment that is deposited where a river flows into an ocean or lake.
delta Accidente geográfico formado por sedimento que se deposita en la desembocadura de un río a un océano o lago.

density The measurement of how much mass of a substance is contained in a given volume.
densidad Medida de la masa de una sustancia que tiene un volumen dado.

dependent variable The factor that changes as a result of changes to the independent variable in an experiment; also called responding variable.
variable dependiente Factor que cambia a causa de los cambios de la variable independiente de un experimento; también se denomina variable de respuesta.

deposition Process in which sediment is laid down in new locations.
sedimentación Proceso por el cual los sedimentos se asientan en nuevos sitios.

dermis The inner layer of the skin.
dermis Capa más interna de la piel.

desert A dry region that on average receives less than 25 centimeters of precipitation per year.
desierto Región seca en la que se registra un promedio menor de 25 centímetros de precipitación anual.

desertification The advance of desert-like conditions into areas that previously were fertile; caused by overfarming, overgrazing, drought, and climate change.
desertificación Paso de condiciones desérticas a áreas que eran fértiles; resulta de la agricultura descontrolada, el uso exagerado de los pastos, las sequías y los cambios climáticos.

destructive force Any natural process that tears down or wears away Earth's surface.
fuerza destructiva Proceso natural que destruye o desgasta la superficie de la Tierra.

destructive interference The interference that occurs when two waves combine to make a wave with an amplitude smaller than the amplitude of either of the individual waves.
interferencia destructiva Interferencia que ocurre cuando dos ondas se combinan para crear una onda con una amplitud menor a la de cualquiera de las ondas individuales.

development The process of change that occurs during an organism's life to produce a more complex organism.
desarrollo Proceso de cambio que ocurre durante la vida de un organismo, mediante el cual se crea un organismo más complejo.

dew point The temperature at which condensation begins.
punto de rocío Temperatura a la que comienza la condensación.

diabetes A condition in which the pancreas fails to produce enough insulin or the body's cells cannot use it properly.
diabetes Condición en la que el páncreas no puede producir suficiente insulina o las células del cuerpo no la pueden usar correctamente.

diaphragm A large, dome-shaped muscle located at the base of the lungs that helps with breathing.
diafragma Músculo grande y redondo situado en la base de los pulmones que ayuda a la respiración.

dicot An angiosperm that has two seed leaves.
dicotiledónea Angiosperma cuyas semillas tienen dos cotiledones.

diffraction The bending or spreading of waves as they move around a barrier or pass through an opening.
difracción Desviación de las ondas al desplazarse alrededor de una barrera o atravesar una abertura.

diffuse reflection Reflection that occurs when parallel rays of light hit an uneven surface and all reflect at different angles.
reflexión difusa Reflexión que ocurre cuando rayos de luz paralelos tocan una superficie rugosa y se reflejan en diferentes ángulos.

diffusion The process by which molecules move from an area of higher concentration to an area of lower concentration.
difusión Proceso por el cual las moléculas se mueven de un área de mayor concentración a otra de menor concentración.

digestion The process that breaks down complex molecules of food into smaller nutrient molecules.
digestión Proceso que descompone las moléculas complejas de los alimentos en moléculas de nutrientes más pequeñas.

digestive system An organ system that has specialized structures for obtaining and digesting food.
sistema digestivo Sistema de órganos que tiene estructuras especializadas para ingerir y digerir alimentos.

dike A slab of volcanic rock formed when magma forces itself across rock layers.
dique discordante Placa de roca volcánica formada cuando el magma se abre paso a través de las capas de roca.

dilute solution A mixture that has only a little solute dissolved in it.
solución diluida Mezcla que sólo tiene un poco de soluto disuelto en ella.

direct current Current consisting of charges that flow in only one direction in a circuit.
corriente directa Corriente de cargas eléctricas que fluyen en una sola dirección en un circuito.

directly proportional A term used to describe the relationship between two variables whose graph is a straight line passing through the point (0, 0).
directamente proporcional Término empleado para describir la relación entre dos variables cuya gráfica forma una línea recta que pasa por el punto (0, 0).

dispersal The movement of organisms from one place to another.
dispersión Traslado de los organismos de un lugar a otro.

distance The length of the path between two points.
distancia Medida del espacio entre dos puntos.

divergent boundary A plate boundary where two plates move away from each other.
borde divergente Borde de una placa donde dos placas se separan.

divide A ridge of land that separates one watershed from another.
divisoria Elevación de terreno que separa una cuenca hidrográfica de otra.

DNA Deoxyribonucleic acid; the genetic material that carries information about an organism and is passed from parent to offspring.
ADN Ácido desoxirribonucleico; material genético que lleva información sobre un organismo y que se transmite de padres a hijos.

DNA replication Before a cell divides, the process in which DNA copies itself.
replicación del ADN Proceso en el que el ADN se duplica, antes de que la célula se divida.

dominant allele An allele whose trait always shows up in the organism when the allele is present.
alelo dominante Alelo cuyo rasgo siempre se manifiesta en el organismo, cuando el alelo está presente.

Doppler effect The change in frequency of a wave as its source moves in relation to an observer.
efecto Doppler Cambio en la frecuencia de una onda a medida que la fuente se mueve en relación al observador.

dormancy A period of time when an organism's growth or activity stops.
latencia Período de tiempo durante el cual se detiene el crecimiento o la actividad de un organismo.

dormant Not currently active but able to become active in the future (as with a volcano).
inactivo Que no está activo en la actualidad pero puede ser activo en el futuro (como un volcán).

double bond A chemical bond formed when atoms share two pairs of electrons.
enlace doble Enlace químico formado cuando los átomos comparten dos pares de electrones.

double helix The shape of a DNA molecule.
doble hélice Forma de una molécula de ADN.

drought A long period of low precipitation.
sequía Período prolongado de baja precipitación.

GLOSSARY

duct A tiny tube through which chemicals are released from a gland.
ducto Conducto diminuto por el cual se liberan sustancias químicas de una glándula.

dwarf planet An object that orbits the sun and is spherical, but has not cleared the area of its orbit.
planeta enano Un cuerpo esférico que orbita alrededor del Sol, pero que no ha despejado las proximidades de su órbita.

------------------ **E** ------------------

ear canal A narrow region leading from the outside of the human ear to the eardrum.
canal auditivo Región estrecha que conecta el exterior del oído humano con el tímpano.

eardrum The small, tightly stretched drumlike membrane that separates the outer ear from the middle ear, and that vibrates when sound waves strike it.
tímpano Membrana pequeña extendida y tensa, como la de un tambor, que separa el oído externo del oído medio y que vibra al percibir ondas de sonido.

earthquake The shaking that results from the movement of rock beneath Earth's surface.
terremoto Temblor que resulta del movimiento de la roca debajo de la superficie de la Tierra.

echinoderm A radially symmetrical marine invertebrate that has an internal skeleton and a system of fluid-filled tubes.
equinodermo Invertebrado marino de simetría radiada que tiene un esqueleto interno y un sistema de apéndices en forma de tubos llenos de líquido.

echolocation The use of reflected sound waves to determine distances or to locate objects.
ecolocación Uso de ondas sonoras reflejadas para determinar distancias o para localizar objetos.

eclipse The partial or total blocking of one object in space by another.
eclipse Bloqueo parcial o total de un cuerpo en el espacio por otro.

eclipsing binary A binary star system in which one star periodically blocks the light from the other.
eclipse binario Sistema estelar binario en el que una estrella bloquea periódicamente la luz de la otra.

ecological footprint The amount of land and water that individuals use to meet their resource needs and to absorb the wastes that they produce.

espacio ecológico Cantidad de tierra y agua que los individuos usan para cubrir sus necesidades y absorber sus desechos.

ecology The study of how organisms interact with each other and their environment.
ecología Estudio de la forma en que los organismos interactúan entre sí y con su medio ambiente.

ecosystem The community of organisms that live in a particular area, along with their nonliving environment.
ecosistema Comunidad de organismos que viven en un área específica, y el medio ambiente que los rodea.

ectotherm An animal whose body temperature is determined by the temperature of its environment.
ectotermo Animal cuya temperatura corporal es determinada por la temperatura de su medio ambiente.

efficiency The percentage of input work that is converted to output work.
eficacia Porcentaje de trabajo aportado que se convierte en trabajo producido.

egg A female sex cell.
óvulo Célula sexual femenina.

El Niño An abnormal climate event that occurs every two to seven years in the Pacific Ocean, causing changes in winds, currents, and weather patterns for one to two years.
El Niño Suceso climático anormal que se presenta cada dos a siete años en el océano Pacífico y que causa cambios de vientos, corrientes y patrones meteorológicos que duran uno o dos años.

elastic potential energy The energy of stretched or compressed objects.
energía elástica potencial Energía de los cuerpos estirados o comprimidos.

electric circuit A complete, unbroken path through which electric charges can flow.
circuito eléctrico Trayecto completo y continuo a través del cual pueden fluir las cargas eléctricas.

electric current The continuous flow of electric charges through a material.
corriente eléctrica Flujo continuo de cargas eléctricas a través de un material.

electric field The region around a charged object where the object's electric force is exerted on other charged objects.
campo eléctrico Región alrededor de un objeto cargado, donde su fuerza eléctrica interactúa con otros objetos cargados eléctricamente.

electric force The force between charged objects.
fuerza eléctrica Fuerza entre cuerpos cargados eléctricamente.

electric motor A device that transforms electrical energy to mechanical energy.
motor eléctrico Instrumento que convierte la energía eléctrica en energía mecánica.

electrical energy The energy of electric charges.
energía eléctrica Energía de las cargas eléctricas.

electromagnet A magnet created by wrapping a coil of wire with a current running through it around a core of material that is easily magnetised.
electroimán Imán creado al enrollar una espiral de alambre, por la cual fluye una corriente eléctrica, alrededor de un núcleo de material que se magnetiza fácilmente.

electromagnetic energy The energy of light and other forms of radiation, which travels through space as waves.
energía electromagnética Energía de la luz y otras formas de radiación, que viaja a través del espacio en forma de ondas.

electromagnetic induction The process of generating an electric current from the motion of a conductor through a magnetic field.
inducción electromagnética Proceso por el cual se genera una corriente eléctrica a partir del movimiento de un conductor a través de un campo magnético.

electromagnetic radiation The energy transferred through space by electromagnetic waves.
radiación electromagnética Energía transferida a través del espacio por ondas electromagnéticas.

electromagnetic spectrum The complete range of electromagnetic waves placed in order of increasing frequency.
espectro electromagnético Gama completa de ondas electromagnéticas organizadas de menor a mayor frecuencia.

electromagnetic wave 1. A wave made up of a combination of a changing electric field and a changing magnetic field. **2.** A wave that can transfer electric and magnetic energy through the vacuum of space.
onda electromagnética 1. Onda formada por la combinación de un campo eléctrico cambiante y un campo magnético cambiante. **2.** Onda que puede transportar energía eléctrica y magnética a través del vacío del espacio.

electromagnetic waves Waves that can transfer electric and magnetic energy through the vacuum of space.

ondas electromagnéticas Ondas que pueden transferir energía eléctrica y magnética a través del vacío del espacio.

electromagnetism The relationship between electricity and magnetism.
electromagnetismo Relación entre la electricidad y el magnetismo.

electron dot diagram A representation of the valence electrons in an atom, using dots.
esquema de puntos por electrones Representación del número de electrones de valencia de un átomo, usando puntos.

element A pure substance that cannot be broken down into other substances by chemical or physical means.
elemento Sustancia que no se puede descomponer en otras sustancias por medios químicos o físicos.

ellipse An oval shape, which may be elongated or nearly circular; the shape of the planets' orbits.
elipse Forma ovalada que puede ser alargada o casi circular; la forma de la órbita de los planetas.

elliptical galaxy A galaxy shaped like a round or flattened ball, generally containing only old stars.
galaxia elíptica Galaxia de forma redonda o semejante a una pelota desinflada, que generalmente sólo contiene estrellas viejas.

embryo 1. The young organism that develops from a zygote. **2.** A developing human during the first eight weeks after fertilization has occurred.
embrión 1. Organismo joven que se desarrolla a partir del cigoto. **2.** Un ser humano en desarrollo durante las primeras ocho semanas después de llevarse a cabo la fertilización.

emergent layer The tallest layer of the rain forest that receives the most sunlight.
capa emergente Capa superior de la selva tropical, que recibe la mayor cantidad de luz solar.

emigration Movement of individuals out of a population's area.
emigración Traslado de individuos fuera del área de una población.

emissions Pollutants that are released into the air.
gases contaminantes Contaminantes liberados al aire.

empirical evidence Data and observations that are collected through scientific processes and that explain a particular observation.
evidencia empírica Datos y observaciones que se recopilan a través de procesos científicos y que explican una observación particular.

GLOSSARY

endangered species A species in danger of becoming extinct in the near future.
especie en peligro de extinción Especie que corre el riesgo de desaparecer en el futuro próximo.

endocytosis The process by which the cell membrane takes particles into the cell by changing shape and engulfing the particles.
endocitosis Proceso en el que la membrana celular absorbe partículas al cambiar de forma y envolver las partículas.

endoplasmic reticulum An organelle that forms a maze of passageways in which proteins and other materials are carried from one part of the cell to another.
retículo endoplasmático Orgánulo que forma un laberinto de conductos que llevan proteínas y otros materiales de una parte de la célula a otra.

endoskeleton An internal skeleton; structural support system within the body of an animal.
endoesqueleto Esqueleto interno; sistema estructural de soporte dentro del cuerpo de un animal.

endospore A structure produced by prokaryotes, such as bacteria, in unfavorable conditions; a thick wall encloses the DNA and some of the cytoplasm.
endospora Estructura que las procariotas, como las bacterias, producen en condiciones desfavorables; capa gruesa que encierra al ADN y parte del citoplasma.

endotherm An animal whose body temperature is regulated by the internal heat the animal produces.
endotermo Animal cuya temperatura corporal es regulada por el calor interno que produce.

endothermic change A change in which energy is absorbed.
cambio endotérmico Cambio en el que se absorbe energía.

endothermic reaction A reaction that absorbs energy.
reacción endotérmica Reacción que absorbe energía.

energy The ability to do work or cause change.
energía Capacidad para realizar un trabajo o producir cambios.

energy conservation The practice of reducing energy use.
conservación de energía Práctica de reducción del uso de energía.

energy pyramid A diagram that shows the amount of energy that moves from one feeding level to another in a food web.

pirámide de energía Diagrama que muestra la cantidad de energía que fluye de un nivel de alimentación a otro en una red alimentaria.

energy transformation A change from one form of energy to another; also called an energy conversion.
transformación de la energía Cambio de una forma de energía a otra; también se le llama conversión de energía.

environmental science The study of the natural processes that occur in the environment and how humans can affect them.
ciencias del medio ambiente Estudio de los procesos naturales que ocurren en el medio ambiente y de cómo los seres humanos pueden afectarlos.

enzyme **1.** A type of protein that speeds up a chemical reaction in a living thing. **2.** A biological catalyst that lowers the activation energy of reactions in cells.
enzima **1.** Tipo de proteína que acelera una reacción química de un ser vivo. **2.** Catalizador biológico que disminuye la energía de activación de las reacciones celulares.

epicenter The point on Earth's surface directly above an earthquake's focus.
epicentro Punto de la superficie de la Tierra directamente sobre el foco de un terremoto.

epidermis The outer layer of the skin.
epidermis Capa externa de la piel.

epiglottis A flap of tissue that seals off the windpipe and prevents food from entering the lungs.
epiglotis Lámina de tejido que sella la tráquea y evita que los alimentos entren en los pulmones.

epithelial tissue A body tissue that covers the interior and exterior surfaces of the body.
tejido epitelial Tejido del cuerpo que cubre las superficies interiores y exteriores.

equinox Either of the two days of the year on which neither hemisphere is tilted toward or away from the sun.
equinoccio Cualquiera de los de dos días del año en el que ningún hemisferio se retrae o inclina hacia el Sol.

era One of the three long units of geologic time between the Precambrian and the present.
era Cada una de las tres unidades largas del tiempo geológico entre el Precámbrico y el presente.

erosion The process by which water, ice, wind, or gravity moves weathered particles of rock and soil.
erosión Proceso por el cual el agua, el hielo, el viento o la gravedad desplazan partículas desgastadas de roca y suelo.

escape velocity The velocity an object must reach to fly beyond a planet's or moon's gravitational pull.
velocidad de escape Velocidad que debe alcanzar un cohete para salir del empuje gravitacional de un planeta o luna.

esophagus A muscular tube that connects the mouth to the stomach.
esófago Tubo muscular que conecta la boca con el estómago.

estimate An approximation of a number based on reasonable assumptions.
estimación Aproximación de un número basada en conjeturas razonables.

estrogen A hormone produced by the ovaries that controls the development of eggs and adult female characteristics.
estrógeno Hormona producida por los ovarios que controla el desarrollo de los óvulos y de las características femeninas adultas.

estuary A kind of wetland formed where fresh water from rivers mixes with salty ocean water.
estuario Tipo de pantanal que se forma donde el agua dulce de los ríos se junta con el agua salada del océano.

ethics The study of principles about what is right and wrong, fair and unfair.
ética Estudio de los principios de qué es lo bueno y lo malo, lo justo y lo injusto.

eukaryote An organism whose cells contain a nucleus.
eucariota Organismo cuyas células contienen un núcleo.

eutrophication The buildup over time of nutrients in freshwater lakes and ponds that leads to an increase in the growth of algae.
eutroficación Acumulación gradual de nutrientes en lagos y estanques de agua dulce que produce un aumento en el crecimiento de algas.

evacuate Moving away temporarily from an area about to be affected by severe weather.
evacuar Desalojar temporalmente un área que será afectada por mal tiempo.

evaluating Comparing observations and data to reach a conclusion about them.
evaluar Comparar observaciones y datos para llegar a una conclusión.

evaporation The process by which molecules at the surface of a liquid absorb enough energy to change to a gas.
evaporación Proceso mediante el cual las moléculas en la superficie de un líquido absorben suficiente energía para pasar al estado gaseoso.

evidence Observations and conclusions that have been repeated.
evidencia Observaciones y conclusiones que se han repetido.

evolution Change over time; the process by which modern organisms have descended from ancient organisms.
evolución Cambios a través del tiempo; proceso por el cual los organismos modernos se originaron a partir de organismos antiguos.

excretion The process by which wastes are removed from the body.
excreción Proceso por el cual se eliminan los desechos del cuerpo.

exocytosis The process by which the vacuole surrounding particles fuses with the cell membrane, forcing the contents out of the cell.
exocitosis Proceso en el que la vacuola que envuelve partículas se funde con la membrana celular, expulsando así el contenido al exterior de la célula.

exoskeleton External skeleton; a tough, waterproof outer covering that protects, supports, and helps prevent evaporation of water from the body of many invertebrates.
exoesqueleto Esqueleto exterior; una cobertura fuerte e impermeable que protege, soporta y ayuda a prevenir la evaporación del agua del cuerpo de muchos invertebrados.

exosphere The outer layer of the thermosphere.
exósfera Capa externa de la termósfera.

exothermic change A change in which energy is released.
cambio exotérmico Cambio en el que se libera energía.

exothermic reaction A reaction that releases energy, usually in the form of heat.
reacción exotérmica Reacción que libera energía generalmente en forma de calor.

exotic species Species that are carried to a new location by people.
especies exóticas Especies que las personas trasladan a un nuevo lugar.

GLOSSARY

experimental bias A mistake in the design of an experiment that makes a particular result more likely.
prejuicio experimental Error en el diseño de un experimento que aumenta la probabilidad de un resultado.

external fertilization When eggs are fertilized outside of a female's body.
fertilización externa Cuando los óvulos se fertilizan fuera del cuerpo de la hembra.

extinct 1. Term used to refer to a group of related organisms that has died out and has no living members. **2.** Term used to describe a volcano that is no longer active and unlikely to erupt again.
extinto 1. Término que se refiere a un grupo de organismos que ha muerto y del cual no queda ningún miembro vivo. **2.** Término que describe un volcán que ya no es activo y es poco probable que vuelva a hacer erupción.

extinction The disappearance of all members of a species from Earth.
extinción Desaparición de la Tierra de todos los miembros de una especie.

extrusion An igneous rock layer formed when lava flows onto Earth's surface and hardens.
extrusión Capa de roca ígnea formada cuando la lava fluye hacia la superficie de la Tierra y se endurece.

extrusive rock Igneous rock that forms from lava on Earth's surface.
roca extrusiva Roca ígnea que se forma de la lava en la superficie de la Tierra.

eyepiece A lens that magnifies the image formed by the objective.
ocular Lente que aumenta la imagen formada por el objetivo.

F

Fahrenheit scale The temperature scale on which water freezes at 32°F and boils at 212°F.
escala Fahrenheit Escala de temperatura en la que el punto de congelación del agua es 32°F y el punto de ebullición es 212°F.

Fallopian tube A passageway for eggs from an ovary to the uterus.
trompa de falopio Pasaje por el que pasan los óvulos de un ovario al útero.

farsighted Having the condition in which a person can see distant objects clearly and nearby objects as blurry.
hipermetropía Condición en la que una persona ve con claridad los objetos lejanos y ve borrosos los objetos cercanos.

fault A break in Earth's crust along which rocks move.
falla Fisura en la corteza terrestre a lo largo de la cual se desplazan las rocas.

feedback Output that changes a system or allows the system to adjust itself.
retroalimentación Salida que cambia un sistema o permite que éste se ajuste.

fermentation The process by which cells release energy by breaking down food molecules without using oxygen.
fermentación Proceso en el que las células liberan energía al descomponer las moléculas de alimento sin usar oxígeno.

fertility A measure of how well soil supports plant growth.
fertilidad Medida de cuán apropiado es un suelo para estimular el crecimiento de las plantas.

fertilization The process in sexual reproduction in which an egg cell and a sperm cell join to form a new cell.
fertilización Proceso de la reproducción sexual en el que un óvulo y un espermatozoide se unen para formar una nueva célula.

fertilizer A substance that provides nutrients to help crops grow better.
fertilizante Sustancia que proporciona nutrientes para ayudar a que crezcan mejor los cultivos.

fetus A developing human from the ninth week of development until birth.
feto Humano en desarrollo desde la novena semana de desarrollo hasta el nacimiento.

field Any area outside of the laboratory.
campo Cualquier área fuera del laboratorio.

filter feeder An animal that strains its food from water.
comedores por suspensión Animal que filtra sus alimentos del agua.

fish A vertebrate whose body temperature is determined by the temperature of its environment, and that lives in the water and has fins.
pez Vertebrado cuya temperatura corporal es determinada por la temperatura de su medio ambiente, que vive en el agua y que tiene aletas.

flagellum A long, whiplike structure that helps a cell to move.
flagelo Estructura larga con forma de látigo, que ayuda a la célula a moverse.

flood An overflowing of water in a normally dry area.
inundación Ocupación de agua en un área que habitualmente permanece seca.

flood plain The flat, wide area of land along a river.
llanura de aluvión Área de tierra extensa y plana a lo largo de un río.

flower The reproductive structure of an angiosperm.
flor Estructura reproductora de una angiosperma.

fluid Any substance that can flow.
fluido Cualquier sustancia que puede fluir.

fluid friction Friction that occurs as an object moves through a fluid.
fricción de fluido Fricción que ocurre cuando un cuerpo se mueve a través de un fluido.

focal point The point at which light rays parallel to the optical axis meet, or appear to meet, after being reflected (or refracted) by a mirror (or a lens).
punto de enfoque Punto en el que se encuentran, o parecen encontrarse, los rayos de luz paralelos al eje óptico después de reflejarse (o refractarse) en un espejo (o lente).

focus The point beneath Earth's surface where rock first breaks under stress and causes an earthquake.
foco Punto debajo de la superficie de la Tierra en el que la roca empieza a romperse debido a una gran fuerza y causa un terremoto.

foliated Term used to describe metamorphic rocks that have grains arranged in parallel layers or bands.
foliación Término que describe las rocas metamórficas con granos dispuestos en capas paralelas o bandas.

follicle Structure in the dermis of the skin from which a strand of hair grows.
folículo Estructura en la dermis de la piel de donde crece un pelo.

food chain A series of events in an ecosystem in which organisms transfer energy by eating and by being eaten.
cadena alimentaria Serie de sucesos en un ecosistema por medio de los cuales los organismos transmiten energía al comer o al ser comidos por otros.

food web The pattern of overlapping feeding relationships or food chains among the various organisms in an ecosystem.
red alimentaria Patrón de las relaciones de alimentación superpuestas o de cadenas alimentarias entre los diferentes organismos de un ecosistema.

force A push or pull exerted on an object.
fuerza Empuje o atracción que se ejerce sobre un cuerpo.

fossil The preserved remains or traces of an organism that lived in the past.
fósil Restos o vestigios conservados de un organismo que vivió en el pasado.

fossil fuel Coal, oil, or natural gas that forms over millions of years from the remains of ancient organisms; burned to release energy.
combustible fósil Carbón, petróleo o gas natural que se forma a lo largo de millones de años a partir de los restos de organismos antiguos; se queman para liberar energía.

fracture 1. The way a mineral looks when it breaks apart in an irregular way. **2.** A break in a bone.
fractura 1. Apariencia de un mineral cuando se rompe de manera irregular. **2.** Fisura de un hueso.

free fall The motion of a falling object when the only force acting on it is gravity.
caída libre Movimiento de un objeto que cae cuando la única fuerza que actúa sobre éste es la gravedad.

freezing The change in state from a liquid to a solid.
congelación Cambio del estado líquido al sólido.

frequency The number of complete waves that pass a given point in a certain amount of time.
frecuencia Número de ondas completas que pasan por un punto dado en cierto tiempo.

frequency modulation A method of transmitting signals by changing the frequency of a wave.
frecuencia modulada Método de transmisión de señales mediante el cambio de la frecuencia de una onda.

friction The force that two surfaces exert on each other when they rub against each other.
fricción Fuerza que dos superficies ejercen una sobre la otra al frotarse.

frond The leaf of a fern plant.
fronda Hoja de un helecho.

front The boundary where unlike air masses meet but do not mix.
frente Límite donde se encuentran, pero no se mezclan, masas de aire diferentes.

frost wedging Process that splits rock when water seeps into cracks, then freezes and expands.
acuñado rocoso Proceso que separa las rocas cuando el agua se filtra entre grietas y luego se congela y expande.

GLOSSARY

fruit The ripened ovary and other structures of an angiosperm that enclose one or more seeds.
fruto Ovario maduro y otras estructuras de una angiosperma que encierran una o más semillas.

fruiting body The reproductive structure of a fungus that contains many hyphae and produces spores.
órgano fructífero Estructura reproductora de un hongo, que contiene muchas hifas y produce esporas.

fuel A substance that provides energy as the result of a chemical change.
combustible Sustancia que libera energía como resultado de un cambio químico.

fuel rod A uranium rod that undergoes fission in a nuclear reactor.
varilla de combustible Varilla de uranio que se somete a la fisión en un reactor nuclear.

fulcrum The fixed point around which a lever pivots.
fulcro Punto fijo en torno al cual gira una palanca.

fundamental tone The lowest natural frequency of an object.
tono fundamental Frecuencia natural más baja de un cuerpo.

fungus A eukaryotic organism that has cell walls, uses spores to reproduce, and is a heterotroph that feeds by absorbing its food.
hongo Organismo eucariótico que posee paredes celulares, usa esporas para reproducirse y es un heterótrofo que se alimenta absorbiendo sus alimentos.

fuse A safety device with a thin metal strip that will melt if too much current passes through a circuit.
fusible Elemento de seguridad que tiene una tira metálica delgada que se derrite si una corriente demasiado fuerte pasa por un circuito.

---------G---------

galaxy A huge group of single stars, star systems, star clusters, dust, and gas bound together by gravity.
galaxia Enorme grupo de estrellas individuales, sistemas estelares, cúmulos de estrellas, polvo y gases unidos por la gravedad.

galvanometer A device that uses an electromagnet to detect small amounts of current.
galvanómetro Instrumento que usa un electroimán para detectar la intensidad de una pequeña corriente.

gametophyte The stage in the life cycle of a plant in which the plant produces gametes, or sex cells.

gametofito Etapa del ciclo vital de una planta en la que produce gametos, es decir, células sexuales.

gamma rays Electromagnetic waves with the shortest wavelengths and highest frequencies.
rayos gamma Ondas electromagnéticas con la menor longitud de onda y la mayor frecuencia.

gas A state of matter with no definite shape or volume.
gas Estado de la materia sin forma ni volumen definidos.

gas giant The name often given to the outer planets: Jupiter, Saturn, Uranus, and Neptune.
gigantes gaseosos Nombre que normalmente se da a los cuatro planetas exteriores: Júpiter, Saturno, Urano y Neptuno.

gasohol A mixture of gasoline and alcohol.
gasohol Mezcla de gasolina y alcohol.

gene A sequence of DNA that determines a trait and is passed from parent to offspring.
gen Secuencia de ADN que determina un rasgo y que se pasa de los progenitores a los hijos.

gene therapy The process of changing a gene to treat a medical disease or disorder. An absent or faulty gene is replaced by a normal working gene.
terapia genética Proceso que consiste en cambiar un gen para tratar una enfermedad o un trastorno médico. El gen ausente o defectuoso se cambia por un gen con función normal.

generator A device that transforms mechanical energy into electrical energy.
generador eléctrico Instrumento que convierte la energía mecánica en energía eléctrica.

genetic engineering The transfer of a gene from the DNA of one organism into another organism, in order to produce an organism with desired traits.
ingeniería genética Transferencia de un gen desde el ADN de un organismo a otro, para producir un organismo con los rasgos deseados.

genetics The scientific study of heredity.
genética Ciencia que estudia la herencia.

genotype An organism's genetic makeup, or allele combinations.
genotipo Composición genética de un organismo, es decir, las combinaciones de los alelos.

genus A classification grouping that consists of a number of similar, closely related species.
género Clase de agrupación que consiste de un número de especies similares y estrechamente relacionadas.

geocentric Term describing a model of the universe in which Earth is at the center of the revolving planets and stars.
geocéntrico Término que describe un modelo del universo en el cual la Tierra se encuentra al centro de los planetas y estrellas que circulan a su alrededor.

geode A hollow rock inside which mineral crystals have grown.
geoda Roca hueca dentro de la que se forman cristales minerales.

geologic time scale A record of the geologic events and life forms in Earth's history.
escala de tiempo geológico Registro de los sucesos geológicos y de las formas de vida en la historia de la Tierra.

geosphere The densest parts of Earth that include the crust, mantle, and core.
geósfera Partes más densos de la Tierra que incluye la corteza, el manto y el núcleo.

geostationary orbit An orbit in which a satellite orbits Earth at the same rate as Earth rotates and thus stays over the same place all the time.
órbita geoestacionaria Órbita en la que un satélite orbita alrededor de la Tierra a la misma velocidad que rota la Tierra y que, por lo tanto, permanece en el mismo lugar todo el tiempo.

geothermal energy The intense heat energy that comes from Earth's interior.
energía geotérmica Energía intensa que proviene del interior de la Tierra.

germination The sprouting of the embryo out of a seed; occurs when the embryo resumes its growth following dormancy.
germinación Brotamiento del embrión a partir de la semilla; ocurre cuando el embrión reanuda su crecimiento tras el estado latente.

gestation period The length of time between fertilization and birth of a mammal.
período de gestación Tiempo entre la fertilización y el nacimiento de un mamífero.

glacier Any large mass of ice that moves slowly over land.
glaciar Cualquier masa grande de hielo que se desplaza lentamente sobre la tierra.

gland An organ that produces and releases chemicals either through ducts or into the bloodstream.
glándula Órgano que produce y libera sustancias químicas por los ductos o al torrente sanguíneo.

global warming A gradual increase in the average temperature of the atmosphere, thought to be caused by an increase in greenhouse gases from human activities.
calentamiento global Aumento gradual de la temperatura promedio de la atmósfera cuya causa se piensa que es el aumento de emisiones de gases de efecto invernadero ocasionados por actividades humanas.

global winds Winds that blow steadily from specific directions over long distances.
vientos globales Vientos que soplan constantemente desde direcciones específicas por largas distancias.

globular cluster A large, round, densely-packed grouping of older stars.
cúmulo globular Conjunto grande y redondo de estrellas viejas densamente agrupadas.

Golgi apparatus An organelle in a cell that receives proteins and other newly formed materials from the endoplasmic reticulum, packages them, and distributes them to other parts of the cell.
aparato de Golgi Orgánulo de la célula que recibe, empaqueta y distribuye a otras partes de la célula las proteínas y otros materiales que se forman en el retículo endoplasmático.

gradualism Pattern of evolution characterized by the slow and steady accumulation of small genetic changes over long periods of time.
gradualismo Evolución de una especie por medio de la acumulación lenta pero continua de cambios genéticos a través de largos períodos de tiempo.

grains The particles of minerals or other rocks that give a rock its texture.
granos Partículas de minerales o de otras rocas que le dan textura a una roca.

granite A usually light-colored igneous rock that is found in continental crust.
granito Roca generalmente de color claro que se encuentra en la corteza continental.

graph A picture of information from a data table; shows the relationship between variables.
gráfica Representación visual de la información de una tabla de datos; muestra la relación entre las variables.

grassland An area populated mostly by grasses and other nonwoody plants that gets 25 to 75 centimeters of rain each year.
pradera Área poblada principalmente por hierbas y otras plantas no leñosas, y donde caen entre 25 y 75 centímetros de lluvia cada año.

GLOSSARY

gravitational potential energy Potential energy that depends on the height of an object.
energía gravitatoria potencial Energía potencial que depende de la altura de un cuerpo.

gravity The attractive force between objects; the force that moves objects downhill.
gravedad Fuerza que atrae a los cuerpos entre sí; fuerza que mueve un cuerpo cuesta abajo.

greenhouse effect The trapping of heat near a planet's surface by certain gases in the planet's atmosphere.
efecto invernadero Retención de calor cerca de la superficie de un planeta debido a la presencia de ciertos gases en la atmósfera.

greenhouse gases Gases in the atmosphere that trap energy.
gases de efecto invernadero Gases presentes en la atmósfera que atrapan la energía.

groin A wall made of rocks or concrete that is built outward from a beach to reduce erosion.
escollera Pared de piedra o concreto que se construye perpendicularmente a una playa para reducir la erosión.

grounded Allowing charges to flow directly from the circuit into the building's ground wire and then into Earth in the event of a short circuit.
conectado a tierra Permitir que las cargas eléctricas fluyan directamente del circuito al cable a tierra del edificio y luego a la Tierra en caso de un cortocircuito.

groundwater Water that fills the cracks and spaces in underground soil and rock layers.
aguas freáticas Agua que llena las grietas y huecos de las capas subterráneas de tierra y roca.

gully A large channel in soil that carries runoff after a rainstorm.
barranco Canal grande en el suelo formado por corrientes de agua durante una tormenta de lluvia.

gymnosperm A plant that produces seeds directly on the scales of cones-not enclosed by a protective fruit.
gimnosperma Planta que produce semillas directamente sobre las escamas de los conos-sin estar encerradas en un fruto protector.

H
---

habitat An environment that provides the things a specific organism needs to live, grow, and reproduce.

hábitat Medio que provee lo que un organismo específico necesita para vivir, crecer y reproducirse.

habitat destruction The loss of a natural habitat.
destrucción del habitat Pérdida de un hábitat natural.

habitat fragmentation The breaking of a habitat into smaller, isolated pieces.
fragmentación del hábitat Desintegración de un hábitat en porciones aisladas más pequeñas.

half-life The time it takes for half of the atoms of a radioactive element to decay.
vida media Tiempo que toma descomponer la mitad de los átomos de un elemento radiactivo.

hazardous waste A material that can be harmful if it is not properly disposed of.
desecho peligroso Material que puede ser dañino si no se elimina adecuadamente.

headland A part of the shore that sticks out into the ocean.
promontorio Parte de la costa que se interna en el mar.

heart A hollow, muscular organ that pumps blood throughout an organism's body.
corazón Órgano hueco y muscular que bombea la sangre por todas partes del cuerpo de un organismo.

heat The transfer of thermal energy from a warmer object to a cooler object.
calor Transferencia de energía térmica de un cuerpo más cálido a uno menos cálido.

heliocentric Term describing a model of the solar system in which Earth and the other planets revolve around the sun.
heliocéntrico Término que describe un modelo del universo en el cual la Tierra y los otros planetas giran alrededor del Sol.

hemoglobin An iron-containing protein that binds chemically to oxygen molecules; makes up most of red blood cells.
hemoglobina Proteína que contiene hierro, y que se enlaza químicamente las moléculas de oxígeno; forma la mayoría de los glóbulos rojos.

herbivore A consumer that obtains energy by eating only plants.
herbívoro Consumidor que come sólo plantas para obtener energía.

heredity The passing of traits from parents to offspring.
herencia Transmisión de rasgos de padres a hijos.

hertz (Hz) Unit of measurement for frequency.
hercio (Hz) Unidad de medida de la frecuencia.

Hertzsprung-Russell diagram A graph relating the surface temperatures and absolute brightnesses of stars.
diagrama Hertzsprung-Russell Gráfica que muestra la relación entre la temperatura de la superficie de una estrella y su magnitud absoluta.

heterotroph An organism that cannot make its own food and gets food by consuming other living things.
heterótrofo Organismo que no puede producir sus propios alimentos y que se alimenta al consumir otros seres vivos.

heterozygous Having two different alleles for a particular gene.
heterocigoto Que tiene dos alelos distintos para un gen particular.

histamine A chemical that is responsible for the symptoms of an allergy.
histamina Sustancia química responsable de los síntomas de una alergia.

HIV (human immunodeficiency virus) The virus that causes AIDS.
VIH (virus de la inmunodeficiencia humana) Virus que causa el SIDA.

homeostasis The condition in which an organism's internal environment is kept stable in spite of changes in the external environment.
homeostasis Condición en la que el medio ambiente interno de un organismo se mantiene estable a pesar de cambios en el medio ambiente externo.

homologous structures Structures that are similar in different species and that have been inherited from a common ancestor.
estructuras homólogas Estructuras parecidas de especies distintas y que se han heredado de un antepasado común.

homozygous Having two identical alleles for a particular gene.
homocigoto Que tiene dos alelos idénticos para un gen particular.

hormone 1. A chemical that affects growth and development. 2. The chemical produced by an endocrine gland.
hormona 1. Sustancia química que afecta el crecimiento y el desarrollo. 2. Sustancia química producida por una glándula endocrina.

host An organism that a parasite lives with, in, or on, and provides a source of energy or a suitable environment for the parasite to live.
huésped Organismo dentro del o sobre el cual vive un parásito y que provee una fuente de energía o un medio apropiado para la existencia del parásito.

hot spot An area where magma from deep within the mantle melts through the crust above it.
punto caliente Área en la que el magma de las profundidades del manto atraviesa la corteza.

Hubble's law The observation that the farther away a galaxy is, the faster it is moving away.
ley de Hubble Observación que enuncia que mientras más lejos se encuentre una galaxia, se aleja con mayor rapidez.

humid subtropical A wet and warm climate found on the edges of the tropics.
subtropical húmedo Clima húmedo y templado que se encuentra en los límites de los trópicos.

humidity The amount of water vapor in a given volume of air.
humedad Cantidad de vapor de agua en cierto volumen de aire.

humus Dark-colored organic material in soil.
humus Material orgánico de color oscuro del suelo.

hurricane A tropical storm that has winds of about 119 kilometers per hour or higher.
huracán Tormenta tropical que tiene vientos de cerca.

hybrid An offspring of crosses that has two different alleles for a trait.
híbrido Descendiente de cruces que tiene dos alelos distintos para un rasgo.

hybridization A selective breeding method that involves crossing different individuals to bring together the best traits from both parents.
hibridación Técnica reproductiva en la que se cruzan individuos distintos para reunir los mejores rasgos de ambos progenitores.

hydrocarbon An organic compound that contains only carbon and hydrogen atoms.
hidrocarburo Compuesto orgánico que contiene átomos de carbón e hidrógeno solamente.

hydroelectric power Electricity produced by the kinetic energy of water moving over a waterfall or dam.
energía hidroeléctrica Electricidad producida a partir de la energía cinética del agua que baja por una catarata o presa.

hydrogen ion A positively charged ion (H+) formed of a hydrogen atom that has lost its electron.
ión hidrógeno Ión de carga positiva (H+) formado por un átomo de hidrógeno que ha perdido su electrón.

hydrosphere The portion of Earth that consists of water in any of its forms, including oceans, glaciers, rivers, lakes, groundwater and water vapor.
hidrósfera Parte de la Tierra formada por agua en cualquiera de sus formas, ya sea océanos, glaciares, ríos, lagos, agua subterránea y vapor de agua.

hydroxide ion A negatively charged ion made of oxygen and hydrogen (OH–).
ión hidróxido Ión de carga negativa formado de oxígeno e hidrógeno (OH–).

hyphae The branching, threadlike tubes that make up the bodies of multicellular fungi.
hifas Delgados tubos ramificados que forman el cuerpo de los hongos multicelulares.

hypothalamus A part of the brain that links the nervous system and the endocrine system.
hipotálamo Parte del encéfalo que une el sistema nervioso con el sistema endocrino.

hypothesis A possible explanation for a set of observations or answer to a scientific question; must be testable.
hipótesis Explicación posible de un conjunto de observaciones o respuesta a una pregunta científica; se debe poder poner a prueba.

I

ice age Time in Earth's history during which glaciers covered large parts of the surface.
glaciación Períodos de la historia de la Tierra en los que los glaciares cubrían grandes partes de la superficie.

igneous rock A type of rock that forms from the cooling of molten rock at or below the surface.
roca ígnea Tipo de roca que se forma cuando se enfrían las rocas fundidas en la superficie o debajo de la superficie.

image A copy of an object formed by reflected or refracted rays of light.
imagen Copia de un objeto formado por rayos de luz que se reflejan y se refractan.

immigration Movement of individuals into a population's area.
inmigración Movimiento de individuos al área de una población.

immune response Part of the body's defense against pathogens in which cells of the immune system react to each kind of pathogen with a defense targeted specifically at that pathogen.
reacción inmunológica Parte de la defensa del cuerpo contra los patógenos, en la que las células del sistema inmunológico reaccionan a cada tipo de patógeno con una defensa específica.

immunity The body's ability to destroy pathogens before they can cause disease.
inmunidad Capacidad del cuerpo para destruir los patógenos antes de que causen enfermedades.

impermeable A characteristic of materials, such as clay and granite, through which water does not easily pass.
impermeable Característica de los materiales, como la arcilla y el granito, que no dejan pasar fácilmente el agua.

impulse An electrical message that carries information in the nervous system.
impulso Mensaje eléctrico que transporta información por el sistema nervioso.

inbreeding A selective breeding method in which two individuals with similar sets of alleles are crossed.
endogamia Técnica reproductiva en la que se cruzan dos individuos con conjuntos de alelos parecidos.

incineration The burning of solid waste.
incineración Quema de desechos sólidos.

inclined plane A simple machine that is a flat, sloped surface.
plano inclinado Máquina simple que consiste en una superficie plana con pendiente.

incomplete dominance A situation in which one allele is not completely dominant over another allele.
dominancia incompleta Situación en la que un alelo no es completamente dominante sobre el otro.

incomplete metamorphosis A type of metamorphosis with three stages: egg, nymph, and adult.
metamorfosis incompleta Tipo de metamorfosis de tres etapas: huevo, ninfa y adulto.

independent variable The one factor that a scientist changes during an experiment; also called manipulated variable.
variable independiente El único factor que un científico altera durante un experimento; también se denomina variable manipulada.

index fossil Fossils of widely distributed organisms that lived during a geologically short period.
fósil guía Fósiles de organismos altamente dispersos que vivieron durante un período geológico corto.

index of refraction A measure of the amount a ray of light bends when it passes from one medium to another.
índice de refracción Medida de la inclinación de un rayo de luz cuando pasa de un medio a otro.

indicator A compound that changes color in the presence of an acid or a base.
indicador Compuesto que cambia de color en presencia de un ácido o una base.

induction A method of redistributing the charge on an object by means of the electric field of another object; the objects have no direct contact.
inducción Método de redistribuir la carga de un cuerpo haciendo uso del campo eléctrico de otro; los cuerpos no están en contacto directo.

inductive reasoning Using specific observations to make generalizations.
razonamiento inductivo Usar observaciones específicas para hacer generalizaciones.

inertia The tendency of an object to resist a change in motion.
inercia Tendencia de un cuerpo de resistirse a cambios de movimiento.

infectious disease A disease caused by the presence of a living thing in the body that can pass from one organism to another.
enfermedad infecciosa Enfermedad causada por la presencia de un ser vivo en el cuerpo y que puede pasar de un organismo a otro.

inferring The process of making an inference, an interpretation based on observations and prior knowledge.
inferir Proceso de hacer una inferencia; interpretación basada en observaciones y conocimientos previos.

inflammatory response Part of the body's defense against pathogens, in which fluid and white blood cells leak from blood vessels into tissues and destroy pathogens by breaking them down.
reacción inflamatoria Parte de la defensa del cuerpo contra los patógenos en la cual los fluidos y los glóbulos blancos salen de los vasos sanguíneos hacia los tejidos y destruyen los patógenos descomponiéndolos.

infrared radiation Electromagnetic waves with wavelengths that are longer than visible light but shorter than microwaves.
radiación infrarroja Ondas electromagnéticas con longitudes de onda más largas que la luz visible, pero más cortas que las microondas.

infrared rays Electromagnetic waves with shorter wavelengths and higher frequencies than microwaves.
rayos infrarrojos Ondas electromagnéticas con longitudes de onda más cortas y frecuencias más altas que las microondas.

inhibitor A material that decreases the rate of a reaction.
inhibidor Material que disminuye la velocidad de una reacción.

inner core A dense sphere of solid iron and nickel at the center of Earth.
núcleo interno Esfera densa de hierro y níquel que se encuentra en el centro de la Tierra.

inorganic Not formed from living things or the remains of living things.
inorgánico Que no está formado por seres vivos o por los restos de seres vivos.

input Material, energy, or information that goes into a system.
entrada Material, energía o informacion que se agrega a un sistema.

input force The force exerted on a machine.
fuerza aplicada Fuerza que se ejerce sobre una máquina.

instantaneous speed The speed of an object at one instant of time.
velocidad instantánea Velocidad de un objeto en un instante del tiempo.

insulation Material that traps air to help block heat transfer between the air inside and outside of a building.
aislante Material que atrapa el aire para ayudar a bloquear el paso del calor del aire adentro y afuera de un edificio.

insulator 1. A material that does not conduct heat well. 2. A material that does not easily allow electric charges to flow.
aislante 1. Material que no conduce bien el calor. 2. Material que no permite fácilmente que las cargas eléctricas fluyan.

insulin A hormone produced in the pancreas that enables the body's cells to take in glucose from the blood and use it for energy.
insulina Hormona producida por el páncreas, que permite que las células del cuerpo absorban glucosa de la sangre y la usen como energía.

GLOSSARY

intensity The amount of energy per second carried through a unit area by a wave.
intensidad Cantidad de energía por segundo que transporta una onda a través de una unidad de área.

interference The interaction between waves that meet.
interferencia Interacción entre dos o más ondas que se encuentran.

internal fertilization When eggs are fertilized inside a female's body.
fertilización interna Cuando los óvulos se fertilizan dentro del cuerpo de la hembra.

International System of Units (SI) A system of units used by scientists to measure the properties of matter.
Sistema Internacional de Unidades (SI) Sistema de unidades que los científicos usan para medir las propiedades de la materia.

interneuron A neuron that carries nerve impulses from one neuron to another.
interneurona Neurona que transporta los impulsos nerviosos de una neurona a otra.

interphase The first stage of the cell cycle that takes place before cell division occurs, during which a cell grows and makes a copy of its DNA.
interfase Primera etapa del ciclo celular que ocurre antes de la división celular y durante la cual la célula crece y duplica su ADN.

intertidal zone An area between the highest high-tide line on land and the point on the continental shelf exposed by the lowest low-tide line.
zona intermareal Área entre el punto más alto de la marea alta y el punto más bajo de la marea baja.

intrusion An igneous rock layer formed when magma hardens beneath Earth's surface.
intrusión Capa de roca ígnea formada cuando el magma se endurece bajo la superficie de la Tierra.

intrusive rock Igneous rock that forms when magma hardens beneath Earth's surface.
roca intrusiva (o plutónica) Roca ígnea que se forma cuando el magma se endurece bajo la superficie de la Tierra.

inversely proportional A term used to describe the relationship between two variables whose product is constant.
inversamente proporcional Término usado para describir la relación entre dos variables cuyo producto es constante.

invertebrate An animal without a backbone.
invertebrado Animal sin columna vertebral.

involuntary muscle A muscle that is not under conscious control.
músculo involuntario Músculo que no se puede controlar conscientemente.

ion An atom or group of atoms that has become electrically charged.
ión Átomo o grupo de átomos que está cargado eléctricamente.

ionic bond The attraction between oppositely charged ions.
enlace iónico Atracción entre iones con cargas opuestas.

ionic compound A compound that consists of positive and negative ions.
compuesto iónico Compuesto que tiene iones positivos y negativos.

ionosphere The lower part of the thermosphere.
ionósfera Parte inferior de la termósfera.

iris The ring of muscle that surrounds the pupil and regulates the amount of light entering the eye; gives the eye its color.
iris Disco de músculo que rodea la pupila y regula la cantidad de luz que entra al ojo; da color al ojo.

irregular galaxy A galaxy that does not have a regular shape.
galaxia irregular Galaxia que no tiene una forma regular.

island arc A string of volcanoes that form as the result of subduction of one oceanic plate beneath a second oceanic plate.
arco de islas Cadena de volcanes formados como resultado de la subducción de una placa oceánica debajo de una segunda placa oceánica.

isobar A line on a weather map that joins places that have the same air pressure.
isobara Línea en un mapa del tiempo que une lugares que tienen la misma presión de aire.

isotherm A line on a weather map that joins places that have the same temperature.
isoterma Línea en un mapa del tiempo que une lugares que tienen la misma temperatura.

J

jet streams Bands of high-speed winds about 10 kilometers above Earth's surface.
corrientes de viento en chorro Bandas de vientos de alta velocidad a unos 10 kilómetros sobre la superficie de la Tierra.

joint A place in the body where two bones come together.
articulación Lugar en el cuerpo en donde se unen dos huesos.

joule The amount of work you do when you exert a force of 1 newton to move an object a distance of 1 meter.
julio Cantidad de trabajo que se produce al aplicar una fuerza de 1 newton para mover un objeto una distancia de 1 metro.

K

karst topography A region in which a layer of limestone close to the surface creates deep valleys, caverns, and sinkholes.
topografía kárstica Región en la que una capa de piedra caliza cerca de la superficie crea valles hundidos, grutas y pozos.

Kelvin scale The temperature scale on which zero is the temperature at which no more energy can be removed from matter.
escala Kelvin Escala de temperatura en la cual el cero es la temperatura a cuyo punto no se puede extraer más energía de la materia.

kettle A small depression that forms when a chunk of ice is left in glacial till.
cazuela Pequeña depresión formada cuando un trozo de hielo se asienta en arcilla glaciárica.

keystone species A species that influences the survival of many other species in an ecosystem.
especie clave Especie que tiene un impacto en la supervivencia de muchas otras especies de un ecosistema.

kidney A major organ of the excretory system; removes urea and other wastes from the blood.
riñón Órgano importante del sistema excretorio; elimina la urea y otros desechos de la sangre.

kinetic energy Energy that an object has due to its motion.

energía cinética Energía que tiene un cuerpo debido a su movimiento.

Kuiper belt A region where many small objects orbit the sun and that stretches from beyond the orbit of Neptune to about 100 times Earth's distance from the sun.
cinturón de Kuiper Región en la cual muchos cuerpos pequeños giran alrededor del Sol y que se extiende desde más allá de la órbita de Neptuno hasta aproximadamente cien veces la distancia entre la Tierra y el Sol.

L

La Niña A climate event in the eastern Pacific Ocean in which surface waters are colder than normal.
La Niña Fenómeno climático que ocurre en la parte este del océano Pacífico, en el cual las aguas superficiales están más frías que lo normal.

land breeze The flow of air from land to a body of water.
brisa terrestre Flujo de aire desde la tierra a una masa de agua.

land reclamation The process of restoring land to a more natural, productive state.
recuperación de la tierra Proceso que consiste en restaurar la tierra y llevarla a un estado productivo más natural.

larva The immature form of an animal that looks very different from the adult.
larva Forma inmadura de un animal que luce muy distinta al adulto.

larynx The voice box; located in the top part of the trachea, underneath the epiglottis.
laringe Caja de la voz; está ubicada en la parte superior de la tráquea debajo de la epiglotis.

latitude The distance in degrees north or south of the equator.
latitud Distancia en grados al norte o al sur del ecuador.

lava Liquid magma that reaches the surface.
lava Magma líquido que sale a la superficie.

lava flow The area covered by lava as it pours out of a volcano's vent.
colada de lava Área cubierta de lava a medida que ésta sale por el ventiladero del volcán.

law of conservation of energy The rule that energy cannot be created or destroyed.
ley de conservación de la energía Regla que dice que la energía no se puede crear ni destruir.

law of conservation of mass The principle that the total amount of matter is neither created nor destroyed during any chemical or physical change.
ley de conservación de la masa Principio que establece que la cantidad total de materia no se crea ni se destruye durante cambios químicos o físicos.

law of conservation of momentum The rule that in the absence of outside forces the total momentum of objects that interact does not change.
principio de la conservación del momento Regla que establece que, en ausencia de fuerzas externas, la cantidad de movimiento total de los cuerpos que se relacionan no cambia.

law of superposition The geologic principle that states that in horizontal layers of sedimentary rock, each layer is older than the layer above it and younger than the layer below it.
ley de la superposición Principio geológico que enuncia que, en las capas horizontales de las rocas sedimentarias, cada capa es más vieja que la capa superior y más joven que la capa inferior.

law of universal gravitation The scientific law that states that every object in the universe attracts every other object.
ley de gravitación universal Ley científica que establece que todos los cuerpos del universo se atraen entre sí.

leachate Polluted liquid produced by water passing through and dissolving chemicals from buried wastes in a landfill.
lixiviado Líquido contaminado producido por el agua que pasa por y disuelve químicos provenientes de desechos bajo la tierra y en rellenos sanitarios.

leeward The side of a mountain range that faces away from the oncoming wind.
sotavento Lado de una cadena montañosa que está resguardado del viento.

lens 1. The flexible structure that focuses light that has entered the eye. **2.** A curved piece of glass or other transparent material that is used to refract light.
lente 1. Estructura flexible que enfoca la luz que entra al ojo. **2.** Trozo curvo de vidrio u otro material transparente que se usa para refractar la luz.

lever A simple machine that consists of a rigid bar that pivots about a fixed point.
palanca Máquina simple que consiste en una barra rígida que gira en torno a un punto fijo.

lichen The combination of a fungus and either an alga or an autotrophic bacterium that live together in a relationship that benefits both organisms.
liquen Combinación de un hongo y una alga o bacteria autotrópica que viven juntos en una relación mutuamente beneficiosa.

ligament Strong connective tissue that holds bones together in movable joints.
ligamentos Tejido conector resistente que une dos huesos en las articulaciones móviles.

light-year The distance that light travels in one year, about 9.5 million million kilometers.
año luz Distancia a la que viaja la luz en un año; aproximadamente 9.5 millones de millones de kilómetros.

lightning A sudden spark, or energy discharge, caused when electrical charges jump between parts of a cloud, between nearby clouds, or between a cloud and the ground.
rayo Chispa repentina o descarga de energía causada por cargas eléctricas que saltan entre partes de una nube, entre nubes cercanas o entre una nube y la tierra.

limiting factor An environmental factor that causes a population to decrease in size.
factor limitante Factor ambiental que causa la disminución del tamaño de una población.

linear graph A line graph in which the data points yield a straight line.
gráfica lineal Gráfica en la cual los puntos de los datos forman una línea recta.

lipid An energy-rich organic compound, such as a fat, oil, or wax, that is made of carbon, hydrogen, and oxygen.
lípido Compuesto orgánico rico en energía, como una grasa, aceite o cera, formado por los elementos carbono, hidrógeno y oxígeno.

liquid A state of matter that has no definite shape but has a definite volume.
líquido Estado de la materia que no tiene forma definida pero sí volumen definido.

lithosphere A rigid layer made up of the uppermost part of the mantle and the crust.
litósfera Capa rígida constituida por la parte superior del manto y la corteza.

litter The very top layer of fertile soil made of dead leaves and grass.
mantillo Capa superior del suelo fértil, que está formada por hojas y pasto muertos.

loam Rich, fertile soil that is made up of about equal parts of clay, sand, and silt.
marga Suelo rico y fértil formado por partes casi iguales de arcilla, arena y limo.

local winds Winds that blow over short distances.
vientos locales Vientos que soplan en distancias cortas.

loess A wind-formed deposit made of fine particles of clay and silt.
loes Depósito de partículas finas de arcilla y limo arrastradas por el viento.

long-day plant A plant that flowers when the nights are shorter than the plant's critical night length.
planta de día largo Planta que florece cuando la duración de la noche es más corta que la duración crítica.

longitudinal wave A wave that moves the medium in a direction parallel to the direction in which the wave travels.
onda longitudinal Onda que mueve al medio en una dirección paralela a la dirección en la que se propaga la onda.

longshore drift The movement of water and sediment down a beach caused by waves coming in to shore at an angle.
deriva litoral Movimiento de agua y sedimentos paralelo a una playa debido a la llegada de olas inclinadas respecto a la costa.

loudness Perception of the energy of a sound.
volumen Percepción de la energía de un sonido.

lunar eclipse The blocking of sunlight to the moon that occurs when Earth is directly between the sun and the moon.
eclipse lunar Bloqueo de la luz solar que ilumina la Luna que ocurre cuando la Tierra se interpone entre el Sol y la Luna.

lung 1. An organ found in air-breathing vertebrates that exchanges oxygen and carbon dioxide with the blood. **2.** In humans, one of two main organs of the respiratory system.
pulmón 1. Órgano que tienen los vertebrados que respiran aire, que intercambia oxígeno y dióxido de carbono en la sangre. **2.** En los humanos, uno de los dos órganos principales del sistema respiratorio.

luster The way a mineral reflects light from its surface.
brillo Manera en la que un mineral refleja la luz en su superficie.

lymphocyte A white blood cell that distinguishes between each kind of pathogen.
linfocito Glóbulo blanco que distingue cada tipo de patógeno.

lysosome A cell organelle which contains chemicals that break down large food particles into smaller ones and that can be used by the rest of the cell.
lisosoma Orgánulo de una célula, que tiene sustancias químicas que convierten partículas grandes de alimentos en partículas más pequeñas que el resto de la célula puede utilizar.

M

machine A device that changes the amount of force exerted, the distance over which a force is exerted, or the direction in which force is exerted.
máquina Dispositivo que altera la cantidad de fuerza ejercida, la distancia sobre que se ejerce la fuerza, o la dirección en la que se ejerce la fuerza.

magma The molten mixture of rock-forming substances, gases, and water from the mantle.
magma Mezcla fundida de las sustancias que forman las rocas, gases y agua, proveniente del manto.

magma chamber The pocket beneath a volcano where magma collects.
cámara magmática Bolsa debajo de un volcán en la que está acumulado el magma.

magnet Any material that attracts iron and materials that contain iron.
imán Material que atrae hierro o materiales que contienen el hierro.

magnetic declination The angle between geographic north and the north to which a compass needle points.
declinación magnética Ángulo (en una ubicación particular) entre el norte geográfico y el polo magnético ubicado en el hemisferio norte de la Tierra.

magnetic field The region around a magnet where the magnetic force is exerted.
campo magnético Área alrededor de un imán donde actúa la fuerza magnética.

GLOSSARY

magnetic field lines Lines that map out the magnetic field around a magnet.
líneas del campo magnético Líneas que representan el campo magnético alrededor de un imán.

magnetic force A force produced when magnetic poles interact.
fuerza magnética Fuerza que se produce cuando hay actividad entre los polos magnéticos.

magnetic pole The ends of a magnetic object, where the magnetic force is strongest.
polo magnético Extremo de un cuerpo magnético, donde la fuerza magnética es mayor.

magnetism The force of attraction or repulsion of magnetic materials.
magnetismo Poder de atracción o repulsión de los materiales magnéticos.

magnitude The measurement of an earthquake's strength based on seismic waves and movement along faults.
magnitud Medida de la fuerza de un sismo basada en las ondas sísmicas y en el movimiento que ocurre a lo largo de las fallas.

main sequence A diagonal area on an Hertzsprung-Russell diagram that includes more than 90 percent of all stars.
secuencia principal Área diagonal en un diagrama de Hertzsprung-Russell que incluye más del 90 por ciento de todas las estrellas.

making models The process of creating representations of complex objects or processes.
hacer modelos Proceso de crear representaciones de objetos o procesos complejos.

mammal A vertebrate whose body temperature is regulated by its internal heat, and that has skin covered with hair or fur and glands that produce milk to feed its young.
mamífero Vertebrado cuya temperatura corporal es regulada por su calor interno, cuya piel está cubierta de pelo o pelaje y que tiene glándulas que producen leche para alimentar a sus crías.

mammary gland An organ in female mammals that produces milk for the mammal's young.
glándula mamaria Órgano de los mamíferos hembra que produce leche para alimentar a sus crías.

manipulated variable The one factor that a scientist changes during an experiment; also called independent variable.
variable manipulada Único factor que el científico cambia durante un experimento; también llamada variable independiente.

mantle The layer of hot, solid material between Earth's crust and core.
manto Capa de material caliente y sólido entre la corteza terrestre y el núcleo.

maria Dark, flat areas on the moon's surface formed from huge ancient lava flows.
maria Áreas oscuras y llanas de la superficie lunar formadas por enormes flujos de lava antiguos.

marine climate The climate of some coastal regions, with relatively warm winters and cool summers.
clima marino Clima de algunas regiones costeras, con inviernos relativamente templados y veranos fríos.

maritime (air mass) A humid air mass that forms over oceans.
masa de aire marítima Masa de aire húmedo que se forma sobre los océanos.

marrow The soft connective tissue that fills the internal spaces in bone.
médula ósea Tejido conector suave que llena los espacios internos de un hueso.

marsupial A mammal whose young are born at an early stage of development, and which usually continue to develop in a pouch on their mother's body.
marsupial Mamífero cuyas crías nacen en una etapa muy temprana del desarrollo, y que normalmente continúan el desarrollo en una bolsa del cuerpo de la madre.

mass A measure of how much matter is in an object.
masa Medida de cuánta materia hay en un cuerpo.

mass extinction When many types of living things become extinct at the same time.
extinción en masa Situación que ocurre cuando muchos tipos de seres vivos se extinguen al mismo tiempo.

mass movement Any one of several processes by which gravity moves sediment downhill.
movimiento en masa Cualquiera de los procesos por los cuales la gravedad desplaza sedimentos cuesta abajo.

matter Anything that has mass and takes up space.
materia Cualquier cosa que tiene masa y ocupa un espacio.

mean The numerical average of a set of data.
media Promedio numérico de un conjunto de datos.

meander A looplike bend in the course of a river.
meandro Curva muy pronunciada en el curso de un río.

mechanical advantage The number of times a machine increases a force exerted on it.
ventaja mecánica Número de veces que una máquina amplifica la fuerza que se ejerce sobre ella.

mechanical energy Kinetic or potential energy associated with the motion or position of an object.
energía mecánica Energía cinética o potencial asociada con el movimiento o la posición de un cuerpo.

mechanical wave A wave that requires a medium through which to travel.
onda mecánica Onda que necesita un medio por el cual propagarse.

mechanical weathering The type of weathering in which rock is physically broken into smaller pieces.
desgaste mecánico Tipo de desgaste en el cual una roca se rompe físicamente en trozos más pequeños.

median The middle number in a set of data.
mediana Número del medio de un conjunto de datos.

medium The material through which a wave travels.
medio Material a través del cual se propaga una onda.

medusa A cnidarian body form characterized by an open umbrella shape and adapted for a freeswimming life.
medusa Cnidario con cuerpo que tiene la forma de una sombrilla abierta y que está adaptado para nadar libremente.

meiosis The process that occurs in the formation of sex cells (sperm and egg) by which the number of chromosomes is reduced by half.
meiosis Proceso durante la formación de las células sexuales (espermatozoide y óvulo) por el cual el número de cromosomas se reduce a la mitad.

melanin A pigment that gives the skin its color.
melanina Pigmento que da color a la piel.

melting The change in state from a solid to a liquid.
fusión Cambio del estado sólido a líquido.

melting point The temperature at which a substance changes from a solid to a liquid; the same as the freezing point, or temperature at which a liquid changes to a solid.
punto de fusión Temperatura a la que una sustancia cambia de estado sólido a líquido; es lo mismo que el punto de congelación (la temperatura a la que un líquido se vuelve sólido).

meniscus The curved upper surface of a liquid in a column of liquid.

menisco Superficie superior curva de un líquido en una columna de líquido.

menstrual cycle The monthly cycle of changes that occurs in the female reproductive system, during which an egg develops and the uterus prepares for the arrival of a fertilized egg.
ciclo menstrual Ciclo mensual de cambios del sistema reproductor femenino, durante el cual se desarrolla un óvulo y el útero se prepara para la llegada del óvulo fecundado.

menstruation The process in which the thickened lining of the uterus breaks down and blood and tissue then pass out of the female body through the vagina.
menstruación Proceso en el cual el recubrimiento grueso del útero se rompe, y sangre y tejido salen del cuerpo femenino a través de la vagina.

mercury barometer An instrument that measures changes in air pressure, consisting of a glass tube partially filled with mercury, with its open end resting in a dish of mercury.
barómetro de mercurio Instrumento que mide los cambios de presión del aire; es un tubo de vidrio parcialmente lleno de mercurio con su extremo abierto posado sobre un recipiente con mercurio.

mesosphere The layer of Earth's atmosphere immediately above the stratosphere.
mesósfera Capa de la atmósfera de la Tierra inmediatamente sobre la estratósfera.

messenger RNA Type of RNA that carries copies of instructions for the assembly of amino acids into proteins from DNA to ribosomes in the cytoplasm.
ARN mensajero Tipo de ARN que lleva, del ADN a los ribosomas del citoplasma, copias de instrucciones para sintetizar a los aminoácidos en proteínas.

metabolism The combination of chemical reactions through which an organism builds up or breaks down materials.
metabolismo Combinación de reacciones químicas mediante las cuales un organismo compone o descompone la materia.

metallic bond An attraction between a positive metal ion and the electrons surrounding it.
enlace metálico Atracción entre un ión metálico positivo y los electrones que lo rodean.

metamorphic rock A type of rock that forms from an existing rock that is changed by heat, pressure, or chemical reactions.
roca metamórfica Tipo de roca que se forma cuando una roca cambia por el calor, la presión o por reacciones químicas.

GLOSSARY

metamorphosis A process in which an animal's body undergoes major changes in shape and form during its life cycle.
metamorfosis Proceso por el cual el cuerpo de un animal cambia de forma radicalmente durante su ciclo vital.

meteor A streak of light in the sky produced by the burning of a meteoroid in Earth's atmosphere.
meteoro Rayo de luz en el cielo producido por el incendio de un meteoroide en la atmósfera terrestre.

meteorite A meteoroid that passes through the atmosphere and hits Earth's surface.
meteorito Meteoroide que pasa por la atmósfera y toca la superficie terrestre.

meteoroid A chunk of rock or dust in space, generally smaller than an asteroid.
meteoroide Un trozo de roca o polvo, generalmente más pequeño que un asteroide, que existe en el espacio.

meteorologists Scientists who study the causes of weather and try to predict it.
meteorólogos Científicos que estudian las causas del tiempo e intentan predecirlo.

metric system A system of measurement based on the number 10.
sistema métrico Sistema de medidas basado en el número 10.

microgravity The condition of experiencing weightlessness in orbit.
microgravedad Manifestación de la falta de pesadez al estar en órbita.

microorganism A living thing too small to see without a microscope.
microorganismo Ser vivo que es tan pequeño que sólo es visible a través de un microscopio.

microscope An instrument that makes small objects look larger.
microscopio Instrumento que permite que los objetos pequeños se vean más grandes.

microwaves Electromagnetic waves that have shorter wavelengths and higher frequencies than radio waves.
microondas Ondas electromagnéticas con longitudes de onda más cortas y frecuencias más altas que las ondas de radio.

mid-ocean ridge An undersea mountain chain where new ocean floor is produced; a divergent plate boundary under the ocean.

cordillera oceánica central Cadena montañosa submarina donde se produce el nuevo suelo oceánico; borde de placa divergente bajo el oceáno.

mineral A naturally occurring, inorganic solid that has a crystal structure and a definite chemical composition.
mineral Cuerpo sólido inorgánico, de estructura cristalina y composición química definida, que se da en la naturaleza.

mirage An image of a distant object caused by refraction of light as it travels through air of varying temperature.
espejismo Imagen de un objeto distante causado por la refracción de la luz cuando viaja por el aire a temperaturas cambiantes.

mitochondria Rod-shaped organelles that convert energy in food molecules to energy the cell can use to carry out its functions.
mitocondria Estructura celular con forma de bastón que transforma la energía de las moléculas de alimentos en energía que la célula puede usar para llevar a cabo sus funciones.

mitosis The second stage of the cell cycle during which the cell's nucleus divides into two new nuclei and one set of DNA is distributed into each daughter cell.
mitosis Segunda etapa del ciclo celular, durante la cual se divide el núcleo de la célula en dos núcleos nuevos y el conjunto del ADN se reparte entre cada célula hija.

mixture Two or more substances that are together in the same place but their atoms are not chemically bonded.
mezcla Dos o más sustancias que están en el mismo lugar pero cuyos átomos no están químicamente enlazados.

mode The number that appears most often in a list of numbers.
moda Número que aparece con más frecuencia en una lista de números.

model A representation of a complex object or process, used to help people understand a concept that they cannot observe directly.
modelo Representación de un objeto o proceso complejo que se usa para explicar un concepto que no se puede observar directamente.

Modified Mercalli scale A scale that rates the amount of shaking from an earthquake.
escala modificada de Mercalli Escala que evalúa la intensidad del temblor de un terremoto.

Mohs hardness scale A scale ranking ten minerals from softest to hardest; used in testing the hardness of minerals.
escala de dureza de Mohs Escala en la que se clasifican diez minerales del más blando al más duro; se usa para probar la dureza de los minerales.

mold A type of fossil that is a hollow area in sediment in the shape of an organism or part of an organism.
molde Tipo de fósil que consiste en una depresión del sedimento que tiene la forma de un organismo o de parte de un organismo.

molecular compound A compound that is composed of molecules.
compuesto molecular Compuesto que tiene moléculas.

molecule A neutral group of two or more atoms held together by covalent bonds.
molécula Grupo neutral de dos o más átomos unidos por medio de enlaces covalentes.

mollusk An invertebrate with a soft, unsegmented body; most are protected by a hard outer shell.
molusco Invertebrado con cuerpo blando y sin segmentos; la mayoría tienen una concha exterior dura que les sirve de protección.

molting The process of shedding an outgrown exoskeleton.
muda de cubierta Proceso de cambiar un exoesqueleto viejo por uno nuevo.

moment magnitude scale A scale that rates earthquakes by estimating the total energy released by an earthquake.
escala de magnitud de momento Escala con la que se miden los sismos estimando la cantidad total de energía liberada por un terremoto.

momentum The product of an object's mass and velocity.
momento Producto de la masa de un cuerpo multiplicada por su velocidad.

monocot An angiosperm that has only one seed leaf.
monocotiledónea Angiosperma cuyas semillas tienen un solo cotiledón.

monotreme A mammal that lays eggs.
monotrema Mamífero que pone huevos.

monsoon Sea or land breeze over a large region that changes direction with the seasons.
monzón Vientos marinos o terrestres que soplan en una región extensa y cambian de dirección según las estaciones.

moraine A ridge formed by the till deposited at the edge of a glacier.
morrena Montículo formado por arcilla glacial depositada en el borde de un glaciar.

motion The state in which one object's distance from another is changing.
movimiento Estado en el que la distancia entre un cuerpo y otro va cambiando.

motor neuron A neuron that sends an impulse to a muscle or gland, causing the muscle or gland to react.
neurona motora Neurona que envía un impulso a un músculo o glándula y hace que el músculo o la glándula reaccione.

multicellular Consisting of many cells.
multicelular Que se compone de muchas células.

multiple alleles Three or more possible alleles of a gene that determine a trait.
alelo múltiple Tres o más alelos posibles del gen que determina un rasgo.

municipal solid waste Waste produced in homes, businesses, schools and in a community.
desechos sólidos urbanos Desechos generados en los hogares, los negocios, las escuelas y las comunidades.

muscle A tissue that contracts or relaxes to create movement.
músculo Tejido que se contrae o relaja para crear movimiento.

muscle tissue A body tissue that contracts, or shortens, making body parts move.
tejido muscular Tejido del cuerpo que se contrae o encoge, y permite que se muevan las partes del cuerpo.

music A set of sounds or notes combined in ways that are pleasing.
música Conjunto de sonidos o notas que se combinan de una manera agradable.

mutation Any change in the DNA of a gene or a chromosome.
mutación Cualquier cambio del ADN de un gen o cromosoma.

mutualism A type of symbiosis in which both species benefit from living together.
mutualismo Tipo de relación simbiótica entre dos especies en la cual ambas especies se benefician de su convivencia.

GLOSSARY

natural resource Anything naturally occuring in the environment that humans use.
recurso natural Cualquier elemento natural en el medio ambiente que el ser humano usa.

natural selection The process by which organisms that are best adapted to their environment are most likely to survive and reproduce.
selección natural Proceso por el cual los organismos que se adaptan mejor a su ambiente tienen mayor probabilidad de sobrevivir y reproducirse.

neap tide The tide with the least difference between consecutive low and high tides.
marea muerta Marea con la mínima diferencia entre las mareas altas y bajas consecutivas.

nearsighted Having the condition in which a person can see nearby objects clearly and distant objects as blurry.
miopía Condición en la que una persona ve con claridad los objetos cercanos y ve borrosos los objetos lejanos.

nebula A large cloud of gas and dust in space.
nebulosa Gran nube de gas y polvo en el espacio.

negative feedback A process in which a system is turned off by the condition it produces.
reacción negativa Proceso en el cual un sistema cesa de funcionar debido a la condición que produce.

nephron Small filtering structure found in the kidneys that removes wastes from blood and produces urine.
nefrona Estructura diminuta de filtración ubicada en los riñones, que elimina los desechos de la sangre y produce la orina.

neritic zone The area of the ocean that extends from the low-tide line out to the edge of the continental shelf.
zona nerítica Área del océano que se extiende desde la línea de bajamar hasta el borde de la plataforma continental.

nerve A bundle of nerve fibers.
nervio Conjunto de fibras nerviosas.

nerve impulse The message carried by a neuron.
impulso nervioso Mensaje que una neurona.

nervous system An organ system that receives information from the environment and coordinates a response.
sistema nervioso Sistema de órganos que recibe información del medio ambiente y coordina una respuesta.

nervous tissue A body tissue that carries electrical messages back and forth between the brain and other parts of the body.
tejido nervioso Tejido del cuerpo que transporta impulsos eléctricos entre el cerebro y otras partes del cuerpo.

net force The overall force on an object when all the individual forces acting on it are added together.
fuerza neta Fuerza total que se ejerce sobre un cuerpo cuando se suman las fuerzas individuales que actúan sobre él.

neuron A cell that carries information through the nervous system.
neurona Célula que transporta información a través del sistema nervioso.

neutralization A reaction of an acid with a base, yielding a solution that is not as acidic or basic as the starting solutions were.
neutralización Reacción de un ácido con una base, que produce una solución que no es ácida ni básica, como lo eran las soluciones originales.

neutron star The small, dense remains of a high-mass star after a supernova.
estrella de neutrones Restos pequeños y densos de una estrella de gran masa tras ocurrir una supernova.

newton A unit of measure that equals the force required to accelerate 1 kilogram of mass at 1 meter per second per second.
newton Unidad de medida equivalente a la fuerza necesaria para acelerar 1 kilogramo de masa a 1 metro por segundo cada segundo.

Newton's first law of motion The scientific law that states that an object at rest will stay at rest and an object in motion will stay in motion with a constant speed and direction unless acted on by a force.
Primera ley de movimiento de Newton Ley científica que establece que un cuerpo en reposo se mantendrá en reposo y un cuerpo en movimiento se mantendrá en movimiento con una velocidad y dirección constantes a menos que se ejerza una fuerza sobre él.

niche How an organism makes its living and interacts with the biotic and abiotic factors in its habitat.
nicho Forma en que un organismo vive e interactúa.

nitrogen bases Molecules that contain nitrogen and other elements.
bases nitrogenadas Moléculas que contienen nitrógeno y otros elementos.

nitrogen fixation The process of changing free nitrogen gas into nitrogen compounds that plants can absorb and use.
fijación del nitrógeno Proceso que consiste en transformar el gas de nitrógeno libre en compuestos de nitrógeno que las plantas pueden absorber y usar.

node A point of zero amplitude on a standing wave.
nodo Punto de amplitud cero de una onda estacionaria.

noninfectious disease A disease that is not caused by a pathogen.
enfermedad no infecciosa Enfermedad que no es causada por un patógeno.

nonlinear graph A line graph in which the data points do not fall along a straight line.
gráfica no lineal Gráfica lineal en la que los puntos de datos no forman una línea recta.

nonpoint source A widely spread source of pollution that is difficult to link to a specific point of origin.
fuente dispersa Fuente muy extendida de contaminación que es difícil vincular a un punto de origen específico.

nonpolar bond A covalent bond in which electrons are shared equally.
enlace no polar Enlace covalente en el que los electrones se comparten por igual.

nonrenewable resource A natural resource that is not replaced in a useful time frame.
recurso no renovable Recurso natural que no se restaura, en un período relativamente corto, una vez se utiliza.

nonvascular plant A low-growing plant that lacks true vascular tissue for transporting materials.
planta no vascular Planta de crecimiento lento que carece de tejido vascular verdadero para el transporte de materiales.

normal fault A type of fault where the hanging wall slides downward; caused by tension in the crust.
falla normal Tipo de falla en la cual el labio elevado o subyacente se desliza hacia abajo como resultado de la tensión de la corteza.

notochord A flexible rod that supports a chordate's back just below the nerve cord.
notocordio Cilindro flexible que sostiene la columna de un cordado, debajo del cordón nervioso.

nuclear energy The potential energy stored in the nucleus of an atom.
energía nuclear Energía potencial almacenada en el núcleo de un átomo.

nuclear fission The splitting of an atom's nucleus into two smaller nuclei and neutrons, releasing a large quantity of energy.
fisión nuclear Separación del núcleo de un átomo en núcleos y neutrones más pequeños, en la cual se libera una gran cantidad de energía.

nuclear fusion The process in which two atomic nuclei combine to form a larger nucleus, forming a heavier element and releasing huge amounts of energy; the process by which energy is produced in stars.
fusión nuclear Unión de dos núcleos atómicos que produce un elemento con una mayor masa atómica y que libera una gran cantidad de energía; el proceso mediante el cual las estrellas producen energía.

nucleic acid A very large organic molecule made of carbon, oxygen, hydrogen, nitrogen, and phosphorus, that contains the instructions cells need to carry out all the functions of life.
ácido nucleico Molécula muy grande formada por carbono, oxígeno, hidrógeno y fósforo, que porta las instrucciones necesarias para que las células realicen todas las funciones vitales.

nucleus 1. In cells, a large oval organelle that contains the cell's genetic material in the form of DNA and controls many of the cell's activities. 2. The central core of an atom which contains protons and neutrons. 3. The solid core of a comet.
núcleo 1. En las células, orgánulo grande y ovalado que contiene el material genético de la célula en forma de ADN y que controla muchas de las funciones celulares. 2. Parte central del átomo que contiene los protones y los neutrones. 3. Centro sólido de un cometa.

nutrient 1. A substance such as nitrogen or phosphorus that enables plants and algae to grow. 2. Substances in food that provide the raw materials and energy needed for an organism to carry out its essential processes.
nutriente 1. Sustancia como el nitrógeno o el fósforo que hace posible que las plantas y algas crezcan. 2. Sustancias de los alimentos que dan el material y la energía que un organismo necesita para sus funciones vitales.

nutrient depletion The situation that arises when more soil nutrients are used than the decomposers can supply.
agotamiento de nutrientes Situación que se produce cuando se usan más nutrientes del suelo de lo que los descomponedores pueden proporcionar.

nymph A stage of incomplete metamorphosis that usually resembles the adult insect.
ninfa Estado de la metamorfosis incompleta que generalmente se asemeja al insecto adulto.

GLOSSARY

―――――――――O―――――――――

objective 1. A lens that gathers light from an object and forms a real image. **2.** Describes the act of decision-making or drawing conclusions based on available evidence.
objetivo 1. Lente que reúne la luz de un objeto y forma una imagen real. **2.** Describe el acto de tomar una decisión o llegar a una conclusión basándose en la evidencia disponible.

objective reasoning Reasoning that is based on evidence.
razonamiento objetivo Razonamiento basado en la evidencia.

observatory A building that contains one or more telescopes.
observatorio Edificio que contiene uno o más telescopios.

observing The process of using one or more of your senses to gather information.
observar Proceso de usar uno o más de tus sentidos para reunir información.

occluded Cut off, as in a front where a warm air mass is caught between two cooler air masses.
ocluido Aislado o cerrado, como un frente donde una masa de aire cálido queda atrapada entre dos masas de aire más frío.

Ohm's law The law that states that resistance in a circuit is equal to voltage divided by current.
ley de Ohm Regla que establece que la resistencia en un circuito es equivalente al voltaje dividido por la corriente.

omnivore A consumer that obtains energy by eating both plants and animals.
omnívoro Consumidor que come plantas y animales para obtener energía.

Oort cloud A spherical region of comets that surrounds the solar system.
nube de Oort Región esférica de cometas que rodea al sistema solar.

opaque A type of material that reflects or absorbs all of the light that strikes it.
material opaco Material que refleja o absorbe toda la luz que llega a él.

open cluster A star cluster that has a loose, disorganized appearance and contains no more than a few thousand stars.
cúmulo abierto Cúmulo de estrellas que tiene una apariencia no compacta y desorganizada, y que no contiene más de unas pocos miles de estrellas.

open system A system in which matter can enter from or escape to the surroundings.
sistema abierto Sistema en el que la materia puede escapar a sus alrededores o entrar desde ahí.

opinion An idea about a situation that is not supported by evidence.
opinión Idea sobre una situación que la evidencia no sustenta.

optic nerve Short, thick nerve that carries signals from the eye to the brain.
nervio óptico Nervio corto y grueso que lleva señales del ojo al cerebro.

optical axis An imaginary line that divides a mirror in half.
eje óptico Recta imaginaria que divide un espejo por la mitad.

optical telescope A telescope that uses lenses or mirrors to collect and focus visible light.
telescopio óptico Telescopio que usa lentes o espejos para captar y enfocar la luz visible.

orbit The path of an object as it revolves around another object in space.
órbita Trayectoria de un cuerpo a medida que gira alrededor de otro en el espacio.

orbital velocity The velocity a rocket must achieve to establish an orbit around a body in space.
velocidad orbital Velocidad que un cohete debe alcanzar para establecer una órbita alrededor de un cuerpo en el espacio.

organ A body structure that is composed of different kinds of tissues that work together.
órgano Estructura del cuerpo compuesta de distintos tipos de tejidos que trabajan conjuntamente.

organ system A group of organs that work together to perform a major function.
sistema de órganos Grupo de órganos que trabajan juntos para realizar una función importante.

organelle A tiny cell structure that carries out a specific function within the cell.
orgánulo Estructura celular diminuta que realiza una función específica dentro de la célula.

organic rock Sedimentary rock that forms from remains of organisms deposited in thick layers.
roca orgánica Roca sedimentaria que se forma cuando los restos de organismos se depositan en capas gruesas.

organism A living thing.
organismo Un ser vivo.

osmosis The diffusion of water molecules across a selectively permeable membrane.
ósmosis Difusión de moléculas de agua a través de una membrana permeable selectiva.

osteoporosis A condition resulting from a loss of minerals in which the body's bones become weak and break easily.
osteoporosis Condición producida por la pérdida de minerales en la que los huesos del cuerpo se vuelven frágiles y se quiebran fácilmente.

outer core A layer of molten iron and nickel that surrounds the inner core of Earth.
núcleo externo Capa de hierro y níquel fundidos que rodea el núcleo interno de la Tierra.

outlier An abnormal or irregular data point; a point on a graph that is clearly not part of the trend.
valor atípico Punto de datos anormal o irregular; punto en una gráfica que se aleja demasiado de los valores esperados.

output Material, energy, result, or product that comes out of a system.
salida Material, energía, resultado o producto que un sistema produce.

output force The force exerted on an object by a machine.
fuerza desarrollada Fuerza que una máquina ejerce sobre un cuerpo.

ovary 1. A flower structure that encloses and protects ovules and seeds as they develop. **2.** Organ of the female reproductive system in which eggs and estrogen are produced.
ovario 1. Estructura de una flor que encierra y protege a los óvulos y las semillas durante su desarrollo. **2.** Órgano del sistema reproductivo femenino en el que se producen los óvulos y el estrógeno.

overtone A natural frequency that is a multiple of the fundamental tone's frequency.
armónico Frecuencia natural que es un múltiplo de la frecuencia del tono fundamental.

ovulation The process in which a mature egg is released from the ovary into a Fallopian tube.
ovulación Proceso en el cual el óvulo maduro sale del ovario y pasa a las trompas de falopio.

ovule A plant structure in seed plants that produces the female gametophyte; contains an egg cell.
óvulo Estructura vegetal de las plantas de semilla que produce el gametofito femenino; contiene una célula reproductora femenina.

oxbow lake A meander cut off from a river.
lago de recodo Meandro que ha quedado aislado de un río.

oxidation A chemical change in which a substance combines with oxygen, as when iron oxidizes, forming rust.
oxidación Cambio químico en el cual una sustancia se combina con el oxígeno, como cuando el hierro se oxida, y produce herrumbre.

ozone A form of oxygen that has three oxygen atoms in each molecule instead of the usual two; toxic to organisms where it forms near Earth's surface.
ozono Forma de oxígeno que tiene tres átomos de oxígeno en cada molécula, en vez de dos; donde se forma en la superficie terrestre, es tóxico para los organismos.

ozone layer The layer of the upper atmosphere that contains a higher concentration of ozone than the rest of the atmosphere.
capa de ozono Capa superior de la atmósfera que contiene una concentración mayor de ozono que el resto de la atmósfera.

P

P wave A type of seismic wave that compresses and expands the ground.
onda P Tipo de onda sísmica que comprime y expande el suelo.

paleontologist A scientist who studies fossils to learn about organisms that lived long ago.
paleontólogo Científico que estudia fósiles para aprender acerca de los organismos que vivieron hace mucho tiempo.

Pangaea The name of the single landmass that began to break apart 200 million years ago and gave rise to today's continents.
Pangea Nombre de la masa de tierra única que empezó a dividirse hace 200 millones de años y que le dio origen a los continentes actuales.

parallax The apparent change in position of an object when seen from different places.
paralaje Cambio aparente en la posición de un cuerpo cuando es visto desde distintos lugares.

parallel circuit An electric circuit in which different parts of the circuit are on separate branches.
circuito paralelo Circuito eléctrico en el que las distintas partes del circuito se encuentran en ramas separadas.

GLOSSARY

parasite An organism that benefits by living with, on, or in a host in a parasitism interaction.
parásito Organismo que se beneficia al vivir dentro de o sobre un huésped en una relación parasítica.

parasitism A type of symbiosis in which one organism lives with, on, or in a host and harms it.
parasitismo Tipo de relación simbiótica en la cual un organismo vive con o en un huésped y le hace daño.

passive immunity Immunity in which antibodies are given to a person rather than produced within the person's own body.
inmunidad pasiva Inmunidad en la que una persona recibe anticuerpos en vez de producirlos en su propio cuerpo.

passive transport The movement of dissolved materials across a cell membrane without using cellular energy.
transporte pasivo Movimiento de materiales a través de una membrana celular sin usar energía celular.

pasteurization A process of heating food to a temperature that is high enough to kill most harmful bacteria without changing the taste of the food.
pasteurización Proceso de calentamiento de los alimentos a una temperatura suficientemente alta como para matar la mayoría de las bacterias dañinas sin que cambie el sabor.

pathogen An organism that causes disease.
patógeno Organismo que causa enfermedades.

peat Compressed layers of dead sphagnum mosses that accumulate in bogs.
turba Capas comprimidas de musgos esfagnáceos muertos que se acumulan en las marismas.

penis The organ through which both semen and urine leave the male body.
pene Órgano por el cual salen del cuerpo masculino tanto el semen como la orina.

penumbra The part of a shadow surrounding the darkest part.
penumbra Parte de la sombra que rodea su parte más oscura.

percent error A calculation used to determine how accurate, or close to the true value, an experimental value really is.
error porcentual Cálculo usado para determinar cuán exacto, o cercano al valor verdadero, es realmente un valor experimental.

perennial A flowering plant that lives for more than two years.
perenne Planta con flores que vive más de dos años.

period **1.** A horizontal row of elements in the periodic table. **2.** One of the units of geologic time into which geologists divide eras.
período **1.** Fila horizontal de los elementos de la tabla periódica. **2.** Una de las unidades del tiempo geológico en las que los geólogos dividen las eras.

peripheral nervous system The division of the nervous system consisting of all of the nerves located outside the central nervous system.
sistema nervioso periférico División del sistema nervioso formada por todos los nervios ubicados fuera del sistema central nervioso.

peristalsis Waves of smooth muscle contractions that move food through the esophagus toward the stomach.
peristalsis Contracciones progresivas de músculo liso que mueven el alimento por el esófago hacia el estómago.

permafrost Permanently frozen soil found in the tundra biome climate region.
permagélido Suelo que está permanentemente congelado y que se encuentra en el bioma climático de la tundra.

permeable Characteristic of a material that contains connected air spaces, or pores, that water can seep through easily.
permeable Característica de un material que contiene diminutos espacios de aire, o poros, conectados por donde se puede filtrar el agua.

personal bias An outlook influenced by a person's likes and dislikes.
prejuicio personal Perspectiva influenciada por las preferencias de un individuo.

pesticide A chemical that kills insects and other crop-destroying organisms.
pesticida Químico usado para matar insectos y otros organismos que destruyen los cultivos.

petal A colorful, leaflike structure of some flowers.
pétalo Estructura de color brillante, similar a una hoja, que algunas flores poseen.

petrified fossil A fossil in which minerals replace all or part of an organism.
fósil petrificado Fósil en el cual los minerales reemplazan todo el organismo o parte de él.

petrochemical A compound made from oil.
petroquímico Compuesto que se obtiene del petróleo.

petroleum Liquid fossil fuel; oil.
petróleo Combustible fósil líquido.

pH scale A range of values used to indicate how acidic or basic a substance is; expresses the concentration of hydrogen ions in a solution.
escala de pH Rango de valores que se usa para indicar cuán ácida o básica es una sustancia; expresa la concentración de iones hidrógeno de una solución.

phagocyte A white blood cell that destroys pathogens by engulfing them and breaking them down.
fagocito Glóbulo blanco que destruye los patógenos envolviéndolos y descomponiéndolos.

pharynx The throat; part of both the respiratory and digestive systems.
faringe Garganta; parte de los sistemas respiratorio y digestivo.

phase One of the different apparent shapes of the moon as seen from Earth.
fase Una de las distintas formas aparentes de la Luna vistas desde la Tierra.

phenotype An organism's physical appearance, or visible traits.
fenotipo Apariencia física, o rasgos visibles, de un organismo.

phloem The vascular tissue through which food moves in some plants.
floema Tejido vascular de algunas plantas por el que circulan los alimentos.

photochemical smog A brownish thick haze that is a mixture of ozone and other chemicals formed when pollutants react with sunlight.
neblina tóxica fotoquímica Nubosidad gruesa de color marrón, resultado de la mezcla del ozono y otras sustancias químicas que se forman cuando los contaminantes reaccionan a la luz del sol.

photoelectric effect The ejection of electrons from a substance when light is shined on it.
efecto fotoeléctrico Expulsión de electrones de una sustancia al ser iluminada.

photon A tiny particle or packet of light energy.
fotón Partícula diminuta o paquete de energía luminosa.

photoperiodism A plant's response to seasonal changes in the length of night and day.
fotoperiodicidad Respuesta de una planta a los cambios estacionales del día y de la noche.

photosphere The inner layer of the sun's atmosphere that gives off its visible light; the sun's surface.

fotósfera Capa más interna de la atmósfera solar que provoca la luz que vemos; superficie del Sol.

photosynthesis The process by which plants and other autotrophs capture and use light energy to make food from carbon dioxide and water.
fotosíntesis Proceso por el cual las plantas y otros autótrofos absorben la energía de la luz para producir alimentos a partir del dióxido de carbono y el agua.

physical change A change that alters the form or appearance of a material but does not make the material into another substance.
cambio físico Cambio que altera la forma o apariencia de un material, pero que no convierte el material en otra sustancia.

physical property A characteristic of a pure substance that can be observed without changing it into another substance.
propiedad física Característica de una sustancia pura que se puede observar sin convertirla en otra sustancia.

pigment 1. A colored chemical compound that absorbs light. 2. A colored substance used to color other materials.
pigmento 1. Compuesto químico de color que absorbe luz. 2. Sustancia de color que se puede usar para dar color a otros materiales.

pioneer species The first species to populate an area during succession.
especies pioneras La primera especie que puebla un área durante la sucesión.

pipe A long tube through which magma moves from the magma chamber to Earth's surface.
chimenea Largo tubo por el que el magma sube desde la cámara magmática hasta la superficie de la tierra.

pistil The female reproductive part of a flower.
pistilo Parte reproductora femenina de una flor.

pitch A description of how a sound is perceived as high or low.
tono Descripción de un sonido que se percibe como alto o bajo.

pituitary gland An endocrine gland that regulates many body activities and controls the actions of several other endocrine glands.
glándula pituitaria Glándula endocrina que regula muchas actividades corporales y controla las acciones de varias otras glándulas endocrinas.

GLOSSARY

placenta An organ in most pregnant mammals, including humans, that links the mother and the developing embryo and allows for the passage of materials between them.
placenta Órgano de la mayoría de los mamíferos preñados, incluyendo a los seres humanos, que conecta a la madre con el embrión en desarrollo y que permite el intercambio de materiales entre ellos.

placental mammal A mammal that develops inside its mother's body until its body systems can function independently.
mamífero placentario Mamífero que se desarrolla dentro del cuerpo de la madre hasta que sus sistemas puedan funcionar por sí solos.

plane mirror A flat mirror that produces an upright, virtual image the same size as the object.
espejo plano Espejo liso que produce una imagen virtual vertical del mismo tamaño que el objeto.

planet An object that orbits a star, is large enough to have become rounded by its own gravity, and has cleared the area of its orbit.
planeta Cuerpo que orbita alrededor de una estrella, que tiene suficiente masa como para permitir que su propia gravedad le dé una forma casi redonda, y que además ha despejado las proximidades de su órbita.

planetesimal One of the small asteroid-like bodies that formed the building blocks of the planets.
planetesimal Uno de los cuerpos pequeños parecidos a asteroides que dieron origen a los planetas.

plate A section of the lithosphere that slowly moves over the asthenosphere, carrying pieces of continental and oceanic crust.
placa Sección de la litósfera que se desplaza lentamente sobre la astenósfera y que se lleva consigo trozos de la corteza continental y de la oceánica.

plate tectonics The theory that pieces of Earth's lithosphere are in constant motion, driven by convection currents in the mantle.
tectónica de placas Teoría según la cual las partes de la litósfera de la Tierra están en continuo movimiento, impulsadas por las corrientes de convección del manto.

plateau A large landform that has high elevation and a more or less level surface.
meseta Accidente geográfico que tiene una elevación alta y cuya superficie está más o menos nivelada.

plucking The process by which a glacier picks up rocks as it flows over the land.

extracción Proceso por el cual un glaciar arranca las rocas al fluir sobre la tierra.

poaching Illegal killing or removal of wildlife from their habitats.
caza ilegal Matanza o eliminación de la fauna silvestre de su hábitat.

point source A specific source of pollution that can be identified.
fuente localizada Fuente específica de contaminación que puede identificarse.

polar (air mass) A cold air mass that forms north of 50¡ north latitude or south of 50¡ south latitude and has high air pressure.
masa de aire polar Masa de aire frío que se forma al norte de los 50¡ de latitud norte o al sur de los 50¡ de latitud sur y que tiene presión alta.

polar bond A covalent bond in which electrons are shared unequally.
enlace polar Enlace covalente en el que los electrones se comparten de forma desigual.

polar zones The areas near both poles from about 66.5° to 90° north and 66.5° to 90° south latitudes.
zona polar Áreas cercanas a los polos desde unos 66.5° a 90° de latitud norte y 66.5° a 90° de latitud sur.

polarization The process through which electrons are attracted to or repelled by an external electric field, causing the electrons to move within their own atoms.
polarización Proceso por el cual un campo eléctrico externo atrae o repele a los electrones y hace que éstos se muevan dentro de su átomo.

polarized light Light that has been filtered so that all of its waves are parallel to each other.
luz polarizada Luz que se ha filtrado de manera que sus ondas queden paralelas unas con otras.

pollen Tiny structure (male gametophyte) produced by seed plants that contain the cell that later becomes a sperm cell.
polen Diminuta estructura (gametofito masculino) producida por las plantas de semilla que contiene la célula que más adelante se convertirá en un espermatozoide.

pollination The transfer of pollen from male reproductive structures to female reproductive structures in plants.
polinización Transferencia del polen de las estructuras reproductoras masculinas de una planta a las estructuras reproductoras femeninas.

pollutant A substance that causes pollution.
contaminante Sustancia que provoca contaminación.

pollution Contamination of Earth's land, water, or air.
polución Contaminación del suelo, el agua o el aire de la Tierra.

polyatomic ion An ion that is made of more than one atom.
ión poliatómico Ión formado por más de un átomo.

polygenic inheritance The inheritance of traits that are controlled by two or more genes, such as height in humans.
herencia poligénica Herencia de los rasgos controlados por dos o más genes, como la altura en los seres humanos.

polyp A cnidarian body form characterized by an upright vase shape and usually adapted for a life attached to an underwater surface.
pólipo Cnidario con cuerpo de forma tubular y que está adaptado para vivir fijo en un fondo acuático.

population All the members of one species living in the same area.
población Todos los miembros de una especie que viven en el mismo lugar.

population density The number of individuals in an area of a specific size.
densidad de población Número de individuos en un área de un tamaño específico.

pore An opening through which sweat reaches the surface of the skin.
poros Aberturas a través de las cuales sale el sudor a la superficie de la piel.

potential energy The energy an object has because of its position; also the internal stored energy of an object, such as energy stored in chemical bonds.
energía potencial Energía que tiene un cuerpo por su posición; también es la energía interna almacenada de un cuerpo, como la energía almacenada en los enlaces químicos.

power The rate at which one form of energy is transformed into another.
potencia Rapidez de la conversión de una forma de energía en otra.

precipitate A solid that forms from a solution during a chemical reaction.
precipitado Sólido que se forma de una solución durante una reacción química.

precipitation Any form of water that falls from clouds and reaches Earth's surface as rain, snow, sleet, or hail.
precipitación Cualquier forma del agua que cae de las nubes y llega a la superficie de la tierra como lluvia, nieve, aguanieve o granizo.

precision How close a group of measurements are to each other.
precisión Cuán cerca se encuentran un grupo de medidas.

predation An interaction in which one organism kills another for food or nutrients.
depredación Interacción en la cual un organismo mata a otro para alimentarse u obtener nutrientes de él.

predator The organism that does the killing in a predation interaction.
depredador Organismo que mata durante la depredación.

predicting The process of forecasting what will happen in the future based on past experience or evidence.
predecir Proceso de pronosticar lo que va a suceder en el futuro, basándose en evidencia o experiencias previas.

pressure The force pushing on a surface divided by the area of that surface.
presión Fuerza que actúa contra una superficie, dividida entre el área de esa superficie.

prey An organism that is killed and eaten by another organism in a predation interaction.
presa Organismo que es consumido por otro organismo en el proceso de depredación.

primary color One of three colors that can be used to make any other color.
color primario Uno de los tres colores que se pueden usar para hacer cualquier color.

primary succession The series of changes that occur in an area where no soil or organisms exist.
sucesión primaria Serie de cambios que ocurren en un área donde no existe suelo ni organismos.

probability A number that describes how likely it is that a particular event will occur.
probabilidad Número que describe cuán probable es que ocurra un suceso.

process A sequence of actions in a system.
proceso Secuencia de acciones en un sistema.

GLOSSARY

producer An organism that can make its own food.
productor Organismo que puede generar su propio alimento.

product A substance formed as a result of a chemical reaction.
producto Sustancia formada como resultado de una reacción química.

prokaryote A unicellular organism that lacks a nucleus and some other cell structures.
procariota Organismo unicelular que carece de un núcleo y otras estructuras celulares.

prominence A huge, reddish loop of gas that protrudes from the sun's surface, linking parts of sunspot regions.
prominencia Enorme burbuja de gas rojiza que sobresale de la superfice solar, y conecta partes de las manchas solares.

protein Large organic molecule made of carbon, hydrogen, oxygen, nitrogen, and sometimes sulfur.
proteína Molécula orgánica grande compuesta de carbono, hidrógeno, oxígeno, nitrógeno y, a veces, azufre.

protist A eukaryotic organism that cannot be classified as an animal, plant, or fungus.
protista Organismo eucariótico que no se puede clasificar como animal, planta ni hongo.

protostar A contracting cloud of gas and dust with enough mass to form a star.
protoestrella Nube de gas y polvo que se contrae, con suficiente masa como para formar una estrella.

protozoan A unicellular, animal-like protist.
protozoario Protista unicelular con características animales.

pseudopod A "false foot" or temporary bulge of cytoplasm used for feeding and movement in some protozoans.
seudópodo "Pie falso" o abultamiento temporal del citoplasma que algunos protozoarios usan para alimentarse o desplazarse.

pseudoscience A set of beliefs that may make use of science but whose conclusions and predictions are not based on observation, objective reasoning, or scientific evidence.
pseudociencia Conjunto de creencias que pueden basarse en la ciencia, pero cuyas conclusiones no se derivan de la observación, el razonamiento objetivo o evidencia científica.

psychrometer An instrument used to measure relative humidity.

psicrómetro Instrumento que se usa para medir la humedad relativa.

pulley A simple machine that consists of a grooved wheel with a rope or cable wrapped around it.
polea Máquina simple que consiste en una rueda con un surco en el que yace una cuerda o cable.

pulsar A rapidly spinning neutron star that produces radio waves.
pulsar Estrella de neutrones que gira rápidamente y produce ondas de radio.

punctuated equilibrium Pattern of evolution in which long stable periods are interrupted by brief periods of more rapid change.
equilibrio puntual Patrón de la evolución en el que los períodos largos estables son interrumpidos por breves períodos de cambio rápido.

Punnett square A chart that shows all the possible combinations of alleles that can result from a genetic cross.
cuadrado de Punnett Tabla que muestra todas las combinaciones posibles de los alelos que se pueden derivar de un cruce genético.

pupa The third stage of complete metamorphosis, in which a larva develops into an adult insect.
pupa Tercera etapa de la metamorfosis completa, en la que la larva se convierte en insecto adulto.

pupil The opening in the center of the iris through which light enters the inside of the eye.
pupila Apertura en el centro del iris por donde entra la luz al ojo.

purebred An offspring of crosses that has the same form of traits.
raza pura Descendiente de cruces, que tiene los mismos rasgos.

pyroclastic flow The flow of ash, cinders, bombs, and gases down the side of a volcano during an explosive eruption.
flujo piroclástico Flujo de ceniza, escoria, bombas y gases que corre por las laderas de un volcán durante una erupción explosiva.

Q

---

qualitative observation An observation that deals with characteristics that cannot be expressed in numbers.
observación cualitativa Observación que se centra en las características que no se pueden expresar con números.

quantitative observation An observation that deals with a number or amount.
observación cuantitativa Observación que se centra en un número o cantidad.

quasar An enormously bright, distant galaxy with a giant black hole at its center.
quásar Galaxia extraordinariamente luminosa y distante con un agujero negro gigante en el centro.

---R---

radar A system that uses reflected radio waves to detect objects and measure their distance and speed.
radar Sistema que usa ondas de radio reflejadas para detectar cuerpos y medir su distancia y velocidad.

radial symmetry A body plan in which any number of imaginary lines that all pass through a central point divide the animal into two mirror images.
simetría radiada Esquema del cuerpo en el que cualquier número de líneas imaginarias que atraviesan un punto central dividen a un animal en dos partes que son el reflejo la una de la otra.

radiation The transfer of energy by electromagnetic waves.
radiación Transferencia de energía por medio de ondas magnéticas.

radiation zone A region of very tightly packed gas in the sun's interior where energy is transferred mainly in the form of electromagnetic radiation.
zona radiactiva Región al interior del Sol de gases densamente acumulados y donde se transmite energía principalmente en la forma de radiación electromagnética.

radio telescope A device used to detect radio waves from objects in space.
radiotelescopio Aparato usado para detectar ondas de radio de los cuerpos en el espacio.

radio waves Electromagnetic waves with the longest wavelengths and lowest frequencies.
ondas de radio Ondas electromagnéticas con las longitudes de onda más largas y las frecuencias más bajas.

radioactive decay The process in which the nuclei of radioactive elements break down, releasing fast-moving particles and energy.
desintegración radiactiva Proceso de descomposición del núcleo de los elementos radiactivos que libera partículas en movimiento y energía.

radon A colorless, odorless, radioactive gas.
radón Gas radioactivo que no tiene color ni olor.

rain forest A forest that receives at least 2 meters of rain per year, mostly occurring in the tropical wet climate zone.
selva tropical Bosque donde caen al menos 2 metros de lluvia al año, principalmente en la zona climática tropical húmeda.

rain gauge An instrument used to measure precipitation.
pluviómetro Instrumento que se usa para medir la precipitación.

range The difference between the greatest value and the least value in a set of data.
rango Diferencia entre el mayor y el menor valor de un conjunto de datos.

rarefaction The part of a longitudinal wave where the particles of the medium are far apart.
rarefacción Parte de una onda longitudinal donde las partículas del medio están muy apartadas entre sí.

ray A straight line used to represent a light wave.
rayo Línea recta que se usa para representar una onda de luz.

reactant A substance that enters into a chemical reaction.
reactante Sustancia que interviene en una reacción química.

reactor vessel The part of a nuclear reactor in which nuclear fission occurs.
cuba de reactor Parte de un reactor nuclear donde ocurre la fisión.

real image An upside-down image formed where rays of light meet.
imagen real Imagen invertida formada en el punto de encuentro de los rayos de luz.

recessive allele An allele that is hidden whenever the dominant allele is present.
alelo recesivo Alelo que no se manifiesta cuando el alelo dominante está presente.

recycling The process of reclaiming and reusing raw materials.
reciclaje Proceso de recuperar y volver a usar materias primas.

reference point A place or object used for comparison to determine if an object is in motion.
punto de referencia Lugar u objeto usado como medio de comparación para determinar si un objeto está en movimiento.

GLOSSARY

refinery A factory in which crude oil is heated and separated into fuels and other products.
refinería Planta en la que el petróleo crudo se calienta y fracciona en combustibles y otros productos.

reflecting telescope A telescope that uses a curved mirror to collect and focus light.
telescopio de reflexión Telescopio que usa un espejo curvado para captar y enfocar la luz.

reflection The bouncing back of an object or a wave when it hits a surface through which it cannot pass.
reflexión Rebote de un cuerpo o una onda al golpear una superficie que no puede atravesar.

reflex An automatic response that occurs rapidly and without conscious control.
reflejo espuesta automática que ocurre rápida e involuntariamente.

refracting telescope A telescope that uses convex lenses to gather and focus light.
telescopio de refracción Telescopio que usa lentes convexas para captar y enfocar la luz.

refraction The bending of waves as they enter a new medium at an angle, caused by a change in speed.
refracción Cambio de dirección de las ondas al entrar en un nuevo medio con un determinado ángulo, y a consecuencia de un cambio de velocidad.

regular reflection Reflection that occurs when parallel rays of light hit a smooth surface and all reflect at the same angle.
reflexión regular Reflexión que ocurre cuando rayos de luz paralelos chocan contra una superficie lisa y se reflejan en el mismo ángulo.

relative age The age of a rock compared to the ages of other rocks.
edad relativa Edad de una roca comparada con la edad de otras rocas.

relative humidity The percentage of water vapor in the air compared to the maximum amount of water vapor that air can contain at a particular temperature.
humedad relativa Porcentaje de vapor de agua del aire comparado con la cantidad máxima de vapor de agua que puede contener el aire a una temperatura particular.

remote sensing The collection of information about Earth and other objects in space using satellites or probes.
percepción remota Recolección de información sobre la Tierra y otros cuerpos del espacio usando satélites o sondas.

renewable resource A resource that is either always available or is naturally replaced in a relatively short time.
recurso renovable Recurso que está siempre disponible o que es restituido de manera natural en un período relativamente corto.

repeated trial A repetition of an experiment to gather additional data and determine whether the experiment's results support the hypothesis.
prueba repetida Repetición de un experimento para recopilar datos adicionales y determinar si los resultados de un experimento sustentan la hipótesis.

replacement A reaction in which one element replaces another in a compound or when two elements in different compounds trade places.
sustitución Reacción en la que un elemento reemplaza a otro en un compuesto o en la que se intercambian dos elementos de diferentes compuestos.

replication The process by which a cell makes a copy of the DNA in its nucleus before cell division.
replicación Proceso en el que la célula copia el ADN de su núcleo antes de la división celular.

reptile A vertebrate whose temperature is determined by the temperature of its environment, that has lungs and scaly skin, and that lays eggs on land.
reptil Vertebrado cuya temperatura corporal es determinada por la temperatura de su medio ambiente, que tiene pulmones y piel escamosa y que pone huevos en la tierra.

reservoir A lake that stores water for human use.
embalse Lago que almacena agua para el uso humano.

resistance The measurement of how difficult it is for charges to flow through an object.
resistencia Medida de la dificultad de una carga eléctrica para fluir por un cuerpo.

resonance The increase in the amplitude of a vibration that occurs when external vibrations match an object's natural frequency.
resonancia Aumento en la amplitud de vibración que ocurre cuando vibraciones externas corresponden con la frecuencia natural de un cuerpo.

resource Anything in the environment that you need to live, such as water, nutrients, light, food, or space.
recurso Cosa en el medio ambiente necesaria para la vida, como agua, nutrientes, luz, comida y espacio.

respiratory system An organ system that enables organisms to exchange gases with their surroundings.
sistema respiratorio Sistema de órganos que permite al organismo intercambiar gases con su entorno.

responding variable The factor that changes as a result of changes to the manipulated, or independent, variable in an experiment; also called dependent variable.
variable de respuesta Factor que cambia como resultado del cambio de la variable manipulada, o independiente, en un experimento; también llamada variable dependiente.

response An action or change in behavior that occurs as a result of a stimulus.
respuesta Acción o cambio del comportamiento que ocurre como resultado de un estímulo.

retina The layer of receptor cells at the back of the eye on which an image is focused.
retina Capa de células receptoras de la parte posterior del ojo donde se enfoca una imagen.

reverse fault A type of fault where the hanging wall slides upward; caused by compression in the crust.
falla inversa Tipo de falla en la cual el labio superior se desliza hacia arriba como resultado de compresión de la corteza.

revolution The movement of an object around another object.
revolución Movimiento de un cuerpo alrededor de otro.

rhizoid A thin, rootlike structure that anchors a moss and absorbs water and nutrients for the plant.
rizoide Estructura fina parecida a una raíz que sujeta un musgo al suelo, y que absorbe el agua y los nutrientes para la planta.

ribosome A small grain-shaped organelle in the cytoplasm of a cell that produces proteins.
ribosoma Orgánulo pequeño con forma de grano en el citoplasma de una célula que produce proteínas.

Richter scale A scale that rates an earthquake's magnitude based on the size of its seismic waves.
escala de ichter Escala con la que se mide la magnitud de un terremoto según el tamaño de sus ondas sísmicas.

rift valley A deep valley that forms where two plates move apart.
valle de fisura Valle profundo que se forma cuando dos placas se separan.

rill A tiny groove in soil made by flowing water.
arroyo Pequeño surco en el suelo causado por el paso del agua.

ring A thin disk of small ice and rock particles surrounding a planet.
anillo Disco fino de pequeñas partículas de hielo y roca que rodea un planeta.

Ring of Fire A major belt of volcanoes that rims the Pacific Ocean.
Cinturón de Fuego Gran cadena de volcanes que rodea el océano Pacífico.

rip current A strong, narrow current that flows briefly from the shore back toward the ocean through a narrow opening.
corriente de resaca Corriente fuerte que fluye por un canal estrecho desde la costa hacia el mar abierto.

rock cycle A series of processes on the surface and inside Earth that slowly changes rocks from one kind to another.
ciclo de la roca Serie de procesos en la superficie y dentro de la Tierra por medio del cual un tipo de roca se convierte lentamente en otro tipo.

rock-forming mineral Any of the common minerals that make up most of the rocks of Earth's crust.
minerales formadores de rocas Uno de los minerales comunes de los que están compuestas la mayoría de las rocas de la corteza de la Tierra.

rocket A device that expels gas in one direction to move in the opposite direction.
cohete Aparato que expulsa gases en una dirección para moverse en la dirección opuesta.

rods Cells in the retina that detect dim light.
bastones Células de la retina que detectan la luz tenue.

rolling friction Friction that occurs when an object rolls over a surface.
fricción de rodamiento Fricción que ocurre cuando un cuerpo rueda sobre una superficie.

root cap A structure that covers the tip of a root, protecting the root from injury as the root grows through soil.
cofia Estructura que cubre la punta de una raíz y la protege de cualquier daño mientras crece en la tierra.

rotation The spinning motion of a planet on its axis.
rotación Movimiento giratorio de un planeta sobre su eje.

GLOSSARY

rover A small robotic space probe that can move about the surface of a planet or moon.
rover Pequeña sonda espacial robótica que puede desplazarse sobre la superficie de un planeta o sobre la Luna.

runoff Water that flows over the ground surface rather than soaking into the ground.
escurrimiento Agua que fluye sobre la superficie en lugar de ser absorbida por el suelo.

S

S wave A type of seismic wave in which the shaking is perpendicular to the direction of the wave.
onda S Tipo de onda sísmica que hace que el suelo se mueva en una dirección perpendicular a la onda.

safety symbols A sign used to alert you to possible sources of accidents in an investigation.
símbolos de seguridad Señal de alerta sobre elementos que pueden causar accidentes durante una investigación.

salinity The total amount of dissolved salts in a water sample.
salinidad Cantidad total de sales disueltas en una muestra de agua.

salt An ionic compound made from the neutralization of an acid with a base.
sal Compuesto iónico formado por la neutralización de un ácido con una base.

sand dune A deposit of wind-blown sand.
duna de arena Depósito de arena arrastrada por el viento.

sanitary landfill A landfill that holds nonhazardous waste such as municipal solid waste, construction debris, and some agricultural and industrial wastes.
relleno sanitario Vertedero que contiene desechos que no son peligrosos, como desechos sólidos municipales, de construcción y algunos tipos de desechos industriales y resultantes de la agricultura.

satellite 1. An object that orbits a planet. 2. Any object that orbits around another object in space.
satélite 1. Cuerpo que orbita alrededor de un planeta. 2. Cualquier cuerpo que orbita alrededor de otro cuerpo en el espacio.

saturated solution A mixture that contains as much dissolved solute as is possible at a given temperature.

solución saturada Mezcla que contiene la mayor cantidad posible de soluto disuelto a una temperatura determinada.

saturated zone The area of permeable rock or soil in which the cracks and pores are totally filled with water.
zona saturada Área de roca o suelo permeable cuyas grietas y poros están totalmente llenos de agua.

savanna A grassland located close to the equator that may include shrubs and small trees and receives as much as 120 centimeters of rain per year.
sabana Pradera que puede tener arbustos y árboles pequeños, ubicada cerca del ecuador y donde pueden caer hasta 120 centímetros de lluvia al año.

scattering Reflection of light in all directions.
dispersión Reflexión de la luz en todas las direcciones.

scavenger A carnivore that feeds on the bodies of dead or decaying organisms.
carroñero Carnívoro que se alimenta de los restos de organismos muertos o en descomposición.

science A way of learning about the natural world through observations and logical reasoning; leads to a body of knowledge.
ciencia Estudio del mundo natural a través de observaciones y del razonamiento lógico; conduce a un conjunto de conocimientos.

scientific explanation A generalization that makes sense of observations by using logical reasoning.
explicación científica Generalización que usa el razonamiento lógico para darle sentido a las observaciones.

scientific inquiry The ongoing process of discovery in science; the diverse ways in which scientists study the natural world and propose explanations based on evidence they gather.
indagación científica Proceso continuo de descubrimiento en la ciencia; diversidad de métodos con los que los científicos estudian el mundo natural y proponen explicaciones del mismo basadas en la evidencia que reúnen.

scientific investigation The process by which a scientist asks a question about the natural world, collects and analyzes data to help answer that question, and communicates the results to the scientific community.
investigación científica Proceso por el que un científico hace preguntas acerca del mundo natural, recopila y analiza datos para responder esas preguntas y comunica los resultados a la comunidad científica.

scientific law A statement that describes what scientists expect to happen every time under a particular set of conditions.
ley científica Enunciado que describe lo que los científicos esperan que suceda cada vez que se da una serie de condiciones determinadas.

scientific literacy The knowledge and understanding of scientific terms and principles required for evaluating information, making personal decisions, and taking part in public affairs.
conocimiento científico Conocimiento y comprensión de los términos y principios científicos necesarios para evaluar información, tomar decisiones personales y participar en actividades públicas.

scientific notation A mathematical method of writing numbers using powers of ten.
notación científica Método matemático de escritura de números que usa la potencia de diez.

scientific theory A well-tested explanation for a wide range of observations or experimental results.
teoría científica Explicación comprobada de una gran variedad de observaciones o resultados de experimentos.

screw A simple machine that is an inclined plane wrapped around a central cylinder to form a spiral.
tornillo Máquina simple que consiste en un plano inclinado enrollado alrededor de un cilindro central para formar una espiral.

scrotum An external pouch of skin in which the testes are located.
escroto Bolsa de piel externa en donde se encuentran los testículos.

sea breeze The flow of cooler air from over an ocean or lake toward land.
brisa marina Flujo de aire frío procedente de un océano o lago hacia la costa.

sea-floor spreading The process by which molten material adds new oceanic crust to the ocean floor.
despliegue del suelo oceánico Proceso mediante el cual la materia fundida añade nueva corteza oceánica al suelo oceánico.

seamount A steep-sided volcanic mountain rising from the deep-ocean floor.
montaña marina Montaña muy inclinada de origen volcánico cuya base es el fondo del mar.

secondary color Any color produced by combining equal amounts of any two primary colors.
color secundario Color producido al combinar iguales cantidades de dos colores primarios cualesquiera.

secondary succession The series of changes that occur in an area where the ecosystem has been disturbed, but where soil and organisms still exist.
sucesión secundaria Serie de cambios que ocurren en un área después de la perturbación de un ecosistema, pero donde todavía hay suelo y organismos.

sediment Small, solid pieces of material that come from rocks or the remains of organisms; earth materials deposited by erosion.
sedimento Trozos pequeños y sólidos de materiales que provienen de las rocas o de los restos de organismos; materiales terrestres depositados por la erosión.

sedimentary rock A type of rock that forms when particles from other rocks or the remains of plants and animals are pressed and cemented together.
roca sedimentaria Tipo de roca que se forma a partir de la compactación y unión de partículas de otras rocas o restos de plantas y animales.

seed The plant structure that contains a young plant and a food supply inside a protective covering.
semilla Estructura vegetal que contiene una planta joven y una fuente alimenticia encerradas en una cubierta protectora.

seismic wave Vibrations that travel through Earth carrying the energy released during an earthquake.
ondas sísmicas Vibraciones que se desplazan por la Tierra, y que llevan la energía liberada durante un terremoto.

seismogram The record of an earthquake's seismic waves produced by a seismograph.
sismograma Registro producido por un sismógrafo de las ondas sísmicas de un terremoto.

seismograph A device that records ground movements caused by seismic waves as they move through Earth.
sismógrafo Aparato con el que se registran los movimientos del suelo ocasionados por las ondas sísmicas a medida que éstas se desplazan por la Tierra.

selective breeding Method of breeding that allows only those organisms with desired traits to produce the next generation.
cruce selectivo Técnica reproductiva por medio de la cual sólo los organismos con rasgos deseados producen la próxima generación.

selectively permeable A property of cell membranes that allows some substances to pass across it, while others cannot.
permeabilidad selectiva Propiedad de las membranas celulares que permite el paso de algunas sustancias y no de otras.

semen A mixture of sperm and fluids.
semen Mezcla de esperma y fluidos.

sensory neuron A neuron that picks up stimuli from the internal or external environment and converts each stimulus into a nerve impulse.
neurona sensorial Neurona que recoge los estímulos del medio ambiente interno o externo y convierte a cada estímulo en un impulso nervioso.

sepal A leaflike structure that encloses and protects the bud of a flower.
sépalo Estructura similar a una hoja que encierra y protege el capullo de una flor.

series circuit An electric circuit in which all parts are connected one after another along one path.
circuito en serie Circuito eléctrico en el que todas las partes se conectan una tras otra en una trayectoria.

sewage The water and human wastes that are washed down sinks, toilets, and showers.
aguas residuales Agua y desechos humanos que son desechados por lavamanos, servicios sanitarios y duchas.

sex chromosomes A pair of chromosomes carrying genes that determine whether a person is male or female.
cromosomas sexuales Par de cromosomas portadores de genes que determinan el sexo (masculino o femenino) de una persona.

sex-linked gene A gene that is carried on a sex
gen ligado al sexo Gen de un cromosoma sexual (X o Y).

sexual reproduction A reproductive process that involves two parents that combine their genetic material to produce a new organism which differs from both parents.
reproducción sexual Proceso de reproducción que involucra a dos reproductores que combinan su material genético para producir un nuevo organismo que es distinto a los dos reproductores.

shared derived characteristic A characteristic or trait, such as fur, that the common ancestor of a group had and passed on to its descendants.
característica derivada compartida Característica o rasgo, como el pelaje, del ancestro común de un grupo que éste pasa a sus descendientes.

shearing Stress that pushes masses of rock in opposite directions, in a sideways movement.
cizallamiento Fuerza que presiona masas de roca en sentidos opuestos, de lado a lado.

shield volcano A wide, gently sloping mountain made of layers of lava and formed by quiet eruptions.
volcán en escudo Montaña ancha de pendientes suaves, compuesta por capas de lava y formada durante erupciones que no son violentas.

short circuit A connection that allows current to take the path of least resistance.
cortocircuito Conexión que permite que la corriente siga el camino de menor resistencia.

short-day plant A plant that flowers when the nights are longer than the plant's critical night length.
planta de día corto Planta que florece cuando la duración de la noche es más larga que la duración crítica.

SI A system of units used by scientists to measure the properties of matter.
SI Sistema de unidades que los científicos usan para medir las propiedades de la materia.

significant figures All the digits in a measurement that have been measured exactly, plus one digit whose value has been estimated.
cifras significativas En una medida, todos los dígitos que se han medido con exactitud, más un dígito cuyo valor se ha estimado.

silica A material found in magma that is formed from the elements oxygen and silicon; it is the primary substance of Earth's crust and mantle.
sílice Material presente en el magma, compuesto por los elementos oxígeno y silicio; es el componente más común de la corteza y el manto de la Tierra.

sill A slab of volcanic rock formed when magma squeezes between layers of rock.
dique concordante Placa de roca volcánica formada cuando el magma a través de capas de roca.

simple machine The most basic device for making work easier, these are the smaller building blocks for complex machines.
máquina simple Aparatos sencillos que facilitan el trabajo; son los componentes de las máquinas compuestas.

skeletal muscle A muscle that is attached to the bones of the skeleton and provides the force that moves the bones; also called striated muscle.
músculo esquelético Músculo que está conectado a los huesos del esqueleto y que proporciona la fuerza que mueve los huesos; llamado también músculo estriado.

skeleton **1.** The inner framework made up of all the bones of the body. **2.** A framework that shapes and supports an animal, protects its internal organs, and allows it to move in its environment.
esqueleto **1.** Estructura interna compuesta de todos los huesos del cuerpo. **2.** Estructura que da forma y soporte a un animal, protege sus órganos internos y le permite moverse en su medio ambiente.

skepticism An attitude of doubt.
escepticismo Actitud de duda.

sliding friction Friction that occurs when one solid surface slides over another.
fricción de deslizamiento Fricción que ocurre cuando una superficie sólida se desliza sobre otra.

slope The steepness of a graph line; the ratio of the vertical change (the rise) to the horizontal change (the run).
pendiente Inclinación de una gráfica lineal; la razón del cambio vertical (el ascenso) al cambio horizontal (el avance).

smooth muscle Involuntary muscle found inside many internal organs of the body.
músculo liso Músculo involuntario que se halla dentro de muchos órganos internos del cuerpo.

soil The loose, weathered material on Earth's surface in which plants can grow.
suelo Material suelto y desgastado de la superficie terrestre donde crecen las plantas.

soil conservation The management of soil to limit its destruction.
conservación del suelo Cuidado del suelo para limitar su destrucción.

soil horizon A layer of soil that differs in color and texture from the layers above or below it.
horizonte de suelo Capa de suelo de color y textura diferentes a las capas que tiene encima o abajo.

solar eclipse The blocking of sunlight to Earth that occurs when the moon is directly between the sun and Earth.
eclipse solar Bloqueo de la luz solar que ilumina la Tierra que ocurre cuando la Luna se interpone entre el Sol y la Tierra.

solar energy Energy from the sun.
energía solar Energía del Sol.

solar flare An eruption of gas from the sun's surface that occurs when the loops in sunspot regions suddenly connect.

destello solar Erupción de los gases de la superficie solar que ocurre cuando las burbujas de las manchas solares se conectan repentinamente.

solar system The system consisting of the sun and the planets and other objects that revolve around it.
sistema solar Sistema formado por el Sol, los planetas y otros cuerpos que giran alrededor de él.

solar wind A stream of electrically charged particles that emanate from the sun's corona.
viento solar Flujo de partículas cargadas que emanan de la corona del Sol.

solenoid A coil of wire with a current.
solenoide Bobina de alambre con una corriente.

solid A state of matter that has a definite shape and a definite volume.
sólido Estado en el que la materia tiene forma y volumen definidos.

solstice Either of the two days of the year on which the sun reaches its greatest distance north or south of the equator.
solsticio Uno de los dos días del año en el que el Sol alcanza la mayor distancia al norte o al sur del ecuador.

solubility A measure of how much solute can dissolve in a given solvent at a given temperature.
solubilidad Medida de cuánto soluto se puede disolver en un solvente a una temperatura dada.

solute The part of a solution that is dissolved by a solvent.
soluto Parte de una solución que se disuelve en un solvente.

solution A mixture containing a solvent and at least one solute that has the same properties throughout; a mixture in which one substance is dissolved in another.
solución Mezcla que contiene un solvente y al menos un soluto, y que tiene Propiedades uniforms mezcla en la que una sustancia se disuelve en otra.

solvent The part of a solution that is usually present in the largest amount and dissolves a solute.
solvente Parte de una solución que, por lo general, está presente en la mayor cantidad y que disuelve a un soluto.

sonar A system that uses reflected sound waves to locate and determine the distance to objects under water.
sónar Sistema que usa ondas sonoras reflejadas para detectar y localizar objetos bajo agua.

GLOSSARY

sonogram An image formed using reflected ultrasound waves.
sonograma Formación de una imagen usando ondas de ultrasonido reflejadas.

space probe A spacecraft that has various scientific instruments that can collect data, including visual images, but has no human crew.
sonda espacial Nave espacial que tiene varios instrumentos científicos que pueden reunir datos e imágenes, pero que no tiene una tripulación.

space shuttle A spacecraft that can carry a crew into space, return to Earth, and then be reused for the same purpose.
transbordador espacial Nave espacial que puede llevar a una tripulación al espacio, volver a la Tierra, y luego volver a ser usada para el mismo propósito.

space spinoff An item that has uses on Earth but was originally developed for use in space.
derivación espacial Objeto que se puede usar en la Tierra, pero que originalmente se construyó para ser usado en el espacio.

space station A large artificial satellite on which people can live and work for long periods.
estación espacial Enorme satélite artificial en el que la gente puede vivir y trabajar durante largos períodos.

species A group of similar organisms that can mate with each other and produce offspring that can also mate and reproduce.
especie Grupo de organismos semejantes que pueden cruzarse y producir descendencia fértil.

specific heat The amount of heat required to raise the temperature of 1 kilogram of a material by 1 kelvin, which is equivalent to 1°C.
calor específico Cantidad de calor que se requiere para elevar la temperatura de 1 kilogramo de un material en 1°C.

spectrograph An instrument that separates light into colors and makes an image of the resulting spectrum.
espectrógrafo Instrumento que separa la luz en colores y crea una imagen del espectro resultante.

spectrum The range of wavelengths of electromagnetic waves.
espectro Gama de las longitudes de ondas electromagnéticas.

speed The distance an object travels per unit of time.
rapidez Distancia que viaja un objeto por unidad de tiempo.

sperm A male sex cell.
esperma Célula sexual masculina.

spiral galaxy A galaxy with a bulge in the middle and arms that spiral outward in a pinwheel pattern.
galaxia espiral Galaxia con una protuberancia en el centro y brazos que giran en espiral hacia el exterior, como un remolino.

spit A beach formed by longshore drift that projects like a finger out into the water.
banco de arena Playa formada por la deriva litoral, que se proyecta como un dedo dentro del agua.

spongy bone Layer of bone tissue that has many small spaces and is found just inside the layer of compact bone.
hueso esponjoso Capa de tejido óseo que tiene muchos orificios pequeños y que se encuentra próxima a la capa de hueso compacto.

spontaneous generation The mistaken idea that living things arise from nonliving sources.
generación espontánea Idea equivocada de que los seres vivos surgen de fuentes inertes.

spore In bacteria, protists, and fungi, a thick-walled, tiny cell capable of surviving unfavorable conditions and then growing into a new organism.
espora En las bacterias, los protistas y los hongos, una minúscula célula de paredes gruesas capaz de sobrevivir condiciones desfavorables y crecer hasta convertirse en un organismo.

sporophyte The stage in the life cycle of a plant in which the plant produces spores.
esporofito Etapa del ciclo vital de una planta en la que produce esporas.

spring tide The tide with the greatest difference between consecutive low and high tides.
marea viva Marea con la mayor diferencia entre las mareas altas y bajas consecutivas.

stalactite An icicle-like structure that hangs from the ceiling of a cavern.
estalactita Estructura en forma de carámbano que cuelga del techo de una caverna.

stalagmite A column-like form that grows upward from the floor of a cavern.
estalagmita Estructura en forma de columna que crece hacia arriba desde el suelo de una caverna.

stamen The male reproductive part of a flower.
estambre Parte reproductora masculina de una flor.

standing wave A wave that appears to stand in one place, even though it is two waves interfering as they pass through each other.
onda estacionaria Onda que parece permanecer en un lugar, y que en realidad es la interferencia de dos ondas que se atraviesan.

star A ball of hot gas, primarily hydrogen and helium, that undergoes nuclear fusion.
estrella Bola de gases calientes, principalmente hidrógeno y helio, en cuyo interior se produce una fusión nuclear.

static discharge The loss of static electricity as electric charges transfer from one object to another.
descarga estática Pérdida de la electricidad estática cuando las cargas eléctricas se transfieren de un cuerpo a otro.

static electricity A buildup of charges on an object.
electricidad estática Acumulación de cargas eléctricas en un cuerpo.

static friction Friction that acts between objects that are not moving.
fricción estática Fricción que actúa sobre los cuerpos que no están en movimiento.

steppe A prairie or grassland found in semiarid regions.
estepa Pradera o pastizal que se encuentra en las regiones semiáridas.

stimulus Any change or signal in the environment that can make an organism react in some way.
estímulo Cualquier cambio o señal del medio ambiente que puede causar una reacción en un organismo.

stoma A small opening on the underside of a leaf through which oxygen, water, and carbon dioxide can move.
estomas Pequeños orificios en la superficie inferior de la hoja a través de los cuales ocurre el intercambio de oxígeno y dióxido de carbono.

stomata A small opening on the underside of a leaf through which oxygen, water, and carbon dioxide can move.
estomas Pequeños orificios en la superficie inferior de la hoja a través de los cuales ocurre el intercambio de oxígeno y dióxido de carbono.

storm A violent disturbance in the atmosphere.
tormenta Alteración violenta en la atmósfera.

storm surge A "dome" of water that sweeps across the coast where a hurricane lands.
marejadas "Cúpula" de agua que se desplaza a lo largo de la costa donde aterriza un huracán.

stratosphere The second-lowest layer of Earth's atmosphere.
estratósfera Segunda capa de la atmósfera de la Tierra.

stratus Clouds that form in flat layers and often cover much of the sky.
estratos Nubes que aparecen como capas planas y que a menudo cubren gran parte del cielo.

streak The color of a mineral's powder.
raya Color del polvo de un mineral.

stream A channel through which water is continually flowing downhill.
riachuelo Canal por el cual el agua fluye continuamente cuesta abajo.

stress 1. A force that acts on rock to change its shape or volume. 2. The reaction of a person's body to potentiallythreatening, challenging, or disturbing events.
presión 1. Fuerza que actúa sobre las rocas y que cambia su forma o volumen. 2. estrés eacción del cuerpo de un individuo a sucesos como posibles amenazas, desafíos o trastornos.

striated muscle A muscle that appears banded; also called skeletal muscle.
músculo estriado Músculo con forma de franjas; también se llama músculo esquelético.

strike-slip fault A type of fault in which rocks on either side move past each other sideways with little up or down motion.
falla transcurrente Tipo de falla en la cual las rocas a ambos lados se deslizan horizontalmente en sentidos opuestos, con poco desplazamiento hacia arriba o abajo.

subarctic A climate zone that lies north of the humid continental climates.
subártico Zona climática situada al norte de las regiones de clima continental húmedo.

subduction The process by which oceanic crust sinks beneath a deep-ocean trench and back into the mantle at a convergent plate boundary.
subducción Proceso mediante el cual la corteza oceánica se hunde debajo de una fosa oceánica profunda y vuelve al manto por el borde de una placa convergente.

subjective Describes the influence of personal feelings on a decision or conclusion.
subjetivo Describe la influencia de sentimientos personales sobre una decisión o conclusión.

GLOSSARY

subjective reasoning Reasoning that is based on personal feelings or personal values.
razonamiento subjetivo Razonamiento basado en los sentimientos o los valores personales.

sublimation The change in state from a solid directly to a gas without passing through the liquid state.
sublimación Cambio del estado sólido directamente a gas, sin pasar por el estado líquido.

subscript A number in a chemical formula that tells the number of atoms in a molecule or the ratio of elements in a compound.
subíndice Número en una fórmula química que indica el número de átomos que tiene una molécula o la razón de elementos en un compuesto.

subsoil The layer of soil below topsoil that has less plant and animal matter than topsoil and contains mostly clay and other minerals.
subsuelo Capa de suelo debajo del suelo superior que tiene menos materia de plantas y animales que el suelo superior, y que principalmente contiene arcilla y otros minerales.

substance A single kind of matter that is pure and has a specific set of properties.
sustancia Tipo único de materia que es pura y tiene propiedades específicas.

succession The series of predictable changes that occur in a community over time.
sucesión Serie de cambios predecibles que ocurren en una comunidad a través del tiempo.

sunspot A dark area of gas on the sun's surface that is cooler than surrounding gases.
mancha solar Área gaseosa oscura de la superficie solar, que es más fría que los gases que la rodean.

supernova The brilliant explosion of a dying supergiant star.
supernova Explosión brillante de una estrella supergigante en extinción.

surface tension The result of an inward pull among the molecules of a liquid that brings the molecules on the surface closer together; causes the surface to act as if it has a thin skin.
tensión superficial Resultado de la atracción hacia el centro entre las moléculas de un líquido, que hace que las moléculas de la superficie se acerquen mucho, y que la superficie actúe como si tuviera una piel delgada.

surface wave A type of seismic wave that forms when P waves and S waves reach Earth's surface.
onda superficial Tipo de onda sísmica que se forma cuando las ondas P y las ondas S llegan a la superficie de la Tierra.

suspension A mixture in which particles can be seen and easily separated by settling or filtration.
suspensión Mezcla en la cual las partículas se pueden ver y separar fácilmente por fijación o por filtración.

sustainable use The use of a resource in ways that maintain the resource at a certain quality for a certain period of time.
uso sostenible Uso de un recurso que permite que ese recurso mantenga cierta calidad por un período de tiempo determinado.

swim bladder An internal gas-filled organ that helps a bony fish stabilize its body at different water depths.
vejiga natatoria Órgano interno lleno de gas que ayuda a un pez con esqueleto a estabilizar su cuerpo a distintas profundidades.

symbiosis Any relationship in which two species live closely together and that benefits at least one of the species.
simbiosis Cualquier relación en la cual dos especies viven muy cerca y al menos una de ellas se beneficia.

synapse The junction where one neuron can transfer an impulse to the next structure.
sinapsis Confluencia donde una neurona puede transferir un impulso a la siguiente estructura.

synthesis A chemical reaction in which two or more simple substances combine to form a new, more complex substance.
síntesis Reacción química en la que dos o más sustancias simples se combinan y forman una sustancia nueva más compleja.

system 1. A group of parts that work together as a whole. 2. A group of related parts that work together to perform a function or produce a result.
sistema 1. Partes de un grupo que trabajan en conjunto. 2. Grupo de partes relacionadas que trabajan conjuntamente para realizar una función o producir un resultado.

T

T cell A lymphocyte that identifies pathogens and distinguishes one pathogen from another.
célula T Linfocito que identifica a los patógenos y distingue un patógeno de otro.

tadpole The larval form of a frog or toad.
renacuajo Estado de larva de una rana o un sapo.

target cell A cell in the body that recognizes a hormone's chemical structure.
célula destinataria Célula del cuerpo que reconoce la estructura química de una hormona.

taxonomy The scientific study of how living things are classified.
taxonomía Estudio científico de cómo se clasifican los seres vivos.

telescope An optical instrument that forms enlarged images of distant objects.
telescopio Instrumento óptico que forma imágenes aumentadas de los objetos lejanos.

temperate zones The areas between the tropical and the polar zones.
área templada Áreas ubicadas entre las zonas tropical y polar.

temperature How hot or cold something is; a measure of the average energy of motion of the particles of a substance; the measure of the average kinetic energy of the particles of a substance.
temperatura Cuán caliente o frío es algo; medida de la energía de movimiento promedio de las partículas de una sustancia; medida de la energía cinética promedio de las partículas de una sustancia.

temperature inversion A condition in which a layer of warm air traps polluted air close to Earth's surface.
inversión térmica Condición en la que una capa de aire caliente atrapa aire contaminado cerca de la superficie de la Tierra.

tendon Strong connective tissue that attaches muscle to bone.
tendón Tejido conectivo resistente que une un músculo a un hueso.

tension Stress that stretches rock so that it becomes thinner in the middle.
tensión Fuerza que estira una roca, de modo que es más delgada en el centro.

terrestrial planets The name often given to the four inner planets: Mercury, Venus, Earth, and Mars.
planetas telúricos Nombre dado normalmente a los cuatro planetas interiores: Mercurio, Venus, Tierra y Marte.

testes Organ of the male reproductive system in which sperm and testosterone are produced.
testículos Órgano del sistema reproductor masculino en el que se producen el esperma y la testosterona.

testis Organ of the male reproductive system in which sperm and testosterone are produced.

testículo Órgano del sistema reproductor masculino en el que se producen el esperma y la testosterona.

testosterone A hormone produced by the testes that controls the development of sperm and adult male characteristics.
testosterona Hormona producida por los testículos que controla el desarrollo del esperma y las características del hombre adulto.

texture The look and feel of a rock's surface, determined by the size, shape, and pattern of a rock's grains.
textura Apariencia y sensación producida por la superficie de una roca, determinadas por el tamaño, la forma y el patrón de los granos de la roca.

thermal energy The total kinetic and potential energy of all the particles of an object.
energía térmica Energía cinética y potencial total de las partículas de un cuerpo.

thermal expansion The expansion of matter when it is heated.
expansión térmica Expansión de la materia cuando se calienta.

thermogram An image that shows regions of different temperatures in different colors.
termograma Imagen que muestra regiones de distintas temperaturas con distintos colores.

thermometer An instrument used to measure temperature.
termómetro Instrumento que se usa para medir la temperatura.

thermosphere The outermost layer of Earth's atmosphere.
termósfera Capa exterior de la atmósfera de la Tierra.

third prong The round prong of a plug that connects any metal pieces in an appliance to the safety grounding wire of a building.
tercera terminal Terminal redondeado de un enchufe que conecta cualquier pieza de metal de un artefacto con el cable a tierra de un edificio.

threatened species A species that could become endangered in the near future.
especie amenazada Especie que puede llegar a estar en peligro de extinción en el futuro próximo.

thrust The reaction force that propels a rocket forward.
empuje Fuerza de reacción que propulsa un cohete hacia delante.

GLOSSARY

thunderstorm A small storm often accompanied by heavy precipitation and frequent thunder and lightning.
tronada Pequeña tormenta acompañada de fuertes precipitaciones y frecuentes rayos y truenos.

tide The periodic rise and fall of the level of water in the ocean.
marea La subida y bajada periódica del nivel de agua del océano.

till The sediments deposited directly by a glacier.
arcilla glacial Sedimentos depositados directamente por un glaciar.

tissue A group of similar cells that perform a specific function.
tejido Grupo de células semejantes que realizan una función específica.

topsoil The crumbly, topmost layer of soil made up of clay and other minerals and humus (nutrients and decaying plant and animal matter).
suelo superior Capa superior desmenuzable del suelo formada por arcilla, otros minerales y humus (nutrientes y materia orgánica de origen vegetal y animal).

tornado A rapidly whirling, funnel-shaped cloud that reaches down to touch Earth's surface.
tornado Nube con forma de embudo que gira rápidamente y que desciende hasta tocar la superficie terrestre.

toxin A poison that can harm an organism.
toxina Veneno que puede dañar un organismo.

trace fossil A type of fossil that provides evidence of the activities of ancient organisms.
vestigios fósiles Tipo de fósil que presenta evidencia de las actividades de los organismos antiguos.

trachea The windpipe; a passage through which air moves in the respiratory system.
tráquea Conducto por el cual circula el aire en el sistema respiratorio.

trait A specific characteristic that an organism can pass to its offspring through its genes.
rasgo Característica específica que un organismo puede transmitir a sus descendientes a través de los genes.

transfer RNA Type of RNA in the cytoplasm that carries an amino acid to the ribosome during protein synthesis.

ARN de transferencia Tipo de ARN del citoplasma que lleva un aminoácido al ribosoma durante la síntesis de proteínas.

transform boundary A plate boundary where two plates move past each other in opposite directions.
borde de transformación Borde de una placa donde dos placas se deslizan, en sentidos opuestos, y se pasan la una a la otra.

transformer A device that increases or decreases voltage, which often consists of two separate coils of insulated wire wrapped around an iron core.
transformador Aparato que aumenta o disminuye el voltaje, que consiste de dos bobinas de alambre aislado y devanado sobre un núcleo de hierro.

translucent A type of material that scatters light as it passes through.
material traslúcido Material que dispersa la luz cuando ésta lo atraviesa.

transparent A type of material that transmits light without scattering it.
material transparente Material que transmite luz sin dispersarla.

transpiration The process by which water is lost through a plant's leaves.
transpiración Proceso por el cual las hojas de una planta pierden agua.

transverse wave A wave that moves the medium at right angles to the direction in which the wave travels.
onda transversal Onda que desplaza a un medio perpendicularmente a la dirección en la que viaja la onda.

trench A deep, steep-sided canyon in the ocean floor.
fosa Cañón profundo, de lados empinados, en el suelo oceánico.

tributary A stream or river that flows into a larger river.
afluente Río o arroyo que desemboca en un río más grande.

triple bond A chemical bond formed when atoms share three pairs of electrons.
enlace triple Enlace químico formado cuando los átomos comparten tres pares de electrones.

tropical (air mass) A warm air mass that forms in the tropics and has low air pressure.

masa de aire tropical Masa de aire templado que se forma en los trópicos y cuya presión atmosférica es baja.

tropical zone The area near the equator between about 23.5° north latitude and 23.5° south latitude.
zona tropical Área cercana al ecuador entre aproximadamente los 23.5° de latitud norte y los 23.5° de latitud sur.

tropism The response of a plant toward or away from a stimulus.
tropismo espuesta de una planta acercándose o apartándose del estímulo.

troposphere The lowest layer of Earth's atmosphere.
troposfera Capa más inferior de la atmósfera de la Tierra.

trough The lowest part of a transverse wave.
valle Parte más baja de una onda transversal.

tsunami A giant wave usually caused by an earthquake beneath the ocean floor.
tsunami Ola gigantesca, generalmente provocada por un sismo que ocurrió debajo de la cuenca oceánica.

tumor A mass of rapidly dividing cells that can damage surrounding tissue.
tumor Masa de células que se dividen rápidamente y que puede dañar los tejidos que la rodean.

tundra An extremely cold, dry biome climate region characterized by short, cool summers and bitterly cold winters.
tundra Bioma de la región climática extremadamente fría y seca, que se caracteriza por veranos cortos y frescos e inviernos sumamente fríos.

U

---

ultrasound Sound waves with frequencies above 20,000 Hz.
ultrasonido Ondas sonoras con frecuencias mayores de 20,000 Hz.

ultraviolet radiation Electromagnetic waves with wavelengths that are shorter than visible light but longer than X-rays.
radiación ultravioleta Ondas electromagnéticas con longitudes de onda más cortas que la luz visible, pero más largas que los rayos X.

ultraviolet rays Electromagnetic waves with wavelengths shorter than visible light but longer than X-rays.

rayos ultravioleta Ondas electromagnéticas con longitudes de onda más cortas que la luz visible pero mas largas que los rayos X.

ultraviolet rays (radiation) Electromagnetic waves with wavelengths shorter than visible light but longer than X-rays.
rayos (radiación) ultravioleta Ondas electromagnéticas con longitudes de onda más cortas que la luz visible pero más largas que los rayos X.

umbilical cord A ropelike structure that forms between the embryo or fetus and the placenta.
cordón umbilical Estructura con forma de cuerda que se forma en el útero entre el embrión o feto y la placenta.

umbra The darkest part of a shadow.
umbra La parte más oscura de una sombra.

unconformity A gap in the geologic record that shows where rock layers have been lost due to erosion.
discordancia Interrupción en el récord geológico que muestra dónde las capas rocosas se han perdido a causa de la erosión.

understory A layer of shorter trees and vines that grows in the shade of a forest canopy.
sotobosque Capa de árboles de poca altura y plantas trepadoras que crecen bajo la sombra del dosel de un bosque.

unicellular Made of a single cell.
unicelular Compuesto por una sola célula.

uniformitarianism The geologic principle that the same geologic processes that operate today operated in the past to change Earth's surface.
uniformitarianismo Principio geológico que enuncia que los mismos procesos geológicos que cambian la superficie de la Tierra en la actualidad ocurrieron en el pasado.

universe All of space and everything in it.
universo Todo el espacio y todo lo que hay en él.

unsaturated zone The layer of rocks and soil above the water table in which the pores contain air as well as water.
zona insaturada Capa de rocas y suelo encima del nivel freático en la que los poros contienen aire además de agua.

urea A chemical that comes from the breakdown of proteins.
urea Sustancia química que resulta de la descomposición de proteínas.

GLOSSARY

ureter A narrow tube that carries urine from one of the kidneys to the urinary bladder.
uretra Conducto estrecho que lleva la orina desde uno de los riñones a la vejiga urinaria.

urethra A small tube through which urine leaves the body.
uretra Conducto pequeño a través del cual la orina sale del cuerpo.

urinary bladder A sacklike muscular organ that stores urine until it is eliminated from the body.
vejiga urinaria Órgano muscular con forma de saco que almacena la orina hasta que se elimine del cuerpo.

urine A watery fluid produced by the kidneys that contains urea and other wastes.
orina Fluido acuoso producido por los riñones que contiene urea y otros materiales de desecho.

uterus The hollow muscular organ of the female reproductive system in which a fertilized egg develops.
útero Órgano muscular hueco del sistema reproductor femenino en el que se desarrolla un óvulo fertilizado.

—————————— **V** ——————————

vaccination The process by which harmless antigens are deliberately introduced into a person's body to produce active immunity; also called immunization.
vacunación Proceso por el cual antígenos inocuos se introducen deliberadamente en el cuerpo de una persona para producir una inmunidad activa; también se le llama inmunización.

vaccine A substance used in a vaccination that consists of pathogens that have been weakened or killed but can still trigger the body to produce chemicals that destroy the pathogens.
vacuna Sustancia que se inyecta en la vacunación; consiste de patógenos débiles o muertos que pueden estimular al cuerpo a producir sustancias químicas que destruyan esos patógenos.

vacuole A sac-like organelle that stores water, food, and other materials.
vacuola Orgánulo en forma de bolsa que almacena agua, alimentos y otros materiales.

vacuum A place that is empty of all matter.
vacío Lugar en donde no existe materia.

vagina A muscular passageway leading to the outside of a female's body; also called the birth canal.
vagina Pasaje muscular que se extiende hasta una abertura del cuerpo de una mujer; también llamada canal de nacimiento.

valence electrons The electrons that are in the highest energy level of an atom and that are involved in chemical bonding.
electrones de valencia Electrones que tienen el nivel más alto de energía de un átomo y que intervienen en los enlaces químicos.

valley glacier A long, narrow glacier that forms when snow and ice build up in a mountain valley.
glaciar de valle Glaciar largo y estrecho que se forma por la acumulación de hielo y nieve en el valle de una montaña.

valve A flap of tissue in the heart or a vein that prevents blood from flowing backward.
válvula Lámina de tejido del corazón o de una vena que impide que la sangre fluya hacia atrás.

vaporization The change of state from a liquid to a gas.
vaporización Cambio del estado de líquido a gas.

variable A factor that can change in an experiment.
variable Factor que puede cambiar en un experimento.

variation Any difference between individuals of the same species.
variación Cualquier diferencia entre individuos de la misma especie.

vascular plant A plant that has true vascular tissue for transporting materials.
planta vascular Planta que tiene tejido vascular verdadero para el transporte de materiales.

vascular tissue The internal transporting tissue in some plants that is made up of tubelike structures that carry water, food, and minerals.
tejido vascular Tejido interno de algunas plantas compuesto de estructuras tubulares que transportan agua, alimentos y minerales.

vein 1. A narrow deposit of a mineral that is sharply different from the surrounding rock. 2. A blood vessel that carries blood back to the heart.
vena 1. Placa delgada de un mineral que es marcadamente distinto a la roca que lo rodea. 2. Vaso sanguíneo que transporta la sangre al corazón.

velocity Speed in a given direction.
velocidad Rapidez en una dirección dada.

vent The opening through which molten rock and gas leave a volcano.
ventiladero Abertura a través de la que la roca derretida y los gases salen de un volcán.

ventricle A lower chamber of the heart that pumps blood out to the lungs or body.
ventrículo Cavidad inferior del corazón que bombea sangre a los pulmones o el cuerpo.

vertebrae The bones that make up the backbone of an organism. In humans, one of the 26 bones that make up the backbone.
vértebras Huesos que componen la columna de un organismo. En los seres humanos, cada uno de los 26 huesos que componen la columna vertebral.

vertebrate An animal with a backbone.
vertebrado Animal con columna vertebral.

vibration A repeated back-and-forth or up-and-down motion.
vibración Movimiento repetido hacia delante y hacia atrás o hacia arriba y hacia abajo.

villi Tiny finger-shaped structures that cover the inner surface of the small intestine and provide a large surface area through which digested food is absorbed.
vellosidades Pequeñas estructuras con forma de dedo que cubren la superficie interna del intestino delgado y proporcionan una superficie amplia a través de la cual se absorbe el alimento digerido.

virtual image An upright image formed where rays of light appear to come from.
imagen virtual Imagen vertical que se forma desde donde parecen provenir los rayos de luz.

virus A tiny, nonliving particle that enters and then reproduces inside a living cell.
virus Partícula diminuta inerte que entra en una célula viva y luego se reproduce dentro de ella.

viscosity A liquid's resistance to flowing.
viscosidad Resistencia a fluir que presenta un líquido.

visible light Electromagnetic radiation that can be seen with the unaided eye.
luz visible Radiación electromagnética que se puede ver a simple vista.

vocal cords Folds of connective tissue that stretch across the opening of the larynx and produce a person's voice.
cuerdas vocales Pliegues de tejido conector que se extienden a lo largo de la abertura de la laringe y que producen la voz de una persona.

volcanic neck A deposit of hardened magma in a volcano's pipe.
cuello volcánico Depósito de magma solidificada en la chimenea de un volcán.

volcano A weak spot in the crust where magma has come to the surface.
volcán Punto débil en la corteza por donde el magma escapa hacia la superficie.

voltage The difference in electrical potential energy per charge between two places in a circuit.
voltaje Diferencia en el potencial eléctrico que hay entre dos áreas de un circuito.

volume The amount of space that matter occupies.
volumen Cantidad de espacio que ocupa la materia.

voluntary muscle A muscle that is under conscious control.
músculo voluntario Músculo que se puede controlar conscientemente.

W

water cycle The continual movement of water among Earth's atmosphere, oceans, and land surface through evaporation, condensation, and precipitation.
ciclo del agua Circulación continua del agua por la atmósfera, los océanos y la superficie de la Tierra mediante la evaporación, la condensación y la precipitación.

watershed The land area that supplies water to a river system.
cuenca hidrográfica Área de terreno que suministra agua a un sistema fluvial.

water table The top of the saturated zone, or depth to the groundwater under Earth's surface.
nivel freático Límite superior de la zona saturada, es decir de la profundidad de las aguas freáticas del subsuelo.

water vapor Water in the form of a gas.
vapor de agua Agua en forma de gas.

water vascular system A system of fluid-filled tubes in an echinoderm's body.
sistema vascular de agua Sistema de vasos llenos de líquido en el cuerpo de un equinodermo.

watt The unit of power when one joule of work is done in one second.
vatio Unidad de potencia equivalente a un julio por segundo.

GLOSSARY

wave 1. A disturbance that transfers energy from place to place. **2.** The movement of energy through a body of water.
onda 1. Perturbación que transfiere energía de un lugar a otro. **2.** Movimiento de energía por un fluido.

wave height The vertical distance from the crest of a wave to the trough.
altura de una ola Distancia vertical desde la cresta de una ola hasta el valle.

wavelength The distance between two corresponding parts of a wave, such as the distance between two crests.
longitud de onda Distancia entre dos partes correspondientes de una onda, por ejemplo la distancia entre dos crestas.

weather The condition of Earth's atmosphere at a particular time and place.
tiempo meteorológico Condición de la atmósfera terrestre en un momento y lugar determinado.

weathering The chemical and physical processes that break down rock and other substances.
desgaste Procesos químicos y físicos que erosionan la roca y descomponen otras sustancias.

wedge A simple machine that is an inclined plane that moves.
cuña Máquina simple que consiste de un plano inclinado que se mueve.

weight A measure of the force of gravity acting on an object.
peso Medida de la fuerza de gravedad que actúa sobre un objeto.

wheel and axle A simple machine that consists of two attached circular or cylindrical objects that rotate about a common axis, each one with a different radius.
rueda y eje Máquina simple que consiste en dos objetos circulares o cilíndricos unidos, de diferente radio, que giran en torno a un eje común.

white dwarf The blue-white hot core of a star that is left behind after its outer layers have expanded and drifted out into space.

enana blanca Núcleo caliente y azul blanquecino de una estrella que queda después de que sus capas externas se han expandido y esparcido por el espacio.

wind The horizontal movement of air from an area of high pressure to an area of lower pressure.
viento Movimiento horizontal de aire de un área de alta presión a una de menor presión.

wind-chill factor A measure of cooling combining temperature and wind speed.
factor de enfriamiento por viento Medida del enfriamiento que combina la temperatura y la velocidad del viento.

windward The side of a mountain range that faces the oncoming wind.
barlovento Lado de una cadena montañosa donde pega el viento de frente.

work Force exerted on an object that causes it to move.
trabajo Fuerza que se ejerce sobre un cuerpo para moverlo.

X

X-rays Electromagnetic waves with wavelengths shorter than ultraviolet rays but longer than gamma rays.
rayos X Ondas electromagnéticas con longitudes de onda más cortas que los rayos ultravioleta pero más largas que los rayos gamma.

xylem The vascular tissue through which water and minerals move in some plants.
xilema Tejido vascular de algunas plantas por el que circulan agua y nutrientes.

Z

zygote A fertilized egg, produced by the joining of a sperm and an egg.
cigoto Óvulo fertilizado, producido por la unión de un espermatozoide y un óvulo.

INDEX

Page numbers for key terms are printed in **boldface** type.

INDEX

Page numbers for key terms are printed in **boldface** type.

INDEX

Page numbers for key terms are printed in **boldface** type.

Index • Index • Index • Index • Index • Index • Index • Index • Index • Index • Index

INDEX

Page numbers for key terms are printed in **boldface** type.

INDEX

INDEX

Page numbers for key terms are printed in **boldface** type.

INDEX

ACKNOWLEDGMENTS

Staff Credits

The people who made up the *Interactive Science* team—representing composition services, core design digital and multimedia production services, digital product development, editorial, editorial services, manufacturing, and production—are listed below:

Jan Van Aarsen, Samah Abadir, Ernie Albanese, Chris Anton, Zareh Artinian, Bridget Binstock, Suzanne Biron, Niki Birbilis, MJ Black, Nancy Bolsover, Stacy Boyd, Jim Brady, Laura Brancky, Katherine Bryant, Michael Burstein, Pradeep Byram, Jessica Chase, Jonathan Cheney, Sitha Chhor, Arthur Ciccone, Allison Cook-Bellistri, Brandon Cole, Karen Corliss, Rebecca Cottingham, AnnMarie Coyne, Bob Craton, Chris Deliee, Paul Delsignore, Michael Di Maria, Diane Dougherty, Nancy Duffner, Kristen Ellis, Kelly Engel, Theresa Eugenio, Amanda Ferguson, Jorgensen Fernandez, Kathryn Fobert, Alicia Franke, Louise Gachet, Julia Gecha, Mark Geyer, Steve Gobbell, Paula Gogan-Porter, Jeffrey Gong, Sandra Graff, Robert M. Graham, Maureen Griffin, Adam Groffman, Lynette Haggard, Christian Henry, Karen Holtzman, Guy Huff, Susan Hutchinson, Sharon Inglis, Marian Jones, Sumy Joy, Chris Kammer, Sheila Kanitsch, Courtenay Kelley, Chris Kennedy, Toby Klang, Alyse Kondrat, Greg Lam, Russ Lappa, Margaret LaRaia, David Leistensnider, Ben Leveillee, Thea Limpus, Charles Luey, Dotti Marshall, Kathy Martin, Robyn Matzke, John McClure, Mary Beth McDaniel, Krista McDonald, Tim McDonald, Rich McMahon, Cara McNally, Bernadette McQuilkin, Melinda Medina, Angelina Mendez, Maria Milczarek, Claudi Mimo, Mike Napieralski, Deborah Nicholls, Dave Nichols, Anthony Nuccio, William Oppenheimer, Jodi O'Rourke, Julie Orr, Ameer Padshah, Lorie Park, Celio Pedrosa, Jonathan Penyack, Linda Zust Reddy, Jennifer Reichlin, Stephen Rider, Charlene Rimsa, Walter Rodriguez, Stephanie Rogers, Marcy Rose, Rashid Ross, Anne Rowsey, Manuel Sanchez, Logan Schmidt, Amanda Seldera, Laurel Smith, Nancy Smith, Ted Smykal, Sandy Schneider, Emily Soltanoff, Cindy Strowman, Dee Sunday, Barry Tomack, Elizabeth Tustian, Patricia Valencia, Ana Sofia Villaveces, Stephanie Wallace, Amanda Watters, Christine Whitney, Brad Wiatr, Heidi Wilson, Heather Wright, James Yagelski, Tim Yetzina, Rachel Youdelman.

Photographs

Every effort has been made to secure permission and provide appropriate credit for photographic material. The publisher deeply regrets any omission and pledges to correct errors called to its attention in subsequent editions.

Unless otherwise acknowledged, all photographs are the property of Pearson Education, Inc.

Photo locators denoted as follows: Top (T), Top right (TR), Top left (TL), Bottom (B), Bottom left (BL), Bottom right (BR), Right (R), Left (L), Center (C), Background (Bkgd)

Front Cover
Alfred Pasieka/Science Photo Library/Photo Researchers, Inc.

Front Matter
vi Michael Newton/Robert Harding, Newscom; **vii** Stephen Dalton, Photo Researchers, Inc./Science Source; **ix** Marko König, Corbis; **x** lazyllama/Shutterstock; **xi** Brian Snyder, Thomson Reuters (Markets) LLC; **xii** spread, Nick Suydam/Alamy; **xiii** Corbis; **xv** Eric Nguyen, Photo Researchers, Inc./Science Source; **xvii** J. Clarke, Z. Levay, NASA; **xviii** Narcis Parfenti/Fotolia, Ulrich Mueller/Shutterstock; **xix** Suzanne Tucker/Shutterstock

Chapter 1 Plants
2–3 (B) Laurent Bouvet, AGE Fotostock America Inc.; **5** (B) Nigel Bean, Nature Picture Library, (TC) Howard Rice, Dorling Kindersley Limited; **9** (L) Paul Paladin, iStockphoto, (R) Theodore Clutter, Photo Researchers, Inc./Science Source; **10** (Inset) Perennou Nuridsany, Photo Researchers, Inc./Science Source, (TL) Shutterstock; **12** Kjell B Sandved, Photo Researchers, Inc./Science Source; **15** (BR) Czamfir, Fotolia, (Inset) John Serrao, Photo Researchers, Inc./Science Source; **16** (BL) Daniel Vega, Getty Images, Inc., (TL) Adrian Davies, Nature Picture Library; **17** (Bkgd) Howard Rice, Getty Images, Inc., (Inset) David Webb, Webb, David T.; **19** (L) Philippe Clement, Nature Picture Library, (R) Albert Aanensen, Nature Picture Library; **21** (B) M Philip Kahl, Photo Researchers, Inc./Science Source, (BC) Joanna Pecha, iStockphoto, (T) Christine M Douglas, Dorling Kindersley Limited, (TC) Peter Anderson, Dorling Kindersley Limited; **22** (BL) Howard Rice, Dorling Kindersley Limited, (R) Subbotina Anna, Shutterstock, (TL) K. Kaplin, Shutterstock; **24** Baylis, Fletcher, Photo Researchers, Inc./Science Source; **25** (L) Lynwood M Chace, Photo Researchers, Inc./Science Source, (R) Derek Croucher, Alamy; **26** (L) Peter Hestbaek, Shutterstock; **28–29** Pakhnyushcha, Shutterstock; **32** (BC) Niall Benvie, Nature Picture Library, (BL) Nature Picture Library, (BR) Simon Williams, Nature Picture Library, (TC) Glenn Bartley, Alamy, (TL) Kim Taylor, Nature Picture Library, (TR) Barry Mansell, Nature Picture Library; **34** (C) Corbis; **37** (B) Christine M Douglas, Dorling Kindersley Limited, (T) Michael Newton/Robert Harding, Newscom; **38–39** Andrew Browne/Ecoscene, Corbis; **39** (B) David R Frazier, Alamy, (C) Breck P Kent, Kent, Breck P.; **40** (Inset) Nigel Cattlin, Alamy (BL) Medio Images/Photodisc/PhotoLibrary Group Inc.; **41** (BC) Peter Chapwick, Dorling Kindersley Limited, (BR) Peter Chapwick, Dorling Kindersley Limited, (L) Nature Picture Library, (TC) Peter Chadwick, Dorling Kindersley Limited, (TR) Peter Chadwick, Dorling Kindersley Limited; **44** Maryann Frazier, Photo Researchers, Inc./Science Source; **45** Mark Turner, Getty Images, Inc.; **46** Theodore Clutter, Photo Researchers, Inc./Science Source; **48** Gary K Smith, Nature Picture Library; **49** Albinger, AGE Fotostock America Inc.; **50** David Tipling, Nature Picture Library; **52** (B) Nature Picture Library, (T) Kjell B Sandved, Photo Researchers, Inc./Science Source; **56** (BL) Tim Messick, iStockphoto, (BR) Susumu Nishinaga, Photo Researchers, Inc./Science Source, (CL) iStockphoto, (TL) Tim Messick, iStockphoto; **57** Ames, NASA

Chapter 2 Animal Life Processes
58 David Grossman, Alamy; **58–59** Stephen Dalton, Photo Researchers, Inc./Science Source; **61** (B) Will, Deni McIntyre, Corbis, (BC) Stephen Dalton, Photo Researchers, Inc./Science Source; (T) HorusVisual/Fotolia, (TC) Fotolia; **64** (B) Alan Carey, Corbis, (T) David A. Northcott, Corbis; **65** Denny Allen, Getty Images, Inc.; **66** (BL) Frank Greenaway, Dorling Kindersley Limited, (BR) Keith Leighton, Alamy, (L) Warren Photographic, (TR) Wayne Mckown, Dreamstime LLC; **66–67** Shutterstock; **68** (L) Fotolia, (R) Steve Bloom, Alamy; **70** Robert

Marien, Corbis; **71** Stephen Dalton, Photo Researchers, Inc./Science Source; **74** (BL) Geoff Brightling, Dorling Kindersley Limited; **74–75** Dave Watts, Nature Picture Library; **75** (BR) Mark Conlin, Alamy, (L) Alamy, (TR) Rod Planck, Photo Researchers, Inc./Science Source; **76** (B) Alamy, (T) D. Hurst, Alamy; **77** (L) Delpho, M./Arco Images GmbH/Alamy, (C) Steve Goodwin, iStockphoto, (R) Peter Burian, Corbis; **79** (BL) Alamy, (BR) Mark Conlin, Alamy, (TL) Will, Deni McIntyre, Corbis, (TR) Alamy; **80** (B) Smaointe, Alamy, (R) Alamy, (TL) Charles Stirling, Alamy; **80–81** Remi Benali, Corbis; **81** (BR) Daryl Balfour, Alamy, (TL) Juergen Hasenkopf, Alamy, (TR) Fotolia; **82** (L) Gijs Bekenkamp, Alamy, (R) Bernd Zoller, Alamy; **82–83** Getty Images, Inc.; **83** (Bkgd) D. Hurst, Alamy, (BL) Ellen McKnight, Alamy, (CL) Alamy, (TL) Bob Jensen, Alamy, (TR) Rolf Richardson, Alamy; **86–87** Kenneth M Highfill, Photo Researchers, Inc./Science Source; **88–89** Mike Raabe/Design Pics/Getty Images; **89** (T) Warren Photographic; **90** (L) Joel Sartore, National Geographic Stock, (R) Eric Isselée, iStockphoto; **91** (BL) Getty Images, Inc., (BR) Getty Images, Inc., (C) Keith Levit, Shutterstock, (TC) PhotoDisc, (TL) PhotoDisc, (TR) Nancy Nehring, Getty Images, Inc.; **92–93** blickwinkel, Alamy, **326** (BL) Fotolia, (BR) Warren Photographic, (TL) Gregory G. Dimijian, Photo Researchers, Inc./Science Source; **93** (BL) Louise Murray, Alamy, (T) AGE Fotostock America Inc.; **94** (TL) Steve Kaufman, Getty Images, Inc., (TR) Gary Lewis, Getty Images, Inc., (BL) George Grall, National Geographic Stock, (TL) Rich Reid, National Geographic Stock; **100** (L) Kathy Keatley Garvey, University of California Davis, (R) Kathy Keatley Garvey, University of California Davis; **101** Colin Milkins, Getty Images, Inc.; **102** (B) Paul Bricknell, Dorling Kindersley Limited; (T) Corbis; **103** (B) David Chapman, Alamy, (T) K L Kohn, Shutterstock; **106–107** Oxford Scientific, Getty Images, Inc.; **108** David G Knowles, Knowles, David; **109** Juniors Bildarchiv, AGE Fotostock America Inc.; **111** (Bkgd) Andrew J. Martinez, Photo Researchers, Inc./Science Source, (Inset L) George D. Lepp, Corbis, (Inset R) Alistair Dove, Alamy; **112** (C) Shutterstock, (L) Rick, Nora Bowers, Alamy (R) Rick, Nora Bowers, Alamy; **113** (L) Thomas Kitchin, Victoria Hurst, Alamy, (R) Victoria Hurst, Thomas Kitchin, Alamy; **115** Patricia Fogden, Corbis; **116** (B) Keren Su, China Span, Alamy, (T) Jin Young Lee, Shutterstock; **118** (B) Rolf Richardson, Alamy, (C) Rod Planck, Photo Researchers, Inc./Science Source, (T) Steve Bloom, Alamy; **120** Alamy; **122** Mark Conlin, Alamy; **123** Niels Poulsen, Alamy

Chapter 3 Populations and Communities

127 (B) Christian Kosanetzky, Alamy, (BC) AGE Fotostock America Inc., (TC) Tom Brakefield, Getty Images, Inc.; **130** (TR) David Haring, DUPC, Getty Images, (B) Ruth Hofshi, Photostock Israel, Alamy, (BL) Köhler, Jörn, (BR) A Visage, J Visage, Getty Images, Inc.; **131** (Bkgd) Bruno Morandi, Corbis, (Inset) Tom Brakefield, Getty Images, Inc.; **134–135** Jason O. Watson, Alamy; **136** Thomas Ash, Shutterstock; **137** Chris Johns, National Geographic Stock; **138** Tom Brakefield, Getty Images, Inc.; **139** Kim Taylor, Nature Picture Library; **141** Wichita Eagle, Getty Images; **142** (T) Tim Mannakee, Corbis; **142–143** (Bkgd) Catolla/Fotolia; **143** (Inset) Taylor S. Kennedy, National Geographic Stock; **144** (C) Alex Wild Photography; **147** (BR) Jim Zipp, Photo Researchers, Inc./Science Source, (CR) Jim Zipp, Photo Researchers, Inc./Science Source, (L) Michael P. Gadomski, Photo Researchers, Inc./Science Source,

(TR) Glenn Bartley, Corbis; **148** (BL) Klaas Lingbeek-van Kranen, Getty Images, Inc., (BR) Christian Kosanetzky, Alamy, (CR) iStockphoto, (T) Bill Curtsinger, National Geographic Stock; **149** (BL) Alamy, (BR) Photo Researchers, Inc./Science Source, (CL) Ethan Daniels, Alamy, (CR) SuperStock, (TL) Jeff Hunter, Getty Images, Inc., (TR) Michael D. Kern, Nature Picture Library; **151** (L) Mogens Trolle, Shutterstock, (R) Steve Byland, Fotolia; **152** (L) Jeff Foott/Getty Images, (TR) WaterFrame/Alamy, (BR) USDA/ARS; **153** (B) Dietmar Nill, Nature Picture Library, (C) Bruce Dale, Getty Images, Inc., (T) Steve Jones, Corbis; **154** (BR) WaterFrame/Alamy; **158** Roger del Moral, del Moral, Roger; **159** (B) Chris Gomersall, Alamy, (T) Dave Jacobs, Les Jacobs, Getty Images, Inc.

Chapter 4 Ecosystems and Biomes

160–161 Marko König, Corbis; **163** (BC) Karen Huntt, Getty Images, Inc., (T) Dorling Kindersley Limited; **168** Ian McAllister, Getty Images, Inc.; **169** (Bkgd) Jerome Wexler, Photo Researchers, Inc./Science Source, (Inset) Ted Kinsman, Photo Researchers, Inc./Science Source; **172** (B) Peter Blottman, iStockphoto, (C) Jerry Young, Dorling Kindersley Limited, (T) Dorling Kindersley Limited; **173** (crayfish) Frank Greenaway, Dorling Kindersley Limited, (fox) Dorling Kindersley Limited, (frog) Geoff Brightling, Dorling Kindersley Limited, (grass) iStockphoto, (grasshopper) Dorling Kindersley Limited, (heron) Judy Ledbetter, iStockphoto, (shrew) Dorling, Kindersley Limited, (snail) Nicholas Homrich, iStockphoto, (snake) Jerry Young, Dorling Kindersley Limited, Neil Fletcher, Dorling Kindersley Limited; **174** (B) Jane Burton, Kim Taylor, Dorling Kindersley Limited, (BC) Frank Greenaway, Dorling Kindersley Limited, (T) Eric Isselée, iStockphoto, (TC) Dorling Kindersley Limited; **178** (C) Juniors Bildarchiv, Alamy; **180** Emma Firth, Dorling Kindersley Limited; **182** Dr. Paul A. Zahl, Photo Researchers, Inc./Science Source; **186** Stefan Wackerhagen, Alamy; **187** (Bkgd) Karen Huntt, Getty Images, Inc., (Inset) Getty Images, Inc.; **188** (C) Ed Reschke, Getty Images, Inc.; **188–189** Peter Chadwick, Dorling Kindersley Limited; **189** (C) Theo Allofs, Corbis; **190** (C) Alamy; **191** (TR) M. Lorenz, Shutterstock, (B) Tim Shepard, Dorling Kindersley Limited; **192** (B) Tom Brakefield, Corbis, (T) Randy Green, Getty Images, Inc.; **193** Deberarr, Fotolia; **194** Blickwinkel, Alamy; **196** (C) Sandy Felsenthal, Corbis; **197** (Bkgd) Pier, Getty Images, Inc.; **200** (T) iStockphoto; **201** Eric Wong, Dreamstime LLC; **205** (L) Jonathan Davies/iStockphoto

Chapter 5 Balance Within Ecosystems

206–207 (Bkgd) lazyllama/Shutterstock; **209** (T) Photodisc/Getty Images; **209** (m1) AGE Fotostock/SuperStock; **212** Ilene MacDonald/Alamy; **218** (Inset) IK Lee/Alamy, (Bkgd) Tengku Mohd Yusof/Alamy; **219** Courtesy of Adrian Burke/Corbis; **220** Peter Miller/Getty Images; **221** (I) Getty Images, (m) Frank Burek/Corbis, (R) Philip Gould/Corbis; **222** (B) Courtesy of Sean Gardner/Corbis; **224** (B) Jerome Whittingham/iStockphoto; **224** Cary Anderson/Getty Images; **225** (L) Burke/Triolo Productions/Brand X/Corbis, (BC) kikkerdirk/fotolia, (TM) Photographer Olympus/iStockphoto, (TR) iStockphoto, (BR) iStockphoto; **227** Kiamsoon/iStockphoto; **228** mbongo/Fotolia; **229** (I) iStockphoto, (R) David A. Hardy/Photo Researchers, Inc.; **231** (TL) Markus Botzek/Zefa/Corbis,

ACKNOWLEDGMENTS

(TC) James Caldwell/Alamy, (TR) Courtesy of belgerdy/fotolia, (BL) Kim Mitchell/Whooping Crane Eastern Partnership, (BM) Operation Migration, (BR) Jason Hahn; **232–233** Wolfgang Amri/Shutterstock; **234** Ken Findlay/Dorling Kindersley; **236** (I) Martin M. Bruce/SuperStock, (R) Geoff du Feu/Getty images; **237** Inge Johnssolamy; **238** Burke/Triolo Productions/BrandX/Corbis

Chapter 6 Forces
244–245 Brian Snyder, Thomson Reuters (Markets) LLC; **247** (B) Zuma Press, (BC) Darryl Leniuk, Getty Images, Inc., (T) Associated Press; **254** Getty Images, Inc.; **257** Mark Humphrey, Associated Press; **261** (BR) Ron Sachs, Newscom, Elena Elisseeva, Shutterstock, Ian Wilson, Shutterstock, Jeff Whyte, iStockphoto; **264** Clive Streeter, Dorling Kindersley Limited, Dorling Kindersley Limited, Steve Gorton, Dorling Kindersley Limited; **265** Darryl Leniuk, Getty Images, Inc.; **267** NASA; **269** Zuma Press; **270** David Trood, Getty Images, Inc.; **272** (L) Mark J Terrill, Associated Press; **273** (B) Kim Kyung Hoon, Thomson Reuters (Markets) LLC, (TR) Steve Helber, Associated Press; **277** Jeremy Woodhouse, Getty Images, Inc.; **280** Tim Platt, Getty Images, Inc.; **281** Richard Megna, Fundamental Photographs; **282** NASA; **283** Alamy; **284** Associated Press; **287** Zuma Press; **288** (Bkgd) Rick Fischer, Masterfile Corporation, (Inset) Corbis; **289** (Bkgd) ©Jose Gil/Shutterstock, (BL) Karen Cochrane/©DK Images

Chapter 7 Electricity
290–291 spread, Nick Suydam/Alamy; **293** (m1) Jim Ketsdever/AP Images; **294** (B Inset), Virgo Productions/Zefa/Corbis, (TL), Peter Menzel/Photo Researchers, Inc.; **294–295** (Bkgd), Jim Ketsdever/AP Images; **296** Moviestore collection Ltd/Alamy; **300** (B Inset), Paul A. Souders/Corbis, (T Inset), Dev Carr/Cultura/Photolibrary New York; **301** (T Inset), GIPhotoStock/Photo Researchers, Inc.; **304** Volker Steger/Photo Researchers, Inc.; **305** Copyright © 2003 Universal/Everett Collection; **306** Google Earth Pro; **307** bracelet, Pixi/iStockphoto.com, glasses, iStockphoto.com, rubber-band ball, iStockphoto.com, skateboard, JulNichols/iStockphoto.com, slinky, Fotko/iStockphoto.com, sneakers, iStockphoto.com; **310** Alan Keohane/Dorling Kindersley; **311** Enrique de la Osa/Reuters; **312** Jeff Horner/AP Images; **313** Sebastianiov/iStockphoto.com; **317** (BR), Liquid Library/JupiterUnlimited; **320** Kim Kyung Hoon/Reuters; **321** laptop, Akirastock/iStockphoto.com, tags, iStockphoto.com, toaster, iStockphoto.com, TV, iStockphoto.com, washer, iStockphoto.com; **322** Emmeline Watkins/SPL/Photo Researchers, Inc.; **323** (BL), Jill Fromer/iStockphoto.com; **324** Paul A. Souders/Corbis; **325** iStockphoto.com; **327** iStockphoto.com; **328** (Bkgd), Silman Snozyk/Photolibrary New York, (Bkgd), Silman Snozyk/Photolibrary New York, (BR Inset), Bettmann/Corbis, (T Inset), Jerry Mason/Photo Researchers, Inc.; **329** (Bkgd), imagebroker/Alamy, (T Inset), Earl Roberge/Photo Researchers, Inc.

Chapter 8 Magnetism and Electromagnetism
330–331 (Bkgd) Liu Xiaoyang, Alamy; **333** (B) Anson, Shutterstock; (T) Alamy; **336** Vikram Hoshing, Alamy; **337** (Bkgd) Galina Barskaya, Alamy, (crane) Paul Ridsdale, Alamy, (logs) Richard Baker, Corbis; **338** (L) Richard Megna, Fundamental Photographs, (R) Richard Megna, Fundamental

Photographs; **339** Alamy; **340** (BL) Corbis, (T) Roger Harris, Photo Researchers, Inc./Science Source; **346** (BR) Master Magnetics, Alamy; **351** (R) Alamy; **352** (Bkgd) Nikkytok, Shutterstock; **354–355** (Bkgd) Richard T Nowitz, Photo Researchers, Inc./Science Source; **355** (TR) Getty Images, Inc.; **358** (Inset) Peter Beck, Corbis; **358–359** (Bkgd) Corbis; **361** (B) Corbis, (C) Clive Streeter, Dorling Kindersley Limited, (T) Corbis; **362** (B) Anson, Shutterstock; **365** (T) Omri Waisman, Corbis; **366** (T) Alamy; **370** (Bkgd) Alamy, (Inset) Photo Researchers, Inc./Science Source; **371** (L) North Wind Picture Archives, (R) Steve Gorton, Dorling Kindersley Limited

Chapter 9 The Atmosphere
372 (Bkgd) Kevin Fleming, Corbis; (B) Shutterstock; (BC) David Wall, Alamy; (T) Corbis, (TC) Van D477, Photo Researchers, Inc./Science Source; **375** Corbis; **378** (C) Charles D Winters, Photo Researchers, Inc./Science Source; **379** Corbis; **380** (B) Alamy, (T) Sean Randall, iStockphoto; **381** (C) NASA; **382** HIGH-G Productions/Stocktrek Images/Getty Images; **385** (T) Van D Bucher, Photo Researchers, Inc./Science Source; **388** (Bkgd) Melissa McManus, Getty Images, Inc.; **389** (C) David Wall, Alamy; **392** (T) Per-Andre Hoffmann, Alamy; **395** (C) Alamy; **397** (CL) Mark Yuill, iStockphoto, (CR) Ideeone, iStockphoto, (L) Ermin Gutenberger, iStockphoto, (R) Jason Major, iStockphoto; **400** (C) Helle Bro Clemmensen, iStockphoto; **402** (L) Mikhail Kokhanchikov, iStockphoto; **402–403** (Bkgd) Xavier Arnau, iStockphoto; **404–405** (Bkgd) Norma Cornes, Shutterstock; **407** (C) Harris Shiffman, Shutterstock; **412** (T) NASA; **416** (Bkgd) NASA; **417** (B) NASA, (T) Stefano Bianchetti, Corbis

Chapter 10 Weather
418 (Bkgd) Eric Nguyen, Photo Researchers, Inc./Science Source; **421** (BC) Rhoden, Gene, (TC) John Howard, Photo Researchers, Inc./Science Source; **425** Jeremy Horner, Corbis; **432** Ng Han Guan, Associated Press; **434** (BL) Liz Leyden, iStockphoto, (BR) John Howard, Photo Researchers, Inc./Science Source, (TL) Don Johnston, Getty Images, Inc., (TR) Tom King, Alamy; **435** (T) Matthias Hauser, Alamy; **437** Paul S Howell, Getty Images, Inc.; **438** Getty Images, Inc.; **441** (C) Gene Rhoden, Rhoden, Gene; **446** Associated Press; **448** (TL) Peter Menzel, Photo Researchers, Inc./Science Source; **449** iStockphoto; **451** (BL) NASA, (TL) NASA, (TR) Joe Raedle, Getty Images, Inc.; **453** Kansas City Star/MCT/Getty Images; **454** Donna McWilliam, Associated Press; **455** (BL) iStockphoto; **456** (B) Tom Sibley, Corbis, (Inset) imac, Alamy; **457** Fitzsimage/Shutterstock; **458** (C) Paul Rapson, Photo Researchers, Inc./Science Source, (L) Photo Researchers, Inc./Science Source, (R) David Parker, Photo Researchers, Inc./Science Source; **462** (BR) David Parker, Photo Researchers, Inc./Science Source; **466** (Bkgd) Brian Cosgrove, Dorling Kindersley Limited

Chapter 11 Earth, Moon, and Sun
471 (B) Getty Images, Inc., (C) John W Bova, Photo Researchers, Inc./Science Source, (CL) John W. Bova, Photo Researchers, Inc./Science Source, (CR) John W Bova, Photo Researchers, Inc./Science Source; **474** Sheila Terry/Science Source; **475** (Bkgd) Corbis, (Inset L) NASA, (Inset R) NASA, (R) NASA; **478** Ted Spiegel, Corbis; **479** Frank Zullo, Photo Researchers, Inc./Science Source; **480** (B) Alamy, (T) Ellen

Rooney, Alamy; **483** (L) A. Dagli Orti, Getty Images, Inc.; **487** Gavin Hellier, Getty Images, Inc.; **492** (Bkgd) Corbis, (Inset T) Jeff Vanuga, Corbis; **494** (C) Eckhard Slawik, Photo Researchers, Inc./Science Source, (CL) John W. Bova, Photo Researchers, Inc./Science Source, (CR) John W. Bova, Photo Researchers, Inc./Science Source, (L) John W. Bova, Photo Researchers, Inc./Science Source, (R) John W. Bova, Photo Researchers, Inc./Science Source; **495** (C) Getty Images, Inc.; **498** (L) Michael P. Gadomski, Photo Researchers, Inc./Science Source, (R) Michael P. Gadomski, Photo Researchers, Inc./Science Source; **501** Klaus Lang/ All Canada Photos/Alamy; **502–503** (Bkgd) NASA; (Inset) Omikron, Photo Researchers, Inc./Science Source; **504** (Chart B) NASA, (Chart T) NASA; **504–505** (Bkgd) NASA; **506** (BR) Photo Researchers, Inc./Science Source; **510** (BL) Andrey Prokhorov, iStockphoto, (CL) Andy Crawford, Dorling Kindersley Limited, (TL) Stephen Laurence Strathdee, iStockphoto; **511** (BL) William King/Getty Images, (Bkgd) NASA

Chapter 12 The Solar System

512–513 J. Clarke, Z. Levay, NASA; **515** (B) NASA, (T) NASA; **520** (BL) ComputerGraphic Vistas, (BR) ComputerGraphic Vistas; **522** (L) Photo Researchers, Inc./Science Source, (R) Detlev van Ravenswaay, Photo Researchers, Inc./Science Source; **523** (L) Photo Researchers, Inc./Science Source, (L) Friedrich Saurer, Alamy, (R) Alamy; **524** (B) NASA; **526–527** NASA; **529** (Bkgd) NASA; **530** (Bkgd) Per-Andre Hoffmann, Alamy; **531** (BL) Michael Melford, Getty Images, Inc.; **532–533** (Bkgd) Getty Images, Inc., (Inset) NASA; **534** (L) NASA, (R) NASA; **536** (CL) Bettmann, Corbis, (CR) Bettmann, Corbis, (L) NASA, (R) Library of Congress (Photoduplication); **537** NASA, (CR) NASA; (L) NASA, (R) NASA; **538** (B) NASA, (TL) NASA, (TR) NASA; **539** (BL) NASA, (BR) NASA, (TL) NASA, (TR) NASA; **542** (T) NASA; **542–543** NASA; **543** (Inset) NASA; **544** (C) Judy Dole, Getty Images, Inc.; **545** (CL) NASA, (CR) K Rages, H Hammel, NASA, (L) NASA, (R) NASA; **546** (BL) NASA, (R) NASA, (TL) NASA; **547** NASA; **548** (BL) NASA, (LC) NASA, (R) NASA, (TL) NASA; **549** (BL) Photo Researchers, Inc./Science Source, (BR) NASA, (TL) NASA, (TR) NASA; **550** (B) Lawrence Sromovsky, W. M. Keck Observatory, (TL) NASA, (TR) NASA; **551** (B) L Sromovsky, NASA, (TL) NASA, (TR) NASA; **552** (B) Alan Sirulnikoff, Getty Images, Inc.; **554** Detlev van Ravenswaay, Photo Researchers, Inc./Science Source; **555** Jerry Lodriguss, Photo Researchers, Inc./Science Source; **556** (Bkgd) NASA, (Inset) NASA; **557** Paolo Koch, Photo Researchers, Inc./Science Source; **558** (BL) NASA, (BR) Jerry Lodriguss, Photo Researchers, Inc./Science Source, (T) NASA; **562** NASA

Part 1 What Is Science?

564 (Bkgd) Narcis Parfenti/Fotolia, (BR) Paulo De Oliveira/ PhotoLibrary Group, Inc.; **565** (Bkgd) Ulrich Mueller/ Shutterstock; **569** (BC) Nature Picture Library, (BC) Charles O'Rear, Corbis, (BL) Richard Haynes, (CTL) Corbis, (TL) Michael Nichols, National Geographic Stock; **572** (Bkgd) Michael Nichols, National Geographic Stock, (L) Alamy, (R) Alamy; **573** (BC) Karl Ammann, Nature Picture Library; **574** (BL) Manoj Shah, Getty Images, Inc., (TL) Anup Shah, Nature Picture Library, (TL) Kevin Oke, Alamy; **575** (C) Christoph Becker, Nature Picture Library, (L) Corbis; **576** (B) Dietrich Rose, Corbis, (B) Kennan Ward, Corbis, (TL) Angelo Cavalli, Corbis; **577** (TR) E D Torial,

Alamy David Jordan, Associated Press; **578** (B) Sarah Holmstrom, iStockphoto, (Bkgd) Bortonia, iStockphoto, (Bkgd) Mukasa, Samuel; **579** (BR) Kurt Lackovic, Alamy, (CL) Stephen Dalton, Photo Researchers, Inc./Science Source, (TR) Karimala, iStockphoto; **580** (TR) Tom Tracy, Alamy, Tracy Frankel, Getty Images, Inc.; **581** (Bkgd) Rick Price, Nature Picture Library, (TR) iStockphoto; **582** (NOP) Jon Helgason, iStockphoto, (Bkgd) Ken Seet, Corbis; **583** (BR) Alamy, (NOP) iStockphoto, (TR) Duncan Walker, iStockphoto; **584** (Bkgd) Stephen Dorey Creative, Alamy; **585** (TL) Richard Megna, Fundamental Photographs, (TR) Redmond Durrell, Alamy; **586** (B) Erik S. Lesser, Newscom, (BL) Leemage/UIG, Getty Images, Inc., Steve Allen, Alamy; **587** (Bkgd) Courtesy of Anna Khomulo/Fotolia; **588** (B) Alamy, (T) Corbis, L: Charles O'Rear, Corbis, R: Charles O'Rear, Corbis; **589** (T) Photo Researchers, Inc./Science Source; **590** (B) Corbis, (TL) Idamini, Alamy, Richard Haynes; **591** (CR) Idamini, Alamy; **592** (L) Kai Uwe Och, Alamy, (TL) Idamini, Alamy; **593** (B) Idamini, Alamy; **594** (B) Michael Wysession, (Bkgd) Daniel Sambraus, Photo Researchers, Inc./ Science Source, (CL) Don Carstens, Getty Images, Inc., (TL) D. Hurst, Alamy; **595** (T) John McConnico, Associated Press, (TR) Getty Images, Inc.; **596** (CR) Courtesy of Images&Stories/ Alamy; **598** (CR) Cardinal, Corbis; **599** (T) Javier Trueba, Photo Researchers, Inc./Science Source

Part 2 The Tools of Science

600 (Bkgd) Suzanne Tucker/Shutterstock, (Inset) Aaron Petersolamy; **601** Mark Thomas/Photo Researchers, Inc.; **602** (B) Kevin Fleming, Corbis, (CR) Rick Bowmer, Associated Press, (Bkgd) Dan Guravich, Getty Images, Inc., (T) Kent, Breck P.; **604** (B) Kent, Breck P., (B) Thomson Reuters (Markets) LLC, (Bkgd) J A Kraulis, Masterfile USA Corporation, (CR) Newscom, (TL) Kent, Breck P., (TR) Andrew J Martinez, Photo Researchers, Inc./Science Source; **605** (C) Chiyacat, Dreamstime LLC, (CL) Miller, Marli, (TCL) SuperStock, (TL) Britvich, Dreamstime LLC; **610** (BC) Philip Dowell, Dorling Kindersley Limited, (BCR) Shattil & Rozinski, Nature Picture Library, (C) Enrique Aguirre, Getty Images, Inc., (CR) Alamy, (R) Anthony Mercieca, Photo Researchers, Inc./Science Source, Loomis Dean, Getty Images, Inc.; **612** (B) Richard Haynes, (Bkgd) Michael Just, AGE Fotostock America Inc.; **612–613** Alexander Mustard, Solent News, Rex Feature, AP Images; **613** (B) Richard Haynes, (CL) Gail Jankus, Photo Researchers, Inc./Science Source, (CR) Gail Jankus, Photo Researchers, Inc./Science Source, (L) Gail Jankus, Photo Researchers, Inc./Science Source, (R) Gail Jankus, Photo Researchers, Inc./Science Source; **614** (L) Darwin Wiggett, AGE Fotostock America Inc.; **615** (TR) Joe Traver, Getty Images, Inc.; **616** (B) Britvich, Dreamstime LLC, (BR) Terex, Dreamstime LLC, (C) Chiyacat, Dreamstime LLC; **619** Francois Gohier, Photo Researchers, Inc./Science Source; **620** (Bkgd) John Casey/Fotolia, (BL) Simon Kwong, Corbis; **621** (BR) Kevin Fleming, Corbis; **622** (B) Paul Zoeller, Associated Press, (T) Photo Researchers, Inc./Science Source, (TL) Chris Jaksa, AGE Fotostock America Inc.; **623** (B) David Nunuk, AGE Fotostock America Inc.; (Bkgd) Dreamstime LLC, (C) Robert Manella, Corbis, Ocean, Corbis, Sandy Felsenthal, Corbis; **624** (B) Getty Images; **625** (Bkgd) Reinhard Dirscherl, Ecoscene, (CR) Frank Greenaway, Dorling Kindersley Limited, (TR) H Lansdown, Alamy; **626** (B) Chris Johnson, Alamy;

ACKNOWLEDGMENTS

627 (TR) Corbis; **628** (Bkgd) Barrie Watts/Dorling Kindersley; **629** NASA/Goddard Space Flight center Scientific Visualization Studio, and Virginia Butcher (SSAI), (Bkgd) Stephen St. John/National Geographic Image Collection; **630** (I) Imagebroker/Alamy; **631** (R) Geoff Brightling/Dorling Kindersley, (I) Ryan M. Bolton/Shutterstock; **632** (Inset) Central Science Laboratory/Photo Researchers, Inc.; **632–633** (Bkgd) Luchschen/Shutterstock; **633** (TR) Daboost/Shutterstock; **634** Dmitry Naumov/Shutterstock; **635** Issei Kato/Reuters; **637** Ahmad Masood/Reuters; **639** Science Source/Photo Researchers, Inc.; **640** (I) Goddard Space Flight Center Scientific Visualization Studio/Additional support provided by Sarah Dewitt (NASA/GSFC) and Fred Kemman (HTSI)/NASA, (Bkgd) Bill Brooks/Alamy; **642–643** (Bkgd) NASA; (B) WILLIAM PHILPOTT, Getty Images, Inc., (TR) Martin Shields, Alamy; **645** (T) Michael Nichols, Getty Images, Inc.; **647** (CB) Michael Szoenyi, Photo Researchers, Inc./Science Source, (CT) Dr. Marli Miller, Getty Images, Inc., (L) Richard Haynes, (T) James L. Amos, Photo Researchers, Inc./Science Source; **648** (Bkgd) Phil Martin, PhotoEdit; **649** (CR) Jian Chen, Newscom, (TR) Lew Robertson, Alamy, David Parker, Photo Researchers, Inc./Science Source; **650** (BC) Kent, Breck P., (L) Charles R. Belinky, Photo Researchers, Inc./Science Source, (T) Richard Haynes, (TC) Charles R. Belinky, Photo Researchers, Inc./Science Source; **650–651** Martin Bond, Photo Researchers, Inc./Science Source; **651** (TR) James L. Amos, Photo Researchers, Inc./Science Source; **652** (BR) John Cancalosi, Getty Images, Inc.; (C) Dell, Dreamstime LLC; (CR) G. Thomas Bishop, Newscom; (L) Bedo, Dreamstime LLC; (R) Dreamstime LLC, Bob Krist, Corbis; **653** (B) Phil Schermeister, Corbis, Michael Nichols, Getty Images, Inc.